Charles Yager
987-5633

DIGITAL IMAGE PROCESSING

DIGITAL IMAGE PROCESSING

WILLIAM K. PRATT

Professor of Electrical Engineering
Image Processing Institute
University of Southern California
Los Angeles, California

A WILEY–INTERSCIENCE PUBLICATION

JOHN WILEY & SONS

New York / Chichester / Brisbane / Toronto

To my son Michael

Library of Congress Cataloging in Publication Data

Pratt, William K.
   Digital image processing.

   "A Wiley–Interscience publication."
   Includes bibliographical references and index.
   1. Image processing.   I. Title.

TA1632.P7 1978   621.3815'42   77–20888
ISBN 0–471–01888–0

Printed in the United States of America

10 9 8 7 6 5 4 3

PREFACE

The field of digital image processing has grown considerably during the past decade with the increased utilization of imagery in myriad applications coupled with improvements in the size, speed, and cost effectiveness of digital computers and related signal processing technologies. Image processing has found a significant role in scientific, industrial, biomedical, space, and governmental applications. Such applications include the digital transmission of spacecraft imagery and personal telephone carrier television; the resolution improvement of electron microscope images and the compensation of sensor and transmission errors of pictures transmitted from deep-space probes; the automatic classification of terrain and detection of resources from earth resources satellite pictures; the formation and enhancement of biomedical imagery, including radiographs, thermograms, and nuclear scanned images; automatic map making from aerial photographs; and the detection of cracks and flaws in machine parts from industrial radiographs. In the future image processing will, no doubt, be utilized to a greater extent to aid medical practitioners in the detection and diagnosis of disease from biomedical images. Industrial applications should abound; image processing systems will analyze scenes from the "eyes" of industrial automatons to control their actions. Efficient image coding techniques offer the promise of scores of personal two-way television channels for homes and businesses. The list is limited only by imagination.

This book is intended to serve as a text for an electrical engineering or computer science graduate course in digital image processing, and as a reference for practicing engineers and scientists engaged in image processing research and development activities. Digital image processing is a broad subject encompassing studies of physics, physiology, electrical engineering, computer science, and mathematics. Readers are assumed to have an undergraduate technical background in one of these areas. Knowledge of linear system theory, vector algebra, probability, and random processes is certainly beneficial, but not absolutely necessary.

The book is divided into six parts. Part 1 contains three chapters concerned with the characterization of continuous images. Topics covered include the mathematical representation of continuous images, the psychophysical properties of human vision, and photometry and colorimetry. In Part 2 image sampling and quantization techniques are explored along with the mathematical representation of discrete images and image quality measures. Part 3 discusses two-dimensional signal processing techniques including general linear operators, pseudoinverse operators, superposition operators, convolution operators, and unitary transform operators such as the Fourier, Hadamard, and Karhunen–Loeve transforms. The final chapter in Part 3 analyzes and compares linear filtering techniques implemented by direct convolution, Fourier transform processing, and recursive filtering.

The last three parts of the book cover the three main application areas of digital image processing. Part 4 presents a discussion of image enhancement and restoration techniques. In image enhancement, picture manipulation processes are performed to provide a more subjectively pleasing image or to convert the image to a form more amenable to human or machine analysis. Image restoration is the task of improving the fidelity of an image in the sense of compensating for image degradations. Part 5, entitled image analysis, concentrates on the general subjects of scene analysis and picture understanding. Specific topics include the isolation and measurement of image features, the detection of objects within pictures, image registration, symbolic image description, and image understanding systems. Image coding, which is the subject of Part 6, involves methods for representing monochrome and color images with a minimal number of code bits for more efficient communication and storage.

Although readers should find this book reasonably comprehensive, many important topics allied to the field of digital image processing have been omitted to limit the size of the book. Among the most prominent omissions are the topics of pattern recognition and classification, digital holography, and image projection reconstruction. References to these topics are provided in Appendix 1.

WILLIAM K. PRATT

Malibu, California
January, 1978

ACKNOWLEDGMENTS

Image processing research at the University of Southern California began in 1962 on a very modest scale, but increased in size and scope with the attendant international interest in the field. In 1971 Dr. Zohrab A. Kaprielian, Dean of the School of Engineering and Vice President of Academic Research and Administration, announced the establishment of the USC Image Processing Institute. Presently, the Image Processing Institute comprises one of the world's largest research groups in image processing with excellent physical facilities. This environment has contributed significantly to this book. I am grateful to Dr. Kaprielian for his role in providing University support of image processing research. Also, I wish to acknowledge the following past and present members of the Institute's scientific staff who rendered invaluable assistance and advice in the preparation of the manuscript: Harry C. Andrews, Lee D. Davisson, Werner Frei, Ali Habibi, Ernest L. Hall, Ronald S. Hershel, Anil K. Jain, Richard P. Kruger, Nasser E. Nahi, Ramakant Nevatia, Guner Robinson, Alexander A. Sawchuk, William B. Thompson, and Lloyd R. Welch. In addition, I sincerely acknowledge the technical help of my graduate students during the writing of the book: Ikram Abdou, Behnam Ashjari, Wen-hsiung Chen, Faramarz Davarian, Michael Huhns, Clanton Mancill, Nelson Mascarenhas, John Roese, Clifford Reader, and Robert Wallis.

This book is an outgrowth of notes developed for the course Image Processing taught in the USC Electrical Engineering Department. I wish to thank the many students who suffered through the early versions of the notes for their valuable comments. Also, I sincerely appreciate the review of the notes provided by Professors Harry C. Andrews, Ernest L. Hall, and Werner Frei of USC and Dr. Ali Habibi, now of TRW Corp., who used the notes when they taught the Image Processing course.

The physical preparation of any book is a formidable task. I have been extremely fortunate to have the assistance of Florence Tebbets, Joyce Seguy, and Marilyn Chan of USC, who typed the manuscript. Mr. Ray Schmidt of the USC Image Processing Institute and his staff provided photographic services for the book, and Mr. Doyle Howland of USC was responsible for drafting and artwork. Mr. Scott Johnston and Mr. Edward Kasanjian assisted greatly in computer programming and preparation of computer-generated examples contained in the book. Many of the digital images have been photographically recorded by Dr. Clifford Reader of Ford Aerospace and Communications Corp. of Palo Alto, California. The gracious assistance of these individuals is sincerely appreciated and acknowledged.

Finally, words of appreciation for my sponsor, the Information Processing Techniques Office of the Advanced Research Projects Agency. This work was supported in part by ARPA and was monitored by the Air Force Range Measurements Laboratory under Contract No. F–08606–72–C–0008 and by the Wright-Patterson Air Force Base under Contract No. F–33615–76–C–1203.

W.K.P.

CONTENTS

Part 1.   Continuous Image Characterization

1.   Mathematical Characterization of Continuous Images   3
2.   Psychophysical Properties of Vision   25
3.   Photometry and Colorimetry   50

Part 2.   Digital Image Characterization

4.   Image Sampling and Reconstruction   93
5.   Mathematical Characterization of Discrete Images   121
6.   Image Quantization   140
7.   Sampled Image Quality Measures   162

Part 3.   Discrete Two-Dimensional Linear Processing

8.   Linear Operators   201
9.   Superposition Operator   214
10.   Two-Dimensional Unitary Transforms   232
11.   Two-Dimensional Linear Processing Techniques   279

Part 4.   Image Enhancement and Restoration

12.   Image Enhancement   307
13.   Image Restoration Models   345
14.   Algebraic Spatial Image Restoration Techniques   378
15.   Specialized Spatial Image Restoration Techniques   426
16.   Luminance, Color, and Spectral Image Restoration   447

Part 5.   Image Analysis

17.   Image Feature Extraction   471
18.   Symbolic Image Description   514
19.   Image Detection and Registration   551
20.   Image Understanding Systems   568

Part 6. Image Coding

21. Analog Processing Image Coding   591
22. Digital Point Processing Image Coding   616
23. Digital Spatial Processing Image Coding   662
24. Image Coding Performance Analysis   710

Appendix

1. Selected References   733
2. Color Coordinate Conversion   736
3. Statistical Source Coding   741

Index   743

DIGITAL IMAGE PROCESSING

1 CONTINUOUS IMAGE CHARACTERIZATION

Although this book is concerned primarily with digital, as opposed to analog, image processing techniques, it must be remembered that most digital images represent continuous natural images. Exceptions are artificial digital images such as test patterns that are numerically created in the computer and images constructed by tomographic systems. Thus it is important to understand the "physics" of image formation by sensors and optical systems including human visual perception. Another important consideration is the measurement of light in order quantitatively to describe images. Finally, it is useful to establish spatial and temporal characteristics of continuous image fields which provide the basis for the interrelationship of digital image samples. These topics are covered in the following chapters. The mathematical characterization of continuous images is the subject of Chapter 1. Chapter 2 discusses the psychophysical properties of vision. Photometry and colorimetry are described in Chapter 3.

1 MATHEMATICAL CHARACTERIZATION OF CONTINUOUS IMAGES

In the design and analysis of image processing systems it is convenient, and often necessary, mathematically to characterize the image to be processed. There are two basic mathematical characterizations of interest: deterministic and statistical. In the deterministic image representation a mathematical image function is defined and point properties of the image are considered. For a statistical representation the image is specified by average properties. The following sections contain a development of the deterministic and the statistical characterization of continuous images. Although the analysis is presented in the context of visual images, many of the results can be extended to general two-dimensional time-varying signals and fields.

1.1. CONTINUOUS IMAGE REPRESENTATION

Let $C(x, y, t, \lambda)$ represent the spatial energy distribution of an image source of radiant energy at spatial coordinates (x, y), at time t, and at wavelength λ. Because light intensity is a real positive quantity, that is, because intensity is proportional to the modulus squared of the electric field, therefore the image light function is real and non-negative. Furthermore, in all practical imaging systems, there is always a small amount of background light present. The physical imaging system also imposes some restriction on the maximum brightness of an image, for example, film saturation and cathode ray tube phosphor heating. Hence it is assumed that

$$0 \le C(x, y, t, \lambda) \le A \tag{1.1-1}$$

where A is the maximum image brightness. A physical image is necessarily limited in extent by the imaging system and image recording media. For mathematical simplicity all images are assumed to be nonzero only over a rectangular region for which

$$-L_x \le x \le L_x \tag{1.1-2a}$$

$$-L_y \le y \le L_y \tag{1.1-2b}$$

3

The physical image is, of course, observable only over some finite time interval. Thus let

$$-T \le t \le T \tag{1.1-2c}$$

The image light function $C(x, y, t, \lambda)$ is therefore a bounded four-dimensional function with bounded independent variables. As a final restriction, it is assumed that the image function is continuous over its domain of definition.

The brightness response of a standard human observer to an image light function is commonly measured in terms of the instantaneous luminance of the light field as defined by

$$Y(x, y, t) = \int_0^\infty C(x, y, t, \lambda) V_S(\lambda) \, d\lambda \tag{1.1-3}$$

where $V_S(\lambda)$ represents the relative luminous efficiency function, that is, the spectral response of human vision. Similarly, the color response of a standard observer is commonly measured in terms of some set of tristimulus values that are linearly proportional to the amounts of red, green, and blue light needed to "match" a colored light. For an arbitrary red-green-blue coordinate system, the instantaneous tristimulus values are

$$R(x, y, t) = \int_0^\infty C(x, y, t, \lambda) R_S(\lambda) \, d\lambda \tag{1.1-4a}$$

$$G(x, y, t) = \int_0^\infty C(x, y, t, \lambda) G_S(\lambda) \, d\lambda \tag{1.1-4b}$$

$$B(x, y, t) = \int_0^\infty C(x, y, t, \lambda) B_S(\lambda) \, d\lambda \tag{1.1-4c}$$

where $R_S(\lambda)$, $G_S(\lambda)$, $B_S(\lambda)$ are spectral tristimulus values for the set of red, green, and blue primaries. The spectral tristimulus values are, in effect, the tristimulus values required to match a unit amount of spectral light at wavelength λ. In a multispectral imaging system the observed image field is modeled as a spectrally weighted integral of the image light function. The ith spectral image field is then given as

$$F_i(x, y, t) = \int_0^\infty C(x, y, t, \lambda) S_i(\lambda) \, d\lambda \tag{1.1-5}$$

where $S_i(\lambda)$ is the spectral response of the ith sensor.

For notational simplicity a single image function $F(x, y, t)$ is selected to represent an image field in a physical imaging system. For a monochrome imaging system the image function $F(x, y, t)$ nominally denotes the image luminance, or some converted or corrupted physical representation of the luminance, while in a color imaging system, $F(x, y, t)$ signifies one of the tristimulus values, or some function of the tristimulus value. The image function $F(x, y, t)$ is also used to denote general three-dimensional fields such as the time-varying noise of an image scanner.

In correspondence with the standard definition for one-dimensional time signals, the time average of an image function at a given point (x, y) is defined as

$$\langle F(x, y, t) \rangle_T = \lim_{T \to \infty} \left\{ \frac{1}{2T} \int_{-T}^{T} F(x, y, t) L(t) \, dt \right\} \qquad (1.1\text{-}6)$$

where $L(t)$ is a time weighting function. Similarly, the average image brightness at a given time is given by the spatial average

$$\langle F(x, y, t) \rangle_S = \lim_{\substack{L_x \to \infty \\ L_y \to \infty}} \left\{ \frac{1}{4 L_x L_y} \int_{-L_x}^{L_x} \int_{-L_y}^{L_y} F(x, y, t) \, dx \, dy \right\} \qquad (1.1\text{-}7)$$

In many imaging systems, such as image projection devices, the image does not change with time, and the time variable may be dropped from the image function. For other types of systems, such as movie pictures, the image function is time sampled. It is also possible to convert the spatial variation into time variation, as in television, by an image scanning process. In the subsequent discussion the time variable is dropped from the image field notation unless specifically required.

1.2. TWO-DIMENSIONAL SYSTEMS

A two-dimensional system, in its most general form, is simply a mapping of some input set of two-dimensional functions $F_1(x, y), F_2(x, y), \ldots,$ $F_N(x, y)$ to a set of output two-dimensional functions $G_1(x, y), G_2(x, y), \ldots, G_M(x, y)$ where $(-\infty < x, y < \infty)$ denotes the independent, continuous spatial variables of the functions. This mapping may be represented by the operators $\mathcal{O}_m\{\cdot\}$ for $m = 1, 2, \ldots, M$, which relate the input to output set of functions by the set of equations

$$G_1(x, y) = \mathcal{O}_1\{F_1(x, y), F_2(x, y), \ldots, F_N(x, y)\}$$
$$\vdots \qquad \vdots \qquad \vdots$$
$$G_m(x, y) = \mathcal{O}_m\{F_1(x, y), F_2(x, y), \ldots, F_N(x, y)\} \qquad (1.2\text{-}1)$$
$$\vdots \qquad \vdots \qquad \vdots$$
$$G_M(x, y) = \mathcal{O}_M\{F_1(x, y), F_2(x, y), \ldots, F_N(x, y)\}$$

In specific cases the mapping may be many-to-few, few-to-many, or one-to-one. The one-to-one mapping is defined as

$$G(x, y) = \mathcal{O}\{F(x, y)\} \qquad (1.2\text{-}2)$$

For one-dimensional physical systems in which the independent variable is time, the system output is a function of the past and the present, but not the future. Such systems are called causal. Two-dimensional systems are generally noncausal; the spatial variables (x, y) may be negative with respect to some reference axis.

To proceed further with a discussion of the properties of two-dimensional systems, it is necessary to direct the discourse toward specific types of operators.

1.3. SINGULARITY OPERATORS

Singularity operators are widely employed in the analysis of two-dimensional systems, especially systems that involve sampling of continuous functions. The two-dimensional Dirac delta function is a singularity operator that possesses the following properties:

$$\delta(x, y) = \begin{cases} \infty, & x = 0, y = 0 \\ 0, & \text{otherwise} \end{cases} \qquad (1.3\text{-}1a)$$

$$\delta(x - \xi, y - \eta) = \begin{cases} \infty, & x = \xi, y = \eta \\ 0, & \text{otherwise} \end{cases} \qquad (1.3\text{-}1b)$$

$$\int\int_{-\varepsilon}^{\varepsilon} \delta(x, y)\, dx\, dy = 1 \qquad \text{for } \varepsilon > 0 \qquad (1.3\text{-}1c)$$

$$\int\int_{-\infty}^{\infty} F(\xi, \eta)\delta(x - \xi, y - \eta)\, d\xi\, d\eta = F(x, y) \qquad (1.3\text{-}1d)$$

In Property (c), ε is an infinitesimally small limit of integration. Property (d) is called the Sifting property of the Dirac delta function.

The two-dimensional delta function can be decomposed into the product of two one-dimensional delta functions defined along orthonormal coordinates. Thus

$$\delta(x, y) = \delta(x)\delta(y) \qquad (1.3\text{-}2)$$

where the one-dimensional delta function satisfies one-dimensional versions of Eq. 1.3-1. The delta function also can be defined as a limit on a family of functions. General examples are given below (1, p. 275).

Rectangle

$$\delta(x, y) = \lim_{\alpha \to \infty} [\alpha^2 \, \text{rect}\{\alpha x\} \, \text{rect}\{\alpha y\}] \qquad (1.3\text{-}3a)$$

Circle

$$\delta(x, y) = \lim_{\alpha \to \infty} \left[\frac{\alpha^2}{\pi} \, \text{circ}\{\alpha\sqrt{x^2 + y^2}\}\right] \qquad (1.3\text{-}3b)$$

Gaussian

$$\delta(x, y) = \lim_{\alpha \to \infty} [\alpha^2 \exp\{-\alpha^2 \pi (x^2 + y^2)\}] \qquad (1.3\text{-}3c)$$

Sinc

$$\delta(x, y) = \lim_{\alpha \to \infty} [\alpha^2 \, \text{sinc}\{\alpha x\} \, \text{sinc}\{\alpha y\}] \qquad (1.3\text{-}3d)$$

Bessel

$$\delta(x, y) = \lim_{\alpha \to \infty} \left[\frac{\alpha J_1(2\pi\alpha\sqrt{x^2 + y^2})}{\sqrt{x^2 + y^2}}\right] \qquad (1.3\text{-}3e)$$

where

$$\text{rect}\{x\} = \begin{cases} 1, & |x| \leq \frac{1}{2} \\ 0, & |x| > \frac{1}{2} \end{cases} \qquad (1.3\text{-}4a)$$

$$\text{circ}\{r\} = \begin{cases} 1, & r \leq 1 \\ 0, & r > 1 \end{cases} \qquad (1.3\text{-}4b)$$

$$\text{sinc}\{x\} = \frac{\sin\{\pi x\}}{\pi x} \qquad (1.3\text{-}4c)$$

Another useful formulation of the delta function is given by the identity (2, p. 99)

$$\delta(x - \xi, y - \eta) = \frac{1}{4\pi^2} \int\limits_{-\infty}^{\infty}\!\!\int \exp\{i[u(x - \xi) + v(y - \eta)]\} \, du \, dv$$

$$(1.3\text{-}5)$$

where $i = \sqrt{-1}$.

1.4. ADDITIVE LINEAR OPERATORS

A two-dimensional system is said to be an additive linear system if the system obeys the law of additive superposition. In the special case of one-to-one mappings, the additive superposition property requires that

$$\mathcal{O}\{a_1 F_1(x, y) + a_2 F_2(x, y)\} = a_1 \mathcal{O}\{F_1(x, y)\} + a_2 \mathcal{O}\{F_2(x, y)\} \quad (1.4\text{-}1)$$

where a_1 and a_2 are constants that are possibly complex. This additive superposition property can easily be extended to the general mapping of Eq. 1.2-1.

A system input function $F(x, y)$ can be represented as a sum of amplitude weighted Dirac delta functions by the Sifting integral,

$$F(x, y) = \int\int_{-\infty}^{\infty} F(\xi, \eta)\delta(x - \xi, y - \eta)\, d\xi\, d\eta \quad (1.4\text{-}2)$$

where $F(\xi, \eta)$ is the weighting factor of the impulse located at coordinates (ξ, η) in the x-y plane as shown in Figure 1.4-1. Then, if the output of a general linear one-to-one system is defined to be

$$G(x, y) = \mathcal{O}\{F(x, y)\} \quad (1.4\text{-}3)$$

then

$$G(x, y) = \mathcal{O}\left\{ \int\int_{-\infty}^{\infty} F(\xi, \eta)\delta(x - \xi, y - \eta)\, d\xi\, d\eta \right\} \quad (1.4\text{-}4a)$$

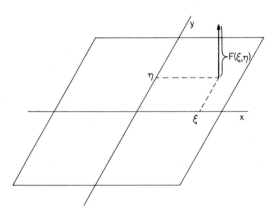

FIGURE 1.4-1. Decomposition of image function.

or

$$G(x, y) = \int\limits_{-\infty}^{\infty}\!\!\int F(\xi, \eta)\mathcal{O}\{\delta(x - \xi, y - \eta)\}\, d\xi\, d\eta \qquad (1.4\text{-}4b)$$

In moving from Eq. 1.4-4a to 1.4-4b, the application order of the general linear operator $\mathcal{O}\{\cdot\}$ and the integral operator have been reversed. Also, the linear operator has been applied only to the term in the integrand that is dependent on the spatial variables (x, y). The second term in the integrand of Eq. 1.4-4b, which is redefined as

$$H(x, y; \xi, \eta) \equiv \mathcal{O}\{\delta(x - \xi, y - \eta)\} \qquad (1.4\text{-}5)$$

is called the impulse response of the two-dimensional system. In optical systems the impulse response is often called the point spread function of the system. Substitution of the impulse response function into Eq. 1.4-4b yields the additive superposition integral

$$G(x, y) = \int\limits_{-\infty}^{\infty}\!\!\int F(\xi, \eta)H(x, y; \xi, \eta)\, d\xi\, d\eta \qquad (1.4\text{-}6)$$

An additive linear two-dimensional system is called space invariant (isoplanatic) if its impulse response depends only on the factors $x - \xi$ and $y - \eta$. In an optical system, as shown in Figure 1.4-2, this implies that the image of a point source in the focal plane will only change in location, not in functional form, as the placement of the point source moves in the object plane. For a space-invariant system

$$H(x, y; \xi, \eta) = H(x - \xi, y - \eta) \qquad (1.4\text{-}7)$$

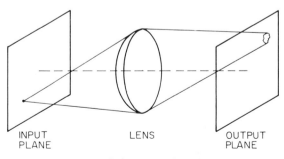

INPUT   LENS   OUTPUT
PLANE   PLANE

FIGURE 1.4-2. Point-source imaging system.

and the superposition integral reduces to the special case called the convolution integral given by

$$G(x, y) = \int\int_{-\infty}^{\infty} F(\xi, \eta) H(x - \xi, y - \eta)\, d\xi\, d\eta \qquad (1.4\text{-}8a)$$

Symbolically

$$G(x, y) = F(x, y) \circledast H(x, y) \qquad (1.4\text{-}8b)$$

denotes the convolution operation. The convolution integral is symmetric in the sense that

$$G(x, y) = \int\int_{-\infty}^{\infty} F(x - \xi, y - \eta) H(\xi, \eta)\, d\xi\, d\eta \qquad (1.4\text{-}9)$$

Figure 1.4-3 provides a visualization of the convolution process. In Figures 1.4-3a and 1.4-3b the input function $F(x, y)$ and impulse response are plotted in the dummy coordinate system (ξ, η). Next, in Figures 1.4-3c and 1.4-3d the coordinates of the impulse response are reversed and the impulse response is offset by the spatial values (x, y). In Figure 1.4-3e the

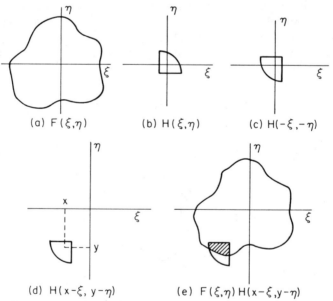

(a) $F(\xi, \eta)$ (b) $H(\xi, \eta)$ (c) $H(-\xi, -\eta)$

(d) $H(x - \xi, y - \eta)$ (e) $F(\xi, \eta) H(x - \xi, y - \eta)$

FIGURE 1.4-3. Graphic example of two-dimensional convolution.

integrand product of the convolution integral of Eq. 1-4.8 is shown as a shaded region. The integral over this region is the value of $G(x, y)$ at the offset coordinate (x, y). The complete function $F(x, y)$ could, in effect, be computed by sequentially scanning the reversed, offset impulse response across the input function and simultaneously integrating the overlapped region.

1.5. DIFFERENTIAL OPERATORS

Edge detection in images is commonly accomplished by performing a spatial differentiation of the image field followed by a thresholding operation to determine points of steep amplitude change. Horizontal and vertical spatial derivatives are defined as

$$d_x = \frac{\partial F(x, y)}{\partial x} \qquad (1.5\text{-}1a)$$

$$d_y = \frac{\partial F(x, y)}{\partial y} \qquad (1.5\text{-}1b)$$

The directional derivative of the image field along a vector direction z subtending an angle Φ with respect to the horizontal axis is given by (3, p. 10)

$$\nabla\{F(x, y)\} = \frac{\partial F(x, y)}{\partial z} = d_x \cos \Phi + d_y \sin \Phi \qquad (1.5\text{-}2)$$

The gradient magnitude is then

$$|\nabla\{F(x, y)\}| = \sqrt{d_x^2 + d_y^2} \qquad (1.5\text{-}3)$$

Spatial second derivatives in the horizontal and vertical directions are defined as

$$d_{xx} = \frac{\partial^2 F(x, y)}{\partial x^2} \qquad (1.5\text{-}4a)$$

$$d_{yy} = \frac{\partial^2 F(x, y)}{\partial y^2} \qquad (1.5\text{-}4b)$$

The second-order derivative is then

$$\nabla^2\{F(x, y)\} = d_{xx} + 2d_x d_y + d_{yy} \qquad (1.5\text{-}5)$$

Continuing further, an nth-order derivative is specified by the definition (3, p. 10)

$$\nabla^n\{F(x, y)\} = \sum_{j=0}^{n} \frac{n!}{(n-j)!j!} \frac{\partial^j F(x, y)}{\partial x^j} \frac{\partial^{n-j}F(x, y)}{\partial y^{n-j}} \qquad (1.5\text{-}6)$$

Spatial second derivatives are often combined to form the Laplacian operator,

$$L\{F(x, y)\} = d_{xx} + d_{yy} = \frac{\partial^2 F(x, y)}{\partial x^2} + \frac{\partial^2 F(x, y)}{\partial y^2} \qquad (1.5\text{-}7)$$

Note that in this definition there are no cross-product terms. In the literature the Laplacian as defined by Eq. 1.5-7 is often represented notationally as $\nabla^2\{F(x, y)\}$, which in this book denotes the second-order spatial derivative containing cross-product terms as seen in Eq. 1.5-5. It should further be noted that the Laplacian is a scalar quantity (not a function of spatial direction), whereas the gradient is a directional-dependent vector quantity.

1.6. TWO-DIMENSIONAL FOURIER TRANSFORM

The two-dimensional Fourier transform of the image function $F(x, y)$ is defined as

$$\mathcal{F}(\omega_x, \omega_y) = \int\limits_{-\infty}^{\infty}\!\!\int F(x, y) \exp\{-i(\omega_x x + \omega_y y)\}\, dx\, dy \qquad (1.6\text{-}1)$$

where ω_x and ω_y are spatial frequencies and $i = \sqrt{-1}$. Notationally, the Fourier transform is written as

$$\mathcal{F}(\omega_x, \omega_y) = \mathcal{O}_{\mathcal{F}}\{F(x, y)\} \qquad (1.6\text{-}2)$$

In general, the Fourier coefficient $\mathcal{F}(\omega_x, \omega_y)$ is a complex number that may be represented in real and imaginary form,

$$\mathcal{F}(\omega_x, \omega_y) = \mathcal{R}(\omega_x, \omega_y) + i\mathcal{I}(\omega_x, \omega_y) \qquad (1.6\text{-}3a)$$

or in magnitude and phase form,

$$\mathcal{F}(\omega_x, \omega_y) = \mathcal{M}(\omega_x, \omega_y) \exp\{i\phi(\omega_x, \omega_y)\} \qquad (1.6\text{-}3b)$$

where

$$\mathcal{M}(\omega_x, \omega_y) = [\mathcal{R}^2(\omega_x, \omega_y) + \mathcal{I}^2(\omega_x, \omega_y)]^{1/2} \qquad (1.6\text{-}4a)$$

$$\phi(\omega_x, \omega_y) = \tan^{-1}\left\{\frac{\mathcal{I}(\omega_x, \omega_y)}{\mathcal{R}(\omega_x, \omega_y)}\right\} \qquad (1.6\text{-}4b)$$

A sufficient condition for the existence of the Fourier transform of $F(x, y)$ is that the function be absolutely integrable. That is,

$$\int\int_{-\infty}^{\infty} |F(x, y)| \, dx \, dy < \infty \tag{1.6-5}$$

Hence, the input function $F(x, y)$ can be recovered from its Fourier transform by the inversion formula

$$F(x, y) = \frac{1}{4\pi^2} \int\int_{-\infty}^{\infty} \mathscr{F}(\omega_x, \omega_y) \exp\{i(\omega_x x + \omega_y y)\} \, d\omega_x \, d\omega_y \tag{1.6-6a}$$

or in operator form

$$F(x, y) = \mathcal{O}_{\mathscr{F}}^{-1}\{\mathscr{F}(\omega_x, \omega_y)\} \tag{1.6-6b}$$

The functions $F(x, y)$ and $\mathscr{F}(\omega_x, \omega_y)$ are called Fourier transform pairs.

The two-dimensional Fourier transform can be computed in two steps as a result of the separability of the kernel. Thus let

$$\mathscr{F}_y(\omega_x, y) = \int_{-\infty}^{\infty} F(x, y) \exp\{-i\omega_x x\} \, dx \tag{1.6-7}$$

then

$$\mathscr{F}(\omega_x, \omega_y) = \int_{-\infty}^{\infty} \mathscr{F}_y(\omega_x, y) \exp\{-i\omega_y y\} \, dy \tag{1.6-8}$$

Several useful properties of the two-dimensional Fourier transform are stated below. Proofs are given in (1, 2).

Functional Properties

If the image function is spatially separable such that

$$F(x, y) = f_x(x) f_y(y) \tag{1.6-9}$$

then

$$\mathscr{F}(\omega_x, \omega_y) = \mathcal{f}_x(\omega_x) \mathcal{f}_y(\omega_y) \tag{1.6-10}$$

where $\mathcal{f}_x(\omega_x)$ and $\mathcal{f}_y(\omega_y)$ are one-dimensional Fourier transforms of $f_x(x)$ and $f_y(y)$, respectively. Also, if $F(x, y)$ and $\mathscr{F}(\omega_x, \omega_y)$ are two-dimensional Fourier transform pairs, the the Fourier transform of $F^*(x, y)$ is $\mathscr{F}^*(-\omega_x, -\omega_y)$.‡ And, if $F(x, y)$ is symmetric such that $F(x, y) = F(-x, -y)$, then $\mathscr{F}(\omega_x, \omega_y) = \mathscr{F}(-\omega_x, -\omega_y)$.

‡ The asterisk symbol * denotes complex conjugation of a variable.

Linearity

The Fourier transform is a linear operator. Thus

$$\mathcal{O}_{\mathscr{F}}\{aF_1(x, y) + bF_1(x, y)\} = a\mathscr{F}_1(\omega_x, \omega_y) + b\mathscr{F}_2(\omega_x, \omega_y) \quad (1.6\text{-}11)$$

where a and b are constants.

Scaling

A linear scaling of the spatial variables results in an inverse scaling of the spatial frequencies as given by

$$\mathcal{O}_{\mathscr{F}}\{F(ax, by)\} = \frac{1}{|ab|}\mathscr{F}\left(\frac{\omega_x}{a}, \frac{\omega_y}{b}\right) \quad (1.6\text{-}12)$$

Hence, stretching of an axis in one domain results in a contraction of the corresponding axis in the other domain plus an amplitude change.

Shift

A positional shift in the input plane results in a phase shift in the output plane. Therefore

$$\mathcal{O}_{\mathscr{F}}\{F(x - a, y - b)\} = \mathscr{F}(\omega_x, \omega_y) \exp\{-i(\omega_x a + \omega_y b)\} \quad (1.6\text{-}13a)$$

Alternatively, a frequency shift in the Fourier plane results in the equivalence

$$\mathcal{O}_{\mathscr{F}}^{-1}\{\mathscr{F}(\omega_x - a_x, \omega_y - b_y)\} = F(x, y) \exp\{i(a_x x + a_y y)\} \quad (1.6\text{-}13b)$$

Convolution

The two-dimensional Fourier transform of two convolved functions is equal to the products of the transforms of the functions. Thus

$$\mathcal{O}_{\mathscr{F}}\{F(x, y) \circledast H(x, y)\} = \mathscr{F}(\omega_x, \omega_y)\mathscr{H}(\omega_x, \omega_y) \quad (1.6\text{-}14)$$

The inverse theorem states that

$$\mathcal{O}_{\mathscr{F}}\{F(x, y)H(x, y)\} = \frac{1}{4\pi^2}\mathscr{F}(\omega_x, \omega_y) \circledast \mathscr{H}(\omega_x, \omega_y) \quad (1.6\text{-}15)$$

Parseval's Theorem

The energy in the spatial and Fourier transform domains is related by

$$\int\limits_{-\infty}^{\infty}\int |F(x, y)|^2 \, dx \, dy = \frac{1}{4\pi^2}\int\limits_{-\infty}^{\infty}\int |\mathscr{F}(\omega_x, \omega_y)|^2 \, d\omega_x \, d\omega_y \quad (1.6\text{-}16)$$

Autocorrelation Theorem

The Fourier transform of the spatial autocorrelation of a function is equal to the absolute value squared of its Fourier transform. Hence

$$\mathcal{O}_\mathscr{F}\left\{\int\limits_{-\infty}^{\infty}\int F(\alpha, \beta)F^*(\alpha - x, \beta - y)\, d\alpha\, d\beta\right\} = |\mathscr{F}(\omega_x, \omega_y)|^2 \quad (1.6\text{-}17)$$

Spatial Differentials

The Fourier transform of the directional derivative of an image function is related to the Fourier transform by

$$\mathcal{O}_\mathscr{F}\left\{\frac{\partial F(x, y)}{\partial x}\right\} = -i\omega_x \mathscr{F}(\omega_x, \omega_y) \qquad (1.6\text{-}18a)$$

$$\mathcal{O}_\mathscr{F}\left\{\frac{\partial F(x, y)}{\partial y}\right\} = -i\omega_y \mathscr{F}(\omega_x, \omega_y) \qquad (1.6\text{-}18b)$$

Consequently, the Fourier transform of the Laplacian of an image function is equal to

$$\mathcal{O}_\mathscr{F}\left\{\frac{\partial^2 F(x, y)}{\partial x^2} + \frac{\partial^2 F(x, y)}{\partial y^2}\right\} = -(\omega_x^2 + \omega_y^2)\mathscr{F}(\omega_x, \omega_y) \qquad (1.6\text{-}19)$$

1.7. FOURIER ANALYSIS OF ADDITIVE LINEAR SYSTEMS

The Fourier transform convolution theorem stated by Eq. 1.6-14 is an extremely useful tool for the analysis of additive linear systems. Consider an image function $F(x, y)$ that is the input to an additive linear system with an impulse response $H(x, y)$. The output image function is given by the convolution integral

$$G(x, y) = \int\limits_{-\infty}^{\infty}\int F(\alpha, \beta)H(x - \alpha, y - \beta)\, d\alpha\, d\beta \qquad (1.7\text{-}1)$$

Taking the Fourier transform of both sides of Eq. 1.7-1 and reversing the order of integration on the right-hand side results in

$$\mathscr{G}(\omega_x, \omega_y) = \int\limits_{-\infty}^{\infty}\int F(\alpha, \beta)\left[\int\limits_{-\infty}^{\infty}\int H(x - \alpha, y - \beta)\right.$$
$$\left. \exp\{-i(\omega_x x + \omega_y y)\}\, dx\, dy\right] d\alpha\, d\beta \qquad (1.7\text{-}2)$$

By the Fourier transform shift theorem of Eq. 1.6-13, the inner integral is equal to the Fourier transform of $H(x, y)$ multiplied by an exponential phase-shift factor. Thus

$$\mathcal{G}(\omega_x, \omega_y) = \int\!\!\!\int\limits_{-\infty}^{\infty} F(\alpha, \beta)\mathcal{H}(\omega_x, \omega_y) \exp\{-i(\omega_x\alpha + \omega_y\beta)\}\, d\alpha\, d\beta$$

$$(1.7\text{-}3)$$

Performing the indicated Fourier transformation gives

$$\mathcal{G}(\omega_x, \omega_y) = \mathcal{H}(\omega_x, \omega_y)\mathcal{F}(\omega_x, \omega_y) \qquad (1.7\text{-}4)$$

Then, an inverse transformation of Eq. 1.7-4 provides the output image function

$$G(x, y) = \frac{1}{4\pi^2}\int\!\!\!\int\limits_{-\infty}^{\infty} \mathcal{H}(\omega_x, \omega_y)\mathcal{F}(\omega_x, \omega_y) \exp\{i(\omega_x x + \omega_y y)\}\, d\omega_x\, d\omega_y$$

$$(1.7\text{-}5)$$

Equations 1.7-1 and 1.7-5 represent two alternative means of determining the output image response of an additive, linear, space-invariant system. The analytic or operational choice between the two approaches, convolution or Fourier processing, is usually problem dependent.

1.8. GENERALIZED LINEAR SYSTEMS

The terms linearity and superposition are commonly applied only to additive linear systems as defined in Section 1.4; however, the concepts of linearity and superposition are more general. Oppenheim (4) has introduced the concept of generalized superposition as a means of extending the additive linearity concept to a broader class of systems.

Consider two image fields $F_1(x, y)$ and $F_2(x, y)$ that are combined according to some undefined operator $(\Diamond)$ to produce an output image field

$$G(x, y) = F_1(x, y) \Diamond F_2(x, y) \qquad (1.8\text{-}1)$$

Let $\mathcal{O}_G\{\cdot\}$ represent a system operation on $G(x, y)$ that possesses the following properties:

$$\mathcal{O}_G\{F_1(x, y) \Diamond F_2(x, y)\} = \mathcal{O}_G\{F_1(x, y)\} \Diamond \mathcal{O}_G\{F_2(x, y)\} \qquad (1.8\text{-}2a)$$

and

$$\mathcal{O}_G\{k : F(x, y)\} = k : \mathcal{O}_G\{F(x, y)\} \qquad (1.8\text{-}2b)$$

where k is a constant and the colon denotes a product operation. It has been shown (4) that if $\diamond$ represents vector space addition and the colon denotes scalar multiplication, then the operator $\mathcal{O}_G\{\cdot\}$ can be decomposed into the cascade of operations shown in Figure 1.8-1, which are collectively called a homomorphic filter. The first operator $\diamond$ follows the rules

$$\mathcal{O}_A\{F_1(x, y) \diamond F_2(x, y)\} = \mathcal{O}_A\{F_1(x, y)\} + \mathcal{O}_A\{F_2(x, y)\} \qquad (1.8\text{-}3a)$$

and

$$\mathcal{O}_A\{k : F(x, y)\} = k : \mathcal{O}_A\{F(x, y)\} \qquad (1.8\text{-}3b)$$

Thus the first stage converts the operator $\diamond$ to algebraic addition. The second stage is an ordinary additive linear system, and the third stage is the inverse of the first stage. That is,

$$\mathcal{O}_A^{-1}\{\mathcal{O}_A\{F(x, y)\}\} = F(x, y) \qquad (1.8\text{-}4)$$

Figure 1.8-1c illustrates a special case of homomorphic filtering for multiplicative systems (5). Suppose that an image field $G(x, y)$ is generated by the algebraic product of image fields $F_1(x, y)$ and $F_2(x, y)$ according to the simple relations

$$G(x, y) = F_1(x, y) \diamond F_2(x, y) \equiv F_1(x, y)F_2(x, y) \qquad (1.8\text{-}5)$$

Taking the logarithm of both sides of Eq. 1.8-5 results in an output

$$\log\{G(x, y)\} = \log\{F_1(x, y)\} + \log\{F_2(x, y)\} \qquad (1.8\text{-}6)$$

in which the logarithms of $F_1(x, y)$ and $F_2(x, y)$ are additively combined.

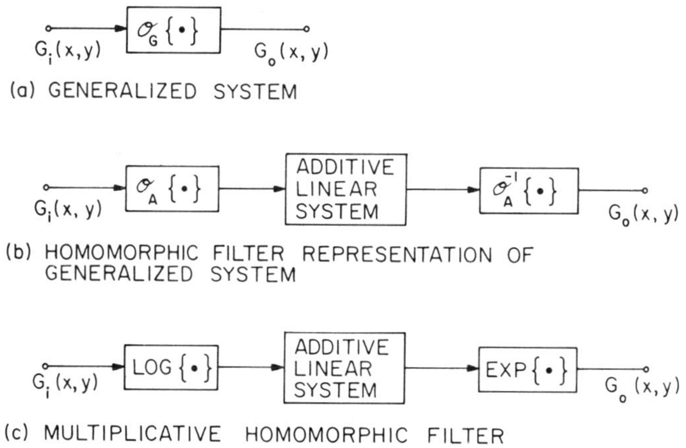

(a) GENERALIZED SYSTEM

(b) HOMOMORPHIC FILTER REPRESENTATION OF GENERALIZED SYSTEM

(c) MULTIPLICATIVE HOMOMORPHIC FILTER

FIGURE 1.8-1. Generalized linear systems.

These image fields are then linearly processed, and a subsequent exponential operation returns the output to the original signal space. For the scalar product operation

$$G(x, y) = k : F(x, y) \equiv [F(x, y)]^k \tag{1.8-7}$$

and the logarithm yields

$$\log \{G(x, y)\} = k \log \{F(x, y)\} \tag{1.8-8}$$

Applications of homomorphic filtering to image restoration are presented in Chapter 15.

1.9. STOCHASTIC CHARACTERIZATION OF CONTINUOUS IMAGES*

It is often convenient to regard an image as a sample of a stochastic process. For continuous images the image function $F(x, y, t)$ is assumed to be a member of a continuous three-dimensional stochastic process with space variables (x, y) and time variable (t).

The stochastic process $F(x, y, t)$ can be completely described by knowledge of its joint probability density

$$p\{F_1, F_2, \ldots, F_J; x_1, y_1, t_1, x_2, y_2, t_2, \ldots, x_J, y_J, t_J\}$$

for all sample points J where (x_j, y_j, t_j) represent space and time samples of image function $F_j(x_j, y_j, t_j)$. In general, high-order joint probability densities of images are usually not known, nor are they easily modeled. The first-order probability density $p(F; x, y, t)$ can sometimes be successfully modeled on the basis of the physics of the process or histogram measurements. For example, the first-order probability density of random noise from an electronic sensor is usually well modeled by a Gaussian density of the form

$$p\{F; x, y, t\} = [2\pi\sigma_F^2(x, y, t)]^{-1/2} \exp\left\{-\frac{[F(x, y, t) - \eta_F(x, y, t)]^2}{2\sigma_F^2(x, y, t)}\right\} \tag{1.9-1}$$

---

* The presentation on the statistical characterization of images assumes general familiarity with probability theory, random variables, and stochastic process. Suitable background references are (2, 6, 7). The primary purpose of the discussion here is to introduce notation and develop stochastic image models.

where the parameters $\eta_F(x, y, t)$ and $\sigma_F^2(x, y, t)$ denote the mean and variance of the process. The Gaussian density is also a reasonably accurate model for the probability density of the amplitude of unitary transform coefficients of an image. The probability density of the luminance function must be a one-sided density since the luminance measure is positive. Models that have found application include the Rayleigh density,

$$p\{F; x, y, t\} = \frac{F(x, y, t)}{\alpha^2} \exp\left\{-\frac{[F(x, y, t)]^2}{2\alpha^2}\right\} \qquad (1.9\text{-}2a)$$

the log-normal density,

$$p\{F; x, y, t\} = [2\pi F^2(x, y, t)\sigma_F^2(x, y, t)]^{-1/2}$$

$$\times \exp\left\{-\frac{[\log[F(x, y, t)] - \eta_F(x, y, t)]^2}{2\sigma_F^2(x, y, t)}\right\} \qquad (1.9\text{-}2b)$$

and the exponential density,

$$p\{F; x, y, t\} = \alpha \exp\{-\alpha|F(x, y, t)|\} \qquad (1.9\text{-}2c)$$

all defined for $F \geq 0$ where α is a constant. The two-sided, or Laplacian, density,

$$p\{F; x, y, t\} = \frac{\alpha}{2} \exp\{-\alpha|F(x, y, t)|\} \qquad (1.9\text{-}3)$$

where α is a constant, is often selected as a model for the probability density of the difference of image samples. Finally, the uniform density

$$p\{F; x, y, t\} = \frac{1}{2\pi} \qquad (1.9\text{-}4)$$

for $-\pi \leq F \leq \pi$ is a common model for phase fluctuations of a random process. Conditional probability densities are also useful in characterizing stochastic process. The conditional density of an image function evaluated at (x_1, y_1, t_1) given knowledge of the image function at (x_2, y_2, t_2) is defined as

$$p\{F_1; x_1, y_1, t_1 | F_2; x_2, y_2, t_2\} = \frac{p\{F_1, F_2; x_1, y_1, t_1, x_2, y_2, t_2\}}{p\{F_2; x_2, y_2, t_2\}}$$

$$(1.9\text{-}5)$$

Higher-order conditional densities are defined in a similar manner.

Another means of describing a stochastic process is through computation of its ensemble averages. The first moment or mean of the image function is defined as

$$\eta_F(x, y, t) = E\{F(x, y, t)\} = \int_{-\infty}^{\infty} F(x, y, t)p\{F; x, y, t\}\, dF \quad (1.9\text{-}6)$$

while the second moment or autocorrelation function is given by

$$R(x_1, y_1, t_1; x_2, y_2, t_2) = E\{F(x_1, y_1, t_1)F^*(x_2, y_2, t_2)\}$$

$$= \int_{-\infty}^{\infty} \int_{-\infty}^{\infty} F(x_1, y_1, t_1)F^*(x_2, y_2, t_2)$$

$$\times p\{F_1, F_2; x_1, y_1, t_1, x_2, y_2, t_2\}\, dF_1\, dF_2 \quad (1.9\text{-}7)$$

The autocovariance of the image process is the autocorrelation about the mean defined as

$$K(x_1, y_1, t_1; x_2, y_2, t_2) = E\{[F(x_1, y_1, t_1) - \eta_F(x_1, y_1, t_1)]$$

$$\times [F^*(x_2, y_2, t_2) - \eta_F^*(x_2, y_2, t_2)]\}$$

$$(1.9\text{-}8a)$$

or

$$K(x_1, y_1, t_1; x_2, y_2, t_2) = R(x_1, y_1, t_1; x_2, y_2, t_2)$$

$$- \eta_F(x_1, y_1, t_1)\eta_F^*(x_2, y_2, t_2)$$

$$(1.9\text{-}8b)$$

Finally, the variance of an image process is

$$\sigma_F^2(x, y, t) = K(x, y, t; x, y, t) \quad (1.9\text{-}9)$$

An image process is called stationary in the strict sense if its moments are unaffected by shifts in the space and time origins. The image process is said to be stationary in the wide sense if its mean is constant and its autocorrelation is dependent on the differences in the image coordinates, $x_1 - x_2$, $y_1 - y_2$, $t_1 - t_2$, and not on their individual values. In other words the image autocorrelation is not a function of position or time. For stationary image processes,

$$E\{F(x, y, t)\} = \eta_F \quad (1.9\text{-}10a)$$

and

$$R(x_1, y_1, t_1; x_2, y_2, t_2) = R(x_1 - x_2; y_1 - y_2; t_1 - t_2) \quad (1.9\text{-}10b)$$

The autocorrelation expression may then be written as

$$R(\tau_x, \tau_y, \tau_t) = E\{F(x + \tau_x, y + \tau_y, t + \tau_t)F^*(x, y, t)\} \quad (1.9\text{-}11)$$

Because

$$R(-\tau_x, -\tau_y, -\tau_t) = R^*(\tau_x, \tau_y, \tau_t) \qquad (1.9\text{-}12)$$

then for an image function with F real, the autocorrelation is real and an even function of τ_x, τ_y, τ_t. The power spectrum of a stationary image process is defined as the three-dimensional Fourier transform of its autocorrelation function as given by

$$\mathcal{W}(\omega_x, \omega_y, \omega_t) = \int_{-\infty}^{\infty} \int_{-\infty}^{\infty} \int_{-\infty}^{\infty} R(\tau_x, \tau_y, \tau_t)$$

$$\times \exp\{-i[\omega_x \tau_x + \omega_y \tau_y + \omega_t \tau_t]\}\, d\tau_x\, d\tau_y\, d\tau_t$$
$$(1.9\text{-}13)$$

In many imaging systems the spatial and time image processes are separable so that the stationary correlation function may be written as

$$R(\tau_x, \tau_y, \tau_t) = R_{xy}(\tau_x, \tau_y)R_t(\tau_t) \qquad (1.9\text{-}14)$$

Furthermore, the spatial autocorrelation function is often considered as the product of x and y axis autocorrelation functions

$$R_{xy}(\tau_x, \tau_y) = R_x(\tau_x)R_y(\tau_y) \qquad (1.9\text{-}15)$$

for computational simplicity. For scenes of man-made objects there is often a large amount of horizontal and vertical image structure, and the spatial separation approximation is quite good. In "natural" scenes, there usually is no preferential direction of correlation; the spatial autocorrelation function tends to be rotationally symmetric, and not separable.

An image field is often modeled as a sample of a first-order Markov process for which the correlation between points on the image field is proportional to their geometric separation. The autocovariance function for the two-dimensional Markov process is

$$K_{x,y}(\tau_x, \tau_y) = K \exp\{-\sqrt{\alpha_x^2 \tau_x^2 + \alpha_y^2 \tau_y^2}\} \qquad (1.9\text{-}16)$$

where K is an energy scaling constant and α_x and α_y are scaling constants. The corresponding power spectrum is

$$\mathcal{W}(\omega_x, \omega_y) = \frac{1}{\alpha_x \alpha_y} \left[\frac{2K}{1 + [\omega_x^2/\alpha_x^2 + \omega_y^2/\alpha_y^2]} \right] \qquad (1.9\text{-}17)$$

As a simplifying assumption, the Markov process is often assumed to be of separable form with an autocovariance function

$$K_{x,y}(\tau_x, \tau_y) = K \exp\{-\alpha_x |\tau_x| - \alpha_y |\tau_y|\} \qquad (1.9\text{-}18)$$

The power spectrum of this process is

$$\mathcal{W}(\omega_x, \omega_y) = \frac{4\alpha_x\alpha_y K}{(\alpha_x^2 + \omega_x^2)(\alpha_y^2 + \omega_y^2)} \tag{1.9-19}$$

In the discussion of the deterministic characteristics of an image, both time and space averages of the image function have been defined. An ensemble average has also been defined for the statistical image characterization. A question of interest is: What is the relationship between the spatial-time averages and the ensemble averages? The answer is that for certain stochastic processes, which are called ergodic processes, the spatial-time averages and the ensemble averages are equal. Proof of the ergodicity of a process in the general case is often difficult; it usually suffices to determine second-order ergodicity in which the first- and second-order space-time averages are equal to the first- and second-order ensemble averages.

1.10. SYSTEM RESPONSE OF STOCHASTIC IMAGES

Often the probability density or moments of a stochastic image field are known at the input to a system, and it is desired to determine the corresponding information at the system output. If the system transfer function is algebraic in nature, the output probability density can be determined in terms of the input probability density by a probability density transformation. For example, let the system output be related to the system input by

$$G(x, y, t) = \mathcal{O}_F\{F(x, y, t)\} \tag{1.10-1}$$

where $\mathcal{O}_F\{\cdot\}$ is a monotonic operator on $F(x, y)$. The probability density of the output field is then

$$p\{G; x, y, t\} = \frac{p\{F(x, y, t)\}}{|d\mathcal{O}_F\{F(x, y)\}/dF|} \tag{1.10-2}$$

The extension to higher-order probability densities is straightforward, but often cumbersome.

The moments of the output of a system can be obtained directly from knowledge of the output probability density, or in certain cases, indirectly in terms of the system operator. For example, if the system operator is additive linear, the mean of the system output is

$$E\{G(x, y, t)\} = E\{\mathcal{O}_L\{F(x, y, t)\}\} = \mathcal{O}_L\{E\{F(x, y, t)\}\} \tag{1.10-3}$$

It can be shown that if a system operator is additive linear and if the system input image field is stationary in the strict sense, the system output is also stationary in the strict sense. Furthermore, if the input is stationary in the wide sense, the output is also wide-sense stationary.

Consider an additive linear space-invariant system whose output is described by the convolution integral

$$G(x, y, t) = \int\int_{-\infty}^{\infty} F(x - \alpha, y - \beta, t-\gamma) H(\alpha, \beta, \gamma) \, d\alpha \, d\beta \, d\gamma$$

$$(1.10\text{-}4)$$

where $H(x, y, t)$ is the system impulse response. The mean of the output is then

$$E\{G(x, y, t)\} = \int\int_{-\infty}^{\infty} E\{F(x - \alpha, y - \beta, t - \gamma)\} H(\alpha, \beta, \gamma) \, d\alpha \, d\beta \, d\gamma$$

$$(1.10\text{-}5)$$

If the input image field is stationary, its mean η_F is a constant that may be brought outside the integral. As a result,

$$E\{G(x, y, t)\} = \eta_F \int\int_{-\infty}^{\infty} H(\alpha, \beta, \gamma) \, d\alpha \, d\beta \, d\gamma = \eta_F \mathcal{H}(0, 0, 0)$$

$$(1.10\text{-}6)$$

where $\mathcal{H}(0, 0, 0)$ is the transfer function of the linear system evaluated at the origin in the spatial-time frequency domain. Following the same techniques, it can be easily shown that the autocorrelation functions of the system input and output are related by

$$R_G(\tau_x, \tau_y, \tau_t) = R_F(\tau_x, \tau_y, \tau_t) \circledast H(\tau_x, \tau_y, \tau_t) \circledast H^*(-\tau_x, -\tau_y, -\tau_t)$$

$$(1.10\text{-}7)$$

Taking Fourier transforms on both sides of Eq. 1.10-7 and invoking the Fourier transform convolution theorem, one obtains the relationship between the power spectra of the input and output image,

$$\mathcal{W}_G(\omega_x, \omega_y, \omega_t) = \mathcal{W}_F(\omega_x, \omega_y, \omega_t) \mathcal{H}(\omega_x, \omega_y, \omega_t) \mathcal{H}^*(\omega_x, \omega_y, \omega_t)$$

$$(1.10\text{-}8a)$$

or

$$\mathcal{W}_G(\omega_x, \omega_y, \omega_t) = \mathcal{W}_F(\omega_x, \omega_y, \omega_t) |\mathcal{H}(\omega_x, \omega_y, \omega_t)|^2 \quad (1.10\text{-}8b)$$

This result is found useful in analyzing the effect of noise in imaging systems.

REFERENCES

1. J. W. Goodman, *Introduction to Fourier Optics*, McGraw-Hill, New York, 1968.

2. A. Papoulis, *Systems and Transforms with Applications in Optics*, McGraw-Hill, New York, 1968.

3. J. M. S. Prewitt, "Object Enhancement and Extraction," in *Picture Processing and Psychopictorics*, B. S. Lipkin and A. Rosenfeld, Eds., Academic Press, New York, 1970.

4. A. V. Oppenheim, "Generalized Superposition," *Information and Control*, **11**, November 1967, 528–536.

5. A. V. Oppenheim, R. W. Schafer, and T. G. Stockham, Jr., "Nonlinear Filtering of Multiplied and Convolved Signals," *Proc. IEEE*, **56**, 8, August 1968, 1264–1291.

6. A. Papoulis, *Probability, Random Variables, and Stochastic Processes*, McGraw-Hill, New York, 1965.

7. J. B. Thomas, *An Introduction to Applied Probability Theory and Random Processes*, John Wiley, New York, 1971.

2 PSYCHOPHYSICAL PROPERTIES OF VISION

To efficiently design imaging systems for which the output is a photograph or display to be viewed by a human observer, it is obviously beneficial to have an understanding of the mechanism of human vision. Such knowledge can be utilized to develop conceptual models of the human visual process. These models are vital in the design of image processing systems and in the construction of measures of image fidelity and intelligibility.

2.1. PERCEPTION OF LIGHT

Light, according to Webster's dictionary (1), is: "radiant energy which, by its action on the organs of vision, enables them to perform their function of sight." Much is known about the physical properties of light, but the mechanisms by which light interacts with the "organs of vision" is not as well understood. Light is known to be a form of electromagnetic radiation lying in a relatively narrow region of the electromagnetic spectrum over a wavelength band of about 350 to 780 nm. A physical light source may be characterized by the rate of radiant energy (radiant intensity) it emits at a particular spectral wavelength. Light entering the human visual system originates either from a self-luminous source, or from light reflected from some object, or from light transmitted through some translucent object. Let $E(\lambda)$ represent the spectral energy distribution of light emitted from some primary light source, and also let $t(\lambda)$ and $r(\lambda)$ denote the wavelength dependent transmissivity and reflectivity, respectively, of an object. Then, for a transmissive object, the observed light spectral energy distribution is

$$C(\lambda) = t(\lambda)E(\lambda) \qquad (2.1\text{-}1)$$

and for a reflective object

$$C(\lambda) = r(\lambda)E(\lambda) \qquad (2.1\text{-}2)$$

Figure 2.1-1 contains plots of the spectral energy distribution of several common sources of light encountered in imaging systems: sunlight, a

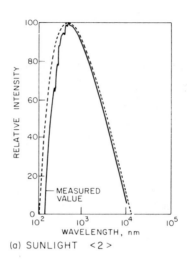

(a) SUNLIGHT < 2 >

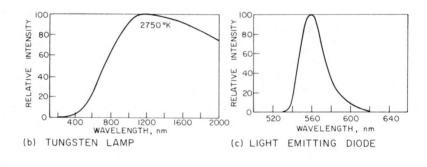

(b) TUNGSTEN LAMP   (c) LIGHT EMITTING DIODE

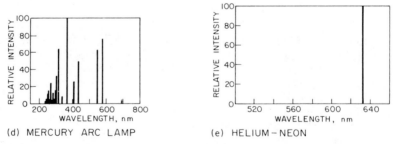

(d) MERCURY ARC LAMP   (e) HELIUM − NEON

FIGURE 2.1-1.   Spectral energy distributions of common physical light sources (2).

tungsten lamp, a light-emitting diode, a mercury arc lamp, and a helium-neon laser. A human viewing each of the light sources will perceive the sources differently. Sunlight appears as an extremely bright yellowish-white light, while the tungsten light bulb appears less bright and somewhat yellowish. The light-emitting diode appears to be a dim green; the mercury arc light is a highly bright bluish-white light; and the laser produces an extremely bright and pure red beam. These observations provoke many questions. What are the attributes of the light sources that cause them to be perceived differently? Is the spectral energy distribution sufficient to explain the differences in perception? If not, what are adequate descriptors of visual perception? As will be seen, answers to these questions are only partially available.

There are three common perceptual descriptors of a light sensation: brightness, hue, and saturation. The characteristics of these descriptors are considered below.

If two light sources with the same spectral shape are observed, the source of greater physical intensity will generally appear to be perceptually brighter. However, there are numerous examples in which an object of uniform intensity appears not to be of uniform brightness. Therefore, intensity is not an adequate quantitative measure of brightness.

The attribute of light that distinguishes a red colored light from a green light or a yellow light, for example, is called the hue of the light. A prism and slit arrangement, as shown in Figure 2.1-2, can produce narrowband wavelength light of varying color. However, it is clear that the light wavelength is not an adequate measure of color since some colored lights encountered in nature are not contained in the rainbow of light produced by a prism. For example, purple light is absent. Purple light can be produced by combining equal amounts of red and blue narrowband lights. Other counterexamples exist. If two light sources with the same spectral energy distribution are observed under identical conditions, they will appear to possess the same hue. However, it is possible to have two light sources with different spectral energy distributions that are perceived identically. Such lights are called metameric pairs.

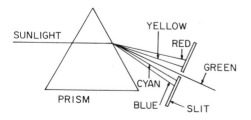

FIGURE 2.1-2. Refraction of light from a prism.

The third perceptual descriptor of a colored light is its saturation. Saturation is the attribute that distinguishes a spectral light from a pastel light of the same hue. In effect, saturation describes the "whiteness" of a light source. Although it is possible to speak of the percentage saturation of a color referenced to a spectral color on a chromaticity diagram of the type shown in Figure 3.4-3, saturation is not usually considered to be a quantitative measure.

As an aid to classifying colors, it is convenient to regard colors as being points in some color solid as shown in Figure 2.1-3. The Munsell system of color classification actually has a form similar in shape to this figure (3). However, to be quantitatively useful, a color solid should possess metric significance. That is, a unit distance within the color solid should represent a constant perceptual color difference regardless of the particular pair of colors considered. The subject of perceptually significant color solids is considered later.

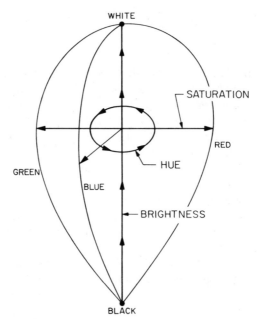

FIGURE 2.1-3.   Perceptual representation of light.

2.2. THE EYE

A conceptual technique for the establishment of a model of the human visual system would be to perform a physiological analysis of the eye, the nerve paths to the brain, and those parts of the brain involved in visual perception. Such a task, of course, is beyond the ability of man because of the large number of infinitesimally small elements in the visual chain. However, much has been learned from physiological studies of the eye that is helpful in the development of visual models (4–7).

Figure 2.2-1 contains a sketch of the horizontal cross section of a human eyeball. The front of the eye is covered by a transparent surface called the cornea. The remaining outer cover, called the sclera, is composed of a fibrous coat that surrounds the choroid, a layer containing blood capillaries. Inside the choroid is the retina, which is composed of two types of receptors: rods and cones. Nerves connecting to the retina leave the eyeball through the optic nerve bundle. Light entering the cornea is focused to the retina surface by a lens that changes shape under muscular control to perform proper focusing of near and distant objects. An iris acts as a diaphram to control the amount of light entering the eye.

The rods in the retina are long slender receptors, while the cones are generally shorter and thicker in structure. There are also important operational distinctions. The rods are more sensitive to light than the cones. At low levels of illumination the rods provide a visual response called scotopic vision. Cones respond to higher levels of illumination; their response is called photopic vision. Figure 2.2-2 illustrates the relative sensitivities of rods and cones as a function of illumination wavelength (7, 8). An eye contains about 6.5 million cones and 100 million rods distributed over the

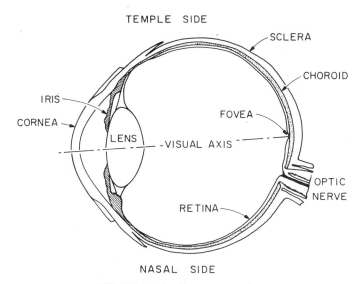

FIGURE 2.2-1. Eye cross section.

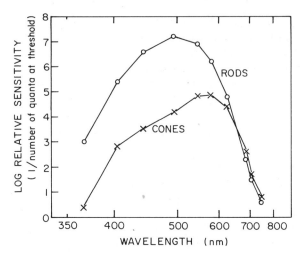

FIGURE 2.2-2. Sensitivity of rods and cones (7) [based upon measurements by Wald (8)].

retina (4). Figure 2.2-3 shows the distribution of rods and cones over a horizontal line on the retina (4). At a point near the optic nerve, called the fovea, the density of cones is greatest. This is the region of sharpest photopic vision. There are no rods nor cones in the vicinity of the optic nerve, and hence the eye has a "blind spot" in this region.

In recent years it has been determined that there are three basic types of cones in the retina (9, 10). These cones have different absorption characteristics as a function of wavelength with peak absorptions in the red, green, and blue regions of the optical spectrum. Figure 2.2-4 contains curves of the measured spectral absorption of pigments in the retina for a particular subject (10). Two major points of note regarding the curves are that the α cones, which are primarily responsible for blue light perception, have relatively low sensitivity, and the absorption curves overlap considerably. The existence of the three types of cones provides a physiological basis for the trichromatic theory of color vision.

When a light stimulus activates a rod or cone, a photochemical transition occurs producing a nerve impulse. The manner in which nerve impulses propagate through the visual system is presently not well established. It is known that the optic nerve bundle contains on the order of 800,000 nerve fibers. Because there are over 100,000,000 receptors in the retina, it is obvious that in many regions of the retina, the rods and cones must be interconnected to nerve fibers. Because neither the photochemistry of the retina nor the propagation of nerve impulses within the eye is well understood, a deterministic characterization of the visual process is unavailable.

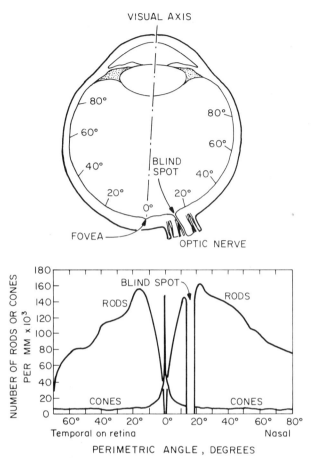

FIGURE 2.2-3. Distribution of rods and cones on retina (4).

One must be satisfied with the establishment of models that characterize, and hopefully predict, human visual response. The following section describes several visual phenomena that should be considered in the modelling of human visual process.

2.3. VISUAL PHENOMENA

The visual phenomena described below are interrelated, in some cases only minimally, but in others, to a very large extent. For simplification in presentation and, in some instances, lack of knowledge, the phenomena are considered disjoint.

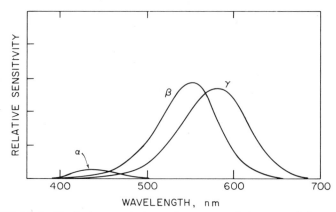

FIGURE 2.2-4. Typical spectral absorption curves of pigments of the retina (10).

Contrast Sensitivity

The response of the eye to changes in the intensity of illumination is known to be nonlinear. Consider a patch of light of intensity $I + \Delta I$ surrounded by a background of intensity I, as shown in Figure 2.3-1a. The just noticeable difference ΔI is to be determined as a function of I. Over a wide range of intensities, it is found that the ratio $\Delta I/I$, called the Weber fraction, is nearly constant at a value of about 0.02 (11). This result does not hold at very low or very high intensities, as illustrated by Figure 2.3-1a (12). Furthermore, contrast sensitivity is dependent on the intensity of the surround. Consider the experiment of Figure 2.3-1b, in which two patches of light, one of intensity I and the other of intensity $I + \Delta I$, are surrounded by light of intensity I_0. The Weber fraction $\Delta I/I$ for this experiment is plotted in Figure 2.3-1b as a function of the intensity of the background. In this situation it is found that the range over which the Weber fraction remains constant is reduced considerably compared to the experiment of Figure 2.3-1a. The envelope of the lower limits of the curves of Figure 2.3-1b is equivalent to the curve of Figure 2.3-1a. However, the range over which $\Delta I/I$ is approximately constant for a fixed background intensity I_0 is still comparable to the dynamic range of most electronic imaging systems.

Because the differential of the logarithm of intensity is

$$d\{\log (I)\} = \frac{dI}{I} \qquad (2.3\text{-}1)$$

equal changes in the logarithm of the intensity of a light can be related to equal just noticeable changes in its intensity over the region of intensities,

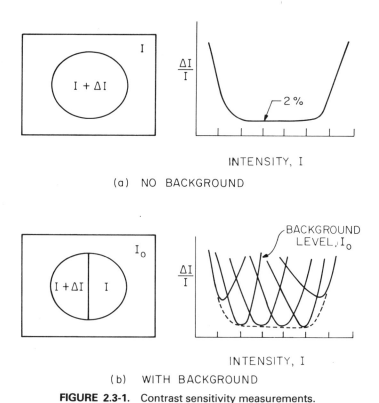

(a) NO BACKGROUND

(b) WITH BACKGROUND

FIGURE 2.3-1. Contrast sensitivity measurements.

for which the Weber fraction is constant. For this reason, in many image processing systems, operations are performed on the logarithm of the intensity of an image point, rather than the intensity.

Mach Band

Consider the set of gray scale strips in the photograph of Figure 2.3-2a. The reflected light intensity from each strip is uniform over its width and differs from its neighbors by a constant amount; nevertheless, the visual appearance is that each strip is darker at its right side than at its left. This is called the Mach band effect (13). Figure 2.3-2c contains a photograph of the Mach band pattern of Figure 2.3-2d. In the photograph a bright bar appears at position B and a dark bar appears at D. Neither bar would be predicted purely on the basis of the intensity distribution. The apparent Mach band overshoot in brightness is a consequence of the spatial frequency response of the eye. As will be seen shortly, the eye possesses a lower sensitivity to high and low spatial frequencies than midfrequencies.

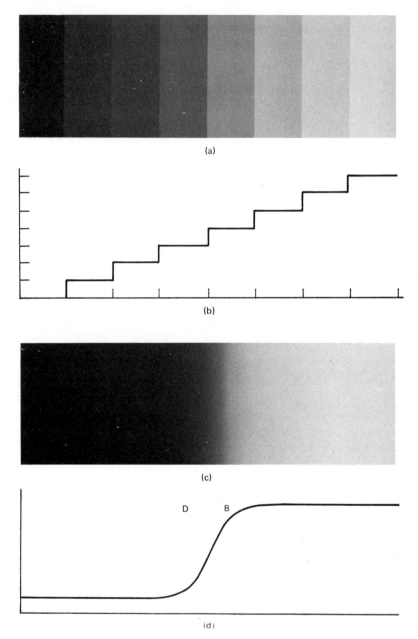

FIGURE 2.3-2. Examples of Mach band effect. (a) Step chart photo. (b) Step chart intensity distribution. (c) Ramp chart photo. (d) Ramp chart intensity distribution.

The implication for the designer of image processing systems is that perfect fidelity of edge contours can be sacrificed to some extent, since the eye has imperfect response to high spatial frequency brightness transitions.

Simultaneous Contrast

The simultaneous contrast phenomenon (7) is illustrated by the photograph of Figure 2.3-3. Each small square is actually the same intensity, but because of the different intensities of the surrounds, the small squares do not appear equally bright. The hue of a patch of light is also dependent on the wavelength composition of surrounding light. A white patch on a black background will appear to be yellowish if the surround is a blue light.

Chromatic Adaption

The hue of a perceived color is dependent on the adaption of a viewer (14). For example, the American flag will not immediately appear red, white, and blue if the viewer has been subjected to high-intensity red light before viewing the flag. The colors of the flag will appear to shift in hue toward the red complement, cyan.

Color Blindness

Approximately 8% of the males and 1% of the females in the world population are subject to some form of color blindness (15, p. 405). There are various degrees of color blindness. Some people, called monochromats, only possess rods or rods plus one type of cone, and therefore are only capable of monochromatic vision. Dichromats are people who possess two of the three types of cones. Both monochromats and dichromats can distinguish colors insofar as they have learned to associate particular colors with particular objects. For example, dark roses are assumed to be red, and light roses are assumed to be yellow. But if a red rose were painted yellow such that its reflectivity was maintained at the same value, the monochromat might still call the rose red. Similar examples illustrate the inability of dichromats to accurately distinguish hue.

FIGURE 2.3-3. Illustration of simultaneous contrast.

Subjective Color (16)

In 1826 Benedict Prevost, a French monk, noticed that when a white sheet of paper was periodically illuminated by waving the sheet through a shaft of sunlight in a darkened room, a spectrum of colored light was observed to be reflected from the sheet of paper. This was the first recorded observation of the phenomenon of subjective color in which intermittent pulses of white light are perceived as colored light. Fechner, in 1838, observed subjective color from a spinning disk painted half black and half white. And in 1894 Benham invented a spinning top which had a pattern of the type shown in Figure 2.3-4 on its upper surface. When the disk is spun counterclockwise, the outer ring appears red, the middle ring appears green, and inner ring appears blue. A reversal of rotation reverses the colors of the inner and outer rings. These phenomena and other related effects are explainable in part by the temporal response of the human visual system to flashing lights.

Land's Experiments

In the early 1950s Land (17) performed some interesting psychophysical experiments involving the reproduction of color with only two primaries. One of these experiments is illustrated in Figure 2.3-5. A positive, monochrome transparency T_1 is made of a scene through a filter with a passband from about 600 to 700 nm. Another monochrome transparency T_2 is made of the same scene through a filter with a passband of 500–600 nm. Then the two transparencies are simultaneously projected onto a screen. Transparency T_1 is illuminated by a red light of wavelength 600–700 nm and transparency T_2 is illuminated by white light. An interesting observation is then made: when the two images are in spatial register, the original scene appears in almost natural color (purple colors in the original scene are the only colors not reproduced well); if the two images are slightly out of register, the color effect is diminished significantly. Thus it is observed that the perception of color is dependent on the spatial content of a scene, and is not a purely local phenomenon.

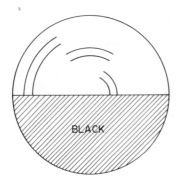

FIGURE 2.3-4. Benham disk.

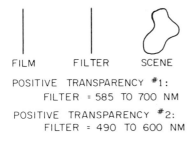

FILM FILTER SCENE

POSITIVE TRANSPARENCY #1:
    FILTER = 585 TO 700 NM

POSITIVE TRANSPARENCY #2:
    FILTER = 490 TO 600 NM

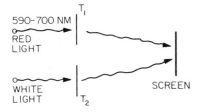

FIGURE 2.3-5. Land's experiment.

2.4. MONOCHROME VISION MODEL

One of the modern techniques of optical system design entails the treatment of an optical system as a two-dimensional linear system that is linear in intensity and can be characterized by a two-dimensional transfer function (18). Consider the linear optical system of Figure 2.4-1. The system input is a spatial light distribution obtained by passing a constant-intensity light beam through a transparency with a spatial sine wave transmittance. Since the system is linear, the spatial output intensity distribution will also exhibit sine wave intensity variations with possible changes in the amplitude and phase of the output intensity compared to the input intensity. By varying the spatial frequency (number of intensity cycles per linear dimension) of the input transparency, and recording the output intensity level and phase, it is possible, in principle, to obtain the optical transfer function (OTF) of the optical system.

Let $\mathcal{H}(\omega_x, \omega_y)$ represent the optical transfer function of a two-dimensional linear system where $\omega_x = 2\pi/T_x$ and $\omega_y = 2\pi/T_y$ are angular spatial frequencies with spatial periods T_x and T_y in the coordinate directions, respectively. Then with $I_i(x, y)$ denoting the input intensity distribution of the object and $I_o(x, y)$ representing the output intensity distribution of the image, the frequency spectra of the input and output signals are defined as

$$\mathcal{I}_i(\omega_x, \omega_y) = \int\int_{-\infty}^{\infty} I_i(x, y) \exp\{-i[\omega_x x + \omega_y y]\} \, dx \, dy \qquad (2.4-1)$$

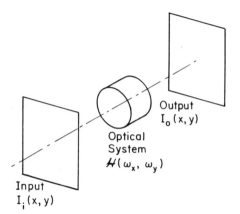

Output
$I_o(x, y)$

Optical
System
$\mathscr{H}(\omega_x, \omega_y)$

Input
$I_i(x, y)$

FIGURE 2.4-1. Linear systems
analysis of an optical system.

and

$$\mathscr{I}_o(\omega_x, \omega_y) = \int\!\!\int_{-\infty}^{\infty} I_o(x, y) \exp\{-i[\omega_x x + \omega_y y]\}\, dx\, dy \qquad (2.4\text{-}2)$$

The input and output intensity spectra are related by

$$\mathscr{I}_o(\omega_x, \omega_y) = \mathscr{H}(\omega_x, \omega_y)\mathscr{I}_i(\omega_x, \omega_y) \qquad (2.4\text{-}3)$$

The spatial distribution of the image intensity can be obtained by an inverse Fourier transformation of Eq. 2.4-1 yielding

$$I_o(x, y) = \frac{1}{4\pi^2} \int\!\!\int_{-\infty}^{\infty} \mathscr{I}_o(\omega_x, \omega_y) \exp\{i[\omega_x x + \omega_y y]\}\, d\omega_x\, d\omega_y \qquad (2.4\text{-}4)$$

In many systems the designer is only interested in the magnitude variations of the output intensity with respect to the magnitude variations of the input intensity, and not the phase variations. The ratio of the magnitudes of the Fourier transforms of the input and output signals,

$$\frac{|\mathscr{I}_o(\omega_x, \omega_y)|}{|\mathscr{I}_i(\omega_x, \omega_y)|} = |\mathscr{H}(\omega_x, \omega_y)| \qquad (2.4\text{-}5)$$

is called the modulation transfer function (MTF) of the optical system.

Much effort has been given to the application of the linear systems concept to the human visual system (19–25). A typical experiment to test the validity of the linear systems model is as follows. An observer is shown two sine wave grating transparencies, a reference grating of constant contrast* and spatial frequency, and a variable-contrast test grating whose spatial frequency is set at some value different from that of the reference. The contrast of the test grating is varied until the brightnesses of the bright and dark regions of the two transparencies appear identical. In this manner it is possible to develop a plot of the MTF of the human visual system. Figure 2.4-2a contains a hypothetical plot of the MTF as a function of the input signal contrast. Another indication of the form of the MTF can be obtained by observation of the composite sine wave grating of Figure 2.4-3 in which spatial frequency increases in one coordinate direction and contrast increases in the other direction. The envelope of the visible bars generally follows the MTF curves of Figure 2.4-2a (24).

Referring to Figure 2.4-2a, it is observed that the MTF measurement is dependent on the input contrast level. Furthermore, if the input sine wave grating is rotated relative to the optic axis of the eye, the shape of the MTF is altered somewhat. Thus it can be concluded that the human visual system, as measured by this experiment, is nonlinear and aniostropic (rotationally variant).

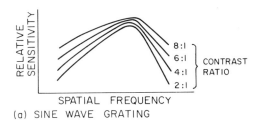

(a) SINE WAVE GRATING

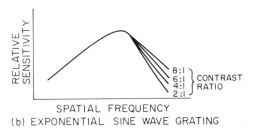

(b) EXPONENTIAL SINE WAVE GRATING

FIGURE 2.4-2. Hypothetical measurements of spatial frequency response of human visual system.

* Contrast is defined as the ratio of the maximum to minimum intensity of the grating.

Contrast →

Spatial frequency →

FIGURE 2.4-3. MTF measurement of human visual process by modulated sine wave grating.

It has been postulated that the nonlinear response of the eye to intensity variations is logarithmic in nature and occurs near the beginning of the visual information processing system, that is, near the rods and cones, before spatial interaction occurs between visual signals from individual rods and cones. Figure 2.4-4 contains a simple logarithmic eye model for monochromatic vision. If indeed the eye exhibits a logarithmic response to input intensity, then if a signal grating contains a recording of an exponential sine wave, that is, $\exp(\sin(I_i(x, y)))$, the human visual system can be "linearized." A hypothetical MTF obtained by measuring an observer's response to an exponential sine wave grating, as shown in Figure 2.4-2*b*,

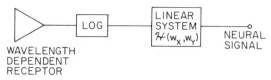

WAVELENGTH
DEPENDENT
RECEPTOR

LOG

LINEAR
SYSTEM
$\mathcal{H}(w_x, w_y)$

NEURAL
SIGNAL

FIGURE 2.4-4. Logarithmic model for monochrome vision.

can be fitted reasonably well by a single curve for low and mid spatial frequencies. Figure 2.4-5 contains a plot of the measured MTF of the human visual system obtained by Davidson (26) for an exponential sine wave test signal. The high spatial frequency portion of the curve has been extrapolated for an average input contrast.

The logarithmic/linear system eye model of Figure 2.4-3 has proved to provide a reasonable prediction of visual response over a wide range of intensities. However, at high spatial frequencies and at very low or very high intensities, observed responses depart from responses predicted by the model. In order to establish a more accurate model, it is necessary to consider the physical mechanisms of the human visual system.

The nonlinear response of rods and cones to intensity variations is still a subject of active research. Hypotheses have been introduced suggesting that the nonlinearity is based on chemical activity, electrical effects, and neural feedback. The basic logarithmic model assumes the form

$$I_o(x, y) = K_1 \log [K_2 + K_3 I_i(x, y)] \tag{2.4-6}$$

where the K_i are constants and $I_i(x, y)$ denotes the input field to the nonlinearity and $I_o(x, y)$ is its output. Another model that has been suggested (7, p. 253) follows the fractional response,

$$I_o(x, y) = \frac{K_1 I_i(x, y)}{K_2 + I_i(x, y)} \tag{2.4-7}$$

where K_1 and K_2 are constants. Mannos and Sakrison (27) have studied the effect of various nonlinearities employed in an analytical visual fidelity measure. Their results, which are discussed in greater detail in Chapter 7, establish that a power-law nonlinearity of the form

$$I_o(x, y) = [I_i(x, y)]^s \tag{2.4-8}$$

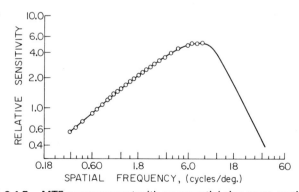

FIGURE 2.4-5. MTF measurement with exponential sine wave grating (26).

where s is a constant, provides good agreement between the visual fidelity measure and subjective assessment. The three models for the nonlinear response of rods and cones defined by Eqs. 2.4-6 to 2.4-8 can be forced to a reasonably close agreement over some mid-intensity range by an appropriate choice of scaling constants.

The physical mechanisms accounting for the spatial frequency response of the eye are partially optical and partially neural. As an optical instrument, the eye has limited resolution because of the finite size of the lens aperture, optical aberrations, and the finite dimensions of the rods and cones. These effects can be modeled by a low-pass transfer function inserted between the receptor and the nonlinear response element. The most significant contributor to the frequency response of the eye is the lateral inhibition process (28). The basic mechanism of lateral inhibition is illustrated in Figure 2.4-6. A neural signal is assumed to be generated by a weighted contribution of many spatially adjacent rods and cones. Some receptors actually exert an inhibitory influence on the neural response. The weighting values are, in effect, the impulse response of the human visual system beyond the retina. The two-dimensional Fourier transform of this impulse response is the post-retina transfer function.

When a light pulse is presented to a human viewer, there is a measurable delay in its perception. Also, perception continues beyond the termination

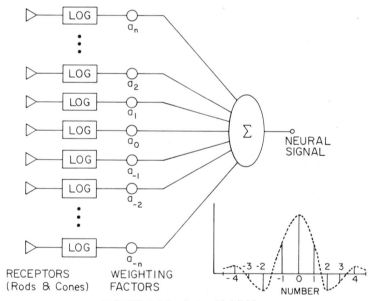

FIGURE 2.4-6. Lateral inhibition.

of the pulse for a short period of time. This delay and lag effect arising from neural temporal response limitations in the human visual system can be modeled by a linear temporal transfer function.

Figure 2.4-7 contains a model for monochromatic vision based on results of the preceding discussion. In the model the output of the wavelength-sensitive receptor is fed to a low-pass type of linear system that represents the optics of the eye. Next follows a general monotonic nonlinearity that represents the nonlinear intensity response of rods or cones. Then, the lateral inhibition process is characterized by a linear system with a band-pass response. Temporal filtering effects are modeled by the following linear system. Hall and Hall (29) have investigated this model extensively, and have found transfer functions for the various elements that accurately model the total system response. The monochromatic vision model of Figure 2.4-7, with appropriately scaled parameters, seems to be sufficiently detailed for most image processing applications. In fact, the simpler logarithmic model of Figure 2.4-3 is probably adequate for the bulk of applications.

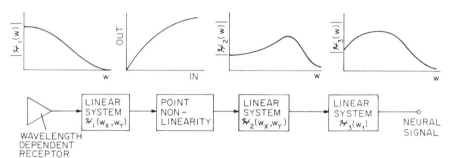

FIGURE 2.4-7. Extended model for monochrome vision.

2.5. COLOR VISION MODEL

There have been many theories postulated to explain human color vision, beginning with the experiments of Newton and Maxwell (30–33). The classical model of human color vision, postulated by Thomas Young in 1802 (32), is the trichromatic model in which it is assumed that the eye possesses three types of sensors, each sensitive over a different wavelength band. It is interesting to note that there was no direct physiological evidence of the existence of three distinct types of sensors until about 1960 (9, 10).

Figure 2.5-1 contains a diagram of a color vision model proposed by Frei (34). In this model three receptors with spectral sensitivities $s_1(\lambda)$, $s_2(\lambda)$,

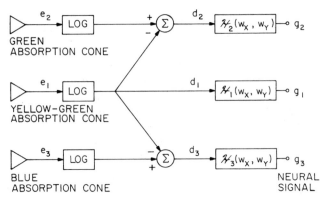

FIGURE 2.5-1   Color vision model.

and $s_3(\lambda)$, which represent the absorption pigments of the retina, produce signals

$$e_1 = \int C(\lambda) s_1(\lambda)\, d\lambda \qquad (2.5\text{-}1a)$$

$$e_2 = \int C(\lambda) s_2(\lambda)\, d\lambda \qquad (2.5\text{-}1b)$$

$$e_3 = \int C(\lambda) s_3(\lambda)\, d\lambda \qquad (2.5\text{-}1c)$$

where $C(\lambda)$ is the spectral energy distribution of the incident light source. The three signals e_1, e_2, e_3 are then subjected to a logarithmic transfer function and combined to produce the outputs

$$d_1 = \log(e_1) \qquad (2.5\text{-}2a)$$

$$d_2 = \log(e_2) - \log(e_1) = \log\left(\frac{e_2}{e_1}\right) \qquad (2.5\text{-}2b)$$

$$d_3 = \log(e_3) - \log(e_1) = \log\left(\frac{e_3}{e_1}\right) \qquad (2.5\text{-}2c)$$

Finally, the signals d_1, d_2, d_3 pass through linear systems with transfer function $\mathcal{H}_1(\omega_x, \omega_y)$, $\mathcal{H}_2(\omega_x, \omega_y)$, and $\mathcal{H}_3(\omega_x, \omega_y)$ to produce output signals g_1, g_2, g_3, that provide the basis for perception of color by the brain.

In the model of Figure 2.5-1 the signals d_2 and d_3 are related to the chromaticity of a colored light while signal d_1 is proportional to its luminance. This model has been found to predict many color vision phenomena quite accurately, and also to satisfy the basic laws of colorimetry. For example, it is known that if the spectral energy of a colored light changes by a constant multiplicative factor, the hue and saturation of the light, as quantitatively described by its chromaticity coordinates, remain invariant over a wide dynamic range. Examination of Eqs. 2.5-1 and 2.5-2 indicates that the chrominance signals d_2 and d_3 are unchanged in this case, and that the luminance signal d_1 increases in a logarithmic manner. Other, more subtle evaluations of the model are described by Frei (34).

As shown in Figure 2.2-4, some indication of the spectral sensitivities $s_i(\lambda)$ of the three types of retinal cones has been obtained by spectral absorption measurements of cone pigments. However, direct physiological measurements are difficult to perform accurately. Indirect estimates of cone spectral sensitivities have been obtained from measurements of the color response of color blind individuals by Konig and Brodhun (35). Judd (36) has used this data to produce a linear transformation relating the spectral sensitivity functions $s_i(\lambda)$ to spectral tristimulus values obtained by colorimetric testing. The resulting sensitivity curves, shown in Figure 2.5-2, are unimodel and strictly positive, as expected from physiological considerations.

The logarithmic color vision model of Figure 2.5-1 may be easily extended, in analogy with the monochromatic vision model of Figure 2.4-7, by inserting a linear transfer function after each cone receptor to account for the optical response of the eye. Also, a general nonlinearity may be substituted for the logarithmic transfer function. It should be noted that the order of the receptor summation and the transfer function operations can be reversed without affecting the output, since both are linear operations. Figure 2.5-3 contains a diagram of the extended model for color vision. It is expected that the spatial frequency response of the g_1 neural signal

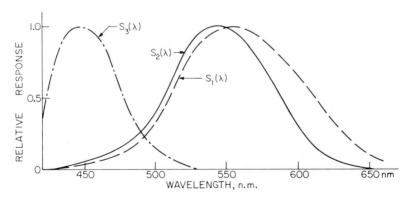

FIGURE 2.5-2. Spectral sensitivity functions of retinal cones based on Konig's data (36).

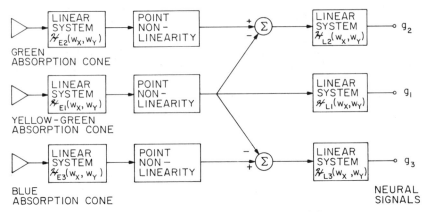

FIGURE 2.5-3. Extended model for color vision.

through the color vision model should be similar to the luminance spatial frequency response discussed in Section 2.4. Sine wave response measurements for colored lights obtained by van der Horst, de Weert, and Bouman (37), shown in Figure 2.5-4, indicate that the chromatic response is shifted toward low spatial frequencies relative to the luminance response. Lateral inhibition effects should produce a low spatial frequency rolloff below the measured response.

Color perception is relative; the perceived color of a given spectral energy distribution is dependent on the viewing surround and state of adaption of the viewer. A human viewer can adapt remarkably well to the surround or viewing illuminant of a scene and essentially normalize perception to some reference white or overall color balance of the scene. This property is known as chromatic adaption.

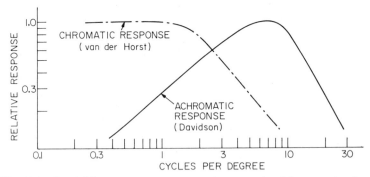

FIGURE 2.5-4. Spatial frequency response measurements of human visual system (26, 37).

The simplest visual model for chromatic adaption, proposed by Von Kries (38, 15, p. 435), involves the insertion of automatic gain controls between the cones and first linear system of Figure 2.5-2. These gains

$$a_i = \left[\int W(\lambda)s_i(\lambda)\, d\lambda \right]^{-1} \tag{2.5-3}$$

for $i = 1, 2, 3$ are adjusted such that the modified cone response is unity when viewing a reference white with spectral energy distribution $W(\lambda)$. Von Kries's model is attractive because of its qualitative reasonableness and simplicity, but chromatic testing (15, p. 438) has shown that the model does not completely predict the chromatic adpation effect. Wallis (39) has suggested that chromatic adaption may, in part, result from a post-retinal neural inhibition mechanism that linearly attenuates slowly varying visual field components. This mechanism could be modeled by the low spatial frequency attenuation associated with the post-retinal transfer functions $\mathcal{H}_{Li}(\omega_x, \omega_y)$ of Figure 2.5-3. Undoubtedly, both retinal and post-retinal mechanisms are responsible for the chromatic adaption effect. Further analysis and testing are required to model the effect adequately.

REFERENCES

1. *Webster's New Collegiate Dictionary*, G. & C. Merriam Co., The Riverside Press, 1960.
2. H. H. Malitson, "The Solar Energy Spectrum," *Sky and Telescope*, **29**, 4, March 1965, 162–165.
3. *Munsell Book of Color*, Munsell Color Co., 2441 North Calvert St., Baltimore, Maryland.
4. M. H. Pirenne, *Vision and the Eye*, 2nd ed., Associated Book Publishers, London, 1967.
5. S. L. Polyak, *The Retina*, University of Chicago Press, Chicago, 1941.
6. L. H. Davson, *The Physiology of the Eye*, McGraw-Hill (Blakiston), New York, 1949.
7. T. N. Cornsweet, *Visual Perception*, Academic Press, New York, 1970.
8. G. Wald, "Human Vision and the Spectrum," *Science*, **101**, 2635, June 29, 1945, 653–658.
9. P. K. Brown and G. Wald, "Visual Pigment in Single Rods and Cones of the Human Retina," *Science*, **144**, 3614, April 3, 1964, 45–52.
10. G. Wald, "The Receptors for Human Color Vision," *Science*, **145**, 3636, September 4, 1964, 1007–1017.
11. S. Hecht, "The Visual Discrimination of Intensity and the Weber–Fechner Law," *J. Gen. Physiol.*, **7**, 1924, 241.
12. S. S. Stevens, *Handbook of Experimental Psychology*, Wiley, New York, 1951.
13. F. Ratliff, *Mach Bands: Quantitative Studies on Neural Networks in the Retina*, Holden-Day, San Francisco, 1965.
14. G. S. Brindley, "Afterimages," *Scientific American*, **209**, 4, October 1963, 84–93.

15. G. Wyszecki and W. S. Stiles, *Color Science*, Wiley, New York, 1967.

16. J. Cohen and D. Gordan, "The Prevost-Fechner-Benham Subjective Colors," *Psychophys. Bull.*, **46**, 2, March 1949, 97–136.

17. E. H. Land, "Experiments in Color Vision," *Scientific American*, **200**, 5, May 1959, 84–99.

18. J. W. Goodman, *Introduction to Fourier Optics*, McGraw-Hill, New York, 1968.

19. F. W. Campbell, "The Human Eye as an Optical filter," *Proc. IEEE*, **56**, 6, June 1968, 1009–1014.

20. O. Bryngdahl, "Characteristics of the Visual System: Psychophysical Measurement of the Response to Spatial Sine-Wave Stimuli in the Mesopic Region," *J. Opt. Soc. Am.*, **54**, 9, September 1964, 1152–1160.

21. E. M. Lowry and J. J. Depalma, "Sine Wave Response of the Visual System, I. The Mach Phenomenom," *J. Opt. Soc. Am.*, **51**, 7, July 1961, 740–746.

22. E. M. Lowry and J. J. DePalma, "Sine Wave Response of the Visual System, II. Sine Wave and Square Wave Contrast Sensitivity," *J. Opt. Soc. Am.*, **52**, 3, March 1962, 328–335.

23. M. B. Sachs, J. Nachmias, and J. G. Robson, "Spatial Frequency Channels in Human Vision," *J. Opt. Soc. Am.*, **61**, 9, September 1971, 1176–1186.

24. T. G. Stockham, Jr., "Image Processing in the Context of a Visual Model," *Proc. IEEE*, **60**, 7, July 1972, 828–842.

25. D. E. Pearson, "A Realistic Model for Visual Communication Systems," *Proc. IEEE*, **55**, 3, March 1967, 380–389.

26. M. L. Davidson, "Perturbation Approach to Spatial Brightness Interaction in Human Vision," *J. Opt. Soc. Am.*, **58**, 9, September 1968, 1300–1308.

27. J. L. Mannos and D. J. Sakrison, "The Effects of a Visual Fidelity Criterion on the Encoding of Images," *IEEE Trans. Inf. Theory*, **IT-20**, 4, July 1974, 525–536.

28. F. Ratliff, H. K. Hartline, and W. H. Miller, "Spatial and Temporal Aspects of Retinal Inhibitory Interaction," *J. Opt. Soc. Am.*, **53**, 1, January 1963, 110–120.

29. C. F. Hall and E. L. Hall, "A Nonlinear Model for the Spatial Characteristics of the Human Visual System," *IEEE Trans. Syst., Man Cybern.*, **SMC-7**, 3, March 1977, 161–170.

30. J. J. McCann, "Human Color Perception," in *Color: Theory and Imaging Systems*, R. A. Enyard, Ed., Society of Photographic Scientists and Engineers, Washington D.C., 1973, 1–23.

31. I. Newton, *Optiks*, 4th ed., 1730; Dover Publications, New York, 1952.

32. T. Young, Philosophical Transactions, **92**, 1802, 12–48.

33. J. C. Maxwell, *Scientific Papers of James Clerk Maxwell*, W. D. Neven, Ed., Dover Publications, New York, 1965.

34. W. Frei, "A New Model of Color Vision and Some Practical Limitations," University of Southern California, Image Processing Institute, USCEE Report 530, March 1974, 128–143.

35. A. Konig and E. Brodhun, "Experimentelle Untersuchungen uber die Psycho-physische Fundamental in Bezug auf den Gesichtssinn," Zweite Mittlg. S. B. Preuss Akademic der Wissenschaften, 1889, 641.

36. D. B. Judd, "Standard Response Functions for Protanopic and Deuteranopic Vision," *J. Opt. Soc. Am.*, **35**, 3, March 1945, 199–221.

37. C. J. C. Van der Horst, C. M. de Weert, and M. A. Bouman, "Transfer of Spatial Chromaticity—Contrast at Threshold in the Human Eye," *J. Opt. Soc. Am.*, **57**, No. 10, October 1967, 1260–1266.

38. J. von Kries, "Die Gesichtsempfindungen," Nagel's Handbuch d. Physiology d. Menchen, Vol. 3, 1904, 211.

39. R. H. Wallis, "Film Recording of Digital Color Images," University of Southern California Image Processing Institute Report No. 570, June 1975.

3 PHOTOMETRY AND COLORIMETRY

Chapter 2 dealt with human vision from a qualitative viewpoint in an attempt to establish models for monochrome and color vision. These models may be made quantitative by specifying measures of human light perception. Luminance measures are the subject of the science of photometry, while color measures are treated by the science of colorimetry. Both topics are discussed in this chapter along with presentations on light sources and color theory.

3.1. LIGHT SOURCES

A source of radiative energy may be characterized by its spectral energy distribution $C(\lambda)$, which specifies the time rate of energy the source emits per unit wavelength interval. The total power emitted by a radiant source, given by the integral of the spectral energy distribution,

$$P = \int_0^\infty C(\lambda)\, d\lambda \qquad (3.1\text{-}1)$$

is called the radiant flux of the source, and is normally expressed in watts (W).

A body that exists at an elevated temperature radiates electromagnetic energy proportional in amount to its temperature. A blackbody is an idealized type of heat radiator whose radiant flux is the maximum obtainable at any wavelength for a body at a fixed temperature. The spectral energy distribution of a blackbody is given by Planck's law (1):

$$C(\lambda) = \frac{C_1}{\lambda^5 [\exp\{C_2/\lambda T\} - 1]} \qquad (3.1\text{-}2)$$

where λ is the radiation wavelength, T is the temperature of the body, and C_1 and C_2 are constants. Figure 3.1-1a is a plot of the spectral energy of a blackbody as a function of temperature and wavelength. In the visible region of the electromagnetic spectrum, the blackbody spectral energy

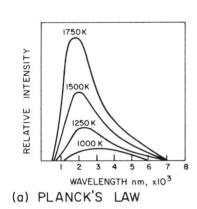

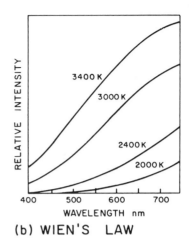

(a) PLANCK'S LAW

(b) WIEN'S LAW

FIGURE 3.1-1. Blackbody radiation functions (1).

distribution function of Eq. 3.1-2 can be approximated by Wien's radiation law (1):

$$C(\lambda) = \frac{C_1}{\lambda^5 \exp\{C_2/\lambda T\}} \qquad (3.1\text{-}3)$$

Wien's radiation function is plotted in Figure 3.1-1b over the visible spectrum.

The most basic physical light source, of course, is the sun. Figure 2.1-1 contains a plot of the measured spectral energy distribution of sunlight (2). The dotted line in this figure, approximating the measured data, is a 6000° K blackbody curve. Incandescent lamps are often approximated as blackbody radiators of a given temperature in the range 1500–3500° K (3).

The Commission Internationale de l'Eclairage (C.I.E.), which is an international body concerned with standards for light and color, has established several standard sources of light as illustrated in Figure 3.1-2 (4). Source S_A is a tungsten filament lamp. Over the wavelength band of 400–700 nm, source S_B approximates direct sunlight, and source S_C approximates light from an overcast sky. A hypothetical source, called illuminant E, is often employed in colorimetric calculations. Illuminant E is assumed to emit constant radiant energy at all wavelengths.

Cathode ray tube phosphors are often utilized as light sources in image processing systems. Figure 3.1-3 describes the spectral energy distributions of several common phosphors (5). Monochrome television receivers generally use a P4 phosphor, which provides a relatively bright blue-white display. The P16 phosphor is popular for monochrome flying spot scanners

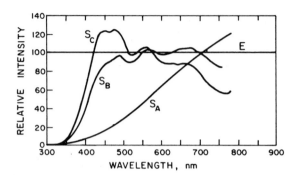

FIGURE 3.1-2.   C.I.E. standard illumination sources (4).

because its persistence is quite short. For color flying spot scanners the P24 phosphor is a common choice because of its relatively wide spectral band and reasonably short persistence. Color television displays utilize cathode ray tubes with red, green, and blue emitting phosphors arranged in triad dots or strips. The P22 phosphor is typical of the spectral energy distribution of commercial phosphor mixtures.

3.2. PHOTOMETRY

Photometric measurements seeks to quantitatively describe the perceptual brightness of visible electromagnetic energy (6–8). The link between photometric measurements and radiometric measurements (physical intensity measurements) is the photoptic luminosity function as shown in Figure 3.2-1a (9). This curve, which is a C.I.E. standard, specifies the spectral sensitivity of the human visual system to optical radiation as a function of wavelength for a typical person referred to as the standard observer. In essence, the curve is a standardized version of the measurement of cone sensitivity given in Figure 2.2-2 for photoptic vision at relatively high levels of illumination. The standard luminosity function for scotoptic vision at relatively low levels of illumination is illustrated in Figure 3.2-1b. Most imaging system designs are based on the photoptic luminosity function, or as commonly called, the relative luminous efficiency.

The perceptual brightness sensation evoked by a light source with spectral energy distribution $C(\lambda)$ is specified by its luminous flux, as defined by

$$F = K_m \int_0^\infty C(\lambda) V(\lambda) \, d\lambda \qquad (3.2\text{-}1)$$

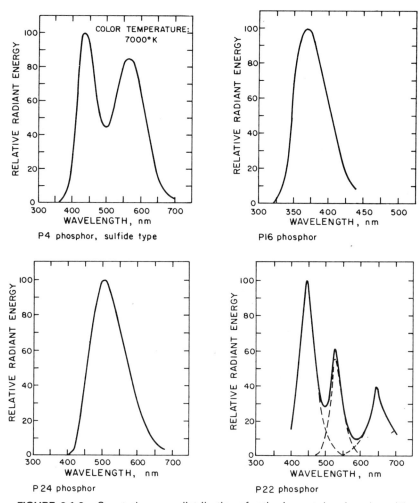

FIGURE 3.1-3.   Spectral energy distribution of cathode ray tube phosphors (5).

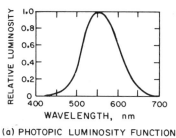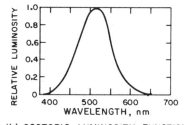

(a) PHOTOPIC LUMINOSITY FUNCTION   (b) SCOTOPIC LUMINOSITY FUNCTION

FIGURE 3.2-1.   Relative luminous efficiency functions (9).

where $V(\lambda)$ represents the relative luminous efficiency and K_m is a scaling constant. The modern unit of luminous flux is the lumen (lm), and the corresponding value for the scaling constant is $K_m = 685$ lm/W. An infinitesimally narrowband source of 1 W of light at the peak wavelength of 555 nm of the relative luminous efficiency curve therefore results in a luminous flux of 685 lm.

Another factor in the perceptual brightness of a radiant source is its emission geometry. Consider a point source of light emitting luminous flux in all directions as shown in Figure 3.2-2a. The incremental amount of flux dF radiated into a unit solid angle $d\omega$ is called the luminous intensity

$$I = \frac{dF}{d\omega} \qquad (3.2\text{-}2)$$

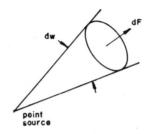

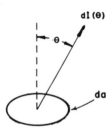

(a) Emission from point source

(b) Emission from an incremental area

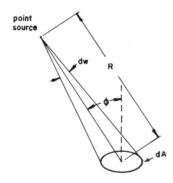

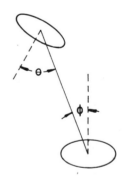

(c) Illuminance from a point source

(d) Illuminance from an extended source

FIGURE 3.2-2. Geometry for photometric measurements.

measured in units of lumens per steradian. The brightness of an extended source, as shown in Figure 3.2-2b, is specified by its luminance defined by

$$B = \frac{dI(\theta)}{da \cos(\theta)} \tag{3.2-3}$$

where $dI(\theta)$ is the incremental luminous intensity of emission from the incremental area da in the direction θ from the normal to the surface. Consistent units of luminance are lumens per steradian per square meter.

An extended radiating surface is said to be diffuse if its incremental luminous intensity follows Lambert's law,

$$dI(\theta) = dI_N \cos(\theta) \tag{3.2-4}$$

where dI_N is the incremental luminous flux normal to the surface. For such surfaces the luminance becomes

$$B = \frac{dI_N}{da} \tag{3.2-5}$$

Thus the luminance of a diffuse source is independent of the direction of observation, and the source appears equally bright from all directions. In imaging systems an illuminated ground-glass plate is often used to approximate an ideal diffuse radiative source.

The luminance of a radiant source is a measure of the light flux emitted from an area on the surface of the source into a solid angle at a particular direction. The amount of light flux from the source that is incident onto a surface of observation is specified by the illuminance. Consider the geometry of Figure 3.2-2c in which a point source emits an incremental flux dF into the solid angle $d\omega$ at an angle ϕ normal to the surface of observation. The angle $d\omega$ subtends an area dA on the observation surface. The illuminance is then defined as

$$E = \frac{dF}{dA} \tag{3.2-6}$$

From Eq. 3.2-2 and the geometry of Figure 3.2-2,

$$dF = I(\theta) \, d\omega = I(\theta) \left[\frac{dA \cos(\phi)}{R^2} \right] \tag{3.2-7}$$

where R is the radial distance from the source to the observation surface point. Hence for illumination by a point source the illuminance becomes

$$E = \frac{I(\theta) \cos(\phi)}{R^2} \tag{3.2-8}$$

This is a form of the inverse square law of radiation. The illuminance of an extended object may be determined by considering the object to be composed of a spatial arrangement of point sources, and then summing together the contributions from the individual point sources. Referring to Figure 3.2-2*d* and Eq. 3.2-8, the incremental illuminance on the observation surface *dA* resulting from emission from the emitting surface *da* is

$$dE = dI(\theta)\frac{\cos\phi}{R^2} \qquad (3.2\text{-}9)$$

Combination of Eqs. 3.2-3 and 3.2-9 then yields

$$dE = \frac{Bda\,\cos(\theta)\cos(\phi)}{R^2} \qquad (3.2\text{-}10)$$

Computation of the illuminance of an object in a physical imaging system generally involves a complicated integration of Eq. 3.2-10 over the object surface and the observation surface.

The preceding theory provides the basis for two important photometric results that are illustrated by the optical systems in Figure 3.2-3. In the generalized imaging system of Figure 3.2-3*a* an incremental surface area *da* of luminance *B* on a diffuse source is imaged onto an incremental observation surface *dA* producing a luminance $\tilde{B}$. It can be shown (8, p. 189) that $\tilde{B} = B$ if the index of refraction in the source space and image space is identical. Thus aside from losses resulting from absorption and scattering, an imaging system does not modify the luminance of images. Figure 3.2-3*b* describes the imaging of an incremental area on an extended diffuse source of luminance *B* onto an extended observation plane by a simple thin lens. The incremental illuminance on an incremental surface area *dA* on the observation plane is given by (8, p. 190)

$$dE = \frac{B\pi D^2}{4x_2^2}\cos^4(\theta) \qquad (3.2\text{-}11)$$

where *D* is the diameter of the lens, θ is the angle of intercept of the principal ray passing through the center of the lens, and x_2 is the distance from the center of the lens to the observation point. This result indicates that the illumination off-axis decreases as the fourth power of the off-axis angle. As a reference, note that $\cos^4(30°) = 0.56$. Additional losses in the illuminance occur from absorption and scattering in the optical system. Illumination loss may also occur because of the lens vignetting effect in which rays from a source with a large skew angle with respect to the optic axis of the lens miss the lens entirely.

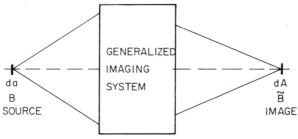

(a) SOURCE AND IMAGE LUMINANCE RELATIONSHIPS

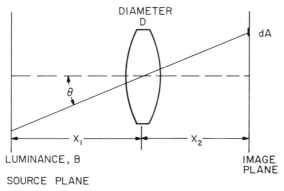

(b) SOURCE AND IMAGE ILLUMINANCE RELATIONSHIPS

FIGURE 3.2-3. Source and image luminance and illuminance relationships.

In the subsequent discussions of image processing systems the geometric considerations of photometry are avoided whenever possible in order to maintain the discussion on a general level. Also, as is common in much of the image processing literature, the single term luminance is employed rather loosely, for descriptive convenience, to denote luminous flux, luminous intensity, and true luminance.

3.3. COLOR MATCHING (10–14)

The basis of the trichromatic theory of color vision is that it is possible to match an arbitrary color by superimposing appropriate amounts of three primary colors. In an additive color reproduction system, such as color television, the three primaries are individual red, green, and blue light sources that are projected onto a common region of space to reproduce a colored light. In a subtractive color system, which is the basis of most color photography and color printing, a white light sequentially passes through cyan, magenta, and yellow filters to reproduce a colored light.

3.3.1. Additive Color Matching

An additive color matching experiment is illustrated in Figure 3.3-1. In Figure 3.3-1*a* a patch of light [*C*] of arbitrary spectral energy distribution $C(\lambda)$, as shown in Figure 3.3-2*a*, is assumed to be imaged onto the surface

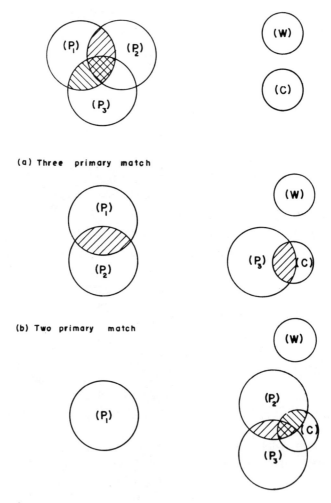

(a) Three primary match

(b) Two primary match

(c) One primary match

FIGURE 3.3-1. Color matching.

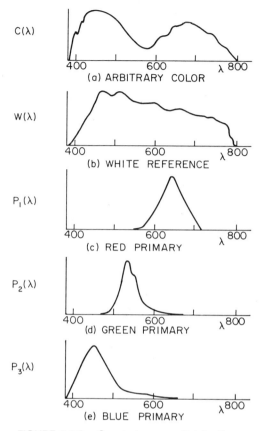

$C(\lambda)$

(a) ARBITRARY COLOR

$W(\lambda)$

(b) WHITE REFERENCE

$P_1(\lambda)$

(c) RED PRIMARY

$P_2(\lambda)$

(d) GREEN PRIMARY

$P_3(\lambda)$

(e) BLUE PRIMARY

FIGURE 3.3-2. Spectral energy distributions.

of an ideal diffuse reflector (a surface that reflects uniformly over all directions and all wavelengths). A reference white light $[W]$ with an energy distribution, as in Figure 3.3-2b, is imaged onto the surface along with three primary lights $[P_1]$, $[P_2]$, $[P_3]$ whose spectral energy distributions are sketched in Figures 3.3-2c to 3.3-2e. The three primary lights are first overlapped and their intensities are adjusted until the overlapping region of the three primary lights perceptually matches the reference white in terms of brightness, hue, and saturation. The amounts of the three primaries $A_1(W)$, $A_2(W)$, $A_3(W)$ are then recorded in some physical units, such as watts. These are the matching values of the reference white. Next, the intensities of the primaries are adjusted until a match is achieved with the colored light $[C]$, if a match is possible. The procedure to be followed if a match cannot be achieved is considered later. The intensities of the primaries $A_1(C)$, $A_2(C)$, $A_3(C)$ when a match is obtained are recorded, and normalized matching values $T_1(C)$, $T_2(C)$, $T_3(C)$, called tristimulus values, are computed as

$$T_1(C) = \frac{A_1(C)}{A_1(W)} \qquad T_2(C) = \frac{A_2(C)}{A_2(W)} \qquad T_3(C) = \frac{A_3(C)}{A_3(W)} \quad (3.3\text{-}1)$$

If a match cannot be achieved by the procedure illustrated in Figure 3.3-1a, then it is often possible to perform the color matching outlined in Figure 3.3-1b. One of the primaries, say $[P_3]$, is superimposed with the light $[C]$, and the intensities of all three primaries are adjusted until a match is achieved between the overlapping region of primaries $[P_1]$ and $[P_2]$ with the overlapping region of $[P_3]$ and $[C]$. If such a match is obtained, then the tristimulus values are

$$T_1(C) = \frac{A_1(C)}{A_1(W)} \qquad T_2(C) = \frac{A_2(C)}{A_2(W)} \qquad T_3(C) = \frac{-A_3(C)}{A_3(W)}$$
$$(3.3\text{-}2)$$

In this case the tristimulus value $T_3(C)$ is negative. If a match cannot be achieved with this geometry, then a match is attempted between $[P_1]$ plus $[P_3]$ and $[P_2]$ plus $[C]$. If a match is achieved by this configuration, tristimulus value $T_2(C)$ will be negative. And if this configuration fails, a match is attempted between $[P_2]$ plus $[P_3]$ and $[P_1]$ plus $[C]$. A correct match is denoted with a negative value for $T_1(C)$.

Finally, in the rare instance in which a match cannot be achieved by either of the configurations of Figure 3.3-1a or 3.3-1b, then two of the primaries are superimposed with $[C]$ and an attempt is made to match the overlapped region with the remaining primary. In the case illustrated in Figure 3.3-1c, if a match is achieved, the tristimulus values become

$$T_1(C) = \frac{A_1(C)}{A_1(W)} \qquad T_2(C) = \frac{-A_2(C)}{A_2(W)} \qquad T_3(C) = \frac{-A_3(C)}{A_3(W)}$$
$$(3.3\text{-}3)$$

If a match is not obtained by this configuration, one of the other two possibilities will yield a match.

The process described above is a direct method for quantitatively specifying a color. It has two drawbacks: the method is cumbersome and the method is dependent upon the perceptual variations of a single observer. Section 3.4 considers standardized quantitative color measurement in detail.

3.3.2. Subtractive Color Matching

A subtractive color matching experiment is shown in Figure 3.3-3. An illumination source with spectral energy distribution $E(\lambda)$ sequentially passes through three dye filters that are nominally cyan, magenta, and yellow. The spectral absorption of the dye filters is a function of the dye concentration. It should be noted that the spectral transmissivities of practical dyes change shape in a nonlinear manner with dye concentration.

In the first step of the subtractive color matching process, the dye concentrations of the three spectral filters are varied until a perceptual match is obtained with a reference white $[W]$. The dye concentrations are the matching values of the color match $A_1(W)$, $A_2(W)$, $A_3(W)$. Next, the three dye concentrations are varied until a match is obtained with a desired color $[C]$. These matching values, $A_1(C)$, $A_2(C)$, $A_3(C)$, then are used to compute the tristimulus values $T_1(C)$, $T_2(C)$, $T_3(C)$, as in Eq. 3.3-1. It should be apparent that there is no fundamental theoretical difference between color matching by additive or subtractive systems. In the subtractive system the yellow dye acts as a variable absorber of blue light, and with ideal dyes, the yellow dye effectively forms a blue primary light. In a similar manner, the magenta filter ideally forms the green primary, and the cyan filter ideally forms the red primary. Subtractive color systems ordinarily utilize cyan, magenta, and yellow dye spectral filters rather than red, green, and blue dye filters because the cyan, magenta, and yellow filters are "notch" filters which permit a greater transmission of light energy than narrowband red, green, and blue "bandpass" filters. In color printing a fourth filter layer of variable gray level density is often introduced in order to achieve a higher contrast in reproduction because common dyes do not

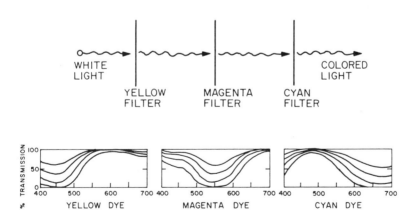

FIGURE 3.3-3. Subtractive color matching.

possess a wide density range. Subtractive color reproduction with practical dyes possessing overlapping spectral characteristics is considered in Chapter 16.

3.3.3. Axioms of Color Matching

The color matching experiments described for additive and subtractive color matching have been performed quite accurately by a number of researchers. It has been found that perfect color matches sometimes cannot be obtained at either very high or very low levels of illumination. Also, the color matching results do depend to some extent on the spectral composition of the surrounding light. Nevertheless, the simple color matching experiments have been found to hold over a wide range of conditions.

Grassman (15) has developed a set of eight axioms that define trichromatic color matching, and that serve as a basis for quantitative color measurements. These axioms are:

1. Any color can be matched by a mixture of no more than three colored lights.
2. A color match at one radiance level holds over a wide range of levels.
3. Components of a mixture of colored lights cannot be resolved by the human eye.
4. The luminance of a color mixture is equal to the sum of the luminance of its components.
5. Law of addition—if color $[M]$ matches color $[N]$ and color $[P]$ matches color $[Q]$, then color $[M]$ mixed with color $[P]$ matches color $[N]$ mixed with color $[Q]$*:

$$\begin{matrix} [M] \triangle [N] \\ [P] \triangle [Q] \end{matrix} \Rightarrow [M] \triangle [P] \triangle [N] \triangle [Q] \qquad (3.3\text{-}4)$$

6. Law of subtraction—if the mixture of $[M]$ plus $[P]$ matches the mixture of $[N]$ plus $[Q]$ and if $[P]$ matches $[Q]$, then $[M]$ matches $[N]$:

$$\begin{matrix} [M] \triangle [P] \triangle [N] \triangle [Q] \\ [P] \triangle [Q] \end{matrix} \Rightarrow [M] \triangle [N] \qquad (3.3\text{-}5)$$

---

* The symbol $\triangle$ indicates a color match; the symbol $\triangle$ indicates an additive color mixture; the symbol $\triangle$ indicates units of a color.

7. Transitive law—if $[M]$ matches $[N]$ and if $[N]$ matches $[P]$, then $[M]$ matches $[P]$:

$$\begin{matrix}[M] \triangleq [N] \\ [N] \triangleq [P]\end{matrix} \Rightarrow [M] \triangleq [P] \qquad (3.3\text{-}6)$$

8. Color matching—(a) C units of $[C]$ matches the mixture of M units of $[M]$ plus N units of $[N]$ plus P units of $[P]$:

$$C \triangleq [C] \triangleq M \triangleq [M] \triangleq N \triangleq [N] \triangleq P \triangleq [P] \qquad (3.3\text{-}7)$$

or, (b) a mixture of C units of $[C]$ plus M units of $[M]$ matches the mixture of N units of $[N]$ plus P units of $[P]$:

$$C \triangleq [C] \triangleq M \triangleq [M] \triangleq N \triangleq [N] \triangleq P \triangleq [P] \qquad (3.3\text{-}8)$$

or (c) a mixture of C units of $[C]$ plus M units of $[M]$ plus N units of $[N]$ matches P units of $[P]$:

$$C \triangleq [C] \triangleq M \triangleq [M] \triangleq N \triangleq [N] \triangleq P \triangleq [P] \qquad (3.3\text{-}9)$$

With Grassman's laws now specified, consideration is given to the development of a quantitative theory for color matching.

3.4. COLORIMETRY

Colorimetry is the science of quantitatively measuring color. In the trichromatic color system, color measurements are in terms of the tristimulus values of a color, or some mathematical function of the tristimulus values.

Referring to Section 3.3.3, the axioms of color matching state that a color $[C]$ can be matched by three primary colors $[P_1]$, $[P_2]$, $[P_3]$. The qualitative match is expressed as

$$[C] \triangleq A_1(C) \triangleq [P_1] \triangleq A_2(C) \triangleq [P_2] \triangleq A_3(C) \triangleq [P_3] \qquad (3.4\text{-}1)$$

where $A_1(C)$, $A_2(C)$, $A_3(C)$ are the matching values of the color $[C]$. Since the intensities of incoherent light sources add linearly, the spectral energy distribution of a color mixture is equal to the sum of the spectral energy distributions of its components. As a consequence of this fact and Eq. 3.4-1, the spectral energy distribution $C(\lambda)$ can be replaced by its color matching equivalent according to the relation

$$C(\lambda) \triangleq A_1(C)P_1(\lambda) + A_2(C)P_2(\lambda) + A_3(C)P_3(\lambda) = \sum_{j=1}^{3} A_j(C)P_j(\lambda) \qquad (3.4\text{-}2)$$

Equation 3.4-2 simply means that the spectral energy distributions on both sides of the equivalence operator $\triangle$ evoke the same color sensation. Color matching is usually specified in terms of tristimulus values, which are normalized matching values, as defined by

$$T_j(C) = \frac{A_j(C)}{A_j(W)} \tag{3.4-3}$$

where $A_j(W)$ represents the matching value of the reference white. By this substitution, Eq. 3.4-2 assumes the form

$$C(\lambda) \triangle \sum_{j=1}^{3} T_j(C)A_j(W)P_j(\lambda) \tag{3.4-4}$$

From Grassman's fourth law the luminance of a color mixture $L(C)$ is equal to the luminance of its primary components. Hence

$$L(C) = \int C(\lambda)V(\lambda)\,d\lambda = \sum_{j=1}^{3} \int A_j(C)P_j(\lambda)V(\lambda)\,d\lambda \tag{3.4-5a}$$

or

$$L(C) = \sum_{j=1}^{3} \int T_j(C)A_j(W)P_j(\lambda)V(\lambda)\,d\lambda \tag{3.4-5b}$$

where $V(\lambda)$ is the relative luminous efficiency and $P_j(\lambda)$ represents the spectral energy distribution of a primary. Equations 3.4-4 and 3.4-5 represents the quantitative foundation for colorimetry.

3.4.1. Verification of Color Vision Model

Before proceeding further with quantitative descriptions of the color matching process, it is instructive to determine whether the matching experiments and the axioms of color matching are satisfied by the color vision model presented in Section 2.5. In that model the responses of the three types of receptors with sensitivities $s_1(\lambda)$, $s_2(\lambda)$, $s_3(\lambda)$ are modeled as

$$e_1(C) = \int C(\lambda)s_1(\lambda)\,d\lambda \tag{3.4-6a}$$

$$e_2(C) = \int C(\lambda)s_2(\lambda)\,d\lambda \tag{3.4-6b}$$

$$e_3(C) = \int C(\lambda)s_3(\lambda)\,d\lambda \tag{3.4-6c}$$

If a viewer observes the primary mixture instead of $[C]$, then from Eq. 3.4-4, substitution for $C(\lambda)$ should result in the same cone signals $e_i(C)$.

Thus

$$e_1(C) = \sum_{j=1}^{3} T_j(C)A_j(W) \int P_j(\lambda)s_1(\lambda)\,d\lambda \qquad (3.4\text{-}7a)$$

$$e_2(C) = \sum_{j=1}^{3} T_j(C)A_j(W) \int P_j(\lambda)s_2(\lambda)\,d\lambda \qquad (3.4\text{-}7b)$$

$$e_3(C) = \sum_{j=1}^{3} T_j(C)A_j(W) \int P_j(\lambda)s_3(\lambda)\,d\lambda \qquad (3.4\text{-}7c)$$

Equation 3.4-7 can be written more compactly in matrix form by defining

$$k_{ij} = \int P_j(\lambda)s_i(\lambda)\,d\lambda \qquad (3.4\text{-}8)$$

Then,

$$\begin{bmatrix} e_1(C) \\ e_2(C) \\ e_3(C) \end{bmatrix} = \begin{bmatrix} k_{11} & k_{12} & k_{13} \\ k_{21} & k_{22} & k_{23} \\ k_{31} & k_{32} & k_{33} \end{bmatrix} \begin{bmatrix} A_1(W) & 0 & 0 \\ 0 & A_2(W) & 0 \\ 0 & 0 & A_3(W) \end{bmatrix} \begin{bmatrix} T_1(C) \\ T_2(C) \\ T_3(C) \end{bmatrix}$$

$$(3.4\text{-}9)$$

Or, in yet more abbreviated form

$$\mathbf{e}(C) = \mathbf{KAT}(C) \qquad (3.4\text{-}10)$$

where the vectors and matrices of Eq. 3.4-10 are defined in correspondence with Eqs. 3.4-7 to 3.4-9. It should be noted that for a given set of primaries, the matrix $\mathbf{K}$ is constant valued, and for a given reference white, the white matching values of the matrix $\mathbf{A}$ are constant. Hence, if a set of cone signals $e_i(C)$ were known for a color $[C]$, then the corresponding tristimulus values $T_j(C)$ could in theory be obtained from

$$\mathbf{T}(C) = (\mathbf{KA})^{-1}\mathbf{e}(C) \qquad (3.4\text{-}11)$$

provided that the matrix inverse of $(\mathbf{KA})$ exists. Thus it has been shown that with proper selection of the tristimulus signals $T_j(C)$, any color can be matched in the sense that the cone signals will be the same for the primary mixture as for the actual color $[C]$. Unfortunately, the cone signals $e_i(C)$ are not easily measurable, physical quantities, and therefore Eq. 3.4-11 cannot be used directly to compute the tristimulus values of a color. However, this has not been the intention of the derivation. Rather, Eq. 3.4-11 has been developed to show the consistency of the color matching experiment with the color vision model.

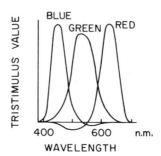

FIGURE 3.4-1. Tristimulus values of typical red, green, and blue primaries required to match unit energy throughout the spectrum.

3.4.2. Tristimulus Value Calculation

It is possible indirectly to compute the tristimulus values of an arbitrary color for a particular set of primaries if the tristimulus values of the spectral colors (narrowband light) are known for that set of primaries. Figure 3.4-1 contains a typical sketch of the tristimulus values required to match a unit energy spectral color with three arbitrary primaries. These tristimulus values, which are fundamental to the definition of a primary system, are denoted as $T_{s1}(\lambda)$, $T_{s2}(\lambda)$, $T_{s3}(\lambda)$ where λ is a particular wavelength in the visible region.

A unit energy spectral light $[C_\psi]$ at wavelength ψ with energy distribution $\delta(\lambda - \psi)$ is matched according to the equation

$$e_i(C_\psi) = \int \delta(\lambda - \psi)s_i(\lambda)\,d\lambda = \sum_{j=1}^{3} \int A_j(W)P_j(\lambda)T_{sj}(\psi)s_i(\lambda)\,d\lambda$$

$$(3.4\text{-}12)$$

Now consider an arbitrary color $[C]$ with spectral energy distribution $C(\lambda)$. At wavelength ψ, $C(\psi)$ units of the color are matched by $C(\psi)T_{s1}(\psi)$, $C(\psi)T_{s2}(\psi)$, $C(\psi)T_{s3}(\psi)$ tristimulus units of the primaries as governed by

$$\int C(\psi)\delta(\lambda - \psi)s_i(\lambda)\,d\lambda = \sum_{j=1}^{3} \int A_j(W)P_j(\lambda)C(\psi)T_{sj}(\psi)s_i(\lambda)\,d\lambda$$

$$(3.4\text{-}13)$$

Integrating each side of Eq. 3.4-13 over ψ and invoking the Sifting integral gives the cone signal for the color $[C]$. Thus

$$\iint C(\psi)\delta(\lambda - \psi)s_i(\lambda)\,d\lambda\,d\psi = e_i(C)$$
$$= \sum_{i=1}^{3} \iint A_j(W)P_j(\lambda)C(\psi)T_{sj}(\psi)s_i(\lambda)\,d\psi\,d\lambda \quad (3.4\text{-}14)$$

By correspondence with Eq. 3.4-7, the tristimulus values of $[C]$ must be equivalent to the second integral on the right of Eq. 3.4-14. Hence

$$T_j(C) = \int C(\psi) T_{sj}(\psi) \, d\psi \qquad (3.4\text{-}15)$$

From Figure 3.4-1 it is seen that the tristimulus values obtained from solution of Eq. 3.4-11 may be negative at some wavelengths. Because the tristimulus values represent units of energy, the physical interpretation to this mathematical result is that a color match can be obtained by adding the primary with negative tristimulus value to the original color, and then matching this resultant color with the remaining primary. In this sense any color can be matched by any set of primaries. However, from a practical viewpoint, negative tristimulus values are not physically realizable, and hence there are certain colors that cannot be matched in a practical color display (e.g., a color television receiver) with fixed primaries. Fortunately, it is possible to choose primaries so that most commonly occurring natural colors can be matched.

The three tristimulus values T_1, T_2, T_3 can be considered to form the three axes of a color space as illustrated in Figure 3.4-2. A particular color may be described as a vector in the color space, but it must be remembered that it is the coordinates of the vectors (tristimulus values), rather than the vector length, that specify the color. In Figure 3.4-2 a triangle, called a Maxwell triangle, has been drawn between the three primaries. The intersection point of a color vector with the triangle gives an indication of the hue and saturation of the color in terms of the distances of the point from the vertices of the triangle.

Often the luminance of a color is not of interest in a color match. In such situations the hue and saturation of a color $[C]$ can be described in terms of

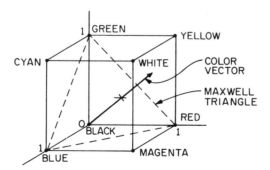

FIGURE 3.4-2. Color space for typical red, green, and blue primaries.

chromaticity coordinates, which are normalized tristimulus values, as defined by

$$t_1 \equiv \frac{T_1}{T_1 + T_2 + T_3} \qquad (3.4\text{-}16a)$$

$$t_2 \equiv \frac{T_2}{T_1 + T_2 + T_3} \qquad (3.4\text{-}16b)$$

$$t_3 \equiv \frac{T_3}{T_1 + T_2 + T_3} \qquad (3.4\text{-}16c)$$

Clearly, $t_3 = 1 - t_1 - t_2$, and hence only two coordinates are necessary to describe a color match. Figure 3.4-3 contains a plot of the chromaticity coordinates of the spectral colors for typical primaries. Only those colors within the triangle defined by the three primaries are realizable by physical primary light sources.

3.4.3. Luminance Calculation

The tristimulus values of a color specify the amounts of the three primaries required to match a color where the units are measured relative to a match of a reference white. Often, it is necessary to determine the absolute, rather than the relative, amount of light from each primary needed to reproduce a color match. This information is found from luminance measurements of calculations of a color match.

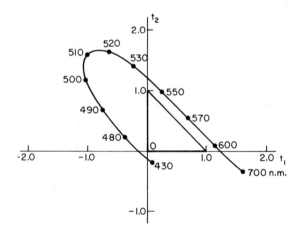

FIGURE 3.4-3. Chromaticity diagram for typical red, green, and blue primaries.

From Eq. 3.4-5 it is noted that the luminance of a matched color $L(C)$ is equal to the sum of the luminances of its primary components according to the relation

$$L(C) = \sum_{i=1}^{3} T_i(C) \int A_i(W)P_i(\lambda)V(\lambda)\, d\lambda \qquad (3.4\text{-}17)$$

The integrals of Eq. 3.4-17,

$$L(P_i) \equiv \int A_i(W)P_i(\lambda)V(\lambda)\, d\lambda \qquad (3.4\text{-}18)$$

are called luminosity coefficients of the primaries. These coefficients represent the luminances of unit amounts of the three primaries for a match to a specific reference white. Hence the luminance of a matched color can be written as

$$L(C) = T_1(C)L(P_1) + T_2(C)L(P_2) + T_3(C)L(P_3) \qquad (3.4\text{-}19)$$

Multiplying the right and left sides of Eq. 3.4-19 by the right and left sides, respectively, of the definition of the chromaticity coordinate

$$t_1(C) = \frac{T_1(C)}{T_1(C) + T_2(C) + T_3(C)} \qquad (3.4\text{-}20)$$

and rearranging gives

$$T_1(C) = \frac{t_1(C)L(C)}{t_1(C)L(P_1) + t_2(C)L(P_2) + t_3(C)L(P_3)} \qquad (3.4\text{-}21a)$$

Similarly,

$$T_2(C) = \frac{t_2(C)L(C)}{t_1(C)L(P_1) + t_2(C)L(P_2) + t_3(C)L(P_3)} \qquad (3.4\text{-}21b)$$

$$T_3(C) = \frac{t_3(C)L(C)}{t_1(C)L(P_1) + t_2(C)L(P_2) + t_3(C)L(P_3)} \qquad (3.4\text{-}21c)$$

Thus the tristimulus values of a color can be expressed in terms of the luminance and chromaticity coordinates of the color.

3.5. TRANSFORMATION OF TRISTIMULUS VALUES

From Eq. 3.4-7 it is clear that there is no unique set of primaries for matching colors. If the tristimulus values of a color are known for one set of primaries, a simple coordinate conversion can be performed to determine the tristimulus values for another set of primaries (16). Let $[P_1], [P_2], [P_3]$

be the original set of primaries with spectral energy distributions $P_1(\lambda)$, $P_2(\lambda)$, $P_3(\lambda)$ with the units of a match determined by a white reference $[W]$ with matching values $A_1(W)$, $A_2(W)$, $A_3(W)$. Now, consider a new set of primaries $[\tilde{P}_1]$, $[\tilde{P}_2]$, $[\tilde{P}_3]$ with spectral energy distributions $\tilde{P}_1(\lambda)$, $\tilde{P}_2(\lambda)$, $\tilde{P}_3(\lambda)$. Matches are made to a reference white $[\tilde{W}]$, which may be different than the reference white of the original set of primaries, by matching values $\tilde{A}_1(W)$, $\tilde{A}_2(W)$, $\tilde{A}_3(W)$. Referring to Eq. 3.4-10, an arbitrary color $[C]$ can be matched by the tristimulus values $T_1(C)$, $T_2(C)$, $T_3(C)$ with the original set of primaries, or by the tristimulus values $\tilde{T}_1(C)$, $\tilde{T}_2(C)$, $\tilde{T}_3(C)$ with the new set of primaries according to the matching matrix relations

$$\mathbf{e}(C) = \mathbf{K}\mathbf{A}(W)\mathbf{T}(C) = \tilde{\mathbf{K}}\tilde{\mathbf{A}}(\tilde{W})\tilde{\mathbf{T}}(C) \qquad (3.5\text{-}1)$$

The tristimulus value units of the new set of primaries, with respect to the original set of primaries, must now be found. This can be accomplished by determining the color signals of the reference white for the second set of primaries in terms of both sets of primaries. The color signal equations for the reference white $[\tilde{W}]$ become

$$\mathbf{e}(\tilde{W}) = \mathbf{K}\mathbf{A}(W)\mathbf{T}(\tilde{W}) = \tilde{\mathbf{K}}\tilde{\mathbf{A}}(\tilde{W})\tilde{\mathbf{T}}(\tilde{W}) \qquad (3.5\text{-}2)$$

where $\tilde{T}_1(\tilde{W}) = \tilde{T}_2(\tilde{W}) = \tilde{T}_3(\tilde{W}) = 1$. Finally, it is necessary to relate the two sets of primaries by determining the color signals of each of the new primary colors $[\tilde{P}_1]$, $[\tilde{P}_2]$, $[\tilde{P}_3]$ in terms of both primary systems. These color signal equations are

$$\mathbf{e}(\tilde{P}_1) = \mathbf{K}\mathbf{A}(W)\mathbf{T}(\tilde{P}_1) = \tilde{\mathbf{K}}\tilde{\mathbf{A}}(\tilde{W})\tilde{\mathbf{T}}(\tilde{P}_1) \qquad (3.5\text{-}3a)$$

$$\mathbf{e}(\tilde{P}_2) = \mathbf{K}\mathbf{A}(W)\mathbf{T}(\tilde{P}_2) = \tilde{\mathbf{K}}\tilde{\mathbf{A}}(\tilde{W})\tilde{\mathbf{T}}(\tilde{P}_2) \qquad (3.5\text{-}3b)$$

$$\mathbf{e}(\tilde{P}_3) = \mathbf{K}\mathbf{A}(W)\mathbf{T}(\tilde{P}_3) = \tilde{\mathbf{K}}\tilde{\mathbf{A}}(\tilde{W})\tilde{\mathbf{T}}(\tilde{P}_3) \qquad (3.5\text{-}3c)$$

where

$$\tilde{T}(\tilde{P}_1) = \begin{bmatrix} \dfrac{1}{\tilde{A}_1(\tilde{W})} \\ 0 \\ 0 \end{bmatrix} \qquad \tilde{T}(\tilde{P}_2) = \begin{bmatrix} 0 \\ \dfrac{1}{\tilde{A}_2(\tilde{W})} \\ 0 \end{bmatrix} \qquad \tilde{T}(\tilde{P}_3) = \begin{bmatrix} 0 \\ 0 \\ \dfrac{1}{\tilde{A}_3(\tilde{W})} \end{bmatrix}$$

Matrix equations 3.5-1 to 3.5-3 may be solved jointly to obtain a relationship between the tristimulus values of the original and new primary system giving

$$
\begin{bmatrix} \tilde{T}_1(C) \\ \tilde{T}_2(C) \\ \tilde{T}_3(C) \end{bmatrix} =
\begin{bmatrix}
\begin{vmatrix} T_1(C) & T_1(\tilde{P}_2) & T_1(\tilde{P}_3) \\ T_2(C) & T_2(\tilde{P}_2) & T_2(\tilde{P}_3) \\ T_3(C) & T_3(\tilde{P}_2) & T_3(\tilde{P}_3) \end{vmatrix} \Big/ \begin{vmatrix} T_1(\tilde{W}) & T_1(\tilde{P}_2) & T_1(\tilde{P}_3) \\ T_2(\tilde{W}) & T_2(\tilde{P}_2) & T_2(\tilde{P}_3) \\ T_3(\tilde{W}) & T_3(\tilde{P}_2) & T_3(\tilde{P}_3) \end{vmatrix} \\[3em]
\begin{vmatrix} T_1(\tilde{P}_1) & T_1(C) & T_1(\tilde{P}_3) \\ T_2(\tilde{P}_1) & T_2(C) & T_2(\tilde{P}_3) \\ T_3(\tilde{P}_1) & T_3(C) & T_3(\tilde{P}_3) \end{vmatrix} \Big/ \begin{vmatrix} T_1(\tilde{P}_1) & T_1(\tilde{W}) & T_1(\tilde{P}_3) \\ T_2(\tilde{P}_1) & T_2(\tilde{W}) & T_2(\tilde{P}_3) \\ T_3(\tilde{P}_1) & T_3(\tilde{W}) & T_3(\tilde{P}_3) \end{vmatrix} \\[3em]
\begin{vmatrix} T_1(\tilde{P}_1) & T_1(\tilde{P}_2) & T_1(C) \\ T_2(\tilde{P}_1) & T_2(\tilde{P}_2) & T_2(C) \\ T_3(\tilde{P}_1) & T_3(\tilde{P}_2) & T_3(C) \end{vmatrix} \Big/ \begin{vmatrix} T_1(\tilde{P}_1) & T_1(\tilde{P}_2) & T_1(\tilde{W}) \\ T_2(\tilde{P}_1) & T_2(\tilde{P}_2) & T_2(\tilde{W}) \\ T_3(\tilde{P}_1) & T_3(\tilde{P}_2) & T_3(\tilde{W}) \end{vmatrix}
\end{bmatrix} \quad (3.5\text{-}4)
$$

Equations 3.5-4 then may be written in terms of the chromaticity coordinates $t_i(\tilde{P}_1)$, $t_i(\tilde{P}_2)$, $t_i(\tilde{P}_3)$ of the new set of primaries referenced to the original primary coordinate system. With this revision

$$
\begin{bmatrix} T_1'(C) \\ T_2'(C) \\ T_3'(C) \end{bmatrix} =
\begin{bmatrix} m_{11} & m_{12} & m_{13} \\ m_{21} & m_{22} & m_{23} \\ m_{31} & m_{32} & m_{33} \end{bmatrix}
\begin{bmatrix} T_1(C) \\ T_2(C) \\ T_3(C) \end{bmatrix} \quad (3.5\text{-}5)
$$

where

$$
m_{ij} = \frac{\Delta_{ij}}{\Delta_i}
$$

$$
\Delta_1 = T_1(\tilde{W})\Delta_{11} + T_2(\tilde{W})\Delta_{12} + T_3(\tilde{W})\Delta_{13}
$$

$$
\Delta_2 = T_1(\tilde{W})\Delta_{21} + T_2(\tilde{W})\Delta_{22} + T_3(\tilde{W})\Delta_{23}
$$

$$
\Delta_3 = T_1(\tilde{W})\Delta_{31} + T_2(\tilde{W})\Delta_{32} + T_3(\tilde{W})\Delta_{33}
$$

$$
\Delta_{11} = t_2(\tilde{P}_2)t_3(\tilde{P}_3) - t_3(\tilde{P}_2)t_2(\tilde{P}_3)
$$

$$
\Delta_{12} = t_3(\tilde{P}_2)t_1(\tilde{P}_3) - t_1(\tilde{P}_2)t_3(\tilde{P}_3)
$$

$$
\Delta_{13} = t_1(\tilde{P}_2)t_2(\tilde{P}_3) - t_2(\tilde{P}_2)t_1(\tilde{P}_3)
$$

$$
\Delta_{21} = t_3(\tilde{P}_1)t_2(\tilde{P}_3) - t_2(\tilde{P}_1)t_3(\tilde{P}_3)
$$

$$
\Delta_{22} = t_1(\tilde{P}_1)t_3(\tilde{P}_3) - t_3(\tilde{P}_1)t_1(\tilde{P}_3)
$$

$$
\Delta_{23} = t_2(\tilde{P}_1)t_1(\tilde{P}_3) - t_1(\tilde{P}_1)t_2(\tilde{P}_3)
$$

$$
\Delta_{31} = t_2(\tilde{P}_1)t_3(\tilde{P}_2) - t_3(\tilde{P}_1)t_2(\tilde{P}_2)
$$

$$
\Delta_{32} = t_3(\tilde{P}_1)t_1(\tilde{P}_2) - t_1(\tilde{P}_1)t_3(\tilde{P}_2)
$$

$$
\Delta_{33} = t_1(\tilde{P}_1)t_2(\tilde{P}_2) - t_2(\tilde{P}_1)t_1(\tilde{P}_2)
$$

Thus if the tristimulus values are known for a given set of primaries, conversion to another set of primaries merely entails a simple linear transformation of coordinates.

3.6. COLOR COORDINATE SYSTEMS

It has been shown that a color $[C]$ can be matched by its tristimulus values $T_1(C)$, $T_2(C)$, $T_3(C)$ for a given set of primaries. Alternatively, the color may be specified by its chromaticity values $t_1(C)$, $t_2(C)$ and its luminance $L(C)$. A third approach in specifying a color is to represent the color by some linear or nonlinear invertible function of its tristimulus or chromaticity values. From Eq. 3.5-5 it is evident that a linear function of the tristimulus values is simply a conversion to a new set of primaries. Appendix 2 presents formulas for color coordinate conversion between tristimulus values and chromaticity coordinates for various representational combinations.

Many different coordinate systems have been employed for the specification of color. Those of historical and analytic significance are discussed in greater detail below.

C.I.E. Spectral Primary Color Coordinate System

In 1931 the C.I.E. developed a standard primary reference system with three monochromatic primaries at wavelengths: red = 700 nm; green = 546.1 nm; and blue = 435.8 nm (4). The units of the tristimulus values are such that the tristimulus values R_c, G_c, and B_c are equal when matching an equal-energy white throughout the visible spectrum. The primary system is defined by tristimulus curves of the spectral colors, as shown in Figure 3.6-1. These curves have been obtained indirectly by experimental color

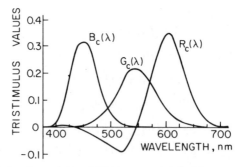

FIGURE 3.6-1. Tristimulus values of C.I.E. spectral primaries required to match unit energy throughout the spectrum. Red = 700 nm, green = 546.1 nm, and blue = 435.8 nm (11).

matching experiments performed by a number of observers. The color matching response of these observers has been denoted as the C.I.E. Standard Observer. The original data published in 1931 apply to color matches over a two-degree field; similar data have been adopted by the C.I.E. for a ten-degree field. For television and facsimile systems the two-degree standard observer data appear adequate. Figure 3.6-2 contains a chromaticity diagram for the C.I.E. spectral primary coordinate system. The N.T.S.C.* color television receiver primaries are plotted in the diagram. A triangle defined by these primaries indicates the gamut of colors reproducible by the N.T.S.C. phosphors.

N.T.S.C. Receiver Primary Color Coordinate System

Commercial United States television receivers employ a cathode ray tube with three phosphors that glow in the red, green, and blue regions of the visible spectrum (14). The standard observer data for the C.I.E. spectral

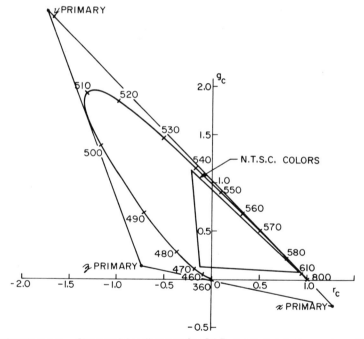

FIGURE 3.6-2. Chromaticity diagram for C.I.E. spectral primary system **(11)**.

---

* National Television Systems Committee, the group that has defined United States television standards.

primary system can be referenced to a primary system utilizing the three N.T.S.C. phosphor primaries by a simple linear transformation of coordinates. Figure 3.6-3 is a chromaticity diagram for the N.T.S.C. primary system. In this system the units of the tristimulus values are normalized so that the tristimulus values are equal when matching the Illuminant C white reference. The N.T.S.C. phosphors are not pure monochromatic sources of radiation, and hence the gamut of colors producible by the N.T.S.C. phosphors is smaller than that available from the C.I.E. spectral primaries.

C.I.E. X-Y-Z- Color Coordinate Systems

The C.I.E. spectral primary system has one defect when analytic colorimetric calculations are performed: the tristimulus values are sometimes negative. Recognizing this problem, the C.I.E. developed an artificial primary coordinate system in which all tristimulus values required to match the spectral colors are positive (4). These artificial primaries are shown in the C.I.E. spectral primary chromaticity diagram of Figure 3.6-2. The X-Y-Z system primaries have been chosen so that the Y tristimulus value is equivalent to the luminance $L(C)$ of the color. Figure 3.6-4 contains the chromaticity diagram for the C.I.E. X-Y-Z primary system referenced to equal-energy white.

N.T.S.C. Transmission Color Coordinate System

In the development of the United States color television system, the N.T.S.C. formulated a color coordinate system composed of three tristimulus values Y-I-Q (14). The Y tristimulus value is the same as the Y of the X-Y-Z coordinate system; it is a measure of the luminance of a color.

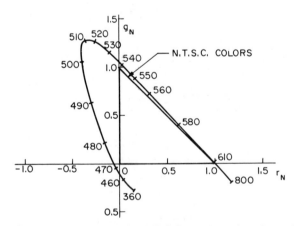

FIGURE 3.6-3. Chromaticity diagram for N.T.S.C. receiver phosphor primary system.

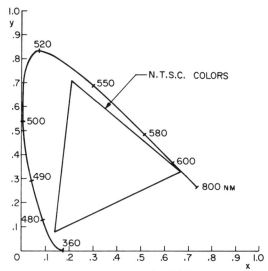

FIGURE 3.6-4.   Chromaticity diagram for C.I.E. *XYZ* primary system (4).

The remaining two tristimulus values I and Q jointly describe the hue and saturation of the image. The reasons for transmitting the Y-I-Q tristimulus values rather than the R_N-G_N-B_N tristimulus values directly from the color camera are twofold: the Y signal alone can be used with existing receivers without modification to display monochrome images; furthermore, it is possible to limit the bandwidth of the I and Q signals without noticeable image degradation. As a result of this latter property, a clever modulation scheme enables the bandwidth of the analog color television carrier to be limited to the same bandwidth as a monochrome carrier.

C.I.E. Uniform Chromaticity Scale Color Coordinate System

A desirable property for any color coordinate system is that any unit change in the chromaticity diagram of that system should be perceived as an equivalently noticeable color shift to an observer. Figure 3.6-5a contains a plot of equally perceived color differences in the x-y chromaticity diagram (12, 17). This figure and other experimental results indicate that a human viewer is most sensitive to color shifts in the blue, moderately sensitive to color shifts in the red, and least sensitive to color shifts in the green. In 1960 the C.I.E. adopted a coordinate system, called the Uniform Chromaticity Scale (UCS), in which equal changes in the chromaticity coordinates result in just noticeable changes in hue and saturation to a good approximation. Figure 3.6-5b shows the data of Figure 3.6-5a replotted in the UCS chromaticity space. The UCS color coordinate system is

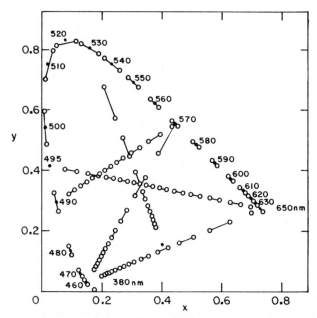

(a) Just noticeable color differences in x–y chromaticity diagram.

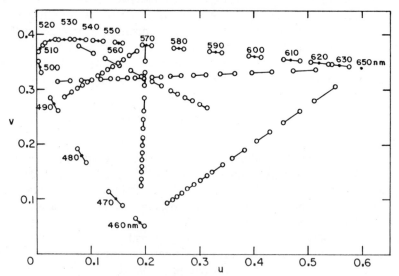

(b) Just noticeable color differences in u–v chromaticity diagram.

FIGURE 3.6-5. Comparison of just noticeable color differences in *X-Y-Z* and *U-V-W* coordinate systems. Lines are 10 times one just noticeable color difference (12).

a linear transformation of the X-Y-Z coordinate system. The chromaticity coordinates of the two systems are related by (18)

$$u = \frac{4x}{-2x + 12y + 3} \tag{3.6-1a}$$

$$v = \frac{6y}{-2x + 12y + 3} \tag{3.6-1b}$$

Figure 3.6-6 contains a UCS chromaticity diagram.

U^*-V^*-W^*- Color Coordinate System

The U^*-V^*-W^* coordinate system is an extension of the U-V-W coordinate system in an attempt to obtain a color solid for which unit shifts in luminance and chrominance are uniformly perceptable The U^*-V^*-W^* coordinates are defined as (19)

$$U^* = 13W^*(u - u_0) \tag{3.6-2a}$$

$$V^* = 13W^*(v - v_0) \tag{3.6-2b}$$

$$W^* = 25(100Y)^{1/3} - 17 \tag{3.6-2c}$$

where the luminance Y is measured over a scale of 0 to 1 and u_0 and v_0 are the chromaticity coordinates of the reference illuminant.

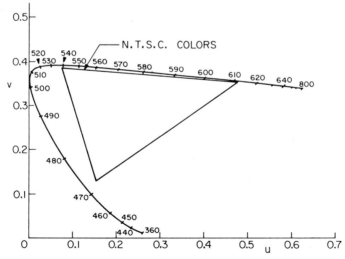

FIGURE 3.6-6. Chromaticity diagram for C.I.E. uniform chromaticity scale primary system (11).

S-θ-W* Color Coordinate System

The S-θ-W^* coordinate system is simply the polar representation of the U^*-V^*-W^* color solid defined by (11)

$$S = [(U^*)^2 + (V^*)^2]^{1/2} = 13W^*[(u - u_0)^2 + (v - v_0)^2]^{1/2} \quad (3.6\text{-}3a)$$

$$\theta = \tan^{-1}\left[\frac{V^*}{U^*}\right] = \tan^{-1}\left(\frac{v - v_0}{u - u_0}\right) \quad (3.6\text{-}3b)$$

In the S-θ-W^* system the S component is proportional to the saturation of a color and the θ component is related to its hue.

L-a-b Coordinate System

The L-a-b cube-root color coordinate system has been developed to provide a relatively accurate measure of color in agreement with the Munsell color system, that would still be simple to calculate (20). The color coordinates are

$$L = 25\left(100\frac{Y}{Y_0}\right)^{1/3} - 16 \quad (3.6\text{-}4a)$$

$$a = 500\left[\left(\frac{X}{X_0}\right)^{1/3} - \left(\frac{Y}{Y_0}\right)^{1/3}\right] \quad (3.6\text{-}4b)$$

$$b = 200\left[\left(\frac{Y}{Y_0}\right)^{1/3} - \left(\frac{Z}{Z_0}\right)^{1/3}\right] \quad (3.6\text{-}4c)$$

where X_0, Y_0, Z_0 are the tristimulus values for the reference white. Basically, L is correlated with brightness, a with redness-greenness, and b with yellowness-blueness. Many manufacturers of colorimeters provide direct readouts in the L-a-b coordinate system.

Karhunen–Loeve Color Coordinate System

The C.I.E. spectral, the X-Y-Z, the U-V-W, and the other tristimulus coordinate systems can be considered linear transformations of the N.T.S.C. receiver primary coordinate system. The R_N, G_N, B_N tristimulus values of the N.T.S.C. receiver primary system are highly correlated with one another (21). In the development of efficient quantization and coding techniques for color image components, it is desirable to work with components that are uncorrelated. If the second-order moments of the R_N, G_N, B_N tristimulus values are known, or at least estimable, it is possible to derive an orthogonal coordinate system, in which the components are uncorrelated, by a Karhunen–Loeve expansion of the covariance matrix of the R_N, G_N, B_N tristimulus values. The transformation matrix with general term m_{ij} is composed of the eigenvectors of the covariance matrix and is defined by

$$
\begin{bmatrix} m_{11} & m_{12} & m_{13} \\ m_{21} & m_{22} & m_{23} \\ m_{31} & m_{32} & m_{33} \end{bmatrix} \begin{bmatrix} u_{11} & u_{12} & u_{13} \\ u_{12} & u_{22} & u_{23} \\ u_{13} & u_{23} & u_{33} \end{bmatrix} \begin{bmatrix} m_{11} & m_{21} & m_{31} \\ m_{12} & m_{22} & m_{32} \\ m_{13} & m_{23} & m_{33} \end{bmatrix}
$$
$$
= \begin{bmatrix} \Lambda_1 & 0 & 0 \\ 0 & \Lambda_2 & 0 \\ 0 & 0 & \Lambda_3 \end{bmatrix} \tag{3.6-5}
$$

where Λ_1, Λ_2, Λ_3 are the eigenvalues of the covariance matrix and

$$u_{11} \equiv E\{(R_N - \bar{R}_N)^2\} \tag{3.6-6a}$$

$$u_{22} \equiv E\{(G_N - \bar{G}_N)^2\} \tag{3.6-6b}$$

$$u_{33} \equiv E\{(B_N - \bar{B}_N)^2\} \tag{3.6-6c}$$

$$u_{12} \equiv E\{(R_N - \bar{R}_N)(G_N - \bar{G}_N)\} \tag{3.6-6d}$$

$$u_{13} \equiv E\{(R_N - \bar{R}_N)(B_N - \bar{B}_N)\} \tag{3.6-6e}$$

$$u_{23} \equiv E\{(G_N - \bar{G}_N)(B_N - \bar{B}_N)\} \tag{3.6-6f}$$

Retinal Cone Color Coordinate System

As indicated in Chapter 2 on the discussion of models of the human visual system for color vision, indirect measurements of the spectral sensitivities $s_1(\lambda)$, $s_2(\lambda)$, $s_3(\lambda)$ have been made for the three types of retinal cones. It has been found that these spectral sensitivity functions can be linearly related to spectral tristimulus values established by colorimetric experimentation. Hence a set of cone signals T_1, T_2, T_3 may be regarded as tristimulus values in a retinal cone color coordinate system. The tristimulus values of the retinal cone color coordinate system are related to the X-Y-Z system by the coordinate conversion (22)

$$
\begin{bmatrix} T_1 \\ T_2 \\ T_3 \end{bmatrix} = \begin{bmatrix} 0.0 & 1.0 & 0.0 \\ -0.460 & 1.359 & 0.101 \\ 0.0 & 0.0 & 1.0 \end{bmatrix} \begin{bmatrix} X \\ Y \\ Z \end{bmatrix} \tag{3.6-7}
$$

Figure 3.6-7 contains examples of the color components of a color image for several color coordinate systems. The red, green, and blue components are observed to be highly correlated. In some of the other coordinate systems one of the planes possesses a large fraction of the image energy, and the remaining planes appear to be reduced in detail.

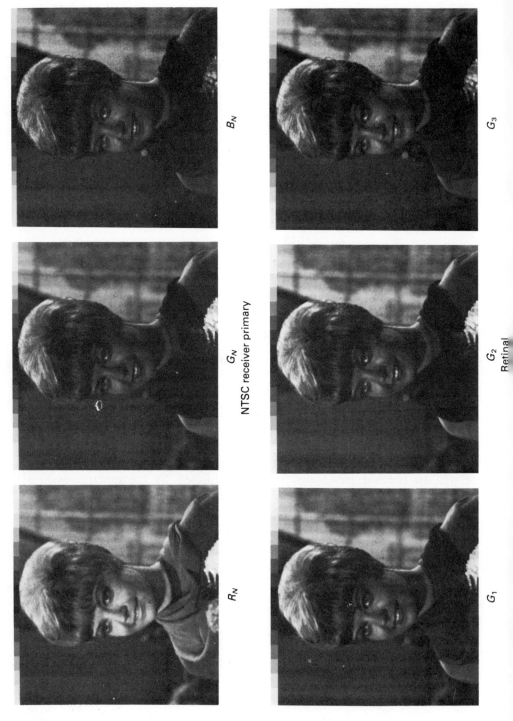

B_N

G_3

G_N
NTSC receiver primary

G_2
Retinal

R_N

G_1

80

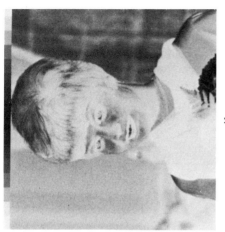

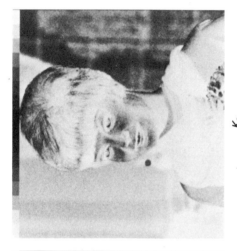

K_1

K_2
Karhunen-Loeve

K_3

FIGURE 3.6-7. Color components of a color image.

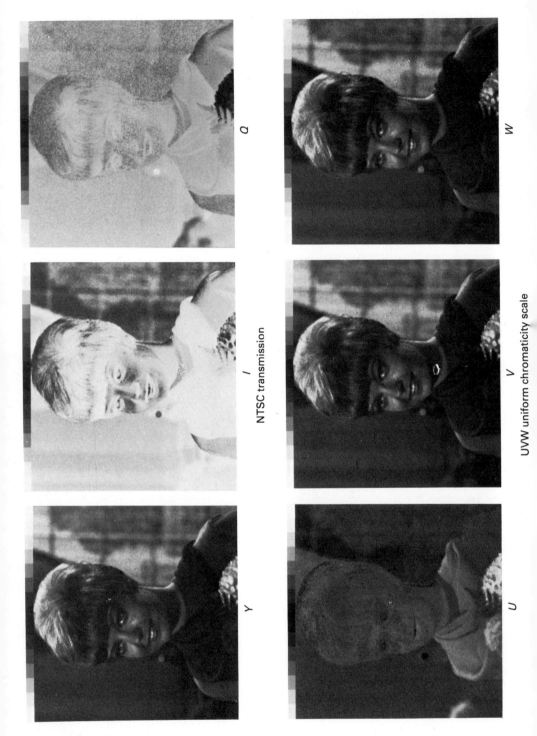

Q

I

NTSC transmission

W

V

UVW uniform chromaticity scale

Y

U

82

L

a

b

L a b uniform tristimulus scale

FIGURE 3.6-7 *(continued).* Color components of a color image.

3.7. COLOR SOLIDS

It is evident from the previous section that there are a number of color coordinate systems that could be employed for the representation of a color. Unfortunately, there appears to be no technique for determining an "optimum" coordinate system for most applications. Rather, one must state the characteristics of the desired coordinate system, and then examine the characteristics of candidate systems. In an effort to quantify the color coordinate selection procedure, consideration will be given to basic limitations in the representation of colors and to methods for discerning the differences between colors.

There are two basic physical restrictions in the representation of natural colors by color imaging systems. First, any set of physical primaries can only emit positive amounts of light. Hence, although the color match may require a negative tristimulus value, it is impossible to satisfy this demand for purely additive color mixtures. Thus colors requiring negative tristimulus values cannot be reproduced by the imaging system. The second restriction in color rendition arises from physical structure limitations on the luminance of light transmitted through transparencies or reflected from objects.

3.7.1. Positive Tristimulus Value Limitation

Consider a color image sensor whose output consists of three tristimulus values $R_N(C)$, $G_N(C)$, $B_N(C)$ of the three N.T.S.C. receiver primary colors $[R_N]$, $[G_N]$, $[B_N]$. The image sensor is capable of rendering any color that results in positive tristimulus values. Such colors lie in a cubic solid as shown in Figure 3.7-1a. The vertices of this cube have been labeled as the N.T.S.C. receiver primary system major colors: red, green, blue, cyan, magenta, yellow, black, white. Now consider a linear coordinate conversion to a new set of primaries $T_1(C)$, $T_2(C)$, $T_3(C)$ given by

$$\begin{bmatrix} T_1(C) \\ T_2(C) \\ T_3(C) \end{bmatrix} = \begin{bmatrix} m_{11} & m_{12} & m_{13} \\ m_{21} & m_{22} & m_{23} \\ m_{31} & m_{32} & m_{33} \end{bmatrix} \begin{bmatrix} R_N(C) \\ G_N(C) \\ B_N(C) \end{bmatrix} \qquad (3.7\text{-}1)$$

Table 3.7-1 contains a listing of the tristimulus and chromaticity values of the N.T.S.C. receiver primary major colors for several coordinate systems. Drawings of tristimulus color solids for various color coordinate systems are shown in Figure 3.7-1 in which the N.T.S.C. receiver primary color solid has been projected onto each color solid. Only those colors within this hexahedron can be produced by the N.T.S.C. receiver phosphors. It should

TABLE 3.7-1. Tristimulus and chromaticity values of N.T.S.C. receiver primary major colors in various color coordinate systems

	Red	Green	Blue	Cyan	Magenta	Yellow	White	Black
R_N	1.000	0.000	0.000	0.000	1.000	1.000	1.000	0.000
G_N	0.000	1.000	0.000	1.000	0.000	1.000	1.000	0.000
B_N	0.000	0.000	1.000	1.000	1.000	0.000	1.000	0.000
r_N	1.000	0.000	0.000	0.000	0.500	0.500	0.333	0.333
g_N	0.000	1.000	0.000	0.500	0.000	0.500	0.333	0.333
b_N	0.000	0.000	1.000	0.500	0.500	0.000	0.333	0.333
X	0.607	0.174	0.201	0.375	0.808	0.781	0.982	0.000
Y	0.299	0.587	0.114	0.701	0.413	0.886	1.000	0.000
Z	0.000	0.066	1.117	1.183	1.117	0.066	1.183	0.000
x	0.670	0.210	0.140	0.166	0.346	0.451	0.310	0.310
y	0.330	0.710	0.080	0.310	0.177	0.511	0.316	0.316
z	0.000	0.080	0.780	0.524	0.477	0.038	0.374	0.374
R_c	0.207	−0.026	−0.026	−0.052	0.180	0.181	0.154	0.000
G_c	0.020	0.133	0.028	0.161	0.048	0.153	0.181	0.000
B_c	0.000	0.010	0.200	0.210	0.199	0.010	0.210	0.000
r_c	0.912	−0.219	−0.132	−0.164	0.421	0.525	0.283	0.283
g_c	0.089	1.130	0.139	0.506	0.113	0.446	0.333	0.333
b_c	0.000	0.089	0.993	0.658	0.466	0.029	0.384	0.384
U	0.405	0.116	0.134	0.250	0.539	0.521	0.655	0.000
V	0.299	0.587	0.114	0.701	0.413	0.886	1.000	0.000
W	0.145	0.827	0.629	1.456	0.774	0.972	1.601	0.000
u	0.477	0.076	0.153	0.104	0.312	0.219	0.201	0.201
v	0.352	0.384	0.130	0.291	0.239	0.373	0.307	0.307
w	0.171	0.540	0.717	0.605	0.449	0.408	0.492	0.492
Y	0.299	0.587	0.114	0.701	0.413	0.886	1.000	0.000
I	0.596	−0.273	−0.322	−0.595	0.272	0.322	0.000	0.000
Q	0.212	−0.522	0.315	−0.207	0.526	−0.312	0.000	0.000
U^*	217.358	−130.319	−24.558	−108.566	100.385	22.144	0.000	0.000
V^*	35.461	79.703	−90.508	−17.913	−61.336	80.125	0.000	0.000
W^*	60.594	80.160	39.265	86.081	69.415	94.451	99.040	−17.000
S	220.232	152.760	93.781	110.034	117.640	83.128	0.000	0.000
θ	0.162	2.609	4.445	3.304	5.733	1.280	0.000	0.000
W^*	60.594	80.160	39.265	86.081	69.415	94.451	99.040	−17.000
L	61.594	81.160	40.265	87.081	70.415	95.451	100.040	−16.000
a	91.577	−137.815	52.227	−81.411	96.177	−16.977	0.000	0.000
b	133.738	91.038	−99.233	−22.335	−47.269	115.670	0.000	0.000

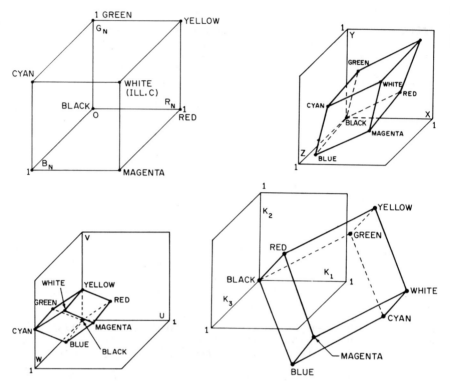

FIGURE 3.7-1. Tristimulus color solids. (a) R_N, G_N, B_N. (b) X, Y, Z. (c) U, V, W. (d) Karhunen-Loeve.

be noted that, in the Karhunen–Loeve coordinate system of Figure 3.7-1d, the hexahedron of the N.T.S.C. receiver primary major colors is a cube rotated with respect to the tristimulus axes.

A particular color may also be represented by its chromaticity values

$$t_1(C) = \frac{T_1(C)}{T_1(C) + T_2(C) + T_3(C)} \tag{3.7-2a}$$

$$t_2(C) = \frac{T_2(C)}{T_1(C) + T_2(C) + T_3(C)} \tag{3.7-2b}$$

and its luminance

$$Y(C) = L(C) = n_{21}R_N(C) + n_{22}G_N(C) + n_{23}B_N(C) \tag{3.7-2c}$$

where the tristimulus values $T_1(C)$, $T_2(C)$, $T_3(C)$ are obtained from Eq. 3.7-1 and the constants n_{ij} are defined in Appendix 2. The tristimulus to chromaticity conversion of Eq. 3.7-2 is a nonlinear coordinate conversion. Figure 3.7-2 contains a sketch of the N.T.S.C. receiver primary color solid in the r_N, g_N, Y luminance/chrominance color space.

3.7.2. Luminance Limitation

Most colors of natural images result from diffuse illumination either reflected from an opaque object or passed through a transparent material. For such non-self-luminous objects there is a physical restriction to the brightness of the object that is dependent upon its color. MacAdam (23, 24) has proved that the maximum color gamut of an object occurs when the object possesses a reflection, or transmission, characteristic of the type shown in Figure 3.7-3. Such objects do not physically exist; hence the gamut of physical object colors will be even less than that indicated by objects with ideal reflectance of transmission characteristics. For simplicity, consideration will only be given to reflective objects. The same results also apply to transmissive objects.

Consider a color $[C]$ to be specified by its X-Y-Z tristimulus values

$$X = \int r_0(\lambda)E(\lambda)X_s(\lambda)\,d\lambda \qquad (3.7\text{-}3a)$$

$$Y = \int r_0(\lambda)E(\lambda)Y_s(\lambda)\,d\lambda \qquad (3.7\text{-}3b)$$

$$Z = \int r_0(\lambda)E(\lambda)Z_s(\lambda)\,d\lambda \qquad (3.7\text{-}3c)$$

where $r_0(\lambda)$ is the object reflectance as a function of wavelength, $E(\lambda)$ is the spectral energy density of the object illumination, and $X_s(\lambda)$, $Y_s(\lambda)$, $Z_s(\lambda)$ are the tristimulus values of one unit of monochromatic light at wavelength λ. The visual efficiency β is defined as the ratio of the luminance of an object with a reflectance $r_0(\lambda)$ to the luminance of an object

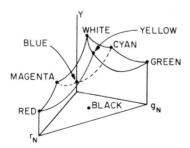

FIGURE 3.7-2. Luminance/chrominance color solid for N.T.S.C. receiver primary system.

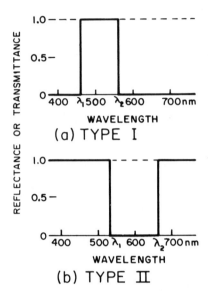

FIGURE 3.7-3.   Spectral reflectance or transmittance curves for optimal colors.

with unity reflectance over all wavelengths. Hence

$$\beta \equiv \frac{\int r_o(\lambda)E(\lambda)Y_s(\lambda)\,d\lambda}{\int E(\lambda)Y_s(\lambda)\,d\lambda} \qquad (3.7\text{-}4)$$

If the object has a reflectance characteristic of the type shown in Figure 3.7-3a, then the luminance of the object is

$$Y = \int_{\lambda_1}^{\lambda_2} E(\psi_k)Y_s(\psi_k)\,d\psi_k = \beta \int_0^\infty E(\psi_k)Y_s(\psi_k)\,d\psi_k \qquad (3.7\text{-}5)$$

Suppose that the spectral energy distribution $E(\lambda)$ of the object illuminant is known. Then for a given value of the visual efficiency β the object luminance may be computed. For an arbitrary lower limit on the wavelength of the object's reflectance λ_1, the upper limit may be found by numerical techniques to satisfy

$$\int_0^{\lambda_2} E(\psi_k)Y_s(\psi_k)\,d\psi_k = Y + \int_0^{\lambda_1} E(\psi_k)Y_s(\psi_k)\,d\psi_k \qquad (3.7\text{-}6)$$

With this value for λ_2 the tristimulus values X and Z may be found from

$$X = \int_{\lambda_1}^{\lambda_2} E(\lambda_k)X_s(\lambda_k)\,d\lambda_k \qquad (3.7\text{-}7)$$

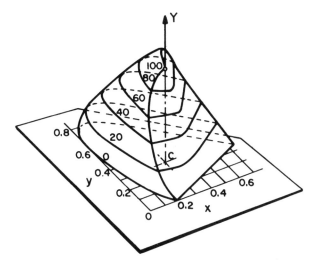

FIGURE 3.7-4. Object color solid in the C.I.E. X, Y, Z luminance/chrominance coordinate system (23).

$$Z = \int_{\lambda_1}^{\lambda_2} E(\lambda_k)Z_s(\lambda_k)\, d\lambda_k \tag{3.7-8}$$

The chromaticity values x and y may then be determined from the tristimulus values. If this procedure is followed for all λ_1 in the visible region for given values of the visual efficiency β, it is possible to obtain the locus of object colors in the tristimulus or luminance/chrominance color solids. Figure 3.7-4 shows a perspective view of the object colors in the luminance/chrominance color solid for illumination by Illuminant C. It should be noted that the maximum luminance only occurs for the reference white illuminant.

REFERENCES

1. T. P. Merrit and F. F. Hall, Jr., "Blackbody Radiation," *Proc. IRE*, **47**, 9, September 1959, 1435–1442.

2. H. H. Malitson, "The Solar Energy Spectrum," *Sky and Telescope*, **29**, 4, March 1965, 162–165.

3. R. D. Larabee, "Spectral Emissivity of Tungsten," *J. Opt. Soc. Am.*, **49**, 6, June 1959, 619–625.

4. *The Science of Color*, Crowell, New York, 1953.

5. D. G. Fink, Ed., *Television Engineering Handbook*, McGraw-Hill, New York, 1957.

6. J. W. T. Walsh, *Photometry*, Constable, London, 1953.

7.   J. Morgan, *Introduction to Geometrical and Physical Optics*, McGraw-Hill, New York, 1953.

8.   M. Born and E. Wolf, *Principles of Optics*, Pergamon, New York, 1970.

9.   K. S. Weaver, "The Visibility of Radiation at Low Intensities," *J. Opt. Soc. Am.*, **27**, 1, January 1937, 39–43.

10. G. Wyszecki and W. S. Stiles, *Color Science*, Wiley, New York, 1957.

11. R. W. G. Hunt, *The Reproduction of Colour*, Wiley, New York, 1957.

12. W. D. Wright, *The Measurement of Color*, Adam Hilger, London, 1944, 204–205.

13. R. A. Enyord, Ed., *Color: Theory and Imaging Systems*, Society of Photographic Scientists and Engineers, Washington D.C., 1973.

14. F. J. Bingley, "Color Vision and Colorimetry," *Television Engineering Handbook*, D. G. Fink, Ed., McGraw-Hill, New York, 1957.

15. H. Grassman, "On the Theory of Compound Colours," *Phil. Mag.*, Ser. 4, **7**, April 1854, 254–264.

16. W. T. Wintringham, "Color Television and Colorimetry," *Proc. IRE*, **39**, 10, October 1951, 1135–1172.

17. D. L. MacAdam, "Visual Sensitivities to Small Color Differences in Daylight," *J. Opt. Soc. Am.*, **32**, 5, May 1942, 247–274.

18. D. L. MacAdam, "Projective Transformations of ICI Color Specifications," *J. Opt. Soc. Am.*, **27**, 8, August 1937, 294–299.

19. G. Wyszecki, "Proposal for a New Color-Difference Formula," *J. Opt. Soc. Am.*, **53**, 11, November 1963, 1318–1319.

20. C.I.E. Colorimetry Committee Proposal for Study of Color Spaces, Tech. Note, *J. Opt. Soc. Am.*, **64**, 6, June 1974, 896–897.

21. W. K. Pratt, "Spatial Transform Coding of Color Images," *IEEE Trans. Commun. Tech.*, **COM-19**, 12, December 1971, 980–992.

22. D. B. Judd, "Standard Response Functions for Protanopic and Deuteranopic Vision," *J. Opt. Soc. Am.*, **35**, 3, March 1945, 199–221.

23. D. L. MacAdam, "The Theory of the Maximum Visual Efficiency of Colored Materials," *J. Opt. Soc. Am.*, **25**, 8, August 1935, 249–252.

24. D. L. MacAdam, "Maximum Visual Efficiency of Colored Materials," *J. Opt. Soc. Am.*, **25**, 11, November 1935, 361–367.

2 DIGITAL IMAGE CHARACTERIZATION

Digital image processing is based on the conversion of a continuous image field to equivalent digital form. This part of the book considers the image sampling and quantization processes that perform the analog image to digital image conversion. The inverse operation of producing continuous image displays from digital image arrays is also analyzed. Vector-space methods of image representation are developed for deterministic and stochastic image arrays. The final topic of image quality is concerned with the establishment of measures of fidelity and intelligibility for discrete image arrays.

4 IMAGE SAMPLING AND RECONSTRUCTION

In digital image processing systems one usually deals with arrays of numbers obtained by spatially sampling points of a physical image. After processing, another array of numbers is produced, and these numbers are then used to reconstruct a continuous image for viewing. Image samples nominally represent some physical measurements of a continuous image field, for example, measurements of the image intensity or photographic density. Measurement uncertainties exist in any physical measurement apparatus. It is important to be able to model these measurement errors in order to specify the validity of the measurements and to design processes for compensation of the measurement errors. Also, it is often not possible to measure an image field directly. Instead, measurements are made of some function related to the desired image field, and this function is then "inverted" to obtain the desired image field. Inversion operations of this nature are discussed in the sections on image restoration. In this chapter the image sampling and reconstruction process is considered both for theoretically exact and practical systems.

4.1. EXACT IMAGE SAMPLING AND RECONSTRUCTION

In the design and analysis of image sampling and reconstruction systems, input images are usually regarded as deterministic fields. However, in some situations it is advantageous to consider the input to an image processing system, especially a noise input, as a sample of a two-dimensional random process. Both viewpoints are developed here for the analysis of image sampling and reconstruction methods.

4.1.1. Sampling Deterministic Fields (1–5)

Let $F_I(x, y)$ denote a continuous, infinite-dimension ideal image field representing the intensity, photographic density, or some desired parameter of a physical image. In a perfect image sampling system, spatial samples of the ideal image would, in effect, be obtained by multiplying the ideal image by a spatial sampling function

$$S(x, y) = \sum_{j_1=-\infty}^{\infty} \sum_{j_2=-\infty}^{\infty} \delta(x - j_1 \Delta x, y - j_2 \Delta y) \qquad (4.1\text{-}1)$$

composed of an infinite array of Dirac delta functions arranged in a grid of spacing $(\Delta x, \Delta y)$ as shown in Figure 4.1-1. The sampled image is then represented as

$$F_P(x, y) = F_I(x, y)S(x, y) = \sum_{j_1=-\infty}^{\infty} \sum_{j_2=-\infty}^{\infty} F_I(j_1 \Delta x, j_2 \Delta y)$$
$$\cdot \delta(x - j_1 \Delta x, y - j_2 \Delta y) \qquad (4.1\text{-}2)$$

where it is observed that $F_I(x, y)$ may be brought inside the summation and evaluated only at the sample points $(j_1 \Delta x, j_2 \Delta y)$. It is convenient, for purposes of analysis, to consider the spatial frequency domain representation $\mathcal{F}_P(\omega_x, \omega_y)$ of the sampled image obtained by taking the continuous two-dimensional Fourier transform of the sampled image. Thus

$$\mathcal{F}_P(\omega_x, \omega_y) = \int\!\!\int_{-\infty}^{\infty} F_P(x, y) \exp\{-i(\omega_x x + \omega_y y)\}\, dx\, dy \qquad (4.1\text{-}3)$$

By the Fourier transform convolution theorem, the Fourier transform of the sampled image can be expressed as the convolution of the Fourier transforms of the ideal image $\mathcal{F}_I(\omega_x, \omega_y)$ and the sampling function $\mathcal{S}(\omega_x, \omega_y)$ as expressed by

$$\mathcal{F}_P(\omega_x, \omega_y) = \frac{1}{4\pi^2}\, \mathcal{F}_I(\omega_x, \omega_y) \circledast \mathcal{S}(\omega_x, \omega_y) \qquad (4.1\text{-}4)$$

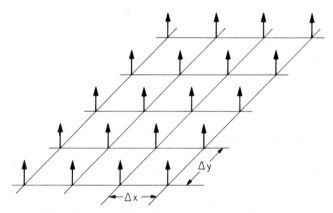

FIGURE 4.1-1. Dirac delta function sampling array.

The two-dimensional Fourier transform of the spatial sampling function is an infinite array of Dirac delta functions in the spatial frequency domain as given by (4, p. 22)

$$\mathcal{S}(\omega_x, \omega_y) = \frac{4\pi^2}{\Delta x\, \Delta y} \sum_{j_1=-\infty}^{\infty} \sum_{j_2=-\infty}^{\infty} \delta(\omega_x - j_1\omega_{xs},\, \omega_y - j_2\omega_{ys}) \quad (4.1\text{-}5)$$

where $\omega_{xs} = 2\pi/\Delta x$ and $\omega_{ys} = 2\pi/\Delta y$ represent the Fourier domain sampling frequencies. It will be assumed that the spectrum of the ideal image is bandlimited to some bounds such that $\mathcal{F}_I(\omega_x, \omega_y) = 0$ for $|\omega_x| > \omega_{xc}$ and $|\omega_y| > \omega_{yc}$. Performing the convolution of Eq. 4.1-4 yields

$$\mathcal{F}_P(\omega_x, \omega_y) = \frac{1}{\Delta x\, \Delta y} \int_{-\infty}^{\infty}\!\!\int \mathcal{F}_I(\omega_x - \alpha,\, \omega_y - \beta)$$

$$\cdot \sum_{j_1=-\infty}^{\infty} \sum_{j_2=-\infty}^{\infty} \delta(\alpha - j_1\omega_{xs},\, \beta - j_2\omega_{ys})\, d\alpha\, d\beta \quad (4.1\text{-}6)$$

Upon changing the order of summation and integration and invoking the Sifting property of the delta function, the sampled image spectrum becomes

$$\mathcal{F}_P(\omega_x, \omega_y) = \frac{1}{\Delta x\, \Delta y} \sum_{j_1=-\infty}^{\infty} \sum_{j_2=-\infty}^{\infty} \mathcal{F}_I(\omega_x - j_1\omega_{xs},\, \omega_y - j_2\omega_{ys}) \quad (4.1\text{-}7)$$

As can be seen from the sketch of Figure 4.1-2, the spectrum of the sampled image consists of the spectrum of the ideal image infinitely repeated over the frequency plane in a grid of resolution $(2\pi/\Delta x, 2\pi/\Delta y)$. It

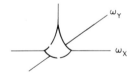

(a) ORIGINAL IMAGE

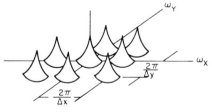

(b) SAMPLED IMAGE

FIGURE 4.1-2. Typical sampled image spectra.

should be noted that if Δx and Δy are chosen too large with respect to the spatial frequency limits of $\mathscr{F}_I(\omega_x, \omega_y)$, then the individual spectra will overlap.

A continuous image field may be obtained from the image samples $F_P(x, y)$ by linear spatial interpolation or by linear spatial filtering of the sampled image. Let $R(x, y)$ denote the impulse response of an interpolation filter and $\mathscr{R}(\omega_x, \omega_y)$ its transfer function. Then the reconstructed image is obtained by a convolution of the samples with the reconstruction filter impulse response. The reconstructed image then becomes

$$F_R(x, y) = F_P(x, y) \circledast R(x, y) \tag{4.1-8}$$

Upon substitution for $F_P(x, y)$ from Eq. 4.1-2 and performing the convolution one obtains

$$F_R(x, y) = \sum_{j_1=-\infty}^{\infty} \sum_{j_2=-\infty}^{\infty} F_I(j_1 \Delta x, j_2 \Delta y) R(x - j_1 \Delta x, y - j_2 \Delta y)$$
$$\tag{4.1-9}$$

Thus it is seen that the impulse response function $R(x, y)$ acts as a two-dimensional interpolation waveform for the image samples. The spatial frequency spectrum of the reconstructed image obtained from Eq. 4.1-8 is equal to the product of the reconstruction filter transform and the spectrum of the sampled image

$$\mathscr{F}_R(\omega_x, \omega_y) = \mathscr{F}_P(\omega_x, \omega_y) \mathscr{R}(\omega_x, \omega_y) \tag{4.1-10}$$

Or from Eq. 4.1-7

$$\mathscr{F}_R(\omega_x, \omega_y) = \frac{1}{\Delta x \, \Delta y} \mathscr{R}(\omega_x, \omega_y) \sum_{j_1=-\infty}^{\infty} \sum_{j_2=-\infty}^{\infty} \mathscr{F}_I(\omega_x - j_1 \omega_{xs}, \omega_y - j_2 \omega_{ys})$$
$$\tag{4.1-11}$$

It is clear from Eq. 4.1-11 that if there is no spectrum overlap and if $\mathscr{R}(\omega_x, \omega_y)$ filters out all spectra for $j_1, j_2 \neq 0$, then the spectrum of the reconstructed image can be made equal to the spectrum of the ideal image, and therefore the images themselves can be made identical. The first condition is met for a bandlimited image if the sampling period is chosen such that the rectangular region bounded by the image cutoff frequencies $(\omega_{xc}, \omega_{yc})$ lies within a rectangular region defined by one-half the sampling frequency $(\omega_{xs}/2, \omega_{ys}/2)$. Hence

$$\omega_{xc} \leq \frac{\omega_{xs}}{2} \qquad \omega_{yc} \leq \frac{\omega_{ys}}{2} \tag{4.1-12a}$$

or, equivalently,

$$\Delta x \leq \frac{\pi}{\omega_{xc}} \qquad \Delta y \leq \frac{\pi}{\omega_{yc}} \qquad (4.1\text{-}12b)$$

In physical terms the sampling period must be equal to or smaller than one-half the period of the finest detail within the image. This sampling condition is equivalent to the one-dimensional sampling theorem constraint for time-varying signals that requires a time-varying signal to be sampled at a rate of at least twice its highest-frequency component. If equality holds in Eq. 4.1-12, the image is said to be sampled at its Nyquist rate; if Δx and Δy are smaller than required by the Nyquist criterion, the image is called oversampled; and if the opposite case holds, the image is undersampled.

If the original image is sampled at a spatial rate sufficient to prevent spectral overlap in the sampled image, then exact reconstruction of the ideal image can be achieved by spatial filtering the samples with an appropriate filter. For example, as shown in Figure 4.1-3, a filter with a transfer function of the form

$$\mathcal{R}(\omega_x, \omega_y) = K \qquad \text{for } |\omega_x| \leq \omega_{xL} \text{ and } |\omega_y| \leq \omega_{yL} \qquad (4.1\text{-}13a)$$

$$\mathcal{R}(\omega_x, \omega_y) = 0 \qquad \text{otherwise} \qquad (4.1\text{-}13b)$$

where K is a scaling constant, satisfies the condition of exact reconstruction if $\omega_{xL} > \omega_{xc}$ and $\omega_{yL} > \omega_{yc}$. The point-spread function or impulse response of this reconstruction filter is

$$R(x, y) = \frac{K\omega_{xL}\omega_{yL}}{\pi^2} \frac{\sin(\omega_{xL}x)}{(\omega_{xL}x)} \frac{\sin(\omega_{yL}y)}{(\omega_{yL}y)} \qquad (4.1\text{-}14)$$

With this filter an image is reconstructed with an infinite sum of sinc functions. Another type of reconstruction filter that could be employed is the cylindrical filter with a transfer function

$$\mathcal{R}(\omega_x, \omega_y) = K \qquad \text{if } \sqrt{\omega_x^2 + \omega_y^2} \leq \omega_0 \qquad (4.1\text{-}15a)$$

$$\mathcal{R}(\omega_x, \omega_y) = 0 \qquad \text{otherwise} \qquad (4.1\text{-}15b)$$

provided that $\omega_0^2 < \omega_{xc}^2 + \omega_{yc}^2$. The impulse response for this filter is

$$R(x, y) = 2\pi\omega_0 \frac{J_1\{\omega_0\sqrt{x^2 + y^2}\}}{\sqrt{x^2 + y^2}} \qquad (4.1\text{-}16)$$

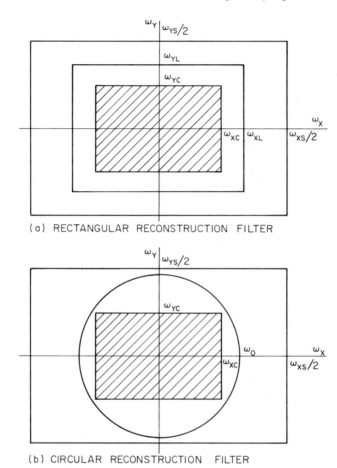

(a) RECTANGULAR RECONSTRUCTION FILTER

(b) CIRCULAR RECONSTRUCTION FILTER

FIGURE 4.1-3. Sampled image reconstruction filters.

where $J_1(\cdot)$ is a first-order Bessel function. There are a number of reconstruction filters, or, equivalently, interpolation waveforms, that could be employed to provide perfect image reconstruction. In practice, however, it is often difficult to implement optimum reconstruction filters for imaging systems. One practical problem is that, although a reconstructed image is strictly positive in amplitude at all points, the common interpolating waveforms such as those given by Eqs. 4.1-14 and 4.1-16 possess negative components. Thus it is impossible sequentially to reconstruct an image by a superposition of such weighted interpolation waveforms, because these waveforms cannot be generated optically. Richards (6) has discovered a family of interpolation functions that are positive in regions in which their magnitude is large, and hence can be employed for sequential optical interpolation.

4.1.2. Sampling Random Image Fields (5, 7, 8)

In the previous discussion on image sampling and reconstruction, the ideal input image field $F_I(x, y)$ has been considered a deterministic function. It has been shown that if the Fourier transform of the ideal image is bandlimited, then discrete image samples taken at the Nyquist rate are sufficient to reconstruct an exact replica of the ideal image with proper sample interpolation. It will now be shown that similar results hold for sampling two-dimensional random fields.

Let $F_I(x, y)$ denote a continuous two-dimensional stationary random process with known mean η_{F_I} and autocorrelation function

$$R_{F_I}(\tau_x, \tau_y) = E\{F_I(x_1, y_1)F_I^*(x_2, y_2)\} \qquad (4.1\text{-}17)$$

where $\tau_x = x_1 - x_2$ and $\tau_y = y_1 - y_2$. This process is spatially sampled by a Dirac sampling array yielding

$$F_P(x, y) = F_I(x, y)S(x, y) = F_I(x, y) \sum_{j_1=-\infty}^{\infty} \sum_{j_2=-\infty}^{\infty} \delta(x - j_1\,\Delta x, y - j_2\,\Delta y)$$

$$(4.1\text{-}18)$$

The autocorrelation of the sampled process is then

$$R_{F_P}(x_1, x_2; y_1, y_2) = E\{F_P(x_1, y_1)F_P^*(x_2, y_2)\}$$

$$= E\{F_I(x_1, y_1)F_I^*(x_2, y_2)\}S(x_1, y_1)S(x_2, y_2)$$
$$(4.1\text{-}19)$$

The first term on the right-hand side of Equation 4.1-19 is the autocorrelation of the stationary ideal image field. It should be observed that the product of the two Dirac sampling functions on the right-hand side of Equation 4.1-19 is itself a Dirac sampling function of the form

$$S(x_1, y_1)S(x_2, y_2) = S(x_1 - x_2, y_1 - y_2) = S(\tau_x, \tau_y) \qquad (4.1\text{-}20)$$

Hence the sampled random field is also stationary with an autocorrelation function

$$R_{F_P}(\tau_x, \tau_y) = R_{F_I}(\tau_x, \tau_y)S(\tau_x, \tau_y) \qquad (4.1\text{-}21)$$

Taking the two-dimensional Fourier transform of Eq. 4.1-21 yields the power spectrum of the sampled random field. By the Fourier transform convolution theorem

$$\mathcal{W}_{F_P}(\omega_x, \omega_y) = \frac{1}{4\pi^2}\mathcal{W}_{F_I}(\omega_x, \omega_y) \circledast \mathcal{S}(\omega_x, \omega_y) \qquad (4.1\text{-}22)$$

where $\mathcal{W}_{F_I}(\omega_x, \omega_y)$ and $\mathcal{W}_{F_P}(\omega_x, \omega_y)$ represent the power spectral densities of the ideal image and sampled ideal image, respectively, and $\mathcal{S}(\omega_x, \omega_y)$ is the Fourier transform of the Dirac sampling array. Then, by the derivation leading to Eq. 4.1-7, it is found that the spectrum of the sampled field can be written as

$$\mathcal{W}_{F_P}(\omega_x, \omega_y) = \frac{4\pi^2}{\Delta x\ \Delta y} \sum_{j_1=-\infty}^{\infty} \sum_{j_2=-\infty}^{\infty} \mathcal{W}_{F_I}(\omega_x - j_1\omega_{xs}, \omega_y - j_2\omega_{ys})$$

(4.1-23)

Thus the sampled image power spectrum is composed of the power spectrum of the continuous ideal image field replicated over the spatial frequency domain at integer multiples of the sampling spatial frequency $(2\pi/\Delta x, 2\pi/\Delta y)$. If the power spectrum of the continuous ideal image field is bandlimited such that $\mathcal{W}_{F_I}(\omega_x, \omega_y) = 0$ for $|\omega_x| > \omega_{xc}$ and $|\omega_y| > \omega_{yc}$, where ω_{xc} and ω_{yc} are cutoff frequencies, then the individual spectra of Eq. 4.1-23 will not overlap if the spatial sampling periods are chosen such that $\Delta x < \pi/\omega_{xc}$ and $\Delta y < \pi/\omega_{yc}$. A continuous random field $F_R(x, y)$ may be reconstructed from samples of the random ideal image field by the interpolation formula

$$F_R(x, y) = \sum_{j_1=-\infty}^{\infty} \sum_{j_2=-\infty}^{\infty} F_I(j_1\ \Delta x, j_2\ \Delta y) R(x - j_1\ \Delta x, y - j_2\ \Delta y)$$

(4.1-24)

where $R(x, y)$ is the deterministic interpolation function. The reconstructed field and the ideal image field can be made equivalent in the mean-square sense (5, p. 284), that is,

$$E\{|F_I(x, y) - F_R(x, y)|^2\} = 0$$

(4.1-25)

if the Nyquist sampling criteria are met and if suitable interpolation functions, such as the sinc functions or Bessel functions of Eqs. 4.1-14 and 4.1-16, are utilized.

The preceding results are directly applicable to the practical problem of sampling a deterministic image field plus additive noise, which is modeled as a random field. Figure 4.1-4 contains a sketch of the spectrum of a sampled noisy image. This sketch indicates a significant potential problem. The spectrum of the noise may be wider than the ideal image spectrum, and if the noise process is undersampled, its tails will overlap into the passband of the image reconstruction filter, leading to additional noise errors. A solution to this problem, of course, is to prefilter the noisy image before sampling to reduce the noise bandwidth.

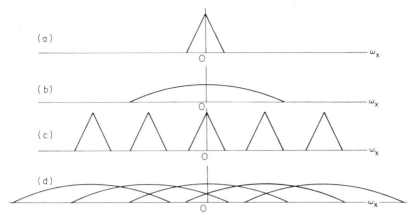

FIGURE 4.1-4. Spectra of sampled noisy image (a) signal, (b) noise, (c) sampled signal, (d) sampled noise.

4.2. PRACTICAL IMAGE SAMPLING SYSTEMS

In a physical image sampling system, the sampling array will be of finite extent, the sampling pulses will be of finite width, and the image may be undersampled. The consequences of nonideal sampling are now explored.

As a basis for the discussion, Figure 4.2-1 illustrates a typical image scanning system. In operation a narrow light beam is discretely scanned across a positive transparency of an ideal image. The light passing through the transparency is collected by a condensor lens and directed toward the

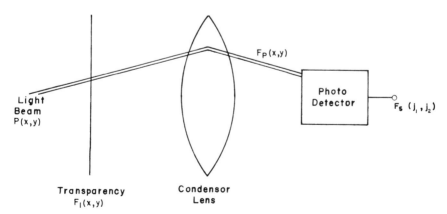

FIGURE 4.2-1. Typical image scanning system.

surface of a photodetector. The electrical output of the photodetector is integrated over the time period during which the light beam strikes a resolution cell. In the analysis it will be assumed that the sampling is noise-free. The results developed in the previous section for sampling noisy images can be combined with the results developed in this section quite easily. Also, it should be noted that the analysis is easily extended to a wide class of physical image sampling systems.

4.2.1. Sampling Pulse Effects

Under the assumptions stated above, the sampled image function is given by

$$F_P(x, y) = F_I(x, y)S(x, y) \qquad (4.2-1)$$

where the sampling array

$$S(x, y) = \sum_{j_1=-J_1}^{J_1} \sum_{j_2=-J_2}^{J_2} P(x - j_1 \Delta x, y - j_2 \Delta y) \qquad (4.2-2)$$

is composed of $(2J_1 + 1)(2J_2 + 1)$ identical pulses $P(x, y)$ arranged in a grid of spacing $\Delta x, \Delta y$. The symmetrical limits on the summation are chosen for notational simplicity. The sampling pulses are assumed scaled such that

$$\int\int_{-\infty}^{\infty} P(x, y)\, dx\, dy = 1 \qquad (4.2-3)$$

For purposes of analysis the sampling function may be assumed to be generated by a finite array of Dirac delta functions $D_T(x, y)$ passing through a linear filter with impulse response $P(x, y)$. Thus

$$S(x, y) = D_T(x, y) \circledast P(x, y) \qquad (4.2-4)$$

where

$$D_T(x, y) = \sum_{j_1=-J_1}^{J_1} \sum_{j_2=-J_2}^{J_2} \delta(x - j_1 \Delta x, y - j_2 \Delta y) \qquad (4.2-5)$$

Combining Eqs. 4.2-1 and 4.2-2 results in an expression for the sampled image function,

$$F_P(x, y) = \sum_{j_1=-J_1}^{J_1} \sum_{j_2=-J_2}^{J_2} F_I(x, y)P(x - j_1 \Delta x, y - j_2 \Delta y) \qquad (4.2-6)$$

The spectrum of the sampled image function is given by

$$\mathscr{F}_P(\omega_x, \omega_y) = \frac{1}{4\pi^2} \mathscr{F}_I(\omega_x, \omega_y) \circledast [\mathscr{D}_T(\omega_x, \omega_y)\mathscr{P}(\omega_x, \omega_y)] \qquad (4.2-7)$$

where $\mathscr{P}(\omega_x, \omega_y)$ is the Fourier transform of $P(x, y)$. The Fourier transform of the truncated sampling array is found to be (5, p. 105)

$$\mathscr{D}_T(\omega_x, \omega_y) = \frac{\sin\left[\omega_x(J_1 + \frac{1}{2})\,\Delta x\right]}{\sin(\omega_x\,\Delta x/2)}\frac{\sin\left[\omega_y(J_2 + \frac{1}{2})\,\Delta y\right]}{\sin(\omega_y\,\Delta y/2)} \qquad (4.2\text{-}8)$$

Figure 4.2-2 contains of sketch of $\mathscr{D}_T(\omega_x, \omega_y)$. In the limit as J_1 and J_2 become large, the right-hand side of Eq. 4.2-7 becomes an array of Dirac delta functions.

In an image reconstruction system an image is reconstructed by interpolation of its samples. Ideal interpolation waveforms such as the sinc function Eq. 4.1-14 or the Bessel function of Eq. 4.1-16 generally extend over the entire image field. If the sampling array is truncated, the reconstructed image will be in error near its boundary because the tails of the interpolation waveforms will be truncated in the vicinity of the boundary (9, 10). However, the error is usually negligibly small at distances of about 8–10 Nyquist samples or greater from the boundary.

The actual numerical samples of an image are obtained by a spatial integration of $F_S(x, y)$ over some finite resolution cell. In the scanning system of Figure 4.2-1 the integration is inherently performed on the photodetector surface. The image sample value of the resolution cell (j_1, j_2) may then be expressed as

$$F_S(j_1\,\Delta x, j_2\,\Delta y) = \int_{j_1\Delta x - A_x}^{j_1\Delta x + A_x}\int_{j_2\Delta y - A_y}^{j_2\Delta y + A_y} F_I(x, y)P(x - j_1\,\Delta x, y - j_2\,\Delta y)\,dx\,dy$$

$$(4.2\text{-}9)$$

where A_x and A_y denote the maximum dimensions of the resolution cell. It is assumed that only one sample pulse exists during the integration time of the detector. If this assumption is not valid, consideration must be given to

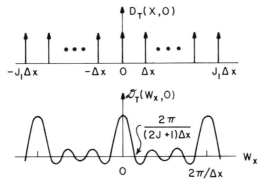

FIGURE 4.2-2. Truncated sampling train and its Fourier spectrum.

the difficult problem of sample "cross-talk." In the sampling system under discussion the width of the resolution cell may be larger than the sample spacing. Thus the model provides for sequentially overlapped samples in time.

By a simple change of variables, Eq. 4.2-9 may be rewritten as

$$F_S(j_1 \Delta x, j_2 \Delta y) = \int_{-A_x}^{A_x} \int_{-A_y}^{A_y} F_I(j_1 \Delta x - \alpha, j_2 \Delta y - \beta) P(-\alpha, -\beta) \, d\alpha \, d\beta$$

$$(4.2\text{-}10)$$

Since only a single sampling pulse is assumed to occur during the integration period, the limits of Eq. 4.2-10 can be infinitely extended. In this formulation Eq. 4.2-10 is recognized to be equivalent to a convolution of the ideal continuous image $F_I(x, y)$ with an impulse response function $P(-x, -y)$ with reversed coordinates, followed by sampling over a finite area with Dirac delta functions. Thus, neglecting the effects of the finite size of the sampling array,

$$F_S(j_1 \Delta x, j_2 \Delta y) = [F_I(x, y) \circledast P(-x, -y)] \, \delta(x - j_1 \Delta x, y - j_2 \Delta y)$$

$$(4.2\text{-}11)$$

In most sampling systems the sampling pulse is symmetric, so that $P(-x, -y) = P(x, y)$.

Equation 4.2-11 provides a simple relation that is useful in assessing the effect of finite extent pulse sampling. If the ideal image is bandlimited and Δx and Δy satisfy the Nyquist criterion, then the finite extent of the sample pulse represents an equivalent linear spatial degradation (an image blur) that occurs before ideal sampling. Part 4 of the book considers methods of compensating for this degradation. A finite extent sampling pulse is not always a detriment, however. Consider the situation in which the ideal image is insufficiently bandlimited so that it is undersampled. The finite extent pulse, in effect, provides a low-pass filtering of the ideal image, which in turn serves to limit its spatial frequency content, and hence to minimize aliasing errors.

4.2.2. Aliasing Effects

In order to achieve perfect image reconstruction in a sampled imaging system, it is necessary to bandlimit the image to be sampled, spatially sample the image at the Nyquist or higher rate, and properly interpolate the image samples. Sample interpolation is considered in the next section; an analysis is presented here of the effect of undersampling an image.

If there is spectral overlap resulting from undersampling, as indicated by the cross-hatched regions in Figure 4.2-3, spurious spatial frequency components will be introduced into the reconstruction. The effect is called an aliasing error (11, 12). Aliasing effects in an actual image are shown in Figure 4.2-4. Spatial undersampling of the image creates artificial low spatial frequency components in the reconstruction. In the field of optics aliasing errors are called Moire effects or Moire patterns.

From Eq. 4.1–7 the spectrum of a sampled image can be written in the form

$$\mathcal{F}_p(\omega_x, \omega_y) = \frac{1}{\Delta x \, \Delta y} \left[\mathcal{F}_I(\omega_x, \omega_y) + \mathcal{F}_Q(\omega_x, \omega_y) \right] \qquad (4.2\text{-}12)$$

where $\mathcal{F}_I(\omega_x, \omega_y)$ represents the spectrum of the original image sampled at period $(\Delta x, \Delta y)$. The term

$$\mathcal{F}_Q(\omega_x, \omega_y) = \sum_{j_1=-\infty}^{\infty} \sum_{j_2=-\infty}^{\infty} \mathcal{F}_I(\omega_x - j_1\omega_{xs}, \omega_y - j_2\omega_{ys}) \qquad (4.2\text{-}13)$$
$$\underbrace{\phantom{\sum_{j_1=-\infty}^{\infty} \sum_{j_2=-\infty}^{\infty}}}_{\substack{j_1 \neq 0 \\ j_2 \neq 0}}$$

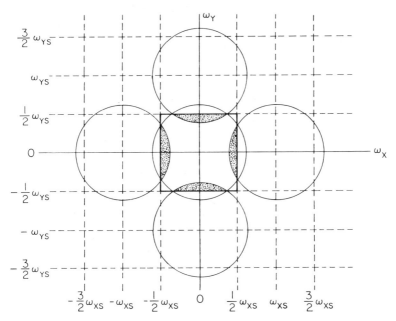

FIGURE 4.2-3. Spectra of undersampled two-dimensional function.

(a)

(b)

FIGURE 4.2-4.   Example of aliasing error in a sampled image. (a) Original image. (b) Sampled image.

describes the spectrum of the higher-order components of the sampled image repeated over spatial frequencies $\omega_{xs} = 2\pi/\Delta x$ and $\omega_{ys} = 2\pi/\Delta y$. If there were no spectral foldover, optimal interpolation of the sampled image components could be obtained by passing the sampled image through a zonal low-pass filter defined by

$$\mathcal{R}(\omega_x, \omega_y) = \begin{cases} K & \text{for } |\omega_x| \leq \dfrac{\omega_{xs}}{2} \text{ and } |\omega_y| \leq \dfrac{\omega_{ys}}{2} & (4.2\text{-}14a) \\ 0 & \text{otherwise} & (4.2\text{-}14b) \end{cases}$$

where K is a scaling constant. Applying this interpolation strategy to an undersampled image yields a reconstructed image field

$$F_R(x, y) = F_I(x, y) + A(x, y) \tag{4.2-15}$$

where

$$A(x, y) = \frac{1}{4\pi^2} \int_{-\omega_{xs}/2}^{\omega_{xs}/2} \int_{-\omega_{ys}/2}^{\omega_{ys}/2} \mathcal{F}_Q(\omega_x, \omega_y) \exp\{i[\omega_x x + \omega_y y]\} \, d\omega_x \, d\omega_y \tag{4.2-16}$$

represents the aliasing error artifact in the reconstructed image. The factor K has absorbed the amplitude scaling factors. The aliasing error component of Eq. 4.2-16 can be substantially reduced by use of an interpolation filter that provides attenuation of its spatial frequency components relative to the components of the ideal image. This technique is discussed in Chapter 15. Another approach, to be considered next, consists of low-pass filtering before sampling to reduce the spectral foldover.

Figure 4.2-5 contains a model for the quantitative analysis of aliasing effects. In this model the ideal image $F_I(x, y)$ is assumed to be a sample of a two-dimensional random process with known power-spectral density $\mathcal{F}_I(\omega_x, \omega_y)$. The ideal image is linearly filtered by a presampling spatial filter with a transfer function $\mathcal{H}(\omega_x, \omega_y)$. This filter is assumed to be a low-pass type of filter with a smooth attenuation of high spatial frequencies (i.e., not a zonal low-pass filter with a sharp cut-off). The filtered image is then spatially sampled by an ideal Dirac delta function sampler at a

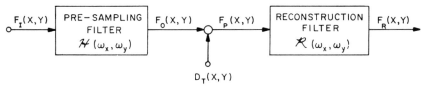

FIGURE 4.2-5. Model for analysis of aliasing effect.

resolution $\Delta x, \Delta y$. Next, a reconstruction filter interpolates the image samples to produce a replica of the ideal image. From Eq. 1.10-8 the power spectral density at the presampling filter output is found to be

$$\mathcal{W}_{\mathcal{F}_O}(\omega_x, \omega_y) = |\mathcal{H}(\omega_x, \omega_y)|^2 \mathcal{W}_{\mathcal{F}_I}(\omega_x, \omega_y) \qquad (4.2\text{-}17)$$

and the Fourier spectrum of the sampled image field is

$$\mathcal{W}_{\mathcal{F}_P}(\omega_x, \omega_y) = \sum_{j_1=-\infty}^{\infty} \sum_{j_2=-\infty}^{\infty} \mathcal{W}_{\mathcal{F}_O}(\omega_x - j_1 \omega_{xs}, \omega_y - j_2 \omega_{ys}) \qquad (4.2\text{-}18)$$

It is desirable to isolate the undersampling effect from the effect of improper reconstruction. Therefore assume for this analysis that the reconstruction filter is an optimal filter of the form given in Eq. 4.2-14. The energy passing through the reconstruction filter for $j_1 = j_2 = 0$, is then

$$E_R = \int_{-\omega_{xs}/2}^{\omega_{xs}/2} \int_{-\omega_{ys}/2}^{\omega_{ys}/2} \mathcal{W}_{\mathcal{F}_I}(\omega_x, \omega_y) |\mathcal{H}(\omega_x, \omega_y)|^2 \, d\omega_x \, d\omega_y \qquad (4.2\text{-}19)$$

Ideally, the presampling filter should be a low-pass zonal filter with a transfer function identical to that of the reconstruction filter as given by Eq. 4.2-14. In this case the sampled image energy would assume the maximum value

$$E_{RM} = \int_{-\omega_{xs}/2}^{\omega_{xs}/2} \int_{-\omega_{ys}/2}^{\omega_{ys}/2} \mathcal{W}_{\mathcal{F}_I}(\omega_x, \omega_y) \, d\omega_x \, d\omega_y \qquad (4.2\text{-}20)$$

Image resolution degradation resulting from the presampling filter may then be measured by the ratio

$$\mathcal{E}_R = \frac{E_{RM} - E_R}{E_{RM}} \qquad (4.2\text{-}21)$$

The aliasing error in a sampled image system is generally measured in terms of the energy from higher-order sidebands that folds over into the passband of the reconstruction filter. Assume, for simplicity, that the sampling rate is sufficient so that the spectral foldover from spectra centered at $(\pm j_1 \omega_{xs}/2, \pm j_2 \omega_{ys}/2)$ is negligible for $j_1 \geq 2$ and $j_2 \geq 2$. The total aliasing error energy, as indicated by the shaded region of Figure 4.2-3, is then

$$E_A = E_0 - E_R \qquad (4.2\text{-}22)$$

where

$$E_0 = \int_{-\infty}^{\infty} \int_{-\infty}^{\infty} \mathcal{W}_{\mathcal{F}_I}(\omega_x, \omega_y) |\mathcal{H}(\omega_x, \omega_y)|^2 \, d\omega_x \, d\omega_y \qquad (4.2\text{-}23)$$

denotes the energy of the output of the presampling filter. The aliasing error is defined as (11)

$$\mathcal{E}_A = \frac{E_A}{E_0} \tag{4.2-24}$$

Aliasing error can be reduced by attenuating high spatial frequencies of $F_I(x, y)$ with the presampling filter. However, any attenuation within the passband of the reconstruction filter represents a system degradation. As a result, there is a tradeoff between sampled image resolution and aliasing error.

Consideration is now given to the aliasing error versus resolution performance of several practical types of presampling filters. Perhaps the simplest means of spatially filtering an image formed by incoherent light is to pass the image through a lens with a restricted aperture. Spatial filtering can then be achieved by controlling the degree of lens misfocus. Figure 13.2-2 contains a plot of the optical transfer function of a circular lens as a function of the degree of lens misfocus. Even a perfectly focused lens produces some blurring because of the diffraction limit of its aperture. The transfer function of a diffraction-limited circular lens of diameter d is given by (13, p. 83)

$$\mathcal{H}(\omega) = \frac{2}{\pi}\left[\cos^{-1}\left(\frac{\omega}{\omega_0}\right) - \frac{\omega}{\omega_0}\sqrt{1 - \left(\frac{\omega}{\omega_0}\right)^2} \right] \qquad 0 \le \omega \le \omega_0 \tag{4.2-25a}$$

$$\mathcal{H}(\omega) = 0 \qquad |\omega| > \omega_0 \tag{4.2-25b}$$

where $\omega_0 = \pi d/R$ and R is the distance from the lens to the focal plane. In the previous section it was noted that sampling with a finite extent sampling pulse is equivalent to ideal sampling of an image that has been passed through a spatial filter whose impulse response is equal to the pulse shape of the sampling pulse, with reversed coordinates. Thus, the sampling pulse may be utilized to perform presampling filtering. A common pulse shape is the rectangular pulse

$$P(x, y) = \begin{cases} \dfrac{1}{T^2} & |x, y| \le \dfrac{T}{2} \\ 0 & |x, y| > \dfrac{T}{2} \end{cases} \tag{4.2-26}$$

obtained with an incoherent light imaging system of a scanning microdensitometer. The transfer function for a square scanning spot is

$$\mathcal{P}(\omega_x, \omega_y) = \frac{\sin(\omega_x T/2)}{(\omega_x T/2)} \frac{\sin(\omega_y T/2)}{(\omega_y T/2)} \tag{4.2-27}$$

Cathode ray tube displays produce display spots with a two-dimensional Gaussian shape of the form

$$P(x, y) = \frac{1}{2\pi\sigma_w^2} \exp\left\{-\frac{(x^2+y^2)}{2\sigma_w^2}\right\} \tag{4.2-28}$$

where σ_w is a measure of the spot spread. The equivalent transfer function of the Gaussian shaped scanning spot is

$$\mathcal{P}(\omega_x, \omega_y) = \exp\left\{-\frac{(\omega_x^2 + \omega_y^2)\sigma_w^2}{2}\right\} \tag{4.2-29}$$

Examples of the aliasing error–resolution tradeoffs for a diffraction-limited aperture, a square sampling spot, and a Gaussian shaped spot are presented in Figure 4.2-6 as a function of the parameter w_0. The square pulse width is set at $T = 2\pi/\omega_0$ so that the first zero of the sinc function coincides with the lens cutoff frequency. The spread of the Gaussian spot is set at $\sigma_w = 2/\omega_0$ corresponding to 2 standard deviation units in cross section. In this example the input image spectrum is modeled as

$$\mathcal{W}_{F_I}(\omega_x, \omega_y) = \frac{A}{1 + (\omega/\omega_c)^{2m}} \tag{4.2-30}$$

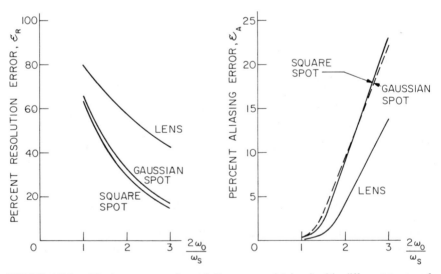

FIGURE 4.2-6. Aliasing error and resolution error obtained with different types of prefiltering, for $m = 1$.

where A is an amplitude constant, m is an integer governing the rate of falloff of the Fourier spectrum, and ω_c is the spatial frequency at the half-amplitude point. The curves of Figure 4.2-6 indicate that the Gaussian spot and square spot scanning prefilters provide about the same results, while the diffraction-limited lens yields a somewhat greater loss in resolution for the same aliasing error level. A defocused lens would give even poorer results.

4.3. PRACTICAL IMAGE RECONSTRUCTION SYSTEMS

In Section 4.1 the conditions for exact image reconstruction were stated: the original image must be spatially sampled at a rate of twice its highest spatial frequency, and the reconstruction filter, or equivalent interpolator, must be designed to pass the spectral component at $j_1 = 0$, $j_2 = 0$ without distortion, and reject all spectra for which $j_1, j_2 \neq 0$. Consideration is now given to the effects of using imperfect reconstruction functions.

In most digital image processing systems, electrical image samples are sequentially output from the computer in a normal raster scan fashion. From these electrical samples it is necessary to drive an optical display such as a cathode ray tube (CRT) or a photographic recorder to record a continuous image. Three implementation techniques are considered below.

4.3.1 Implementation Techniques

Figure 4.3-1 illustrates an incoherent optical image reconstruction system. In this system extremely small points of light are raster scanned onto a CRT with the intensity of each point set proportional to the image sample magnitude. The light array on the CRT can then be imaged onto a ground-glass screen for viewing or onto photographic film for recording with a light

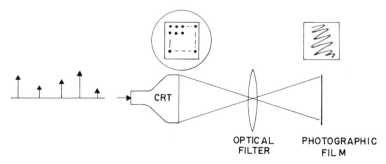

FIGURE 4.3-1. Incoherent optical filtering image reconstruction system.

projection system incorporating an incoherent spatial filter with the desired optical transfer function. Optimal transfer functions with a perfectly flat passband over the image spectrum and a sharp cutoff to zero outside the spectrum generally cannot be physically implemented.

For monochromatic image reconstruction it is possible to utilize a coherent optical filtering system, as shown in Figure 4.3-2. In this system the dot representation of an image on a CRT is photographed and a positive transparency is produced. Then the positive transparency is illuminated by a collimated laser beam. The light passing through the transparency continues through a lens that produces a light distribution at its back focal plane proportional to the two-dimensional Fourier transform of the transparency transmittance. An optical filter may then be designed to modify appropriately the light amplitude and phase distribution at the filter plane to achieve a desired reconstruction filter. A second lens performs a Fourier transform to reconstruct the interpolated image on the surface of a photographic plate. A major advantage of the coherent optical system implementation is the relative simplicity in the fabrication of the reconstruction filter. An optimal reconstruction filter is simply a clear aperture that passes only the zero-order diffraction pattern.

The most common means of image reconstruction is by the use of electrooptical techniques. For example, image reconstruction can be performed quite simply by electrically defocusing the writing spot of a cathode ray tube display. Drawbacks of this technique are the difficulty of accurately controlling the spot shape over the image field, and the fact that the interpolation is usually suboptimal. In a scanning microdensitometer, image reconstruction is usually accomplished by projecting a rectangularly shaped spot of light onto photographic film. Generally, the spot size is set at the same size as the sample spacing to completely fill the image field. The resulting interpolation is simple to perform, but not optimal. If a small

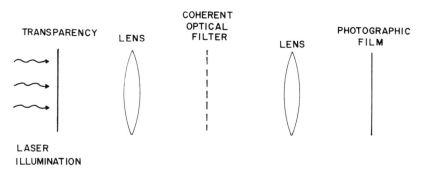

FIGURE 4.3-2.   Coherent optical filtering image reconstruction system.

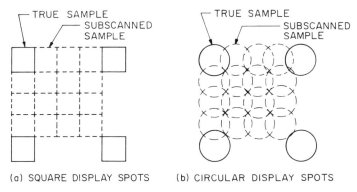

(a) SQUARE DISPLAY SPOTS   (b) CIRCULAR DISPLAY SPOTS

FIGURE 4.3-3.   Image reconstruction by subscanning.

writing spot can be achieved with a CRT display or a projected light display, then it is possible approximately to synthesize any desired interpolation function by subscanning a resolution cell, as shown in Figure 4.3-3. There are three methods of generating interpolation pixel values for subscan interpolation: spatial function fitting, convolution, and Fourier domain filtering. Chapters 11 and 15 consider implementation of these techniques in detail.

4.3.2.   Interpolation Functions

Figure 4.3-4 illustrates several one-dimensional interpolation functions. The sinc function, as stated previously, provides an exact reconstruction, but is usually difficult to produce in an imaging system. The simplest interpolation waveform is the pulse function that results in a zero-order interpolation of the samples. A triangle function provides first-order linear sample interpolation with triangular-shaped interpolation waveforms. The triangle function may be considered to be the result of convolving a pulse function with itself. Convolution of the triangle function with the pulse function yields a bell-shaped interpolation waveform, as shown in Figure 4.3-4d. This process quickly converses to the Gaussian-shaped interpolation waveform of Figure 4.3-4f. Polynomials of order two or greater can also be employed as interpolation waveforms. The cubic B-spline is a particularly attractive candidate for image interpolation because of its properties of continuity and smoothness at its extremities. The cubic B-spline is defined as (14)

$$R(x) = (x)_+^3 - 4(x - \Delta x)_+^3 + 6(x - 2\,\Delta x)_+^3 - 4(x - 3\,\Delta x)_+^3 \quad (4.3\text{-}1)$$

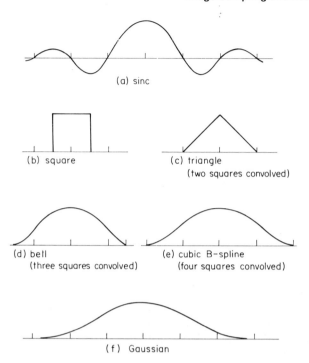

FIGURE 4.3-4.   One-dimensional interpolation waveforms.

where

$$(z)_+^m = \begin{cases} z^m & z > 0 \\ 0 & z \leq 0 \end{cases}$$

(4.3-2a)

(4.3-2b)

This spline function, which is nonzero only over a span of four samples, can be obtained by a convolution of four square pulses. Figure 4.3-5 illustrates one-dimensional interpolation using sinc, square, and triangle functions.

Table 4.3-1 defines several orthogonally separable two-dimensional interpolation functions for which $R(x, y) = R(x)R(y)$. It should be noted that two-dimensional, first-order linear interpolation, analogous to the one-dimensional linear interpolation example of Figure 4.3-5c, does not result from interpolation with the two-dimensional triangular functions of Table 4.3-1. Rather, the interpolation must be performed in a piecewise fashion, as shown in Figure 4.3-6a. In region I of Figure 4.3-6a, points are linearly interpolated in the plane defined by pixels A, B, C, while in region II, interpolation is performed in the plane defined by pixels B, C, D.

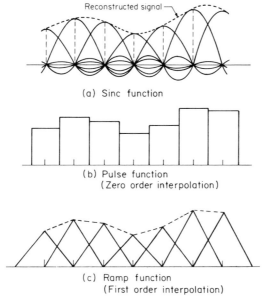

(a) Sinc function

(b) Pulse function
(Zero order interpolation)

(c) Ramp function
(First order interpolation)

FIGURE 4.3-5. One-dimensional interpolation.

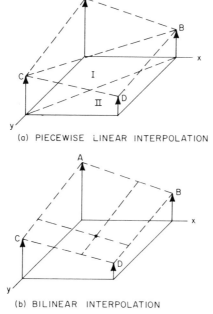

(a) PIECEWISE LINEAR INTERPOLATION

(b) BILINEAR INTERPOLATION

FIGURE 4.3-6. Two-dimensional linear interpolation.

Continuous bilinar interpolation, shown in Figure 4.3-6b, is performed by linearly interpolating points along separable orthogonal coordinates of the continuous image field. The resultant interpolated surface of Figure 4.3-6b, connecting pixels A, B, C, D, is generally nonplanar.

TABLE 4.3-1.   Two-dimensional interpolation functions

Function	Definition
Separable sinc	$R(x, y) = \dfrac{4}{T_x T_y} \dfrac{\sin(2\pi x/T_x)}{(2\pi x/T_x)} \dfrac{\sin(2\pi y/T_y)}{(2\pi y/T_y)}$ $\quad T_x = \dfrac{2\pi}{\omega_{xs}}$ $\quad T_y = \dfrac{2\pi}{\omega_{ys}}$
	$\mathscr{R}(\omega_x, \omega_y) = \begin{cases} 1 & |\omega_x| \le \omega_{xs}, \quad |\omega_y| \le \omega_{ys} \\ 0 & \text{otherwise} \end{cases}$
Separable square	$R_0(x, y) = \begin{cases} \dfrac{1}{T_x T_y} & |x| \le \dfrac{T_x}{2} \quad |y| \le \dfrac{T_y}{2} \\ 0 & \text{otherwise} \end{cases}$
	$\mathscr{R}_0(\omega_x, \omega_y) = \dfrac{\sin(\omega_x T_x/2) \sin(\omega_y T_y/2)}{(\omega_x T_x/2)(\omega_y T_y/2)}$
Separable triangle	$R_1(x, y) = R_0(x, y) \circledast R_0(x, y)$
	$\mathscr{R}_1(\omega_x, \omega_y) = \mathscr{R}_0^2(\omega_x, \omega_y)$
Separable bell	$R_2(x, y) = R_0(x, y) \circledast R_1(x, y)$
	$\mathscr{R}_2(\omega_x, \omega_y) = \mathscr{R}_0^3(\omega_x, \omega_y)$
Separable cubic B-spline	$R_3(x, y) = R_0(x, y) \circledast R_2(x, y)$
	$\mathscr{R}_3(\omega_x, \omega_y) = \mathscr{R}_0^4(\omega_x, \omega_y)$
Gaussian	$R(x, y) = [2\pi\sigma_w^2]^{-1} \exp\left\{ -\dfrac{x^2 + y^2}{2\sigma_w^2} \right\}$
	$\mathscr{R}(\omega_x, \omega_y) = \exp\left\{ -\dfrac{\sigma_w^2(\omega_x^2 + \omega_y^2)}{2} \right\}$

4.3.3.   Effect of Imperfect Reconstruction Filters

The performance of practical image reconstruction systems will now be analyzed. It will be assumed that the input to the image reconstruction system is composed of samples of an ideal image obtained by sampling with a finite array of Dirac samples at the Nyquist rate. From Eq. 4.1-9 the reconstructed image is found to be

$$F_R(x, y) = \sum_{j_1=-J_1}^{J_1} \sum_{j_2=-J_2}^{J_2} F_I(j_1 \Delta x, j_2 \Delta y) R(x - j_1 \Delta x, y - j_2 \Delta y)$$

(4.3-3)

where $R(x, y)$ is the two-dimensional interpolation function of the image reconstruction system. Ideally, the reconstructed image would be the exact replica of the ideal image as obtained from Eq. 4.1-9. That is,

$$\hat{F}_R(x, y) = \sum_{j_1=-\infty}^{\infty} \sum_{j_2=-\infty}^{\infty} F_I(j_1 \Delta x, j_2 \Delta y) R_I(x - j_1 \Delta x, y - j_2 \Delta y)$$

(4.3-4)

where $R_I(x, y)$ represents an optimum interpolation function such as given by Eq. 4.1-14 or 4.1-16. The reconstruction error over the bounds of the sampled image is then

$$\mathcal{E}_D(x, y) = \sum_{j_1=-J_1}^{J_1} \sum_{j_2=-J_2}^{J_2} F_I(j_1 \Delta x, j_2 \Delta y)$$
$$\cdot [R(x - j_1 \Delta x, y - j_2 \Delta y) - R_I(x - j_1 \Delta x, y - j_2 \Delta y)] \quad (4.3-5)$$

There are two contributors to the reconstruction error: (a) the physical system interpolation function $R(x, y)$ may differ from the ideal inter-polation function $R_I(x, y)$, and (b) the finite bounds of the reconstruction, which cause truncation of the interpolation functions at the boundary. In most sampled imaging systems the boundary reconstruction error is ig-nored because the error generally becomes negligible at distances of a few samples from the boundary. The utilization of nonideal interpolation func-tions leads to a potential loss of image resolution and to the introduction of high spatial frequency artifacts.

The effect of an imperfect reconstruction filter may be conveniently analyzed by examination of the frequency spectrum of a reconstructed image, as derived in Eq. 4.1-11:

$$\mathcal{F}_R(\omega_x, \omega_y) = \frac{4\pi^2}{\Delta x \, \Delta y} \mathcal{R}(\omega_x, \omega_y) \sum_{j_1=-\infty}^{\infty} \sum_{j_2=-\infty}^{\infty} \mathcal{F}_I(\omega_x - j_1 \omega_{xs}, \omega_y - j_2 \omega_{ys})$$

(4.3-6)

Ideally, $\mathcal{R}(\omega_x, \omega_y)$ should select the spectral component for $j_1 = 0, j_2 = 0$ with uniform attenuation at all spatial frequencies, and should reject all other spectral components. An imperfect filter may attenuate the frequency components of the zero-order spectra, causing a loss of image resolution, and may also permit higher-order spectral modes to contribute to the restoration, and therefore introduce distortion in the restoration.

Figure 4.3-7 provides a graphic example of the effect of an imperfect image reconstruction filter. A typical cross section of a sampled image is shown in Figure 4.3-7a. With an ideal reconstruction filter employing sinc functions for interpolation, the central image spectrum is extracted and all side bands are rejected, as shown in Figure 4.3-7c. Figure 4.3-7d is a plot of the transfer function for a zero-order interpolation reconstruction filter in which the reconstructed pixel amplitudes over the pixel sample area are set at the sample value. The resulting spectrum shown in Figure 4.3-7e exhibits distortion from attenuation of the central spectral mode and spurious high-frequency signal components.

Following the analysis leading to Eq. 4.2-21, the resolution loss resulting from the use of a nonideal reconstruction function $R(x, y)$ may be quantitatively specified as

$$\mathcal{E}_R = \frac{E_{RM} - E_R}{E_{RM}} \tag{4.3-7}$$

where

$$E_R = \int_{-\omega_{xs}/2}^{\omega_{xs}/2} \int_{-\omega_{ys}/2}^{\omega_{ys}/2} W_{\mathcal{F}_I}(\omega_x, \omega_y) |\mathcal{R}(\omega_x, \omega_y)|^2 \, d\omega_x \, d\omega_y \tag{4.3-8}$$

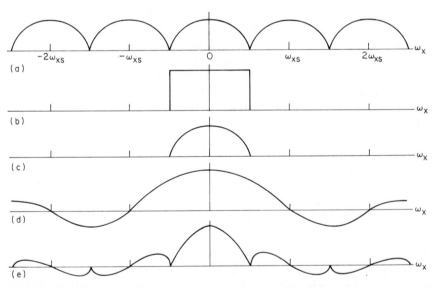

FIGURE 4.3-7. Example of power spectra for perfect and imperfect reconstruction. (a) Sampled image, (b) sinc function reconstruction filter, (c) sinc function reconstruction, (d) zero-order interpolation reconstruction filter, (e) zero-order interpolator reconstruction.

represents the actual interpolated image energy in the Nyquist sampling band limits, and

$$E_{RM} = \int_{-\omega_{xs}/2}^{\omega_{xs}/2} \int_{-\omega_{ys}/2}^{\omega_{ys}/2} \mathcal{W}_{\mathcal{F}_I}(\omega_x, \omega_y) \, d\omega_x \, d\omega_y \qquad (4.3\text{-}9)$$

is the ideal interpolated image energy. The interpolation error attributable to high spatial frequency artifacts may be defined as

$$\mathcal{E}_H = \frac{E_H}{E_T} \qquad (4.3\text{-}10)$$

where

$$E_T = \int_{-\infty}^{\infty} \int_{-\infty}^{\infty} \mathcal{W}_{\mathcal{F}_P}(\omega_x, \omega_y) |\mathcal{R}(\omega_x, \omega_y)|^2 \, d\omega_x \, d\omega_y \qquad (4.3\text{-}11)$$

denotes the total energy of the interpolated image and

$$E_H = E_T - E_R \qquad (4.3\text{-}12)$$

is that portion of the interpolated image energy lying outside the Nyquist band limits.

Table 4.3-2 contains a list of the resolution error and interpolation error obtained with several separable two-dimensional interpolation functions.

TABLE 4.3-2. Interpolation error and resolution error for various separable two interpolation functions

Function	Percent Resolution Error $\mathcal{E}_R$	Percent Interpolation Error $\mathcal{E}_H$
Sinc	0.0	0.0
Square	26.9	15.7
Triangle	44.0	3.7
Bell	55.4	1.1
Cubic B-spline	63.2	0.3
Gaussian $\sigma_w = \dfrac{3T}{8}$	38.6	10.3
Gaussian $\sigma_w = \dfrac{T}{2}$	54.6	2.0
Gaussian $\sigma_w = \dfrac{5T}{8}$	66.7	0.3

In this example the power spectral density of the ideal image is assumed to be of the form

$$\mathcal{W}_{\mathcal{F}_I}(\omega) = \sqrt{\left(\frac{\omega_s}{2}\right)^2 - \omega^2} \qquad \omega^2 \le \left(\frac{\omega_s}{2}\right)^2$$

$$\mathcal{W}_{\mathcal{F}_I}(\omega) = 0 \qquad\qquad \omega^2 > \left(\frac{\omega_s}{2}\right)^2$$

(4.3-13)

The interpolation error contribution of higher-order components, $j_1, j_2 > 2$, is assumed negligible. The table indicates that zero-order interpolation with a square interpolation function results in a significant amount of resolution error. Interpolation error reduces significantly for higher-order convolutional interpolation functions, but at the expense of resolution error.

REFERENCES

1. E. T. Whittaker, "On the Functions which are Represented by the Expansions of the Interpolation Theory," *Proc. Roy. Soc. Edinburgh, Section A*, **35**, 1915, 181–194.

2. C. E. Shannon, "Communication in the Presence of Noise," *Proc. IRE*, **37**, 1, January 1949, 10–21.

3. H. J. Landa, "Sampling, Data Transmission, and the Nyquist Rate," *Proc. IEEE*, **55**, 10, October 1967, 1701–1706.

4. J. W. Goodman, *Introduction to Fourier Optics*, McGraw-Hill, New York, 1968.

5. A. Papoulis, *Systems and Transforms with Applications in Optics*, McGraw-Hill, New York, 1966.

6. P. J. Richards, "Sampling Positive Functions," *Proc. IEEE* (*Letters*), **54**, 1, January 1966, 81–82.

7. S. P. Lloyd, "A Sampling Theorem for Stationary (Wide Sense) Stochastic Processes," *Trans. Am. Math. Soc.*, **92**, 1, July 1959, 1–12.

8. H. S. Shapiro and R. A. Silverman, "Alias-Free Sampling of Random Noise," *J. SIAM*, **8**, 2, June 1960, 225–248.

9. J. L. Brown, Jr., "Bounds for Truncation Error in Sampling Expansions of Band-Limited Signals," *IEEE Trans. Inf. Theory*, **IT-15**, 4, July 1969, 440–444.

10. H. D. Helms and J. B. Thomas, "Truncation Error of Sampling Theory Expansions," *Proc. IRE*, **50**, 2, February 1962, 179–184.

11. J. J. Downing, "Data Sampling and Pulse Amplitude Modulation," in *Aerospace Telemetry*, H. L. Stiltz, Ed., Prentice-Hall, Englewood Cliffs, N.J., 1961.

12. D. G. Childers, "Study and Experimental Investigation on Sampling Rate and Aliasing in Time Division Telemetry Systems,' *IRE Trans. Space Electronics and Telemetry*, **SET-8**, December 1962, 267–283.

13. E. L. O'Neill, *Introduction to Statistical Optics*, Addison-Wesley, Reading, Massachusetts, 1963.

14. T. N. E. Greville, "Introduction to Spline Functions," in *Theory and Applications of Spline Functions* (*T. N. E. Greville, ed.*), Academic Press, New York, 1969.

5 MATHEMATICAL CHARACTERIZATION OF DISCRETE IMAGES

Chapter 1 presented a mathematical characterization of continuous image fields. In this chapter a formalism is developed for representing discrete image fields from a deterministic and statistical viewpoint.

5.1. VECTOR ALGEBRA

This section provides a summary of vector and matrix algebraic manipulation procedures utilized in the text. References 1–5 may be consulted for formal derivations and proofs of the statements of definition presented here.

Vector

An $N \times 1$ column vector $\mathbf{f}$ is a one-dimensional vertical arrangement

$$\mathbf{f} = \begin{bmatrix} f(1) \\ f(2) \\ \vdots \\ f(j) \\ \vdots \\ f(N) \end{bmatrix} \qquad (5.1\text{-}1)$$

of the elements $f(n)$, where $n = 1, 2, \ldots, N$. A $1 \times N$ row vector $\mathbf{h}$ is a one-dimensional horizontal arrangement

$$\mathbf{h} = [h(1) \quad h(2) \cdots h(j) \cdots h(N)] \qquad (5.1\text{-}2)$$

of the element $h(n)$, where $n = 1, 2, \ldots, N$. In this book, unless otherwise indicated, all boldface lower case letters denote column vectors. Row vectors are indicated by the transpose relation

$$\mathbf{f}^T = [f(1) \quad f(2) \cdots f(j) \cdots f(N)] \qquad (5.1\text{-}3)$$

Matrix

An $M \times N$ matrix $\mathbf{F}$ is a two-dimensional arrangement

$$
\mathbf{F} = \begin{bmatrix}
F(1,1) & F(1,2) & \cdots & F(1,N) \\
F(2,1) & F(2,2) & \cdots & F(2,N) \\
\vdots & \vdots & & \vdots \\
F(M,1) & F(M,2) & \cdots & F(M,N)
\end{bmatrix}
\tag{5.1-4}
$$

of the elements $F(m, n)$ into rows and columns, where $m = 1, 2, \ldots, M$ and $n = 1, 2, \ldots, N$. The symbol $\mathbf{0}$ indicates a null matrix whose terms are all zeros. A diagonal matrix is a square matrix, $M = N$, for which all off-diagonal terms are zero; that is, $F(m, n) = 0$ if $m \neq n$. An identity matrix denoted by $\mathbf{I}$ is a diagonal matrix whose diagonal terms are unity. The identity symbol is often subscripted to indicate its dimension; $\mathbf{I}_N$ is an $N \times N$ identity matrix. A submatrix $\mathbf{F}_{pq}$ is a matrix partition of a larger matrix $\mathbf{F}$ of the form

$$
\mathbf{F} = \left[\begin{array}{c:c:c:c}
\mathbf{F}_{1,1} & \mathbf{F}_{1,2} & \cdots & \mathbf{F}_{1,Q} \\ \hdashline
\vdots & \vdots & \vdots & \vdots \\ \hdashline
\mathbf{F}_{P,1} & \mathbf{F}_{P,2} & \cdots & \mathbf{F}_{P,Q}
\end{array} \right]
\tag{5.1-5}
$$

Matrix Addition

The sum $\mathbf{C} = \mathbf{A} + \mathbf{B}$ of two matrices is defined only for matrices of the same size. The sum matrix $\mathbf{C}$ is an $M \times N$ matrix whose elements are $C(m, n) = A(m, n) + B(m, n)$.

Matrix Multiplication

The product $\mathbf{C} = \mathbf{AB}$ of two matrices is defined only when the number of columns of $\mathbf{A}$ equals the number of rows of $\mathbf{B}$. The $M \times N$ product matrix $\mathbf{C}$ of the $M \times P$ matrix $\mathbf{A}$ and the $P \times N$ matrix $\mathbf{B}$ is a matrix whose general element is given by

$$
C(m, n) = \sum_{p=1}^{P} A(m, p) B(p, n)
\tag{5.1-6}
$$

Multiplication of a matrix by a scalar k, that is, $\mathbf{C} = k\mathbf{A}$, produces a matrix of elements $C(m, n) = kA(m, n)$.

Matrix Inverse

The matrix inverse, denoted by A^{-1}, of a square matrix A has the property that $AA^{-1} = I$ and $A^{-1}A = I$. If such a matrix A^{-1} exists, the matrix A is said to be nonsingular; otherwise A is singular. If a matrix possesses an inverse, the inverse is unique. The matrix inverse of a matrix inverse is the original matrix. Thus

$$[A^{-1}]^{-1} = A \tag{5.1-7}$$

If matrices A and B are nonsingular,

$$[AB]^{-1} = B^{-1}A^{-1} \tag{5.1-8}$$

If matrix A is nonsingular, and the scalar $k \neq 0$, then

$$[kA]^{-1} = \frac{1}{k}A^{-1} \tag{5.1-9}$$

Inverse operators of singular square matrices and of nonsquare matrices are considered in Chapter 8. The inverse of the partitioned square matrix

$$F = \left[\begin{array}{c|c} F_{11} & F_{12} \\ \hline F_{21} & F_{22} \end{array} \right] \tag{5.1-10}$$

may be expressed as

$$F^{-1} = \left[\begin{array}{c|c} [F_{11} - F_{12}F_{22}^{-1}F_{21}]^{-1} & -F_{11}^{-1}F_{12}[F_{22} - F_{21}F_{11}^{-1}F_{12}]^{-1} \\ \hline -F_{22}^{-1}F_{21}[F_{11} - F_{12}F_{22}^{-1}F_{21}]^{-1} & [F_{22} - F_{21}F_{11}^{-1}F_{12}]^{-1} \end{array} \right] \tag{5.1-11}$$

provided that F_{11} and F_{22} are nonsingular.

Matrix Transpose

The transpose of an $M \times N$ matrix A is an $N \times M$ matrix denoted by A^T, whose rows are the columns of A and whose columns are the rows of A. For any matrix A,

$$[A^T]^T = A \tag{5.1-12}$$

If $A = A^T$, then A is said to be symmetric. The matrix products AA^T and A^TA are symmetric. For any matrices A and B,

$$[AB]^T = B^TA^T \tag{5.1-13}$$

If A is nonsingular, then A^T is nonsingular and

$$[A^T]^{-1} = [A^{-1}]^T \tag{5.1-14}$$

Matrix Direct Product

The left direct product of a $P \times Q$ matrix $\mathbf{A}$ and a $M \times N$ matrix $\mathbf{B}$ is a $PM \times QN$ matrix defined by

$$\mathbf{C} = \mathbf{A} \otimes \mathbf{B} = \begin{bmatrix} B(1,1)\mathbf{A} & B(1,2)\mathbf{A} & \cdots & B(1,N)\mathbf{A} \\ B(2,1)\mathbf{A} & B(2,2)\mathbf{A} & \cdots & B(2,N)\mathbf{A} \\ \vdots & \vdots & & \\ & & & \\ B(M,1)\mathbf{A} & \cdots & \cdots & B(M,N)\mathbf{A} \end{bmatrix} \quad (5.1\text{-}15)$$

A right direct product can also be defined in a complementary manner. In this book only the left direct product will be employed. The direct products $\mathbf{A} \otimes \mathbf{B}$ and $\mathbf{B} \otimes \mathbf{A}$ are not necessarily equal. The product, sum, transpose, and inverse relations are stated below:

$$(\mathbf{A} \otimes \mathbf{B})(\mathbf{C} \otimes \mathbf{D}) = (\mathbf{AC}) \otimes (\mathbf{BD}) \quad (5.1\text{-}16)$$

$$(\mathbf{A} + \mathbf{B}) \otimes \mathbf{C} = \mathbf{A} \otimes \mathbf{C} + \mathbf{B} \otimes \mathbf{C} \quad (5.1\text{-}17)$$

$$[\mathbf{A} \otimes \mathbf{B}]^T = \mathbf{A}^T \otimes \mathbf{B}^T \quad (5.1\text{-}18)$$

$$[\mathbf{A} \otimes \mathbf{B}]^{-1} = [\mathbf{A}^{-1} \otimes \mathbf{B}^{-1}] \quad (5.1\text{-}19)$$

Matrix Trace

The trace of an $N \times N$ square matrix $\mathbf{F}$ is the sum of its diagonal elements denoted as

$$\mathrm{tr}\,[\mathbf{F}] = \sum_{n=1}^{N} F(n,n) \quad (5.1\text{-}20)$$

If $\mathbf{A}$ and $\mathbf{B}$ are square matrices,

$$\mathrm{tr}\,[\mathbf{AB}] = \mathrm{tr}\,[\mathbf{BA}] \quad (5.1\text{-}21)$$

The trace of the direct product of two matrices equals

$$\mathrm{tr}\,(\mathbf{A} \otimes \mathbf{B}) = \mathrm{tr}\,(\mathbf{A})\,\mathrm{tr}\,(\mathbf{B}) \quad (5.1\text{-}22)$$

Vector Norm

The Euclidean vector norm of the $N \times 1$ vector $\mathbf{f}$ is a scalar defined as

$$\|\mathbf{f}\| = \mathbf{f}^T \mathbf{f} \quad (5.1\text{-}23)$$

Matrix Norm

The Euclidean matrix norm of the $M \times N$ matrix $\mathbf{F}$ is a scalar defined as

$$\|\mathbf{F}\| = \mathrm{tr}\,[\mathbf{F}^T \mathbf{F}] \quad (5.1\text{-}24)$$

Matrix Rank

An $N \times N$ matrix $\mathbf{A}$ is a rank R matrix if the largest nonsingular square submatrix of $\mathbf{A}$ is an $R \times R$ matrix. The rank of a matrix is utilized in the inversion of matrices. If matrices $\mathbf{A}$ and $\mathbf{B}$ are nonsingular, and $\mathbf{C}$ is an arbitrary matrix, then

$$\text{rank}\,[\mathbf{C}] = \text{rank}\,[\mathbf{AC}] = \text{rank}\,[\mathbf{CA}] = \text{rank}\,[\mathbf{ACB}] \qquad (5.1\text{-}25)$$

The rank of the product of matrices $\mathbf{A}$ and $\mathbf{B}$ satisfies the relations

$$\text{rank}\,[\mathbf{AB}] \le \text{rank}\,[\mathbf{A}] \qquad (5.1\text{-}26a)$$

$$\text{rank}\,[\mathbf{AB}] \le \text{rank}\,[\mathbf{B}] \qquad (5.1\text{-}26b)$$

The rank of the sum of matrices $\mathbf{A}$ and $\mathbf{B}$ satisfies the relations

$$\text{rank}\,[\mathbf{A} + \mathbf{B}] \le \text{rank}\,[\mathbf{A}] + \text{rank}\,[\mathbf{B}] \qquad (5.1\text{-}27)$$

Vector Inner Product

The inner product of the $N \times 1$ vectors $\mathbf{f}$ and $\mathbf{g}$ is a scalar

$$k = \mathbf{g}^T \mathbf{f} \qquad (5.1\text{-}28)$$

where

$$k = \sum_{n=1}^{N} g(n)f(n) \qquad (5.1\text{-}29)$$

Vector Outer Product

The outer product of the $M \times 1$ vector $\mathbf{g}$ and the $N \times 1$ vector $\mathbf{f}$ is a matrix

$$\mathbf{A} = \mathbf{g}\mathbf{f}^T \qquad (5.1\text{-}30)$$

where $A(m, n) = g(m)f(n)$.

Quadratic Form

The quadratic form of an $N \times 1$ vector $\mathbf{f}$ is a scalar

$$k = \mathbf{f}^T \mathbf{A}\mathbf{f} \qquad (5.1\text{-}31)$$

where $\mathbf{A}$ is an $N \times N$ matrix. Often the matrix $\mathbf{A}$ is selected to be symmetric.

Vector Differentiation

The derivative of the inner product $\mathbf{a}^T \mathbf{x}$ with respect to $\mathbf{x}$ is

$$\frac{\partial [\mathbf{a}^T \mathbf{x}]}{\partial \mathbf{x}} = \mathbf{a} \qquad (5.1\text{-}32)$$

and the derivative of the inner product $\mathbf{x}^T \mathbf{a}$ with respect to $\mathbf{x}$ is

$$\frac{\partial[\mathbf{x}^T \mathbf{a}]}{\partial \mathbf{x}} = \mathbf{a} \qquad (5.1\text{-}33)$$

The derivative of the quadratic form $\mathbf{x}^T \mathbf{A}\mathbf{x}$ with respect to $\mathbf{x}$ is

$$\frac{\partial[\mathbf{x}^T \mathbf{A}\mathbf{x}]}{\partial \mathbf{x}} = 2\mathbf{A}\mathbf{x} \qquad (5.1\text{-}34)$$

5.2. SINGULAR VALUE MATRIX DECOMPOSITION

It is known that any arbitrary $M \times N$ matrix $\mathbf{F}$ of rank R can be decomposed into the sum of a weighted set of unit rank $M \times N$ matrices by a singular value decomposition (SVD) (6–8). Applications of this concept to image processing are explored in subsequent sections.

According to the SVD matrix decomposition, there exist an $M \times M$ unitary matrix $\mathbf{U}$ and an $N \times N$ unitary matrix $\mathbf{V}$ for which

$$\mathbf{U}^T \mathbf{F} \mathbf{V} = \mathbf{\Lambda}^{1/2} \qquad (5.2\text{-}1)$$

where

$$\mathbf{\Lambda}^{1/2} = \left[\begin{array}{ccc:c} \overbrace{\lambda^{1/2}(1) \quad\quad}^{R} & & & \overbrace{\quad\quad}^{N-R} \\ & \ddots & & 0 \\ & & \lambda^{1/2}(R) & \\ \hdashline & 0 & & 0 \end{array} \right] \begin{array}{l} \left.\vphantom{\begin{array}{c}a\\b\\c\end{array}}\right\} R \\[6pt] \left.\vphantom{a}\right\} M-R \end{array} \qquad (5.2\text{-}2)$$

is an $M \times N$ matrix with a general diagonal entry $\lambda^{1/2}(j)$, called a singular value of $\mathbf{F}$. Since $\mathbf{U}$ and $\mathbf{V}$ are unitary matrices, $\mathbf{U}\mathbf{U}^T = \mathbf{I}_M$ and $\mathbf{V}\mathbf{V}^T = \mathbf{I}_N$. Consequently,

$$\mathbf{F} = \mathbf{U}\mathbf{\Lambda}^{1/2}\mathbf{V}^T \qquad (5.2\text{-}3)$$

The columns of the unitary matrix $\mathbf{U}$ are composed of the eigenvectors $\mathbf{u}_m$ of the symmetric matrix $\mathbf{F}\mathbf{F}^T$. The defining relation is

$$\mathbf{U}^T[\mathbf{F}\mathbf{F}^T]\mathbf{U} = \left[\begin{array}{ccc:c} \overbrace{\lambda(1) \quad\quad}^{R} & & & \overbrace{\quad\quad}^{M-R} \\ & \ddots & & 0 \\ & & \lambda(R) & \\ \hdashline & 0 & & 0 \end{array} \right] \begin{array}{l} \left.\vphantom{\begin{array}{c}a\\b\\c\end{array}}\right\} R \\[6pt] \left.\vphantom{a}\right\} M-R \end{array} \qquad (5.2\text{-}4)$$

where the $\lambda(j)$ are the nonzero eigenvalues of $\mathbf{F}\mathbf{F}^T$. Similarly, the columns of $\mathbf{V}$ are the eigenvectors $\mathbf{v}_n$ of the symmetric matrix $\mathbf{F}^T\mathbf{F}$ as defined by

$$\mathbf{V}^T[\mathbf{F}^T\mathbf{F}]\mathbf{V} = \left[\begin{array}{ccc|c} \lambda(1) & & & \\ & \ddots & & \mathbf{0} \\ & & \lambda(R) & \\ \hline & \mathbf{0} & & \mathbf{0} \end{array} \right] \begin{array}{l} \left.\vphantom{\begin{array}{c}a\\a\\a\end{array}}\right\} R \\ \\ \left.\vphantom{\begin{array}{c}a\end{array}}\right\} N-R \end{array} \tag{5.2-5}$$

where the $\lambda(j)$ are the corresponding nonzero eigenvalues of $\mathbf{F}^T\mathbf{F}$. Consistency is easily established between Eqs. 5.2-3 to 5.2-5.

It is possible to express the matrix decomposition of Eq. 5.2-3 in the series form

$$\mathbf{F} = \sum_{j=1}^{R} \lambda^{1/2}(j)\mathbf{u}_j\mathbf{v}_j^T \tag{5.2-6}$$

The outer products $\mathbf{u}_i\mathbf{v}_j^T$ of the eigenvectors form a set of unit rank matrices each of which is scaled by a corresponding singular value of $\mathbf{F}$. The consistency of Eq. 5.2-6 with the previously stated relations can be shown by its substitution into Eq. 5.2-1, which yields

$$\mathbf{\Lambda}^{1/2} = \mathbf{U}^T\mathbf{F}\mathbf{V} = \sum_{j=1}^{R} \lambda^{1/2}(j)\mathbf{U}^T\mathbf{u}_j\mathbf{v}_j^T\mathbf{V} \tag{5.2-7}$$

It should be observed that the vector product $\mathbf{U}^T\mathbf{u}_j$ is a column vector with unity in its jth elements and zeros elsewhere. The row vector resulting from the product $\mathbf{v}_j^T\mathbf{V}$ is of similar form. Hence upon final expansion, the right-hand side of Eq. 5.2-7 reduces to a diagonal matrix containing the singular values of $\mathbf{F}$.

The SVD matrix decomposition of Eq. 5.2-3 and the equivalent series representation of Eq. 5.2-6 apply for any arbitrary matrix. Hence the SVD expansion can be applied directly to discrete images represented as matrices. Another application is the decomposition of linear operators that perform superposition, convolution, or general transformation of images in vector form. Applications of the SVD to image restoration and coding are presented in subsequent chapters.

5.3. VECTOR-SPACE IMAGE REPRESENTATION

In Chapter 1 a generalized continuous image function $F(x, y, t)$ was selected to represent the luminance, tristimulus value, or some other appropriate parameter of a physical imaging system. Image sampling techniques, discussed in Chapter 4, indicated means by which a discrete array

$F(j_1, j_2)$ could be extracted from the continuous image field at some time instant over some rectangular area $-J_i \leq j_i \leq J_i$. It is often helpful to regard this sampled image array as an $N_1 \times N_2$ element matrix

$$\mathbf{F} = [F(n_1, n_2)] \qquad (5.3\text{-}1)$$

for $1 \leq n_i \leq N_i$ where the indices of the sampled array are reindexed for consistency with standard vector-space notation.

For purposes of analysis it is convenient to convert the image matrix to vector form by column (or row) scanning $\mathbf{F}$ and then stringing the elements together in a long vector (9). An equivalent scanning operation can be expressed in quantitative form by the use of an $N_2 \times 1$ operational vector $\mathbf{v}_n$ and $N_1 N_2 \times N_1$ matrix $\mathbf{N}_n$ defined as

$$
\mathbf{v}_n =
\begin{bmatrix}
0 \\ \vdots \\ 0 \\ 1 \\ 0 \\ \vdots \\ 0
\end{bmatrix}
\begin{matrix}
1 \\ \vdots \\ n-1 \\ n \\ n+1 \\ \vdots \\ N_2
\end{matrix}
\qquad
\mathbf{N}_n =
\begin{bmatrix}
\mathbf{0} \\ \vdots \\ \mathbf{0} \\ \mathbf{I} \\ \mathbf{0} \\ \vdots \\ \mathbf{0}
\end{bmatrix}
\begin{matrix}
1 \\ \vdots \\ n-1 \\ n \\ n+1 \\ \vdots \\ N_2
\end{matrix}
\qquad (5.3\text{-}2)
$$

Then the vector representation of the data matrix $\mathbf{F}$ is given by the stacking operation

$$\mathbf{f} = \sum_{n=1}^{N_2} \mathbf{N}_n \mathbf{F} \mathbf{v}_n \qquad (5.3\text{-}3)$$

In essence the vector $\mathbf{v}_n$ extracts the nth column from $\mathbf{F}$ and the matrix $\mathbf{N}_n$ places this column into the nth segment of the vector $\mathbf{f}$. Thus $\mathbf{f}$ contains the column-scanned elements of $\mathbf{F}$. The inverse relation of casting the vector $\mathbf{f}$ into matrix form is obtained from

$$\mathbf{F} = \sum_{n=1}^{N_2} \mathbf{N}_n^T \mathbf{f} \mathbf{v}_n^T \qquad (5.3\text{-}4)$$

With the matrix to vector operator of Eq. 5.3-3 and the vector to matrix operator of Eq. 5.3-4, it is now possible easily to convert between vector and matrix representations of a two-dimensional array. The advantages of dealing with images in vector form are a more compact notation and the ability readily to apply previously derived results for one-dimensional signal processing applications. It should be recognized that Eqs. 5.3-3 and

5.3-4 represent more than a lexicographic ordering between an array and a vector; these equations define mathematical operators that may be analytically manipulated. Numerous examples of the application of the stacking operators are given in subsequent sections.

5.4. STATISTICAL CHARACTERIZATION OF DISCRETE IMAGES (5, 10)

The statistical descriptors of continuous images presented in Chapter 1 can be directly applied to characterize discrete images. In this section expressions are developed for the statistical moments of discrete image arrays. Joint probability density models for discrete image fields are described in the following section.

The moments of a discrete image process may be conveniently expressed in vector-space form. The mean value of the discrete image function is a matrix of the form

$$E\{\mathbf{F}\} = [E\{F(n_1, n_2)\}] \tag{5.4-1}$$

If the image array is written as a column-scanned vector, then the mean of the image vector is

$$\boldsymbol{\eta}_f = E\{\mathbf{f}\} = \sum_{n=1}^{N_2} \mathbf{N}_n E\{\mathbf{F}\} \mathbf{v}_n \tag{5.4-2}$$

and the correlation function of the image array is given by

$$R(n_1, n_2; n_3, n_4) = E\{F(n_1, n_2)F^*(n_3, n_4)\} \tag{5.4-3}$$

where the n_i represent points of the image array. Similarly, the covariance function of the image array is

$$K(n_1, n_2; n_3, n_4) = E\{[F(n_1, n_2) - E\{F(n_1, n_2)\}]$$
$$\cdot [F^*(n_3, n_4) - E\{F^*(n_3, n_4)\}]\} \tag{5.4-4}$$

And finally, the variance function of the image array is obtained directly from the covariance function as

$$\sigma^2(n_1, n_2) = K(n_1, n_2; n_1, n_2) \tag{5.4-5}$$

Again, if the image array is represented in vector form, the correlation matrix of $\mathbf{f}$ can be written in terms of the correlation of elements of $\mathbf{F}$ as

$$\mathbf{R}_f = E\{\mathbf{f}\mathbf{f}^{*T}\} = E\left\{\left[\sum_{m=1}^{N_2} \mathbf{N}_m \mathbf{F} \mathbf{v}_m\right]\left[\sum_{n=1}^{N_2} \mathbf{v}_n^T \mathbf{F}^{*T} \mathbf{N}_n^T\right]\right\} \tag{5.4-6a}$$

or

$$\mathbf{R}_f = \sum_{m=1}^{N_2} \sum_{n=1}^{N_2} \mathbf{N}_m E\{\mathbf{F}\mathbf{v}_m \, \mathbf{v}_n^T \mathbf{F}^{*T}\} \mathbf{N}_n^T \qquad (5.4\text{-}6b)$$

The term

$$E\{\mathbf{F}\mathbf{v}_m \, \mathbf{v}_n^T \mathbf{F}^{*T}\} = \mathbf{R}_{m,n} \qquad (5.4\text{-}7)$$

is the $N_1 \times N_2$ correlation matrix of the mth and nth columns of $\mathbf{F}$. Hence it is possible to express $\mathbf{R}_f$ in partitioned form as

$$\mathbf{R}_f = \begin{bmatrix} \mathbf{R}_{1,1} & \mathbf{R}_{1,2} & \cdots & \mathbf{R}_{1,N_2} \\ \mathbf{R}_{2,1} & \mathbf{R}_{2,2} & \cdots & \mathbf{R}_{2,N_2} \\ \vdots & \vdots & & \\ \mathbf{R}_{N_2,1} & \mathbf{R}_{N_2,2} & \cdots & \mathbf{R}_{N_2,N_2} \end{bmatrix} \qquad (5.4\text{-}8)$$

The covariance matrix of $\mathbf{f}$ can be found from its correlation matrix and mean vector by the relation

$$\mathbf{K}_f = \mathbf{R}_f - \boldsymbol{\eta}_f \boldsymbol{\eta}_f^{*T} \qquad (5.4\text{-}9)$$

A variance matrix $\mathbf{V}_F$ of the array $F(n_1, n_2)$ is defined as a matrix whose elements represent the variances of the corresponding elements of the array. The elements of this matrix may be extracted directly from the covariance matrix partitions of $\mathbf{K}_f$. That is,

$$\mathbf{V}_F(n_1, n_2) = \mathbf{K}_{n_1,n_2}(n_1, n_1) \qquad (5.4\text{-}10)$$

If the image array $\mathbf{F}$ is wide-sense stationary, the correlation function can be expressed as

$$R(n_1, n_2; n_3, n_4) = R(n_1 - n_3, n_2 - n_4) = R(j, k) \qquad (5.4\text{-}11)$$

where $j = n_1 - n_3$ and $k = n_2 - n_4$. Correspondingly, the covariance matrix partitions of Eq. 5.4-9 are related by

$$\mathbf{K}_{m,n} = \mathbf{K}_k \qquad m \geq n \qquad (5.4\text{-}12a)$$

$$\mathbf{K}_{m,n} = \mathbf{K}_k^* \qquad m < n \qquad (5.4\text{-}12b)$$

where $k = |m - n| + 1$. Hence, for a wide-sense stationary image array

$$\mathbf{K}_f = \begin{bmatrix} \mathbf{K}_1 & \mathbf{K}_2 & \mathbf{K}_3 & \cdots & \mathbf{K}_{N_2} \\ \mathbf{K}_2^* & \mathbf{K}_1 & \mathbf{K}_2 & \cdots & \mathbf{K}_{N_2-1} \\ \vdots & \vdots & \vdots & & \vdots \\ \mathbf{K}_{N_2}^* & \mathbf{K}_{N_2-1}^* & \mathbf{K}_{N_2-2}^* & \cdots & \mathbf{K}_1 \end{bmatrix} \qquad (5.4\text{-}13)$$

The matrix of Eq. 5.4-13 is of block Toeplitz form (11). Finally, if the correlation between elements is separable into the product of row and column correlation functions, then the covariance matrix of the data vector **f** can be expressed as the direct product of row and column covariance matrices. Under this condition

$$\mathbf{K}_f = \mathbf{K}_C \otimes \mathbf{K}_R = \begin{bmatrix} \mathbf{K}_R(1,1)\mathbf{K}_C & \mathbf{K}_R(1,2)\mathbf{K}_C & \cdots & \mathbf{K}_R(1,N_2)\mathbf{K}_C \\ \mathbf{K}_R(2,1)\mathbf{K}_C & \mathbf{K}_R(2,2)\mathbf{K}_C & \cdots & \mathbf{K}_R(2,N_2)\mathbf{K}_C \\ \vdots & \vdots & & \vdots \\ \mathbf{K}_R(N_2,1)\mathbf{K}_C & \mathbf{K}_R(N_2,2)\mathbf{K}_C & \cdots & \mathbf{K}_R(N_2,N_2)\mathbf{K}_C \end{bmatrix}$$

$$(5.4\text{-}14)$$

where $\mathbf{K}_C$ is an $N_1 \times N_1$ covariance matrix of each column of **F** and $\mathbf{K}_R$ is an $N_2 \times N_2$ covariance matrix of the rows of **F**.

As a special case consider the situation in which adjacent pixels along an image row have a correlation of $(0 \le \rho_R \le 1)$ and a self-correlation of unity. Then the covariance matrix reduces to

$$\mathbf{K}_R = \sigma_R^2 \begin{bmatrix} 1 & \rho_R & \rho_R^2 & \rho_R^3 & \cdots & \rho_R^{N_2-1} \\ \rho_R & 1 & \rho_R & \rho_R^2 & \cdots & \rho_R^{N_2-2} \\ \vdots & & & & & \vdots \\ \rho_R^{N_2-1} & \cdot & \cdot & \cdot & \cdots & 1 \end{bmatrix}$$

$$(5.4\text{-}15)$$

where σ_R^2 denotes the variance of pixels along a row. This is an example of the covariance matrix of a Markov process, analogous to the continuous autocovariance function $\exp(-\alpha|x|)$. Figure 5.4-1 contains a plot of the measured correlation of pixels along an image line for a typical image obtained by Davisson (12). The data points can be fit quite well with a Markov covariance function with $\rho = 0.953$. Likewise, the correlation between lines can be modeled well with a Markov covariance function with $\rho = 0.965$. If the horizontal and vertical correlations were exactly separable, then the covariance function for pixels along the image diagonal would be equal to the product of the horizontal and vertical axis correlation functions. In this example the approximation was found to be reasonably accurate for up to five pixel separations.

The discrete power-spectral density of a discrete image random process may be defined, in analogy with the continuous power spectrum of Eq. 1.8-11, as the two-dimensional discrete Fourier transform* of its stationary

---

* Chapter 10 discusses the properties of discrete two-dimensional Fourier transforms.

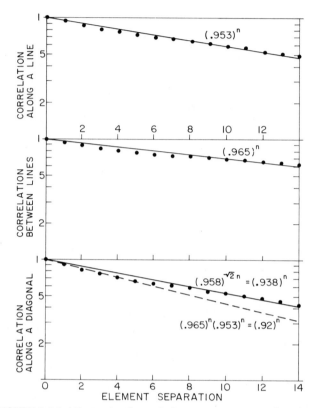

FIGURE 5.4-1. Example of correlation measurements of a scene.

autocorrelation function. Thus from Eq. 5.4-11

$$\mathcal{W}(u, v) = \frac{1}{\sqrt{N_1 N_2}} \sum_{j=0}^{N_1-1} \sum_{k=0}^{N_2-1} R(j, k) \exp\left\{ -2\pi i \left(\frac{ju}{N_1} + \frac{kv}{N_2} \right) \right\}$$

$$(5.4\text{-}16)$$

Figure 5.4-2 contains perspective plots of the power-spectral densities for separable and circularly symmetric Markov processes.

5.5 PROBABILITY DENSITY MODELS FOR DISCRETE IMAGES

A discrete image array $F(n_1, n_2)$ can be completely characterized statistically by its joint probability density written in matrix form as

$$p(\mathbf{F}) \equiv p\{F(1, 1), F(2, 1), \ldots, F(N_1, N_2)\} \qquad (5.5\text{-}1a)$$

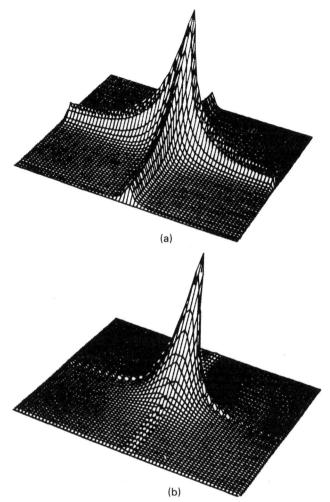

(a)

(b)

FIGURE 5.4-2. Power spectral densities of Markov process sources. $N = 256$, log magnitude displays. (a) Separable. (b) Circularly symmetric.

or in corresponding vector form as

$$p(\mathbf{f}) = p\{f(1), f(2), \ldots, f(Q)\} \tag{5.5-1b}$$

where $Q = N_1 \cdot N_2$ is the order of the joint density. If all pixel values are satistically independent, then the joint density factors into the product

$$p(\mathbf{f}) = p\{f(1)\}p\{f(2)\} \cdots p\{f(Q)\} \tag{5.5-2}$$

of its first-order marginal densities.

The most common joint probability density is the joint Gaussian, which may be expressed as

$$p(\mathbf{f}) = (2\pi)^{-Q/2}|\mathbf{K}_f|^{-1/2} \exp\{-\tfrac{1}{2}(\mathbf{f} - \boldsymbol{\eta}_f)^T \mathbf{K}_f^{-1}(\mathbf{f} - \boldsymbol{\eta}_f)\} \qquad (5.5\text{-}3)$$

where $\mathbf{K}_f$ is the covariance matrix of $\mathbf{f}$, $\boldsymbol{\eta}_f$ is the mean of $\mathbf{f}$, and $|\mathbf{K}_f|$ denotes the determinant of $\mathbf{K}_f$. The joint Gaussian density is useful as a model for the density of unitary transform coefficients of an image. However, the Gaussian density is not an adequate model for the luminance values on an image because luminance is a positive quantity and the Gaussian variables are bipolar.

Expressions for joint densities, other than the Gaussian density, are rarely found in the literature. Huhns (13) has developed a technique of generating high-order densities in terms of specified first-order marginal densities and a specified covariance matrix between the ensemble elements. The procedure for a zero mean density involves a linear transformation of a set of uncorrelated variables $\mathbf{g}$ whose probability density

$$p(\mathbf{g}) = p[g(1)]p[g(2)] \cdots p[g(Q)] \qquad (5.5\text{-}4)$$

can be written as the product of desired marginals. Then the desired joint probability density assumes the form

$$p_f(\mathbf{f}) = |\mathbf{A}|p_g(\mathbf{A}\mathbf{f}) \qquad (5.5\text{-}5)$$

where

$$\mathbf{A} = \mathbf{E}\boldsymbol{\Lambda}^{-1/2}\mathbf{E}^T \qquad (5.5\text{-}6)$$

and $|\mathbf{A}|$ denotes the determinant of $\mathbf{A}$. The matrix $\mathbf{E}$ is a matrix of column eigenvectors and $\boldsymbol{\Lambda}$ is a diagonal matrix of corresponding eigenvalues of the specified covariance matrix $\mathbf{K}_f$ satisfying

$$\mathbf{E}^T\mathbf{K}_f\mathbf{E} = \boldsymbol{\Lambda} \qquad (5.5\text{-}7)$$

Figure 5.5-1 contains perspective views of two-dimensional correlated densities whose marginals are Rayleigh and Laplacian densities. The joint "Rayleigh" model is useful for modeling the joint density of pixel luminance values, while the joint "Laplacian" model has application for the statistical description of a sequence of difference signals generated by a predictive image coding system.

In the next chapter techniques are developed for quantizing variables to some discrete set of values called reconstruction levels. Let $r_{j_q}(q)$ denote the reconstruction level of the pixel at vector coordinate (q). Then the probability of occurrence of the possible states of the image vector can be written in terms of the joint probability distribution as

$$P(\mathbf{f}) = P_R\{\mathbf{f}(1) = r_{j_1}(1), f(2) = r_{j_2}(2), \ldots, f(Q) = r_{jQ}(Q)\} \qquad (5.5\text{-}8)$$

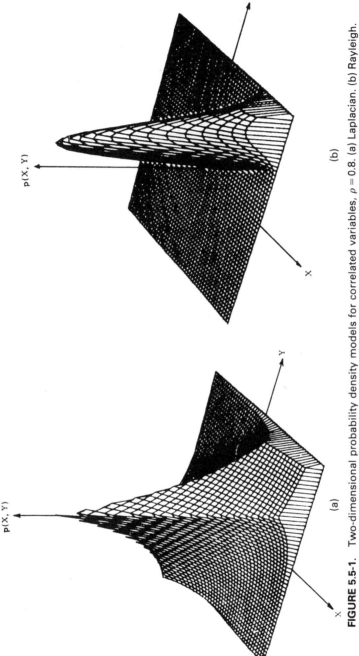

FIGURE 5.5-1. Two-dimensional probability density models for correlated variables, $\rho = 0.8$. (a) Laplacian. (b) Rayleigh.

where $0 \leq j_q \leq j_Q = J - 1$. Normally the reconstruction levels are set identically for each vector component and the joint probability distribution reduces to

$$P(\mathbf{f}) = P_R\{f(1) = r_{j_1}, f(2) = r_{j_2}, \ldots, f(Q) = r_{j_Q}\} \qquad (5.5\text{-}9)$$

Probability distributions of image values can be estimated by histogram measurements. For example, the first-order probability distribution

$$P\{f(q)\} = P_R\{f(q) = r_j\} \qquad (5.5\text{-}10)$$

of the amplitude value at vector coordinate q can be estimated by examining a large collection of images representative of a given image class, for example, chest X rays, aerial scenes of crop, and so on. The first-order histrogram estimate of the probability distribution is the frequency ratio

$$H_E(j;q) = \frac{N_p(j)}{N_p} \qquad (5.5\text{-}11)$$

where N_P represents the total number of images examined and $N_P(j)$ denotes the number for which $f(q) = r_j$ for $j = 0, 1, \ldots, J - 1$. If the image source is satistically stationary, the first-order probability distribution of Eq. 5.5-10 will be the same for all vector components q. Furthermore, if the image source is ergodic, ensemble averages (measurements over a collection of pictures) can be replaced by spatial averages. Under the ergodic assumption the first-order probability distribution can be estimated by measurement of the spatial histogram

$$H_S(j) = \frac{N_S(j)}{Q} \qquad (5.5\text{-}12)$$

where $N_S(j)$ denotes the number of pixels in a test image for which $f(q) = r_j$ for $1 \leq q \leq Q$ and $0 \leq j \leq J - 1$.

Figure 5.5-2 contains first-order histograms of the red, green, and blue tristimulus values of the girl picture. Most natural images possess many more dark pixels than bright pixels, and their histograms tend to fall off exponentially at higher luminance levels.

Estimates of the second-order probability distribution for ergodic image sources can be obtained by measurement of the second-order spatial histogram, which is a measure of the joint occurrence of pairs of pixels separated by a specified distance. With reference to Figure 5.5-3, let $F(m_1, m_2)$ amd $F(m_3, m_4)$ denote a pair of pixels separated by r radial units at an angle θ with respect to the horizontal axis. As a consequence of the rectilinear grid, the separation parameters may only assume certain

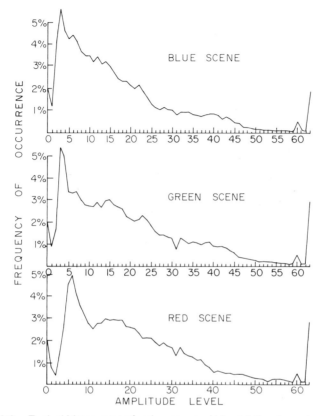

FIGURE 5.2-2.   Typical histograms of red, green, and blue tristimulus values of a color image.

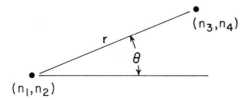

FIGURE 5.5-3.   Geometric relationships of pixel pairs.

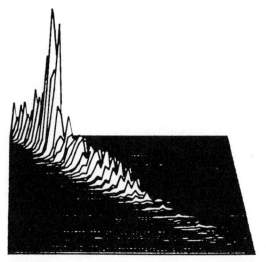

FIGURE 5.5-4.   Second-order histogram of GIRL picture.

discrete values. The second-order spatial histogram is then the frequency ratio

$$H_S(j_1, j_2; r, \theta) = \frac{N_S(j_1, j_2)}{Q_T} \qquad (5.5\text{-}13)$$

where $N_S(j_1, j_2)$ denotes the number of pixel pairs for which $F(m_1, m_2) = r_{j_1}$ and $F(m_3, m_4) = r_{j_2}$. The factor Q_T in the denominator of Eq. 5.5-13 represents the total number of pixels lying in an image region for which the separation is (r, θ). Because of boundary effects, $Q_T < Q$.

Second-order spatial histograms of the girl picture are presented in Figure 5.5-4 as a function of pixel separation distance and angle. As the separation increases, the pairs of pixels become less correlated and the histogram energy tends to spread more uniformly about the plane.

REFERENCES

1. F. Ayres, Jr., *Schaum's Outline of Theory and Problems of Matrices*, McGraw-Hill, New York, 1962.

2. R. E. Bellman, *Introduction to Matrix Analysis*, McGraw-Hill, New York, 1970.

3. H. G. Campbell, *An Introduction to Matrices, Vectors, and Linear Programming*, Appleton, New York, 1965.

4. C. G. Cullen, *Matrices and Linear Transformations*, Addison-Wesley, Reading, Mass., 1966.

5. F. A. Graybill, *Introduction to Matrices with Applications in Statistics*, Wadsworth, Belmont, Calif., 1969.

6. C. R. Rau and S. K. Mitra, *Generalized Inverse of Matrices and its Applications*, Wiley, New York, 1971.

7. G. H. Golub and C. Reinsch, "Singular Value Decomposition and Least Squares Solutions," *Numer. Math.*, **14**, 1970, 403–420.

8. H. C. Andrews and C. L. Patterson, "Outer Product Expansions and their Uses in Digital Image Processing," *Am. Math. Monthly*, **1**, 82, January 1975, 1–13.

9. W. K. Pratt, "Vector Formulation of Two Dimensional Signal Processing Operations," *J. Comput. Graphics Image Proc.*, **4**, No. 1, March 1975, 1–24 (Academic Press, New York).

10. A. Papoulis, *Probability, Random Variables, and Stochastic Processes*, McGraw-Hill, New York, 1965.

11. U. Grenander and G. Szego, *Toeplitz Forms and Their Applications*, University of California Press, Berkeley, 1958.

12. L. D. Davisson (private communication).

13. M. N. Huhns, "Optimum Restoration of Quantized Correlated Signals," University of Southern California, Image Processing Institute, Report USCIPI 600, August 1975.

6 IMAGE QUANTIZATION

Any analog quantity that is to be processed by a digital computer or digital system must be represented as an integer number proportional to its amplitude. The conversion process between analog samples and discrete-valued samples is called quantization. The following two sections contain an analytic treatment of the quantization process, which is applicable not only for images, but for a wide class of signals encountered in image processing systems. The next section considers the processing of quantized variables. The last two sections discuss the subjective effects of quantizing monochrome and color images.

6.1. SCALAR QUANTIZATION

Figure 6.1-1 illustrates a typical example of quantization of a scalar signal. In the quantization process the amplitude of an analog signal sample is compared to a set of decision levels. If the sample amplitude falls between two decision levels, it is quantized to a fixed reconstruction level lying in

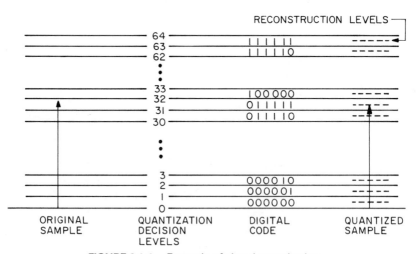

FIGURE 6.1-1. Example of signal quantization.

the quantization band. In a digital system each quantized sample is assigned a binary code. An equal length binary code is indicated in the example.

For the development of quantitative scalar signal quantization techniques let f and $\hat{f}$ represent the amplitude of a real, scalar signal sample and its quantized value, respectively. It is assumed that f is a sample of a random process with known probability density $p(f)$. Furthermore, it is assumed that f is constrained to lie in the range

$$a_L \leq f \leq a_U \qquad (6.1\text{-}1)$$

where a_U and a_L represent upper and lower limits.

The quantization problem entails specification of a set of decision levels d_j and a set of reconstruction levels r_j such that if

$$d_j \leq f < d_{j+1} \qquad (6.1\text{-}2)$$

then the sample is quantized to a reconstruction value r_j. Figure 6.1-2a illustrates the placement of decision and reconstruction levels along a line for J quantization levels. The staircase representation of Figure 6.2-2b is another common form of representation.

Decision and reconstruction levels are chosen to minimize some desired quantization error measure between f and $\hat{f}$. The quantization error

DECISION LEVELS

RECONSTRUCTION LEVELS

(a) LINE REPRESENTATION

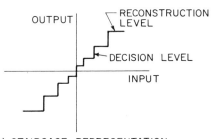

(b) STAIRCASE REPRESENTATION

FIGURE 6.1-2. Quantization decision and reconstruction levels.

measure usually selected is the mean-square error because this measure is tractable, and it usually correlates reasonably well with subjective criteria. For J quantization levels the mean-square quantization error is

$$\mathscr{E} = E\{(f - \hat{f})^2\} = \int_{a_L}^{a_U} (f - \hat{f})^2 p(f) \, df = \sum_{j=0}^{J-1} \int_{d_j}^{d_{j+1}} (f - r_j)^2 p(f) \, df$$

(6.1-3)

For a large number of quantization levels J, the probability density may be represented as a constant value $p(r_j)$ over each quantization band. Hence

$$\mathscr{E} = \sum_{j=0}^{J-1} p\{r_j\} \int_{d_j}^{d_{j+1}} (f - r_j)^2 \, df$$

(6.1-4)

which evaluates to

$$\mathscr{E} = \frac{1}{3} \sum_{j=0}^{J-1} p\{r_j\}[(d_{j+1} - r_j)^3 - (d_j - r_j)^3]$$

(6.1-5)

The optimum placing of the reconstruction level r_j within the range d_{j-1} to d_j can be determined by minimization of $\mathscr{E}$ with respect to r_j. Setting

$$\frac{d\mathscr{E}}{dr_j} = 0$$

(6.1-6)

yields

$$r_j = \frac{d_{j+1} + d_j}{2}$$

(6.1-7)

Therefore, the optimum placement of reconstruction levels is at the midpoint between each pair of decision levels. Substitution for this choice of reconstruction level into the expression for the quantization error yields

$$\mathscr{E} = \frac{1}{12} \sum_{j=0}^{J-1} p\{r_j\}[d_{j+1} - d_j]^3$$

(6.1-8)

The optimum choice for decision levels may be found by minimization of $\mathscr{E}$ in Eq. 6.1-8 by the method of Lagrange multipliers. Following this procedure, Panter and Dite (1) found that the decision levels may be computed to a good approximation from the integral equation

$$d_j = \frac{(a_U - a_L) \int_{a_L}^{a_j} [p\{f\}]^{-1/3} \, df}{\int_{a_L}^{a_U} [p\{f\}]^{-1/3} \, df} + a_L$$

(6.1-9a)

where

$$a_j = \frac{j(a_U - a_L)}{J} + a_L \qquad (6.1\text{-}9b)$$

for $j = 0, 1, \ldots, J$. If the probability density of the sample is uniform, the decision levels will be uniformly spaced. For nonuniform probability densities the spacing of decision levels is narrow in large-amplitude regions of the probability density function and widens in low-amplitude portions of the density. Equation 6.1-9 does not reduce to closed form for most probability density functions commonly encountered in image processing systems models, and hence the decision levels must be obtained by numerical integration.

If the number of quantization levels is not large, the approximation of Eq. 6.1-4 becomes inaccurate, and exact solutions must be explored. From Eq. 6.1-3, setting the partial derivatives of the error expression with respect to the decision and reconstruction levels equal to zero yields

$$\frac{\partial \mathscr{E}}{\partial d_j} = (d_j - r_j)^2 p(d_j) - (d_j - r_{j-1})^2 p(d_j) = 0 \qquad (6.1\text{-}10a)$$

$$\frac{\partial \mathscr{E}}{\partial r_j} = 2 \int_{d_j}^{d_{j+1}} (f - r_j) p(f) \, df = 0 \qquad (6.1\text{-}10b)$$

Upon simplification the set of equations

$$r_j = 2d_j - r_{j-1} \qquad (6.1\text{-}11a)$$

$$r_j = \frac{\displaystyle\int_{d_j}^{d_{j+1}} f p(f) \, df}{\displaystyle\int_{d_j}^{d_{j+1}} p(f) \, df} \qquad (6.1\text{-}11b)$$

is obtained. Recursive solution of these equations for a given probability distribution $p(f)$ provides optimum values for the decision and reconstruction levels. Max (2) has developed a solution for optimum decision and reconstruction levels for a Gaussian density, and has computed tables of optimum levels as a function of the number of quantization steps. Table 6.1-1 lists placements of decision and quantization levels for uniform, Gaussian, Laplacian, and Rayleigh densities for the Max quantizer.

TABLE 6.1-1. Placement of decision and reconstruction levels for Max quantizer

Bits	Uniform d_i	Uniform r_i	Gaussian d_i	Gaussian r_i	Laplacian d_i	Laplacian r_i	Rayleigh d_i	Rayleigh r_i
1	−1.0000	−0.5000	−∞	−0.7979	−∞	−0.7071	0.0000	1.2657
	0.0000	0.5000	0.0000	0.7979	0.0000	0.7071	2.0985	2.9313
	1.0000		∞		∞		∞	
2	−1.0000	−0.7500	−∞	−1.5104	−∞	−1.8340	0.0000	0.8079
	−0.5000	−0.2500	−0.9816	−0.4528	−1.1269	−0.4198	1.2545	1.7010
	−0.0000	0.2500	0.0000	0.4528	0.0000	0.4198	2.1667	2.6325
	0.5000	0.7500	0.9816	1.5104	1.1269	1.8340	3.2465	3.8604
	1.0000		∞		∞		∞	
3	−1.0000	−0.8750	−∞	−2.1519	−∞	−3.0867	0.0000	0.5016
	−0.7500	−0.6250	−1.7479	−1.3439	−2.3796	−1.6725	0.7619	1.0222
	−0.5000	−0.3750	−1.0500	−0.7560	−1.2527	−0.8330	1.2594	1.4966
	−0.2500	−0.1250	−0.5005	−0.2451	−0.5332	−0.2334	1.7327	1.9688
	0.0000	0.1250	0.0000	0.2451	0.0000	0.2334	2.2182	2.4675
	0.2500	0.3750	0,5005	0.7560	0.5332	0.8330	2.7476	3.0277
	0.5000	0.6250	1.0500	1.3439	1.2527	1.6725	3.3707	3.7137
	0.7500	0.8750	1.7479	2.1519	2.3796	3.0867	4.2124	4.7111
	1.0000		∞		∞		∞	
4	−1.0000	−0.9375	−∞	−2.7326	−∞	−4.4311	0.0000	0.3057
	−0.8750	−0.8125	−2.4008	−2.0690	−3.7240	−3.0169	0.4606	0.6156
	−0.7500	−0.6875	−1.8435	−1.6180	−2.5971	−2.1773	0.7509	0.8863
	−0.6250	−0.5625	−1.4371	−1.2562	−1.8776	−1.5778	1.0130	1.1397
	−0.5000	−0.4375	−1.0993	−0.9423	−1.3444	−1.1110	1.2624	1.3850
	−0.3750	−0.3125	−0.7995	−0.6568	−0.9198	−0.7287	1.5064	1.6277
	−0.2500	−0.1875	−0.5224	−0.3880	−0.5667	−0.4048	1.7499	1.8721
	−0.1250	−0.0625	−0.2582	−0.1284	−0.2664	−0.1240	1.9970	2.1220
	0.0000	0.0625	0.0000	0.1284	0.0000	0.1240	2.2517	2.3814
	0.1250	0.1875	0.2582	0.3880	0.2644	0.4048	2.5182	2.6550
	0.2500	0.3125	0.5224	0.6568	0.5667	0.7287	2.8021	2.9492
	0.3750	0.4375	0.7995	0.9423	0.9198	1.1110	3.1110	3.2729
	0.5000	0.5625	1.0993	1.2562	1.3444	1.5778	3.4566	3.6403
	0.6250	0.6875	1.4371	1.6180	1.8776	2.1773	3.8588	4.0772
	0.7500	0.8125	1.8435	2.0690	2.5971	3.0169	4.3579	4.6385
	0.8750	0.9375	2.4008	2.7326	3.7240	4.4311	5.0649	5.4913
	1.0000		∞		∞		∞	

If the decision and reconstruction levels are selected to satisfy Eq. 6.1-11, it can be easily shown that the mean-square quantization error becomes

$$\mathscr{E}_{MIN} = \sum_{j=0}^{J-1} \left[\int_{d_j}^{d_{j+1}} f^2 p\{f\} \, df - r_j^2 \int_{d_j}^{d_{j+1}} p\{f\} \, df \right] \qquad (6.1\text{-}12a)$$

or in a more compact form

$$\mathscr{E}_{\text{MIN}} = E\{f^2\} - \sum_{j=0}^{J-1} r_j^2 P\{d_j \leq f < d_{j+1}\} \qquad (6.1\text{-}12b)$$

In the special case of a uniform probability density, the minimum mean-square quantization error becomes

$$\mathscr{E}_{\text{MIN}} = \frac{1}{12J^2} \qquad (6.1\text{-}13)$$

Quantization errors for most other densities must be determined by computation.

It is possible to perform nonlinear quantization by a companding operation, as shown in Figure 6.1-3, in which the sample is transformed nonlinearly, linear quantization is performed, and the inverse nonlinear transformation is taken (3). In the companding system of quantization, the probability density of the transformed samples is forced to be uniform. Thus, from Figure 6.1-3, the transformed sample value is

$$g = T\{f\} \qquad (6.1\text{-}14)$$

where the nonlinear transformation $T(\cdot)$ is chosen such that the probability density of g is uniform.

$$p\{g\} = 1 \qquad (6.1\text{-}15)$$

for $-\frac{1}{2} \leq g \leq \frac{1}{2}$. If f is a zero mean random variable, the proper transformation function is (4)

$$T\{f\} = \int_{-\infty}^{f} p\{z\}\, dz - \tfrac{1}{2} \qquad (6.1\text{-}16)$$

That is, the nonlinear transformation function is equivalent to the cumulative probability distribution of f. Table 6.1-2 contains the companding transformations and inverses for the Gaussian, Rayleigh, and Laplacian probability densities.

FIGURE 6.1-3. Companding quantizer.

TABLE 6.1-2. Companding quantization transformation

	Probability Density	Forward Transformation	Inverse Transformation
Gaussian	$p(f) = (2\pi\sigma^2)^{-1/2} \exp\left\{-\dfrac{f^2}{2\sigma^2}\right\}$	$g = \dfrac{1}{2}\,\mathrm{erf}\left\{\dfrac{f}{\sqrt{2}\sigma}\right\}$	$\hat{f} = \sqrt{2}\sigma\,\mathrm{erf}^{-1}\{2\hat{g}\}$
Rayleigh	$p(f) = \dfrac{f}{\sigma^2}\exp\left\{-\dfrac{f^2}{2\sigma^2}\right\}$	$g = \dfrac{1}{2} - \exp\left\{-\dfrac{f^2}{2\sigma^2}\right\}$	$\hat{f} = [\sqrt{2}\sigma^2 \ln[1/(\tfrac{1}{2}-\hat{g})]]^{1/2} \quad \hat{g} \geq 0$
Laplacian	$p(f) = \dfrac{\alpha}{2}\exp\{-\alpha|f|\}$ $\alpha = \dfrac{\sqrt{2}}{\sigma}$	$g = \dfrac{1}{2}[1-\exp\{-\alpha f\}] \quad f \geq 0$ $g = -\dfrac{1}{2}[1-\exp\{\alpha f\}] \quad f < 0$	$\hat{f} = -\dfrac{1}{\alpha}\ln[1-2\hat{g}] \quad \hat{g} \geq 0$ $\hat{f} = \dfrac{1}{\alpha}\ln[1+2\hat{g}] \quad \hat{g} < 0$

where $\mathrm{erf}(x) = \dfrac{2}{\sqrt{\pi}}\displaystyle\int_0^x \exp(-y^2)\,dy$

6.2. VECTOR QUANTIZATION

Quantization of a sequence of continuous amplitude samples is normally performed on a sequential basis. Each member of the sequence is treated as a scalar variable and quantized separately according to the techniques outlined in the previous section. It is often possible, however, to reduce the quantization error by jointly quantizing and reconstructing the elements of the sequence.

Consider the $N \times 1$ element signal vector $\mathbf{f}$, which is assumed to be a sample of a vector random process with known Nth-order probability density

$$p(\mathbf{f}) = p\{f_1, f_2, \ldots, f_N\} \qquad (6.2\text{-}1)$$

Vector quantization of $\mathbf{f}$ involves subdivision of the N-dimensional vector space into J decision regions D_j each enclosing one of the J reconstruction values. The signal vector $\mathbf{f}$ is quantized to the reconstruction vector $\mathbf{r}_j$ if $\mathbf{f}$ lies in the decision region D_j. Figure 6.2-1 presents an illustration of vector quantization for one-, two-, and three-dimensional space. In this general

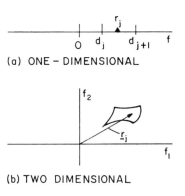

(a) ONE – DIMENSIONAL

(b) TWO DIMENSIONAL

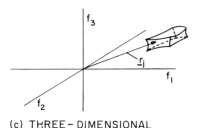

(c) THREE – DIMENSIONAL

FIGURE 6.2-1. Vector quantization decision regions.

formulation of vector quantization, the vector **f** is mapped into a vector $\mathbf{r}_j$; the individual elements of f are not necessarily individually quantized over a set of decision levels.

For vector quantization the mean-square quantization error can be written as

$$\mathscr{E} = \sum_{j=0}^{J-1} \int_{D_j} \text{tr}\, [(f - r_j)(\mathbf{f} - \mathbf{r}_j)^T] p(\mathbf{f})\, d\mathbf{f} \qquad (6.2\text{-}2)$$

The optimal reconstruction vector $\mathbf{r}_j$ can be determined for a fixed decision region D_j by setting to zero the partial derivatives of the quantization error expression with respect to $\mathbf{r}_j$. The resultant integral equation is given by

$$\frac{\partial \mathscr{E}}{\partial \mathbf{r}_j} = 0 = \int_{D_j} (\mathbf{f} - \mathbf{r}_j) p(\mathbf{f})\, d\mathbf{f} \qquad (6.2\text{-}3)$$

On rearrangement, one obtains

$$\mathbf{r}_j = \frac{\int_{D_j} \mathbf{f} p(\mathbf{f})\, d\mathbf{f}}{\int_{D_j} p(\mathbf{f})\, d\mathbf{f}} \qquad (6.2.4)$$

Equation 6.2-4 should be recognized as the definition of the conditional mean estimate

$$\mathbf{r}_j = E\{\mathbf{f} \,|\, \mathbf{f} \in D_j\} \qquad (6.2\text{-}5)$$

of **f** conditioned upon the information that **f** lies in the region D_j. The minimum mean-square quantization error is then found to be

$$\mathscr{E}_{\text{MIN}} = \text{tr} \left[\mathbf{R}_f - \sum_{j=0}^{J-1} \mathbf{r}_j \mathbf{r}_j^T P\{\mathbf{f} \in D_j\} \right\} \qquad (6.2\text{-}6)$$

where $\mathbf{R}_f$ is the correlation matrix of **f**. It should be recognized that in one dimension, Eq. 6.2-4 reduces to the scalar case given by Eq. 6.1-11, and similarly the error expression of Eq. 6.2-6 reduces to the scalar form of Eq. 6.1-12.

Determination of the optimum reconstruction vector $\mathbf{r}_j$ for a fixed decision region requires knowledge of the joint probability density $p(\mathbf{f})$. Often, this information is not available. Another major difficulty is the actual evaluation of the integral equation in Eq. 6.2-4. As a result, simplifications of the general vector quantization procedure are often necessitated. One simplification is to quantize each element of **f** separately, but form the reconstruction vector $\mathbf{r}_j$ in terms of the decision region D_j. In three-dimensional space the resultant decision regions become rectangular parallelpipeds. Under these circumstances if the elements of **f** are uncorrelated, vector quantization reduces to sequential scalar quantization. For correlated samples, however, the reconstruction problem of optimally determining the vector of reconstruction levels r_j usually remains formidable without further simplifying assumptions. Curry (4) has obtained solutions for joint Gaussian densities in which the decision regions are reasonably small. Huhns (5) has investigated a recursive solution, applicable to a wide variety of probability densities, in which each vector element is recursively estimated on the basis of the remaining quantized vector components. This method is discussed further in Part 6 as a means of quantization error reduction for PCM, DPCM, and transform image coding.

Attention will now be given to the selection of the decision regions D_j to minimize the mean-square quantization error. Bruce (6) has developed a dynamic programming solution to the problem. However, the optimal regions are complex shaped and difficult to compute in the general case. For this reason most vector quantization methods rely on the suboptimal approach in which each coefficient is assigned a fixed number of quantization levels $J(i)$ for $i = 1, 2, \ldots, N$ and quantized separately. The optimization problem then reduces to the choice of the $J(i)$ for a fixed sum

$$J = \sum_{i=1}^{N} J(i) \qquad (6.2\text{-}7)$$

of quantization levels to be assigned to the vector. The quantization error of the ith sample then becomes

$$\mathscr{E}(i) = E\{f^2(i)\} - \sum_{j=0}^{J(i)-1} r_j^2(i) P\{d_j(i) \le f(i) < d_{j+1}(i)\} \qquad (6.2\text{-}8)$$

For digital coding applications the number of quantization levels is usually restricted to be a binary number of the form

$$J(i) = 2^{b(i)} \qquad (6.2\text{-}9)$$

where $b(i)$ is the integer number of code bits allotted to the ith vector component. The bit allotments must sum to a fixed bit assignment

$$B = \sum_{i=1}^{N} b(i) \qquad (6.2\text{-}10)$$

The resultant quantization procedure is called block quantization.

Several authors (7–9) have developed algorithms for choosing the bit assignment $b(i)$ for fixed B to minimize the mean-square quantization error. The algorithm suggested by Ready and Wintz (9) which applies to Max quantization of independent Gaussian variables, is as follows:

1. Compute the bit assignment from

$$b(i) = \frac{B}{N} + 2\log_{10}[\sigma^2(i)] - \frac{2}{N}\sum_{j=1}^{N}\log_{10}[\sigma^2(j)] \qquad (6.2\text{-}11)$$

where $\sigma^2(i)$ denotes the variance of the ith sample.
2. Round off each bit $b(i)$ to its nearest integer value.
3. Modify the resultant bit assignments until Eq. 6.2-10 is satisfied.

The derivation leading to Eq. 6.2-10 is based on an exponential approximation of the error expression of Eq. 6.1-12 between the quantization error of the ith sample and its bit assignment $b(i)$. This approximation is relatively poor if $b(i)$ is small. Better results can be obtained with the minimal error algorithm developed by Pratt (10). In this algorithm bits are sequentially assigned to the sample with the largest differential error as specified by Eq. 6.2-8. The algorithm for zero-mean variables is as follows:

STEP 1. Initial conditions:
        B = total number of block code bits
        N = block length
        $\sigma^2(n)$ = component variance
        $p\{f(n)\}$ = component probability density model
        B_s = bit index (initially zero)

STEP 2. Compute and store differential error factors

$$\tilde{D}[b(n)] \equiv \tilde{F}[2J(n)] - \tilde{F}[J(n)]$$

where $J(n) = 2^{b(n)}$ and

$$\tilde{F}[J(n)] = \sum_{j=0}^{J(n)-1} \tilde{r}_j^2[J(n)]P\left[\tilde{d}_j[J(n)] \le \frac{f(n)}{\sigma(n)} < \tilde{d}_{j+1}[J(n)]\right]$$

is the error factor for unit variance random variables and the tilde sign (˜) indicates reconstruction and decision levels for such variables.

STEP 3. Assign one bit to that component for which $\sigma^2(n)\tilde{D}[b(n)]$ is largest, increment $b(n)$ by one and increment B_s by one.

STEP 4. If $B_s = B$, exit; otherwise go to step 3.

With this algorithm the differential error factors $\tilde{D}(\,\cdot\,)$ can be precomputed and stored in a table of size N. The algorithm then proceeds through B sorting steps. The advantages of the algorithm are that it is easily computed and it avoids the approximation and roundoff errors associated with the log variance algorithm. Furthermore, the minimal error algorithm utilizes knowledge of the probability density model, and therefore can be effectively used for bit assignment of nonidentically distributed samples.

6.3. PROCESSING QUANTIZED VARIABLES

Numbers within a digital computer that represent image variables, such as luminance or tristimulus values, normally are input as the integer codes corresponding to the quantization reconstruction levels of the variables. For example, the black to white scale for luminance in a monochrome image is usually linear scaled as an integer between 0 and 255. However, these integer codes should not be treated as arithmetic variables; rather, the integer codes should be converted to real decimal number reconstruction levels before arithmetic operations. Failure to follow this simple suggestion can lead to serious processing errors. Actually, if the integer codes were nonmonotonic along the gray scale, one would not consider using them as processing variables. The consequences of arithmetic processing of monotonic integer codes rather than decimal number reconstruction levels are now considered.

In a digital computer there are two major forms of numeric representation: integer and real. Integer numbers range in magnitude from 0 to some maximum value. In a 16-bit minicomputer, for example, the maximum positive integer is 32,768 (2^{15}). If an integer arithmetic operation results in a fractional part, the remainder is simply truncated. Thus, for example, the ratio 8/3 is represented as the integer 2 without a trailing decimal point. With real number computation the fractional part of an operation is retained up to the numerical accuracy of the computer. The ratio of the real numbers 8./3. is represented as $2.66\cdots66$.

Figure 6.3-1 offers a comparison of three signal processing strategies. In Figure 6.3-1*a* a continuous scalar signal f in the range $a_L \leq f \leq a_U$ is subject to a point transformation $\mathcal{O}_p\{\,\cdot\,\}$, which yields the continuous signal output variable

$$g = \mathcal{O}_p\{f\} \tag{6.3-1}$$

Figure 6.3-1*b* describes a processing system in which the scalar variable f is uniformly quantized and coded before processing. The integer code value

(a) CONTINUOUS SIGNAL PROCESSING

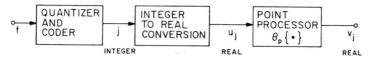

(b) QUANTIZED REAL NUMBER SIGNAL PROCESSING

(c) QUANTIZED AND CODED REAL NUMBER SIGNAL PROCESSING

FIGURE 6.3-1. Comparison of processing techniques for quantized signals.

is given by

$$j = \left[(J-1) \left(\frac{f - a_L}{a_U - a_L} \right) \right]_N \qquad (6.3\text{-}2)$$

where $[\cdot]_N$ denotes the nearest integer value of the argument. The integer code j is reconstructed to the real number r_j according to the relation

$$r_j = \left(\frac{r_{J-1} - r_0}{J-1} \right) j + r_0 \qquad (6.3\text{-}3a)$$

or equivalently

$$r_j = \left(\frac{a_U - a_L}{J} \right) j + \left(\frac{a_U - a_L}{2J} \right) + a_L \qquad (6.3\text{-}3b)$$

Next, the point processing operation is performed on the reconstructed signal r_j to produce the quantized output signal

$$g_j = O_p\{r_j\} \qquad (6.3\text{-}4)$$

which is equivalent to the continuous output signal g of Eq. 6.3-1 except for the quantization error introduced by Eq. 6.3-2.

Figure 6.3-1b represents the desired form of computer processing of quantized variables. Unfortunately, all too often, quantized variable signal processing is erroneously performed according to the procedure described in Figure 6.3-1c. The integer code j is converted to a real number u_j over the range $0., 1., 2., \ldots, J-1$. Then, the real number output signal v_j is computed according to the relation

$$v_j = \mathcal{O}_p\{u_j\} \tag{6.3-5}$$

In general, v_j contains a fractional as well as a whole number part. For example, if $u_j = 17.$, and the point processor performs a square root operation, then $v_j = 4.12311$ to five-place accuracy. It is certainly clear that the output variable v_j is subject to the quantization error of u_j. However, even more serious problems arise if v_j is meant to be a reasonably accurate approximation of the continuous output variable g. Suppose that the number of quantization levels is sufficiently large so that

$$u_j \approx (J-1)\frac{f-a_L}{a_U-a_L} \tag{6.3-6}$$

Then the output variable becomes

$$v_j \approx \mathcal{O}_p\{k_1 f + k_2\} \tag{6.3-7}$$

where k_1 and k_2 are constants defined by

$$k_1 = \frac{J-1}{a_U-a_L} \tag{6.3-8a}$$

$$k_2 = \frac{-(J-1)a_L}{a_U-a_L} \tag{6.3-8b}$$

If the point operator $\mathcal{O}_p\{\cdot\}$ is linear,

$$v_j \approx k_1 \mathcal{O}_p\{f\} + k_2 \tag{6.3-9}$$

and

$$g \approx g_j \approx \frac{v_j - k_2}{k_1} \tag{6.3-10}$$

Thus a good approximation to the continuous processed output variable f can be obtained with the processing system of Figure 6.3-1c if the point transformation is linear. On the other hand, the approximation is generally quite poor if the point transformation is nonlinear. For example, there is usually considerable difference between the logarithm of a quantized variable r_j and the logarithm of the real number version of its code number u_j.

6.4. MONOCHROME IMAGE QUANTIZATION

In basic pulse-code modulation (PCM) transmission of monochrome images, each image sample is quantized, usually over a linear scale, and assigned a binary code group for transmission. Normally, uniform-length codes are used for each brightness level, and therefore the number of brightness levels L is chosen to satisfy the relation

$$L = 2^b \qquad (6.4\text{-}1)$$

where b represents the number of bits allowed per image sample.

A bit rate compression can be achieved for PCM by the simple expedient of restricting the number of bits assigned to each sample. If the image quality of the transmission system is to be judged by an analytic measure, then b is simply taken as the smallest value that satisfies the minimal acceptable image quality measure. For a subjective assessment, b is lowered until quantization effects become unacceptable. The eye is only capable of judging the absolute brightness of about 10 to 15 shades of gray, but it is much more sensitive to the difference in the brightness of adjacent gray shades. For a reduced number of quantization levels, the first noticeable effect is a gray scale contouring caused by a jump in the reconstructed image brightness between quantization levels in a region where the original image is slowly changing in brightness. The minimal number of quantization bits required for basic PCM coding to prevent gray scale contouring is dependent on a variety of factors including the linearity of the image display and noise effects before and after the image sensor.

Assuming that an image sensor produces an output pixel sample proportional to the image intensity, a question of concern then is: Should the image intensity itself, or some function of the image intensity, be quantized? Furthermore, should the quantization scale be linear or nonlinear? Linearity or nonlinearity of the quantization scale can be viewed as a matter of implementation. A given nonlinear quantization scale can be realized by the companding operation of Figure 6.1-3 in which a nonlinear amplification weighting of the continuous signal to be quantized is performed, followed by linear quantization, followed by an inverse weighting of the quantized amplitude. Thus consideration is limited here to linear quantization of companded pixel samples.

There have been many experimental studies to determine the number and placement of quantization levels required to minimize the effect of gray scale contouring (11–14). Goodall (11) performed some of the earliest experiments on digital television and concluded that 6 bits of intensity quantization (64 levels) were required for good quality and that 5 bits (32 levels) would suffice for a moderate amount of contouring. Other investigators have reached similar conclusions. In most studies, however, there has been some question as to the linearity and calibration of the imaging system. Most television cameras and monitors exhibit a nonlinear response to light intensity. Also, the photographic film that is often used to record the experimental results is highly nonlinear. Finally, any camera or monitor noise tends to diminish the effects of contouring.

Figures 6.4-1 and 6.4-2 contain photographs of the girl picture quantized with a variable number of quantization levels. In Figure 6.4-1 the luminance signal of the image has been uniformly quantized with from two to 64 levels (1 bit and 6 bits). Gray scale contouring in these pictures is apparent in black regions of the picture for five or fewer bits. Figure 6.4-2 presents results of a computer simulation of uniform quantization of image density. In the experiment the 8 bit, 256 quantization level image was linearly rescaled to the range $0 \le F(j, k) \le 1.0$ and logarithmically modified according to the relation

$$G(j, k) = \frac{\ln\left[1 + F(j, k)\right]}{\ln\left[2\right]} \qquad (6.4-2)$$

The logarithmically scaled image $G(j, k)$ was then uniformly quantized with a variable number of levels to produce the reconstruction $\hat{G}(j, k)$. Next, the reconstructed luminance image was created by the operation

$$\hat{F}(j, k) = \exp\{\hat{G}(j, k) \ln(2)\} - 1 \qquad (6.4-3)$$

In the displayed photographs of Figure 6.4-2 for uniform density quantization the gray scale contouring effect appears to be less noticeable than for the corresponding example of Figure 6.4-1 for uniform luminance quantization.

Chapter 19 contains a discussion of digital image coding techniques designed to suppress gray scale contouring caused by an insufficient number of quantization levels.

6.5. COLOR IMAGE QUANTIZATION

A color image may be represented by its red, green, and blue source tristimulus values or any linear or nonlinear, invertible function of the source tristimulus values. If the red, green, and blue tristimulus values are to be individually quantized, then the selection of the number and placement of quantization levels follows the same general considerations as for a monochrome image. The eye exhibits a nonlinear response to spectral

6 Bit, 64 levels

5 Bit, 32 levels

4 Bit, 16 levels

3 Bit, 8 levels

2 Bit, 4 levels

1 Bit, 2 levels

FIGURE 6.4-1. Example of uniform quantization of
image intensity.

6 Bits, 64 levels

5 Bits, 32 levels

4 Bits, 32 levels

3 Bits, 8 levels

2 Bits, 4 levels

1 Bit, 2 levels

FIGURE 6.4-2.   Example of uniform quantization of image density.

lights as well as white light, and therefore it is subjectively preferable to compand the tristimulus values before quantization. It is known, however, that the eye is most sensitive to brightness changes in the blue region of the spectrum, moderately sensitive to brightness changes in the green spectral region, and least sensitive to red changes. Thus it is possible to assign quantization levels on this basis more efficiently than simply using an equal number for each tristimulus value.

Figure 6.5-1 contains a general block diagram for a color image quantization system. A source image described by source tristimulus values R_N, G_N, B_N is converted to three components $x(1)$, $x(2)$, $x(3)$, which are then quantized. Next, the quantized components $\hat{x}(1)$, $\hat{x}(2)$, $\hat{x}(3)$ are converted back to the original color coordinate system, producing the tristimulus values $\hat{R}_N$, $\hat{G}_N$, $\hat{B}_N$. The quantizer in Figure 6.5-2 effectively partitions the color space of the color coordinates $x(1)$, $x(2)$, $x(3)$ into quantization cells and assigns a single color value to all colors within a cell. To be most efficient, the three color components $x(1)$, $x(2)$, $x(3)$ should be quantized jointly. However, implementation problems often dictate separate quantization of the color components. In such a system $x(1)$, $x(2)$, $x(3)$ are individually quantized over their maximum ranges. In effect, the physical color solid is enclosed in a rectangular solid, which is then divided into rectangular quantization cells.

If the source tristimulus values are converted to some other coordinate system for quantization, some immediate problems arise. As an example consider the quantization of the U-V-W tristimulus values. Figure 6.5-2 contains the locus of reproducible colors for the R_N-G_N-B_N source tristimulus values plotted as a cube, and the transformation of this color cube into the U-V-W coordinate system. It is seen that the R_N-G_N-B_N cube becomes a parallepiped. If the U-V-W tristimulus values are to be individually quantized over their maximum and minimum limits, then many of the quantization cells represent nonreproducible colors, and hence are wasted. It is only worthwhile to quantize colors within the parallelpiped, but this generally is a difficult operation to efficiently implement.

In the present analysis it is assumed that each color component is linearly quantized over its maximum range into $2^{b(i)}$ levels, where $b(i)$ represents the number of bits assigned to the component $x(i)$. The total number of

FIGURE 6.5-1.   Color image quantization model.

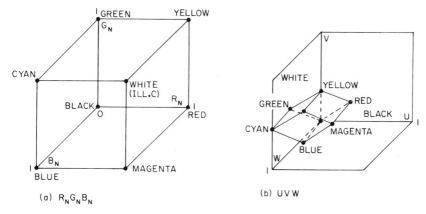

FIGURE 6.5-2. Loci of reproducible colors for $R_N G_N B_N$ and UVW coordinate systems.

bits allotted to the coding is fixed at

$$B = b(1) + b(2) + b(3) \qquad (6.5\text{-}1)$$

Let $a_U(i)$ represent the upper bound of $x(i)$ and $a_L(i)$ the lower bound. Then each quantization cell has dimension

$$q(i) = \frac{a_U(i) - a_L(i)}{2^{b(i)}} \qquad (6.5\text{-}2)$$

Any color with color component $x(i)$ within the quantization cell will be quantized to the color component value $\hat{x}(i)$. The maximum quantization error along each color coordinate axis is then

$$\varepsilon(i) = |x(i) - \hat{x}(i)| = \frac{a_U(i) - a_L(i)}{2^{b(i)+1}} \qquad (6.5\text{-}3)$$

Thus the coordinates of the quantized color become

$$\hat{x}(i) = x(i) \pm \varepsilon(i) \qquad (6.5\text{-}4)$$

subject to the conditions $a_L(i) \le \hat{x}(i) \le a_U(i)$. It should be observed that the values of $\hat{x}(i)$ will always lie within the smallest cube enclosing the color solid for the given color coordinate system. Figure 6.5-3 illustrates chromaticity shifts of various colors for quantization in the $R_N\text{-}G_N\text{-}B_N$ and $Y\text{-}u\text{-}v$ coordinate systems (15).

Jain and Pratt (15) have investigated the optimal assignment of quantization decision levels for color images in order to minimize the geodesic

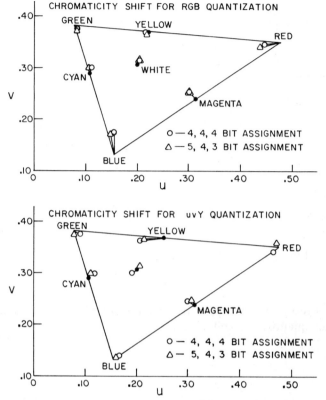

FIGURE 6.5-3. Chromaticity shifts resulting from uniform quantization of GIRL image (15).

color distance between an original color and its reconstructed representation. Interestingly enough, it was found that quantization of the R_N-G_N-B_N color coordinates provided the best results as compared to other common color coordinate systems. The primary reason was that all quantization levels were occupied in the R_N-G_N-B_N system, but many levels were unoccupied with the other systems. This consideration seemed to override the metric nonuniformity of the R_N-G_N-B_N space.

REFERENCES

1. P. F. Panter and W. Dite, "Quantization Distortion in Pulse Code Modulation with Non-uniform Spacing of Levels," *Proc. IRE*, **39**, 1, January 1951, 44–48.

2. J. Max, "Quantizing for Minimum Distortion," *IRE Trans. Inf. Theory*, **IT-6**, 1, March 1960, 7–12.

3. V. R. Algazi, "Useful Approximations to Optimum Quantization," *IEEE Trans. Commun. Tech.*, **COM-14**, 3, June 1966, 297–301.

4. R. Curry, *Estimation and Control with Quantized Measurements*, M.I.T. Press, Cambridge, Mass. 1970.

5. M. Huhns, "Optimum Quantization Restoration," University of Southern California, Image Processing Institute Report 600, September 1975.

6. J. D. Bruce, "Optimum Quantization," M.I.T. Research Laboratory of Electronics, Technical Report 429, March 1965.

7. J. J. Y. Huang and P. M. Schutheiss, "Block Quantization of Correlated Gaussian Random Variables," *IEEE Trans. Commun. Syst.*, **CS-11**, 3, September 1963, 289–296.

8. P. J. Ready and P. A. Wintz, "Multispectral Data Compression Through Transform Coding and Block Quantization," Purdue University, Laboratory for Applications of Remote Sensing, Information Note 050572, May 1972.

9. P. A. Wintz and A. J. Kurtenbach, "Waveform Error Control in PCM Telemetry," *IEEE Trans. Inf. Theory*, **IT-14**, 5, September 1968, 650–661.

10. W. K. Pratt, "Block Quantization Bit Assignment," private notes.

11. W. M. Goodall, "Television by Pulse Code Modulation," *Bell Syst. Tech. J.*, January 1951.

12. R. L. Cabrey, "Video Transmission over Telephone Cable Pairs by Pulse Code Modulation," *Proc. IRE*, **48**, 9, September 1960, 1546–1551.

13. L. H. Harper, "PCM Picture Transmission," *IEEE Spectrum*, **3**, 6, June 1966, 146.

14. F. W. Scoville and T. S. Huang, "The Subjective Effect of Spatial and Brightness Quantization in PCM Picture Transmission," *NEREM Record*, 1965, 234–235.

15. A. K. Jain and W. K. Pratt, "Color Image Quantization," National Telecommunications Conference 1972 Record, IEEE Publication No. 72 CHO 601-5-NTC, Houston, Texas, December 1972.

7 SAMPLED IMAGE QUALITY MEASURES

The objective of image coding is to code an image for storage or transmission with as few code symbols as possible, but maintain the quality of the coded image at some acceptable level. Image enhancement systems are designed to improve the visual appearance of an image. Image restoration systems seek to compensate for image degradations and to generate a reconstructed image that closely approximates an ideal image that would be produced by a degradation-free imaging system. The common factor in all three applications is image quality; to maintain, improve, or restore the quality of processed images.

There are two subdivisions of image quality: image fidelity and image intelligibility. Image fidelity characterizes the departure of a processed image from some standard image, while image intelligibility denotes the ability of man or machine to extract relevant information from an image. Most often, image fidelity is concerned with small-scale differences between a processed and a standard image; conversely, image intelligibility generally involves gross differences between the standard and processed images.

Clearly, it is desirable to formulate quantitative measures of image fidelity and intelligibility as a basis for the design and evaluation of imaging systems. Such quantitative measures would eliminate much of the present cumbersome, and often inaccurate, efforts of image rating by human observers. Also, quantitative measures could form the framework for the optimization of image processing systems.

Much progress has been made toward the development of quantitative measures of image fidelity and intelligibility. However, those measures that have been developed are not perfect; counter example images can often be generated that possess a high quality rating, but that are subjectively poor in quality, or vice versa. The key to the formulation of improved image quality measures is, no doubt, a better understanding of the human visual system.

7.1. SUBJECTIVE RATING OF IMAGE QUALITY

Presently, the most common and most reliable judgment of image quality is subjective rating by human observers (1–7). In some instances, untrained, "nonexpert" observers are utilized so that the judgment represents image quality as perceived by an average viewer. Tests are also conducted with trained "expert" observers who are experienced in processing images and allegedly better able to provide a critical judgment of image quality. Presumably, expert viewers have acquired the ability to notice small-scale image degradations that a nonexpert viewer might overlook.

There are two common types of subjective evaluation: absolute and comparative. In the former case, observers are shown an image and are asked to judge its quality according to some predefined rating scale. In some instances the observer may also be provided with a set of standard reference images that assist in a subjective calibration of quality judgment, while in other experimental situations, the observer may be forced to provide judgments based only on prior viewing experience. Comparative evaluation involves observer ranking of a set of images from best to worst in a particular group of images.

A common type of rating scale is the "overall goodness" scale, in which an image is numerically rated from unsatisfactory to excellent according to the categories in Table 7.1-1 (1). In practice, each image is viewed by an

TABLE 7.1-1. Overall goodness scale

5. Excellent
4. Good
3. Fair
2. Poor
1. Unsatisfactory

observer who assigns the numerical value of the category in which the image best fits. A variant of this scale is the "group goodness" scale of Table 7.1-2 in which an observer rates the quality of an image with respect

TABLE 7.1-2. Group goodness scale

7. Best in group
6. Well above average for this group
5. Slightly above average for this group
4. Average for this group
3. Slightly below average for this group
2. Well below average for this group
1. Worst in group

to all other images in the group under consideration (2). Another prevalent rating scale is the impairment scale, in which the observer is asked to judge the numerical level of impairment from not perceptible to extremely objectionable. The scale devised by Mertz, Fowler, and Christoper (3) is given in Table 7.1-3. Several other quality rating scales are summarized by Pearson (1).

TABLE 7.1-3. Impairment scale

1. Not perceptible
2. Just perceptible
3. Definitely perceptible, but only slight impairment to picture
4. Impairment to picture but not objectionable
5. Somewhat objectionable
6. Definitely objectionable
7. Extremely objectionable

Subjective rating results are normally presented as a mean opinion score defined as

$$\bar{C} = \frac{\sum\limits_{k=1}^{K} n_k C_k}{\sum\limits_{k=1}^{K} n_k} \tag{7.1-1}$$

where n_k is the number of images judged to be in the kth category and C_k is the numerical category value. At least 20 subjects are considered necessary to ensure statistical confidence in subjective image quality experiments. One of the difficulties with the category scaling system is the potential nonlinearity of the scale. Figure 7.1-1 shows a comparison between the overall goodness scale of Table 7.1-1, the impairment scale of Table 7.1-3, and another three-category impairment scale, as determined by subjective testing (1).

It should be emphasized that the results of subjective testing are influenced by the types of images presented to the viewer and the experimental conditions. If the images are familiar to the observer, the observer is apt to be more critical of impairments because of preconceived notions of the image structure. On the other hand, impairments may go unnoticed in nonfamiliar imagery unless actually brought to the attention of the observer. Obviously, the experimental conditions should be designed to match the viewing conditions in practice as closely as possible. Also, care must be taken in the application of subjective ratings from one set of

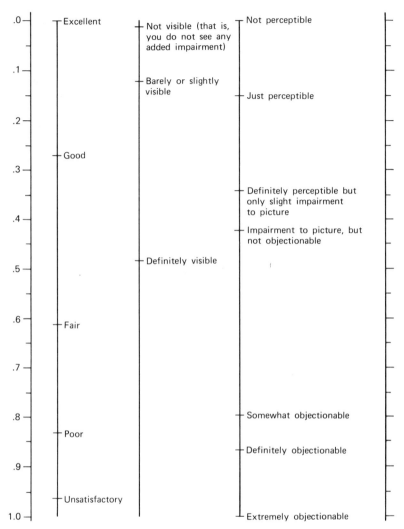

FIGURE 7.1-1. Comparison of impairment and goodness scales for subjective image evaluation (1).

viewing conditions to another. For example, an image displayed on a standard television monitor might be judged to be of "good" quality with "just perceptible" impairment. But, if the same image were viewed as a photograph recorded by a high-quality recorder, impairments that were masked by nonlinearities in the television display might suddenly become quite apparent.

7.2. WAVEFORM AND TEST PATTERN QUALITY RATING

Television systems are most commonly tested and evaluated by observing their performance when displaying images generated by electronic test waveforms or from cameras viewing test pattern charts. This approach has the advantage of simplicity, but the connection to subjective quality is usually tenuous.

For analog television transmission the effect of signal degradation in the transmission channel is often evaluated by comparing a transmitted signal and its degraded version at the receiver. Figure 7.2-1 illustrates a semiquantitative approach to this comparison (8). The test signal in Figure 7.2-1a is called a $2T$ sine-squared pulse. After passing through the channel the received signal of Figure 7.2-1b is fitted with a template scaled by a factor K. Signal degradation is then specified as a K rating.

Geometric distortion, luminance linearity, and spatial resolution can be tested by injecting appropriate electronic test signals into a television display. Figures 7.2-2a and 7.2-2b contain photographs of electronically generated dot and line grid patterns that are useful for detecting geometric distortion. Such patterns also provide an indication of color primary misregistration in a color television display. A photograph of an electronically

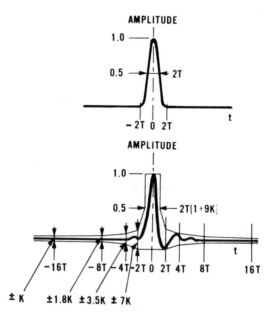

FIGURE 7.2-1. Example of K factor rating of signal degradation (8).

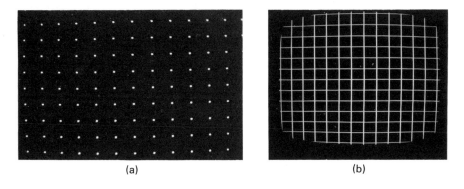

(a) (b)

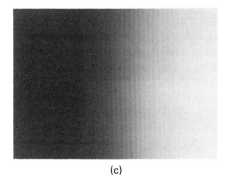

(c)

FIGURE 7.2-2. Photographs of electronically generated test patterns on a shadow mask CRT. (a) Dot pattern. (b) Line pattern. (c) Gray scale.

generated gray scale chart is shown in Figure 7.2-2c. Gray scale linearity can be checked by comparing the signal steps to the measured radiance from each bar. A standard color bar chart with bars of white, yellow, cyan, green, magenta, red, and blue has been developed for color television testing (9–11, p. 17–85). Spatial resolution response can be inferred by measuring the radiance response across a step transition.

Results obtained by waveform and test pattern testing of imaging systems are useful in measuring certain physical properties of an imaging system such as its gray scale linearity, geometric distortion, and spatial resolution. In this sense such test results are invaluable in calibration and compensating image acquisition and display devices. However, waveform and test pattern results have not proved to be adequate general indicators of image quality.

7.3. BRIGHTNESS AND COLOR METRICS

The first stage in the determination of an image fidelity measure is the development of some metric for the quantitative specification of perceptual differences in the brightness, hue, and saturation of a point source of light. There are two types of light difference measures: global and local. A global measure is valid for all light sources regardless of their perceptual attributes, while a local measure is restricted to small changes in the perceptual descriptors.

7.3.1. Brightness Metrics

Consider a white light source $[L_1]$ of luminance Y that is placed in close proximity to another white light source $[L_2]$ with an identical spectral energy distribution and luminance $Y + \Delta Y$. Contrast sensitivity measurements, as reported in Section 2.3, indicate that the Weber fraction ratio $\Delta Y/Y$ of just noticeable luminance differences is constant at a value of about 1–2% over a reasonably wide range of luminance Y. This result leads to the postulate that the incremental brightness between the sources of light should be based upon some base b logarithmic metric of the form

$$\Delta\{L_1, L_2\} = \log_b (Y + \Delta Y) - \log_b (Y) \qquad (7.3\text{-}1)$$

rather than a linear difference. Since the differential of the logarithmic luminance is

$$d[\log_b (Y)] = \lim_{\Delta Y \to 0} [\log_b (Y + \Delta Y) - \log_b (Y)] = \log_b (e)\frac{dY}{Y} \qquad (7.3\text{-}2)$$

incremental changes in the logarithm of the luminances are equal to the Weber fraction. Manos and Sakrison (2) have investigated the power-law nonlinearity given by Eq. 2.4-8 for use in a monochrome image fidelity measure. For this power law the incremental brightness metric becomes

$$\Delta\{L_1, L_2\} = (Y + \Delta Y)^\nu - (Y)^\nu \qquad (7.3\text{-}3)$$

where ν is a constant. Also, it has been suggested (12, p. 253) that the luminance response of the photoreceptors of the retina follows the nonlinearity of Eq. 2.4-7. The corresponding brightness metric would then be

$$\Delta\{L_1, L_2\} = \frac{K_1(Y + \Delta Y)}{K_2 + (Y + \Delta Y)} - \frac{K_1 Y}{K_2 + Y} \qquad (7.3\text{-}4)$$

where K_1 and K_2 are constants.

The incremental brightness metrics of Eqs. 7.3-1, 7.3-3, and 7.3-4 provide a local measure of brightness changes. Global measures are also often required for light sources separated in luminance by large percentage differences. Such measures have been developed from empirical models based on experimentation. Figure 7.3-1 contains several plots of perceptual brightness measured in terms of a lightness scale Λ as a function of luminance for an achromatic light source. The simple square-root scale proposed by Priest, Gibson, and MacNicholas (13) follows the equation

$$\Lambda = (Y)^{1/2} \qquad (7.3\text{-}5)$$

where the luminance is measured on a percentage scale ($0 \le Y \le 100$) and the lightness ranges from 0 to 10. Ladd and Pinney (14) have suggested a cube-root scale

$$\Lambda = 2.468(Y)^{1/3} - 1.636 \qquad (7.3\text{-}6)$$

for Y measured on a percentage scale. A modified logarithmic scale

$$\Lambda = 5 \log_{10}(T) + 0.25 \qquad (7.3\text{-}7)$$

has also been proposed by Foss (15). The divergence between the three curves of Figure 7.3-1 stems largely from the different levels of background illumination employed in the corresponding experiments (16, p. 453). Judd (17) has introduced a lightness scale that incorporates the background luminance level Y_B. For this scale the lightness formula is

$$\Lambda = \frac{0.1\,Y(Y_B + 100)}{Y_B + Y} \qquad (7.3\text{-}8)$$

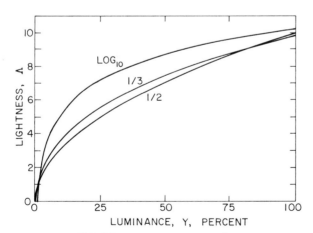

FIGURE 7.3-1. Lightness scales.

It is interesting to note that Judd's empirical scale is similar in form to the model of the nonlinear response of photoreceptors of the retina given by Eq. 2.4-7.

7.3.2. Color Metrics

A deterministic color difference measure may be obtained by considering the color solid defined by the three tristimulus values of a color to be an Euclidean space. Then a color $[C_1]$ specified by tristimulus values T_1, T_2, T_3 will be separated by an incremental distance $\Delta\{C_1, C_2\}$ from a color $[C_2]$ with tristimulus values $T_1 + \Delta T_1$, $T_2 + \Delta T_2$, $T_3 + \Delta T_3$ according to the relation

$$\Delta^2\{C_1, C_2\} = (\Delta T_1)^2 + (\Delta T_2)^2 + (\Delta T_3)^2 \qquad (7.3\text{-}9)$$

If this color difference measure is to be subjectively valid, the incremental color difference $\Delta\{C_1, C_2\}$ should correspond to equal "just noticeable color differences" (jncd) for equal shifts ΔT_1, ΔT_2, ΔT_3 in the tristimulus values for all tristimulus values. In other words the equation $\Delta^2\{C_1, C_2\} = 1$ should represent a sphere of unit radius one jncd about T_1, T_2, T_3. This is not the case when the tristimulus values correspond to red, green, and blue primaries. Subjective testing indicates that the human viewer is most sensitive to unit changes in the blue tristimulus value and least sensitive to unit changes in the green tristimulus value (18).

As a next step to correct Eq. 7.3-9 to better correspond to the results of subjective testing, one might consider the tristimulus color solid to be a Riemannian space. In a Riemannian color space the incremental color difference is defined as

$$\Delta^2\{C_1, C_2\} = \sum_{i=1}^{3} \sum_{j=1}^{3} g_{ij}(\Delta T_i)(\Delta T_j) \qquad (7.3\text{-}10)$$

where the coefficients g_{ij} are functions of T_1, T_2, T_3. Setting Eq. 7.3-10 to unity results in an ellipsoid centered at T_1, T_2, T_3. It has been found that measured just noticeable color differences can be modeled reasonably accurately as ellipsoids for the tristimulus solids of physical primaries.

In colorimetry Eq. 7.3-10 is accepted as a measure of the incremental color difference between two colors separated by distances on the order of a few jncd. For colors separated by a greater distance, one must sum the incremental color distances along the shortest path between the colors. The global color difference is then

$$d\{C_1, C_2\} = \underbrace{\sum_{i} \Delta_i\{C_1, C_2\}}_{\text{over min. path}} \qquad (7.3\text{-}11)$$

In an Euclidean space the shortest path is a straight line, but in Riemannian space, the shortest path, called the geodesic, is generally a curved line. Muth and Persels (19) and Jain (20) have developed computer programs for calculating the color difference between colors, based upon computation of color geodesics. The programs provide quite accurate color metrics, but the computations are rather lengthy.

The Riemannian metric of Eq. 7.3-10 is awkward to handle. Hence the following question naturally arises: Is it possible to map the tristimulus values T_1, T_2, T_3 into another three-dimensional space with coordinates $\tilde{T}_1$, $\tilde{T}_2$, $\tilde{T}_3$ that is Euclidean, such that the color difference measure is preserved? In the new space the incremental tristimulus values should satisfy

$$\Delta^2\{C_1, C_2\} = (\Delta \tilde{T}_1)^2 + (\Delta \tilde{T}_1)^2 + (\Delta \tilde{T}_3)^2 \qquad (7.3\text{-}12)$$

so that the loci of jncd are spheres centered about $\tilde{T}_1$, $\tilde{T}_2$, $\tilde{T}_3$. It has been shown (16, p. 513) that, in general, no linear coordinate conversion for the desired mapping exists. However, several linear coordinate conversions with approximately the desired properties have been introduced. The C.I.E. has adopted a tristimulus coordinate system, called the U-V-W system, based upon work by Judd (21) and MacAdam (22) in which the incremental perceptual distance between the chromaticities of a color is reasonably uniform. Figure 7.3-2a contains a plot of just noticeable color differences measured by MacAdam (23) that are fitted by ellipses and plotted in the x-y chromaticity diagram. When this same data is replotted in the u-v chromaticity diagram, as shown in Figure 7.3-2b, it is seen that the ellipses of Figure 7.3-2a become much more circular and tend to uniform size. However, it is apparent that there are still considerable variations in the loci of the just noticeable color differences over the u-v diagram. Farnsworth (24) has performed a nonlinear transformation, illustrated in Figure 7.3-3, of MacAdam's ellipses that has produced just noticeable color differences that are circular to within the accuracy of MacAdam's data. Unfortunately, the nonlinear transformation is a complex function of the x-y chromaticity coordinates, and not easily computed.

In the U-V-W coordinate system the incremental color distance

$$\Delta^2\{C_1, C_2\} = k_1(\Delta U)^2 + k_2(\Delta V)^2 + k_3(\Delta W)^2 \qquad (7.3\text{-}13)$$

where the k_i are constants, is not uniform; the human viewer is more sensitive to color changes of dim colors than to bright colors. In an effort to accommodate this characteristic, the C.I.E. has provisionally adopted the L-a-b and the U^*-V^*-W^* coordinate systems as standards in which chromaticity and brightness changes are expected to be uniformly

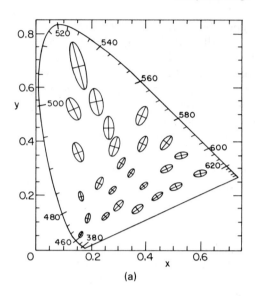

(a)

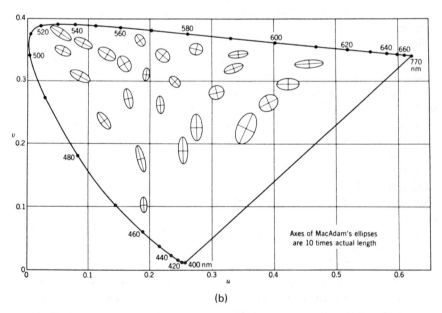

(b)

FIGURE 7.3-2. MacAdam's ellipses of just noticeable color differences in *X-Y-Z* and *U-V-W* coordinate systems (23). Axes of ellipses are 10 times actual length. (a) *x-y* chromaticity diagram. (b) *u-v* chromaticity diagram.

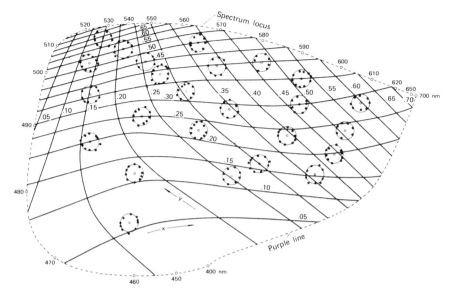

FIGURE 7.3-3. Nonlinear transformation of MacAdam's ellipses in *X-Y-Z* chromaticity diagram (24).

noticeable (25). The color difference in these coordinate systems is defined as

$$\Delta^2\{C_1, C_2\} = k_1(\Delta L)^2 + k_2(\Delta a)^2 + k_3(\Delta b)^2 \qquad (7.3\text{-}14a)$$

$$\Delta^2\{C_1, C_2\} = k_1(\Delta U^*)^2 + k_2(\Delta V^*)^2 + k_3(\Delta W^*)^2 \qquad (7.3\text{-}14b)$$

One difficulty with the U^*, V^*, W^* color difference measure is that differences in hue and saturation of a color are not distinguished. It is believed that differences in hue are much more noticeable than differences in saturation. As a result, the S, θ, W coordinate system, in which S is proportional to the saturation and θ is proportional to the hue of a color, has been developed (26, p. 152). The color difference in this coordinate system is

$$\Delta^2\{C_1, C_2\} = k_1(\Delta S)^2 + k_2(\Delta\theta)^2 + k_3(\Delta W^*)^2 \qquad (7.3\text{-}15)$$

If the saturation of a color is very small, that is, the light is nearly gray, then changes in hue are relatively unimportant. This fact has led to the definition of still another color difference measure (26, p. 152),

$$\Delta^2\{C_1, C_2\} = k_1(\Delta S)^2 + k_2\left(\frac{S_1+S_2}{2}\right)^2 (\Delta\theta)^2 + k_3(\Delta W^*)^2 \qquad (7.3\text{-}16)$$

All of the formulas presented above are ad hoc attempts to provide a subjectively uniform color difference measure. There has been relatively little testing to prove their relative worth. At present, the selection of a subjective color difference formula is still an open question.

7.4. MONOCHROME IMAGE FIDELITY

There has been much effort toward the development and assessment of quantitative measures of monochrome image fidelity (27–32). A useful measure should correlate well with subjective testing for a broad class of imagery and be reasonably calculable. It is also highly desirable that the measure be analytic so that it can be used as an objective performance function in the optimization or parametric design of image processing systems.

Quantitative measures of monochrome image fidelity may be classed as univariate or bivariate. A univariate measure is a numerical rating assigned to a single image based upon measurements of the image field, and a bivariate measure is a numerical comparison between a pair of images.

Fidelity measurements in a digital image processing system may either be made on the continuous image field that is generated from an array of discrete image samples, or by measurements of the sample array itself. The latter approach is normally preferred from the standpoint of implementation simplicity. However, if the discrete array measurement is to be subjectively meaningful, it is necessary that any degradation in the display be small, or at least predictable. In the following, fidelity measures are first defined for continuous displayed image fields. Subsequently, discrete versions of these measures are presented and related to their continuous image counterparts.

Consider a continuous image field $F(x, y)$ that is defined over a rectangular region $-L_x \leq x \leq L_x$ and $-L_y \leq y \leq L_y$. This image field is assumed to be generated by two-dimensional interpolation of an array of image samples $F(j, k)$ for $-J \leq j \leq J$ and $-K \leq k \leq K$ according to the equation

$$F(x, y) = \sum_{j=-J}^{J} \sum_{k=-K}^{K} F(j, k)R(x - j\,\Delta x, y - k\,\Delta y) \qquad (7.4\text{-}1)$$

where $R(x, y)$ is the continuous interpolation function and $\Delta x, \Delta y$ are the sample spacings.

A spatial domain, univariate fidelity rating may then be expressed in generalized form as

$$Q = \int_{-L_x}^{L_x} \int_{-L_y}^{L_y} \mathcal{O}\{F(x, y)\} \, dx \, dy \qquad (7.4\text{-}2)$$

where $\mathcal{O}\{\cdot\}$ is some operator, possibly nonlinear, possessing point and spatial properties. Fidelity measures are also often defined in the Fourier transform domain. A general form of such a univariate fidelity measure can be defined as

$$Q = \int_{-\infty}^{\infty} \int_{-\infty}^{\infty} \mathcal{O}\{\mathcal{F}(\omega_x, \omega_y)\} \, d\omega_x \, d\omega_y \qquad (7.4\text{-}3)$$

where $\mathcal{F}(\omega_x, \omega_y)$ is the continuous two-dimensional Fourier transform of $F(x, y)$. One of the simplest fidelity measures of this nature is the Strehl definition (33, p. 461) of an image

$$Q = \frac{\int_{-\infty}^{\infty} \int_{-\infty}^{\infty} \mathcal{F}(\omega_x, \omega_y) \, d\omega_x \, d\omega_y}{\int_{-\infty}^{\infty} \int_{-\infty}^{\infty} \mathcal{F}_I(\omega_x, \omega_y) \, d\omega_x \, d\omega_y} \qquad (7.4\text{-}4)$$

where $\mathcal{F}_I(\omega_x, \omega_y)$ is an ideal image field. The genesis of the Strehl definition lies in the field of optical component evaluation. As an optical image passes through the various stages of some physical optical system, its Fourier components will usually decrease in magnitude, and perhaps polarity, in comparison to the Fourier image components passed through an ideal, diffraction-limited optical system. Those components of the highest spatial frequency generally decrease by the greatest percentage amount. From the definition of the Fourier transform, stated in Eq. 1.6-6a, the Strehl definition given by Eq. 7.4-4 reduces to the ratio $F(0, 0)/F_I(0, 0)$ of the actual and ideal image fields at the image center. Thus the Strehl measure is really just a simple measure of the reduction of contrast of an actual image in comparison to some ideal image. The Strehl definition tends to correlate with subjective image quality, but testing indicates that the correlation is not always high. In fact, counterexample images have been generated that possess a low Strehl measure, yet are still highly intelligible (34).

Another classical measure of univariate image fidelity is the equivalent rectangular passband measure, defined as (35)

$$Q = \int_{-\infty}^{\infty} \int_{-\infty}^{\infty} |\mathcal{F}(\omega_x, \omega_y)|^2 \, d\omega_x \, d\omega_y \qquad (7.4\text{-}5)$$

The squaring operation of this measure gives a higher weighting to the low spatial frequency image components, which are generally of high magnitude. Again, however, the measure has not proved to be well correlated with subjective testing.

Attempts at the development of bivariate measures of image quality have met with somewhat more success. Consider a pair of image fields composed of some standard or ideal image $F(x, y)$ and a field $\hat{F}(x, y)$ that is an approximate or degraded version of the reference field. One measure of the "closeness" of the two image fields is the cross-correlation function, defined as

$$\mathcal{K} = \int_{-L_x}^{L_x} \int_{-L_y}^{L_y} F(x, y)\hat{F}(x, y)\, dx\, dy \qquad (7.4\text{-}6)$$

Usually, the cross-correlation function is normalized by the reference image energy so that the peak correlation is unity. The normalized cross-correlation measure is given by

$$\mathcal{K} = \frac{\int_{-L_x}^{L_x}\int_{-L_y}^{L_y} F(x, y)\hat{F}(x, y)\, dx\, dy}{\int_{-L_x}^{L_x}\int_{-L_y}^{L_y} [F(x, y)]^2\, dx\, dy} \qquad (7.4\text{-}7)$$

From Parseval's theorem, Eq. 1.6-16, it is found that the normalized cross correlation can also be computed in terms of the Fourier transforms of the images according to the relation

$$\mathcal{K} = \frac{\displaystyle\iint_{-\infty}^{\infty} \mathcal{F}(\omega_x, \omega_y)\hat{\mathcal{F}}^*(\omega_x, \omega_y)\, d\omega_x\, d\omega_y}{\displaystyle\iint_{-\infty}^{\infty} |\mathcal{F}(\omega_x, \omega_y)|^2\, d\omega_x\, d\omega_y} \qquad (7.4\text{-}8)$$

Since edge rendition is of importance in image perception, Andrews (36) has proposed a Laplacian correlation measure for image evaluation defined by

$$\mathcal{K} = \frac{\displaystyle\iint_{-\infty}^{\infty} (\omega_x^2 + \omega_y^2)\mathcal{F}(\omega_x, \omega_y)\hat{\mathcal{F}}^*(\omega_x, \omega_y)\, d\omega_x\, d\omega_y}{\displaystyle\iint_{-\infty}^{\infty} (\omega_x^2 + \omega_y^2)|\mathcal{F}(\omega_x, \omega_y)|^2\, d\omega_x\, d\omega_y} \qquad (7.4\text{-}9)$$

As indicated in Eq. 1.6-19, multiplication of the Fourier spectra $\mathcal{F}(\omega_x, \omega_y)$ by the quadratic frequency factor is equivalent to performing an edge sharpening Laplacian operation on the spatial domain fields $F(x, y)$ before correlation. Experiments by Andrews on low-pass and high-pass linearly filtered images demonstrate that the basic correlation measure remains quite high even when an image is severely low-pass filtered and is of subjectively poor quality, but that the Laplacian correlation measure drops off rapidly as the degree of low-pass filtering increases. Conversely, however, it is possible to generate subjectively poor quality images with severe low spatial frequency distortion that yield a relatively large Laplacian correlation measure.

Another bivariate fidelity measure is the normalized difference or error between the reference and degraded image fields, defined as

$$\mathcal{E} = \frac{\int_{-L_x}^{L_x}\int_{-L_y}^{L_y}\left|\mathcal{O}\{F(x, y)\} - \mathcal{O}\{\hat{F}(x, y)\}\right| dx\, dy}{\int_{-L_x}^{L_x}\int_{-L_y}^{L_y}\left|\mathcal{O}\{F(x, y)\}\right| dx\, dy} \tag{7.4-10}$$

The most common error measure in image processing is the normalized mean-square error, given by*

$$\mathcal{E} = \frac{\int_{-L_x}^{L_x}\int_{-L_y}^{L_y}\left[\mathcal{O}\{F(x, y)\} - \mathcal{O}\{\hat{F}(x, y)\}\right]^2 dx\, dy}{\int_{-L_x}^{L_x}\int_{-L_y}^{L_y}\left[\mathcal{O}\{F(x, y)\}\right]^2 dx\, dy} \tag{7.4-11}$$

The mean-square error expression is generally preferred to the absolute error equation because the former is analytically tractable, while the latter is difficult to manipulate. For this reason there has been great effort to determine transformations of the image field that yield a mean-square error measure that correlates well with subjective results. The most basic transformation, of course, is the linear point transformation. The power-law transformation has also received considerable attention, along with the logarithmic transformation. Spatial transformations that have been investigated include the gradient operator, the Laplacian operator, and the convolution system operation. Combinations of the point and spatial transformations mentioned above have also been considered.

Image error expressions can also be formulated in the Fourier transform domain. The normalized Fourier domain mean square is defined as

$$\mathcal{E} = \frac{\iint\limits_{-\infty}^{\infty}\left|\mathcal{O}\{\mathcal{F}(\omega_x, \omega_y)\} - \mathcal{O}\{\hat{\mathcal{F}}(\omega_x, \omega_y)\}\right|^2 d\omega_x\, d\omega_y}{\iint\limits_{-\infty}^{\infty}\left|\mathcal{O}\{\mathcal{F}(\omega_x, \omega_y)\}\right|^2 d\omega_x\, d\omega_y} \tag{7.4-12}$$

---

* Strictly speaking, the proper term is least-square error when applied to deterministic fields, but the term mean-square error is pervasive in the literature.

A special case of interest involves a linear weighting transformation of the form

$$\mathcal{O}\{\mathcal{F}(\omega_x, \omega_y)\} = \mathcal{W}(\omega_x, \omega_y)\mathcal{F}(\omega_x, \omega_y) \qquad (7.4\text{-}13)$$

where $\mathcal{W}(\omega_x, \omega_y)$ is a spatial frequency weighting function. The resulting mean-square error expression becomes

$$\mathscr{E} = \frac{\displaystyle\iint_{-\infty}^{\infty} |\mathcal{W}(\omega_x, \omega_y)|^2 |\mathcal{F}(\omega_x, \omega_y) - \hat{\mathcal{F}}(\omega_x, \omega_y)|^2 \, d\omega_x \, d\omega_y}{\displaystyle\iint_{-\infty}^{\infty} |\mathcal{W}(\omega_x, \omega_y)|^2 |\mathcal{F}(\omega_x, \omega_y)|^2 \, d\omega_x \, d\omega_y} \qquad (7.4\text{-}14)$$

It should be observed that Eq. 7.4-14 is exactly equivalent to the spatial domain mean-square error expression for a convolution system operation transformation in which the system transfer function is

$$\mathcal{H}(\omega_x, \omega_y) = |\mathcal{W}(\omega_x, \omega_y)|^2 \qquad (7.4\text{-}15)$$

Wilder (37) has performed a comprehensive evaluation of the absolute magnitude error and mean-square error measures evaluated in discrete form for power-law, logarithmic, gradient, and Laplacian transformations. The degraded pictures in the study were obtained by source coding simulations with a variety of coding algorithms. It was found that point transformations coupled with either the absolute error or mean-square error did not provide subjectively meaningful fidelity criteria. The gradient and Laplacian error measures resulted in the best correlation with subjective testing, but the correlation factor was only about 0.8, which is insufficient to be a reliable measure.

Most attempts to find worthwhile image fidelity measures have been ad hoc in nature. A measure is postulated, perhaps on the basis of some physiological evidence, but more often upon analytical and computation expediency, and then evaluated. Another branch of thought on the problem is that an image fidelity measure that is to mimic human evaluation should operate in the same "geodesic space" as does the human brain. Following this concept a preprocessing operation is performed on the image to be evaluated before invoking the fidelity measure. This operation approximates, as well as possible, the processes that actually occur in the initial stages of the human visual system. In Chapter 2 the "front end" of the human visual system was modeled as a two-dimensional linear system with impulse response $H_0(x, y)$ representing effects of the optical elements of the eye, followed by a point nonlinearity $\mathcal{O}_N\{\cdot\}$ modeling the response of the eye's photoreceptors, followed next by another two-dimensional system with impulse response $H_L(x, y)$, which represents the lateral inhibition process. For this model the total transformation becomes

$$\mathcal{O}\{F(x, y)\} = H_L(x, y) \circledast \mathcal{O}_N\{H_0(x, y) \circledast F(x, y)\} \qquad (7.4\text{-}16)$$

Mannos and Sakrison (2) have conducted an extensive series of tests to determine a valid mean-square error fidelity criterion for monochrome images based upon a model of the human visual system. The spatial frequency degradation of the optical effects of the eye was ignored, so that Eq. 7.4-16 reduced to the simpler form

$$\mathcal{O}\{F(x, y)\} = H_L(x, y) \circledast \mathcal{O}_N\{F(x, y)\} \qquad (7.4\text{-}17)$$

In the experiments a given original intensity domain image was subjected to a point nonlinearity of power-law or logarithmic form, and the resulting image field was spatially filtered with a transfer function whose parametric form is

$$\mathcal{H}_L(\omega) = \left[c + \left(\frac{\omega}{\omega_0}\right)^{k_1} \right] \exp \left\{ -\left(\frac{\omega}{\omega_0}\right)^{k_2} \right\} \qquad (7.4\text{-}18)$$

where c, k_1, k_2, and ω_0 are constants. Next, a controlled amount of distortion was introduced into the image field to simulate optimal coding at a fixed channel rate measured in terms of the average number of bits per pixel required to code the image. Following this, the degraded image field was spatially filtered by an inverse filter of the transfer function $\mathcal{H}_L(\omega)$, and then an inverse point nonlinear transformation was performed to reproduce a degraded image in the standard spatial intensity domain. All operations were performed on discrete image arrays. This procedure was repeated for several images, coding rates, and parameter variations. The subjective quality of the resultant images was then judged on an absolute seven-level group goodness scale (Table 7.1-3) and a group ranking. It was found that the highest ratings and rankings for all pictures at a fixed coding rate were obtained for a spatial transfer function as given in Figure 7.4-1. Furthermore, the one-third power law proved to be significantly better than a logarithmic nonlinearity. The experiments of Manos and Sakrison also indicate that a preprocessing operation according to Eq. 7.4-17 performed before image coding is beneficial in terms of improved coding performance. In addition their results lend credence to the validity of a mean-square fidelity measure in the geodesic space of the human visual system. Further work is needed to evaluate this fidelity measure quantitatively.

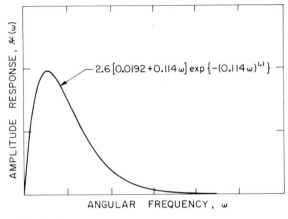

(a) Spatial frequency response

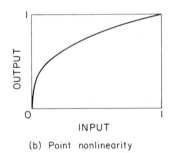

(b) Point nonlinearity

FIGURE 7.4-1. Transfer functions for $\mathcal{H}_L(w)$ and $\mathcal{O}_N\{\cdot\}$ that produced simulated coded images judged to be of best subjective quality in tests conducted by Sakrison and Mannos (2).

In a digital image processing system it is usually much more convenient to specify image fidelity in terms of the discrete samples of the image to be output for display, rather than the continuous image field that is displayed. Thus it is important to develop measures of image fidelity based on discrete image samples that correlate well with subjective testing of continuous image fields.

A straightforward approach to the development of discrete measures of image fidelity would be simply to "discretize" the appropriate continuous measures. For example, the mean-square error between samples $F(j, k)$ on a continuous reference image field $F(x, y)$ and samples $\hat{F}(j, k)$ on a continuous degraded image field $\hat{F}(x, y)$ could be defined in normalized form as

$$\mathcal{E} = \frac{\sum\limits_{j=1}^{J} \sum\limits_{k=1}^{K} [\mathcal{O}\{F(j,k)\} - \mathcal{O}\{\hat{F}(j,k)\}]^2}{\sum\limits_{j=1}^{J} \sum\limits_{k=1}^{K} [\mathcal{O}\{F(j,k)\}]^2} \tag{7.4-19}$$

It can be shown that this error measure is identical to the corresponding continuous image field error measure of Eq. 7.4-11 provided that the sampling of the two fields satisfies the Nyquist criteria. The problem in practical image processing systems is that the digital samples that generate a continuous image are not Nyquist samples of the continuous displayed image because of degradation in the display system and difficulties in generating optimal two-dimensional reconstruction waveforms. Nevertheless, expediency often dictates the use of such imprecise measures.

Table 7.4-1 lists several of the most common discrete image fidelity normalized mean-square error measures. Another common discrete image fidelity measure is the peak mean-square error defined as

$$\text{PMSE} = \frac{(1/JK) \sum\limits_{j=1}^{J} \sum\limits_{k=1}^{K} [G(j,k) - \hat{G}(j,k)]^2}{A^2} \tag{7.4-20}$$

where $G(j,k)$ is a transformed image field, as defined in Table 7.4-1, and A represents the maximum value of $G(j,k)$. The mean-square error is often expressed in decibel form as an equivalent signal-to-noise ratio

$$\text{NSNR} = -10 \log_{10} (\text{NMSE}) \tag{7.4-21a}$$

or

$$\text{PSNR} = -10 \log_{10} (\text{PMSE}) \tag{7.4-21b}$$

An important point that should be observed in dealing with spatial transformations such as the Laplacian operator or the convolution operator of Table 7.4-1 is that image arrays are of finite bounds. Thus it is necessary to limit the summation to the centermost regions of the processed arrays $G(j,k)$ and $\hat{G}(j,k)$ in order to avoid edge error effects such as the "wrap around" error that is inherent in the discrete approximation to continuous convolution. This subject is considered in detail in Chapter 11.

TABLE 7.4-1. Normalized mean-square error measures for discrete monochrome images

Mean-Square Error

$$\text{NMSE} = \frac{\sum\limits_{j=1}^{J}\sum\limits_{k=1}^{K}[F(j,k)-\hat{F}(j,k)]^2}{\sum\limits_{j=1}^{J}\sum\limits_{k=1}^{K}[F(j,k)]^2}$$

Point-Transformed Mean-Square Error

$$\text{NMSE} = \frac{\sum\limits_{j=1}^{J}\sum\limits_{k=1}^{K}[G(j,k)-\hat{G}(j,k)]^2}{\sum\limits_{j=1}^{J}\sum\limits_{k=1}^{K}[G(j,k)]^2}$$

Power Law

$$G(j,k) = [F(j,k)]^r$$

Logarithmic

$$G(j,k) = k_1 \log_b [k_2 + k_3 F(j,k)]$$

Laplacian Mean-Square Error

$$\text{NMSE} = \frac{\sum\limits_{j=2}^{J-1}\sum\limits_{k=2}^{K-1}[G(j,k)-\hat{G}(j,k)]^2}{\sum\limits_{j=2}^{J-1}\sum\limits_{k=2}^{K-1}[G(j,k)]^2}$$

where

$$G(j,k) = F(j+1,k) + F(j-1,k) + F(j,k+1) + F(j,k-1) - 4F(j,k)$$

Convolution Mean-Square Error

$$\text{NMSE} = \frac{\sum\limits_{j=1}^{J}\sum\limits_{k=1}^{K}[G(j,k)-\hat{G}(j,k)]^2}{\sum\limits_{j=1}^{J}\sum\limits_{k=1}^{K}[G(j,k)]^2}$$

where

$$G(j,k) = [F(x,y) \circledast H(x,y)]\delta(x - j\Delta x, y - k\Delta y)$$

7.5. COLOR IMAGE FIDELITY

Development of a quantitative measure of color image fidelity is much more difficult than the development of such a measure for monochrome images not only because of the increase in dimensionality, but also because of the larger number of perceptual phenomena that must be satisfied. The color fidelity measure should quantitatively measure just noticeable color differences on a point-by-point basis, and also be consistent with spatial effects such as color Mach bands and color adaptation.

In the discussion of color metrics an incremental color difference formula

$$\Delta^2\{C_1, C_2\} = \sum_{i=1}^{3} \sum_{j=1}^{3} g_{ij} \Delta T_i \Delta T_j \tag{7.5-1}$$

was developed in which ΔT_i denotes the difference in tristimulus values T_i between two colors and g_{ij} is the weighting coefficient dependent on the tristimulus values. This color difference formula can be used as the basis for a normalized mean-square error fidelity measure defined as

$$\mathscr{E} = \frac{\displaystyle\iint_{-\infty}^{\infty} \sum_{i=1}^{3} \sum_{j=1}^{3} g_{ij}[T_i(x, y) - \hat{T}_i(x, y)][T_j(x, y) - \hat{T}_j(x, y)]\, dx\, dy}{\displaystyle\iint_{-\infty}^{\infty} \sum_{i=1}^{3} \sum_{j=1}^{3} g_{ij} T_i(x, y) T_j(x, y)\, dx\, dy}$$

$$\tag{7.5-2}$$

where $T_i(x, y)$ and $\hat{T}_i(x, y)$ are the tristimulus planes of the reference and degraded images, respectively. This version of the mean-square error is cumbersome to compute because of the cross-product terms involved, and the fact that the weighting constants g_{ij} are dependent on the tristimulus values. As noted in the discussion of color metrics, no linear transformation exists for which the cross-product terms completely disappear. The nonlinear coordinate conversions to the U^*-V^*-W^* space and to the L-a-b space, as defined in Chapter 3, have been provisionally adopted as standard C.I.E. uniform luminance-chromaticity spaces. In the U^*-V^*-W^* space, for example, the mean-square error becomes

$$\mathscr{E} = \frac{\displaystyle\iint_{-\infty}^{\infty} \left(h_1[U^*(x, y) - \hat{U}^*(x, y)]^2 + h_2[V^*(x, y) - \hat{V}^*(x, y)]^2 + h_3[W^*(x, y) - \hat{W}^*(x, y)]^2 \right) dx\, dy}{\displaystyle\iint_{-\infty}^{\infty} \left(h_1[U^*(x, y)]^2 + h_2[V^*(x, y)]^2 + h_3[W^*(x, y)]^2 \right) dx\, dy} \tag{7.5-3}$$

Another approach toward the formulation of a color image mean-square error measure is to perform the measurement on transformed tristimulus value planes that are uncorrelated. The decorrelation may be accomplished by the Karhunen–Loeve expansion described in Chapter 3. For this measure the elimination of the cross-product terms is intuitively justified because the planes are statistically uncorrelated. The Karhunen–Loeve coordinate transformation depends on the covariance matrix of the original set of tristimulus planes $T_i(x, y)$, which must either be measured, estimated, or modeled for a given class of color images. The Y-I-Q coordinate system, which is the N.T.S.C. standard for color television transmission of tristimulus values, has been found to be quite similar to the Karhunen–Loeve coordinate system from the standpoint of decorrelation and energy compaction (38). For this reason the Y-I-Q mean-square error has often been used as a color image fidelity measure. Unfortunately, a common link between all of the color image fidelity measures previously defined is the lack of subjective evaluation.

A third approach to the formulation of a color image fidelity measure is to compute the mean-square error in the color geodesic space according to some model of human color vision. For the color vision model of Figure 2.5-3, the mean-square error measure becomes

$$\mathscr{E} = \frac{\displaystyle\iint_{-\infty}^{\infty} \sum_{i=1}^{3} [g_i(x, y) - \hat{g}_i(x, y)]^2 \, dx \, dy}{\displaystyle\iint_{-\infty}^{\infty} \sum_{i=1}^{3} [g_i(x, y)]^2 \, dx \, dy} \tag{7.5-4}$$

where the $g_i(x, y)$ are the geodesic signals. The geodesic signals are related to the cone signals $e_i(x, y)$ by the transformations

$$g_1(x, y) = H_1(x, y) \circledast \log [e_1(x, y)] \tag{7.5-5a}$$

$$g_2(x, y) = H_2(x, y) \circledast \log \left[\frac{e_2(x, y)}{e_1(x, y)} \right] \tag{7.5-5b}$$

$$g_3(x, y) = H_3(x, y) \circledast \log \left[\frac{e_3(x, y)}{e_1(x, y)} \right] \tag{7.5-5c}$$

Finally, variables $e_i(x, y)$ are related to the image tristimulus values, $T_i(x, y)$, by some coordinate conversion of the form

$$\mathbf{e} = \mathbf{MT} \tag{7.5-6}$$

where $\mathbf{M}$ is the 3×3 conversion matrix. Again, there has been very little testing of the geodesic error measure to determine its validity.

The continuous color image fidelity measures described previously can be extended to discrete color images following the same techniques discussed for the discretization of monochrome image fidelity measures.

7.6. ENTROPY REPRESENTATION

Subjectively, it is clear that some images are more meaningful than others in that they contain more "detail" or perhaps they yield more "data" on analysis. Detail, data, and similar terms are vague and qualitative. There is often a need to quantify the state of an image to establish performance bounds for coding, restoration, and analysis algorithms. Information theory (39–42) provides one approach to quantitative image representation and assessment.

Following the techniques outlined in Section 5.3, let the $N \times N$ image matrix $\mathbf{F}$ of quantized pixels be represented as the $Q \times 1$ $(Q = N^2)$ column vector $\mathbf{f}$ obtained by column scanning of $\mathbf{F}$. Conceptually, image vectors may be considered as the output of a digital image source that is capable of the generation of any vector state. At one extreme is the blank image of minimum luminance, at the opposite extreme is the bright image of maximum luminance, and in between are a huge set of brightness patterns. If each pixel of an $N \times N$ element image is quantized to J luminance levels, a total of $T = J^Q$ different luminance patterns could be generated by the image source. The vast majority of the T possible luminance patterns are relatively unstructured, and resemble two-dimensional fields of random noise. Only a minority of the possible patterns would ever be generated by a physical digital image sensor viewing real world scenes. Accordingly, one might consider the conceptual specification of an a priori probability of occurrence $P(\mathbf{f}_t)$, for $t = 1, 2, \ldots, T$, of each luminance state of $\mathbf{f}$. In practice, such information is not easily measured or modeled, but the concept does ultimately lead to useful results.

In 1948 Shannon (39) published the famous paper, "A Mathematical Theory of Information," which opened the door to the quantitative analysis of data sources and transmission systems. The foundations of Shannon's information theory rest on the concept of entropy. In the context of the vector image source, the average information of the source is specified by its entropy defined as

$$H(\mathbf{f}) = - \sum_{t=1}^{T} P(\mathbf{f}_t) \log_2 P(\mathbf{f}_t) \qquad (7.6\text{-}1)$$

This entropy definition utilizes a base-two logarithm and specifies an entropy measure in bits (binary digits). The source entropy is a useful measure for image coding, because by the "noiseless coding theorem" (39) of information theory it is theoretically possible to code a source of entropy $H(\mathbf{f})$ bits without distortion using $H(\mathbf{f}) + \varepsilon$ code bits, where ε is a positive infinitesimally small quantity. Conversely, it is not possible to code the source with fewer than $H(\mathbf{f})$ bits without distortion.

The probability of occurrence of the tth image vector can be expressed in terms of the joint probability distribution of pixel luminance levels as

$$P(\mathbf{f}_t) = P_R\{(\mathbf{f}(1) = r_{j_1}(1), f(2) = r_{j_2}(2), \ldots, f(Q) = r_{j_Q}(Q)\} \quad (7.6\text{-}2)$$

where $r_{j_q}(q)$ represents the jth reconstruction level at pixel location q.* Alternatively, the a priori source probability can be expanded in terms of conditional source probabilities by the chain rule. This expansion gives

$$P(\mathbf{f}) = P_R\{f(1) = r_{j_1}(1)\}P_R\{f(2) = r_{j_2}(2)|f(1)\}P_R\{f(3) = r_{j_3}(3)|f(2), f(1)\}$$

$$\cdots P_R\{f(q) = r_{j_q}(q)|f(q-1), f(q-2), \ldots, f(2), f(1)\}$$

$$\cdots P_R\{f(Q) = r_{j_Q}(Q)|f(Q-1), f(Q-2), \ldots, f(2), f(1)\} \quad (7.6\text{-}3)$$

Taking the base-two logarithm of Eq. 7.6-3 and substituting into the entropy definition of Eq. 7.6-1 gives

$$H(\mathbf{f}) = -\sum_{t=1}^{T} P(\mathbf{f}_t) \log\left[P_R\{f(1) = r_{j_1}(1)\}\right]$$

$$-\sum_{t=1}^{T} P(\mathbf{f}_t) \log\left[P_R\{f(2) = r_{j_2}(2)|f(1)\}\right] \cdots$$

$$-\sum_{t=1}^{T} P(\mathbf{f}_t) \log\left[P_R\{f(q) = r_{j_q}(q)|f(q-1), \ldots, f(1)\}\right] \cdots$$

$$(7.6\text{-}4)$$

The general term of Eq. 7.6-4, which is given the notation $H[f(q)|f(q-1), \ldots, f(1)]$, may be regarded as the average information of the pixel at vector coordinate q when complete knowledge of the luminance state of the other $q-1$ pixels of the vector $\mathbf{f}$ is known. Thus

$$H(\mathbf{f}) = \sum_{q=1}^{Q} H[f(q)|f(q-1), \ldots, f(1)] \quad (7.6\text{-}5)$$

Equation 7.6-5 is a general result that specifies the image source entropy without regard to the image data orgainzation. Consideration is now given to the evaluation of Eq. 7.6-5 for column raster-scanned images and for image sources for which all pixels are simultaneously available.

For a column-scanned image source it can be shown that

$$H[f(q)|f(q-1), \ldots, f(q-j)] \geq H[f(q)|f(q-1), \ldots, f(q-k)] \quad (7.6\text{-}6)$$

---

* The image source is assumed memoryless in the sense that the probability distribution of an image luminance pattern is independent of all past luminance patterns generated.

where $j > k$. That is, if the entropy history increases, the average information provided by the pixel $f(q)$ decreases. In Eq. 7.6-6 equality holds only if all pixels are independently distributed. The right-hand side of Eq. 7.6-6 approaches some nonzero limiting value, denoted by $H[f(q)|\infty]$, as knowledge is gained from more and more preceding pixels.

Neglecting the end of sequence effect, which is minimal for large-size images, the image entropy can be approximated by

$$H(\mathbf{f}) \approx QH[f(q)|\infty] \tag{7.6-7}$$

Thus the total image entropy is assumed to be equal to the limiting conditional entropy of a single pixel multiplied by the number of image pixels.

In a raster-scanned imaging system the limiting conditional entropy is determined for a limited sequence of previously scanned pixels. Thus for a history of k pixels,

$$H[f(q)|\infty] \approx H[f(q)|f(q-1), \ldots, f(q-k)] \tag{7.6-8}$$

In explicit form

$$H[f(q)|f(q-1), \ldots, f(q-k)]$$

$$= \sum_{j_0=0}^{J-1} \cdots \sum_{j_k=0}^{J-1} P[f(q), \ldots, f(q-k)] \log \left\{ \frac{P[f(q), \ldots, f(q-k)]}{P[f(q-1), \ldots, f(q-k)]} \right\} \tag{7.6-9}$$

where the joint probability distribution

$$P[f(q), \ldots, f(q-k)] = P_R\{f(q) = r_{j_0}(q), \ldots, f(q-k) = r_{j_k}(q-k)\} \tag{7.6-10}$$

is specified in terms of the luminance reconstruction levels r_{jq}. To compute the conditional entropy of Eq. 7.6-10, it is necessary either to model the required joint probability distributions or to measure the corresponding histograms of an image or particular class of images.

Schreiber (43) has estimated the first-, second-, and third-order entropy of several 64-level images by measuring the first-, second-, and third-order luminance histograms of a particular image with zero, one, and two pixel neighbors, respectively. The resulting histogram data were substituted for the probability distributions in Eq. 7.6-10. This measurement procedure assumes ergodicity of the image source; ensemble averages of multiple images are replaced by spatial averages. Results of Schreiber's measurements for a particular image are presented in Table 7.6-1. This image, which has been coded with a six-bit PCM code, could theoretically be coded with 4.4 bits/pixel on a pixel-by-pixel basis. If knowledge of the past pixel were utilized, the coding requirement would drop to 1.9 bits/pixel. Alternatively, the previous pixel can be considered to provide an additional 2.5 bits of information about the state of $f(q)$. Continuing on to the next pixel provides only an additional 0.4 bits of information. It appears, therefore, that in this image most of the information that is available is obtained by only a few previously scanned neighbors.

TABLE 7.6-1.   Schreiber's image entropy estimates

		Entropy
Order	Entropy Function	(bits/pixel)
First	$H[f(q)]$	4.4
Second	$H[f(q)\|f(q-1)]$	1.9
Third	$H[f(q)\|f(q-1), f(q-2)]$	1.5

The preceding discussion has presented a method of estimating the entropy of a column-scanned image by approximating the limiting conditional entropy function $H[f(q)|\infty]$ by the conditional entropy utilizing a few neighboring pixels along the column. This approach can be extended to provide an entropy estimate for an image for which all pixels are simultaneously available.

The chain rule for decimating joint probability densities can be invoked in a variety of forms. Letting $q = (Q+1)/2$ denote the center pixel of an odd length image vector $\mathbf{f}$, the joint distribution may be expressed as

$$P(\mathbf{f}) = P[f(1)]P[f(Q)|f(1)]P[f(2)|f(Q), f(1)]$$
$$\cdots P[f(q)|f(Q), f(Q-1), \ldots, f(q+1), f(q-1), \ldots, f(2), f(1)]$$
$$(7.6\text{-}11)$$

Following the same reasoning that led to Eq. 7.6-7, the entropy of the image source may be approximated as

$$H(\mathbf{f}) \approx QH[f(q)|f(Q), f(Q-1), \ldots, f(q+1), f(q-1), \ldots, f(2), f(1)]$$
$$(7.6\text{-}12)$$

This bidirectional conditional entropy expression may, in turn, be approximated by its nearest column neighbors yielding

$$H(\mathbf{f}) \approx QH[f(q)|f(q+k), \ldots, f(q+1), f(q-1), \ldots, f(q-k)]$$
$$(7.6\text{-}13)$$

Adopting this concept, the entropy estimate may be logically extended to involve those pixels of the column sequence that exhibit the greatest statistical dependence with $f(q)$. In many instances, these would likely be the nearest geometrical neighbors. Hence a reasonable entropy estimate might take the form

$$H(\mathbf{f}) \approx QH[f(q)|f(q-1), f(q+1), f(q-N), f(q+N)] \quad (7.6\text{-}14)$$

where N is the pixel raster dimension, and the entropy of $f(q)$ is conditioned on its nearest North, South, East, and West neighbors.

Preuss (44) has computed the conditional entropy of black or white facsimile documents using several previously scanned neighbors. Unfortunately, estimation of the entropy of a gray level image, even with the approximation of Eq. 7.6-14, is difficult because of excessive computational requirements. Equation 7.6-14 requires measurement of a fifth-order image histogram in which each histogram dimension is quantized to as many levels as the image luminance! The sad conclusion is that entropy calculations offer a conceptual means of assessing the structural content of an image, but practical calculations are infeasible for gray scale images.

7.7. RATE DISTORTION FUNCTION REPRESENTATION

The rate distortion function of a source provides a measure of the minimum channel capacity required to transmit the source at a given level of permissible distortion or error between the source output and destination input (45, 46). There have been some efforts (2, 47–50) to adapt the general theory to image sources in order to establish performance bounds for image coding systems. The summary of rate distortion theory applied to imagery presented in this section is based upon Davisson's review (50).

Figure 7.7-1 contains a simplified block diagram of an image transmission system. In operation the source generates a $Q \times 1$ vector sequence $\mathbf{f}$ of pixels, each of which is quantized to one of J^Q levels. The coder makes code word assignments to each pixel luminance pattern $\mathbf{f}_i$, for $i = 1, 2, \ldots, T = J^Q$. After decoding, a received luminance pattern $\hat{\mathbf{f}}_k$ is reconstructed. The coder-decoder performance may be described by a conditional probability $P[\hat{\mathbf{f}}_k|\mathbf{f}_i]$ of the pixel vector $\hat{\mathbf{f}}_k$ being reconstructed given that the pixel vector $\mathbf{f}_i$ was coded. If no coding-decoding distortion is

FIGURE 7.7-1. Block diagram for rate distortion analysis.

permitted, the input and output pixel vectors will be identical in the absence of channel errors. The conditional probability $P[\hat{\mathbf{f}}_k|\mathbf{f}_i]$ is simply a means of describing the coder-decoder operation when a controlled amount of distortion is permitted. From the conditional probability and source a priori probability, the marginal probability of a reconstructed pixel sequence is found to be

$$P(\hat{\mathbf{f}}_k) = \sum_{i=1}^{T} P(\hat{\mathbf{f}}_k|\mathbf{f}_i)P(\mathbf{f}_i) \tag{7.7-1}$$

The channel capacity requirements are specified by the mutual information function defined as

$$I_Q(\mathbf{f}, \hat{\mathbf{f}}) = \sum_{i=1}^{T} \sum_{k=1}^{T} P(\mathbf{f}_i)P(\hat{\mathbf{f}}_k|\mathbf{f}_i) \log\left[\frac{P(\hat{\mathbf{f}}_k|\mathbf{f}_i)}{P(\hat{\mathbf{f}}_k)}\right] \tag{7.7-2}$$

For error-free encoding the expression for the mutual information reduces to

$$I_Q(\mathbf{f}, \hat{\mathbf{f}}) = -\sum_{i=1}^{T} P(\mathbf{f}_i) \log[P(\mathbf{f}_i)] \equiv H(\mathbf{f}) \tag{7.7-3}$$

which is the source entropy of the pixel vector. When distortion is introduced in the coding process, the reconstructed pixel sequence f_i contains only statistical information about the state of $\hat{f}_i$. Hence the channel capacity requirement will decrease.

Let $D(\mathbf{f}, \hat{\mathbf{f}})$ represent some measure of the distortion between the source and destination. The average distortion per pixel block sequence is then defined as

$$D = \frac{1}{Q}E\{D(\mathbf{f}, \hat{\mathbf{f}})\} = \frac{1}{Q} \sum_{i=1}^{T} \sum_{k=1}^{T} D(\mathbf{f}_i, \hat{\mathbf{f}}_k)P(\mathbf{f}_i)P(\hat{\mathbf{f}}_k|\mathbf{f}_i) \tag{7.7-4}$$

and the corresponding rate distortion function for the sequence of Q pixels is*

$$R_Q(D_*) = \inf\left[\frac{1}{Q}I_Q(\mathbf{f}, \hat{\mathbf{f}})\right] \tag{7.7-5}$$

for $D < D_*$. Conceptually, $R_Q(D_*)$ is the minimum channel rate required to transmit the source information over the channel while maintaining the average distortion to some maximum limit D_*. The rate distortion function

---

* inf [·] represents the infinum of the argument.

may be determined by a minimization of the mutual information function $I_Q(\mathbf{f}, \hat{\mathbf{f}})$ for the maximum acceptable distortion D_*. The source rate distortion is then found by letting the block length increase to infinity. Hence

$$R(D_*) = \lim_{Q \to \infty} [R_Q(D_*)] \qquad (7.7\text{-}6)$$

In general, minimization of the mutual information function, with the constraint that the average distortion is limited to some acceptable value D_*, is a difficult analytical or numerical problem. Few solutions exist for practical communication channels. One solution that has been found is for the source with Gaussianly distributed symbols and a mean-square distortion measure. This solution is not directly applicable to the coding of pixel luminances because such pixel values are non-negative. Another limitation is the possible inadequacy of the mean-square distortion measure. However, the Gaussian source mean-square error solution does provide an upper bound on achievable coding performance for any source with specified second moments. Also, the solution is directly applicable to transform image coding. For these reasons characteristics of the Gaussian source mean-square error rate distortion function will be investigated further.

Consider a vector data sequence $\mathbf{f}$ of zero mean, independent, Gaussian elements of known variance σ^2. The average mean-square error is defined as

$$D(\mathbf{f}, \hat{\mathbf{f}}) = \frac{1}{Q} \sum_{q=1}^{Q} E\{[f(q) - \hat{f}(q)]^2\} \qquad (7.7\text{-}7)$$

The rate distortion function has been found to be (45)

$$R(D_*) = R_Q(D_*) = \begin{cases} \frac{1}{2} \log_2 \left(\dfrac{\sigma^2}{D_*} \right) & \sigma^2 > D_* \qquad (7.7\text{-}8a) \\[2mm] 0 & \sigma^2 \leq D_* \qquad (7.7\text{-}8b) \end{cases}$$

Thus the rate distortion function is equal to one-half the logarithm of the signal power to distortion power ratio if the ratio is greater than unity, and zero otherwise. If the elements of the Gaussian source sequence are correlated with known covariance matrix $\mathbf{K}_f$, the rate distortion function for a sequence of Q pixels becomes (50)

$$R_Q(D_*) = \frac{1}{Q} \sum_{q=1}^{Q} \frac{1}{2} \log_2 \left[\frac{\lambda(q)}{\text{MIN}\,[\lambda(q), D_{**}]} \right] \qquad (7.7\text{-}9)$$

where $\lambda(q)$ is the qth eigenvalue of $\mathbf{K}_f$ and D_{**} is chosen such that

$$D_* = \frac{1}{Q} \sum_{q=1}^{Q} \mathrm{MIN}\,[\lambda(q), D_{**}] \qquad (7.7\text{-}10)$$

A special source of common interest in image processing is the separable Markovian source whose elements possess equal variance σ^2 and possess adjacent pixel correlation factors ρ_R ahd ρ_C along rows and columns, respectively. Under the assumption of low distortion the rate distortion function for one-dimensional processing is (50)

$$R(D_*) = \tfrac{1}{2} \log_2 \left[\frac{\sigma^2(1 - \rho_R^2)}{D_*} \right] \qquad (7.7\text{-}11)$$

and for two-dimensional processing

$$R(D_*) = \tfrac{1}{2} \log_2 \left[\frac{\sigma^2(1 - \rho_R^2)(1 - \rho_C^2)}{D_*} \right] \qquad (7.7\text{-}12)$$

Figure 7.7-2 contains a plot of these rate distortion functions for various correlation factors. In Chapter 24 the performance of several image coding systems is compared to these performance bounds.

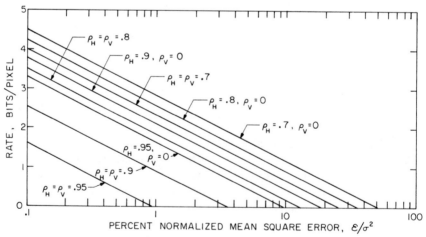

FIGURE 7.7-2.   Rate distortion functions for one- and two-dimensional coding of Markov image source.

7.8. IMAGE INTELLIGIBILITY

Quantitative determination of the intelligibility of an image in terms of its ability to convey information to an observer is a much more difficult task than measuring image fidelity. Considerations affecting image intelligibility penetrate deeply into the human visual system. The ability of a human viewer to extract information from an image is obviously dependent on physical factors of vision: the optical effects of the eye, the luminance nonlinearity of the photoreceptors, and the lateral inhibition process. However, the "processing" of visual data from the eye by the brain plays an important and perhaps dominant role in human visual perception in regard to visual information extraction. Since the mechanisms of human visual perception beyond the retina remain poorly understood, it seems hopeless, at present, to attempt to formulate an image intelligibility measure based on a perceptual model. Rather, it is necessary to resort to ad hoc measures that correlate reasonably well with subjective testing.

Most subjective testing of image intelligibility involves simple black on white targets, for example, the optometrist's chart of different size random letters. Figure 7.8-1 illustrates four test charts that have been utilized in target identification tests (51). The Landolt C-type charts (52, 53) contain rows of the letter C in one of four or eight orientations with the letters diminishing in size from row to row. The numeral chart is composed of the "curved" numerals 3, 5, 6, 8, 9 in random orientations. In the spoke chart one of six possible spoke positions is missing in each symbol. With each chart an observer is asked to identify the proper symbols, and results are recorded in terms of the measured probability of detection as a function of symbol size. Barnard (51) has made such measurements, illustrated in Figure 7.8-2, for sampled versions of the four images of Figure 7.8-1. In this set of experiments, the image transparencies were sampled, Gaussian noise was added, and the images were recorded on film transparencies. As expected, the probability of detection decreases in a reasonably monotonic manner as the symbol size decreases. Barnard has also observed that there is more variation associated with the numerals chart than in the spokes of Landolt C-type chart. Also, the detection of numerals was found to be angle sensitive. For example, a rotated numeral 3 was misnamed more often than an upright numeral 3 of the same size. Presumably, detection results with the spokes and Landolt C-type charts do not exhibit this variability because the symbols do not possess a "standard" orientation. Barnard (51) has applied the theory of matched filtering* to predict the performance of a human observer for detection of Landolt C targets. The

---

* An analysis of two-dimensional matched filters is presented in Chapter 19.

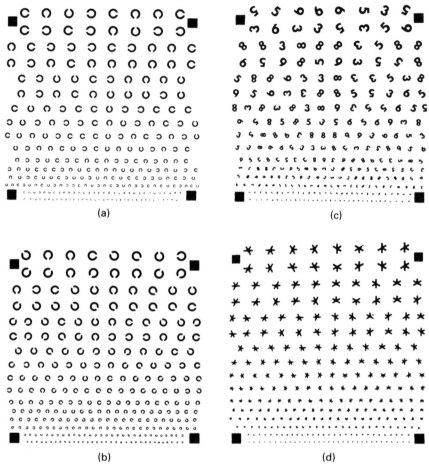

FIGURE 7.8-1. Target identification testing targets (51). (a) Landolt-C Four orientations. (b) Landolt-C Eight orientations. (c) Numerals. (d) Spokes.

probability of detection of M orthogonal signals (M target orientations) in the presence of additive Gaussian noise has been modeled as (54)

$$P = \frac{1}{\sqrt{\pi}} \int_{-\infty}^{\infty} \exp\{-z^2\} \left[\frac{1}{2} + \frac{1}{2} \operatorname{erf} \left\{ \sqrt{\frac{1}{2}\frac{S}{N}} + z \right\} \right]^{M-1} dz \qquad (7.8\text{-}1)$$

where S/N is the power signal-to-noise ratio. As indicated by the dotted lines in Figures 7.8-2b and 7.8-2c, theoretical and experimental results are in reasonably close agreement.

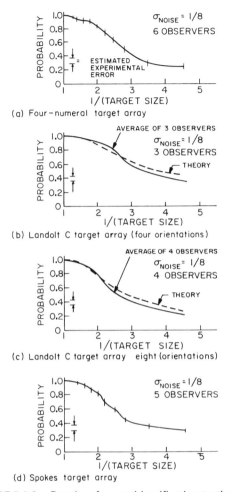

FIGURE 7.8-2. Results of target identification testing (51).

There have been some experimental studies to evaluate the legibility of scanned alphanumeric characters for facsimile transmission. Arps et al. (55) have found that the sample resolution of a character should be about one-tenth of its maximum dimension to achieve a 97.5% probability of correct recognition. Erdman and Neal (56) have investigated the legibility of words as a function of character legibility and other contextual factors.

Studies have also been undertaken to assess the performance of a human observer for gray scale imagery (57). However, research in this field is still in its infancy.

REFERENCES

1. D. E. Pearson, "Methods for Scaling Television Picture Quality," in *Picture Bandwidth Compression*, T. S. Huang and O. J. Tretiak, Eds., Gordon and Breach, New York, 1972.

2. J. L. Mannos and D. J. Sakrison, "The Effects of a Visual Fidelity Criterion on the Encoding of Images," *IEEE Trans. Inf. Theory*, **IT-20**, 4 July 1974, 525–536.

3. P. Mertz, A. D. Fowler, and H. N. Christoper, "Quality Rating of Television Images," *Proc. IRE*, **38**, 11, November 1950, 1269–1283.

4. G. L. Fredenhall and W. L. Behrend, "Picture Quality-Procedures for Evaluating Subjective Effects of Interference," *Proc. IRE*, **48**, 6, June 1960, 1030–1034.

5. C. E. Dean, "Measurements of the Subjective Effects of Interference in Television Reception," *Proc. IRE*, **48**, 6, June 1960, 1035–1050.

6. R. D. Prosser, J. W. Allnatt, and N. W. Lewis, "Quality Grading of Impaired Television Pictures," *Proc. IEE*, **111**, 3, March 1964, 491–502.

7. L. E. Weaver, "The Quality Rating of Color Television Pictures," *J. Soc. Motion Picture Television Engineers*, **77**, 6, June 1968, 610–612.

8. N. W. Lewis, "Waveform Responses of Television Links," *Proc. IEE*, **101**, part III, 1954, 258–270.

9. J. F. Fisher, "Generation of NTSC Color Signals," *Proc. IRE*, **41**, 3, March 1953, 338–343.

10. A. C. Luther, "Methods of Verifying Adherence to the NTSC Color Signal Specifications," *Proc. IRE*, **42**, 1, January 1954, 235–240.

11. D. G. Fink, Ed., *Television Engineering Handbook*, McGraw-Hill, New York, 1957.

12. T. N. Cornsweet, *Visual Perception*, Academic Press, New York, 1970.

13. I. G. Priest, K. S. Gibson, and H. J. McNicholas, "An Examination of the Munsell Color System, I. Spectral and Total Reflection and the Munsell Scale of Value," U.S. National Bureau of Standards, Technical Paper 167, 1920.

14. J. H. Ladd and J. E. Pinney, "Empirical Relationships with the Munsell Value Scale," *Proc. IRE (Correspondence)*, **43**, 9, 1955, 1137.

15. C. E. Foss, D. Nickerson, and W. C. Granville, "Analysis of the Ostwald Color System," *J. Opt. Soc. Am.*, **34**, 7, July 1944, 361–381.

16. G. W. Wyszecki and W. S. Stiles, *Color Science*, Wiley, New York, 1967.

17. D. B. Judd, "Hue, Saturation, and Lightness of Surface Colors with Chromatic Illumination," *J. Opt. Soc. Am.*, **30**, 1, January 1940, 2–32.

18. W. D. Wright, "The Sensitivity of the Eye to Small Colour Differences," *Proc. Phys. Soc. (London)*, **53**, 1941, 93.

19. E. J. Muth and C. G. Persels, "Computation of Geodesics in Color 3-Space by Dynamic Programming," *Proceedings 4th Hawaii Conference on System Sciences*, January 1971, 155–157.

20. A. K. Jain, "Color Distance and Geodesics in Color 3 Space," *J. Opt. Soc. Am.*, **62**, 11, November 1972, 1287–1290.

21. D. B. Judd, "A Maxwell Triangle Yielding Uniform Chromaticity Scales," *J. Opt. Soc. Am.*, **25**, 1, January 1935, 24–35.

22. D. L. MacAdam, "Projective Transformations of ICI Color Specifications," *J. Opt. Soc. Am.*, **27**, 9, August 1937, 294–299.

23. D. L. MacAdam, "Visual Sensitivities to Color Differences in Daylight," *J. Opt. Soc. Am.*, **32**, 5, May 1942, 247–274.

24. D. Farnsworth, "A Temporal Factor in Colour Discrimination," Visual Problems in Colour, II. National Phys. Lab. Symposium, No. 8, London, Her Majesty's Stationary Office, 1958, 429.

25. G. Wyszecki, "Proposal for a New Color-Difference Formula," *J. Opt. Soc. Am.*, **53**, 11, November 1963, 1318–1319.

26. R. W. G. Hunt, *The Reproduction of Colour*, Wiley, New York, 1967.

27. T. W. Barnard, "A Literature Survey on Image Quality Evaluation," The Perkin Elmer Corporation, Engineering Report ER-177, June 1971.

28. B. R. Frieden, "Image Evaluation by Use of the Sampling Theorem," *J. Opt. Soc. Am.*, **56**, 10, October 1966, 1355–1362.

29. E. H. Linfoot, "Quality Evaluations of Optical Systems," *Optica Acta*, **5**, 1–2, March–June 1958, 1–14.

30. E. L. O'Neill, *Introduction to Statistical Optics*, Addison-Wesley, Reading, Mass., 1963.

31. J. L. Harris, Sr., "Image Evaluation and Restoration," *J. Opt. Soc. Am.*, **56**, 5, May 1966, 569–574.

32. J. L. Harris, Sr., "Resolving Power and Decision Theory," *J. Opt. Soc. Am.*, **54**, 5, May 1964, 606–611.

33. M. Born and E. Wolf, *Principles of Optics*, 4th ed., Pergamon, New York, 1970.

34. B. Boyce, "A Summary Measure of Image Quality," Proceedings of a Symposium on Current Mathematical Problems in Image Science, Naval Postgraduate School, Monterey, California, November 1976.

35. O. H. Schade, "Modern Image Evaluation and Television," *Appl. Opt.*, **3**, 1, January 1964, 17–23.

36. H. C. Andrews, *Computer Techniques in Image Processing*, Academic Press, New York, 1970.

37. W. C. Wilder, "Subjectively Relevant Error Criteria for Pictorial Data Processing," Purdue University, School of Electrical Engineering, Report TR-EE 72–34, December 1972.

38. W. K. Pratt, "Spatial Transform Coding of Color Images," *IEEE Trans. Commun. Tech.*, **COM-19**, 6, December 1971, 980–992.

39. C. E. Shannon, *The Mathematical Theory of Communication*, University of Illinois Press, Urbana, Illinois, 1949. (Orig. Pub., *Bell Syst. Tech. J.*, 1948.)

40. N. Abramson, *Information Theory and Coding*, McGraw-Hill, New York, 1963.

41. R. B. Ash, *Information Theory and Reliable Communication*, Wiley, New York, 1968.

42. R. G. Gallagher, *Information Theory*, Wiley-Interscience, New York, 1965.

43. W. F. Schreiber, "The Measurement of Third Order Probability Distributions of Television Signals," *IRE Trans. Inf. Theory*, **IT-2**, 3, September 1956, 94–105.

44. D. Preuss, "Comparison of Two-Dimensional Facsimile Coding Schemes," *International Communications Conference*, 1975 Conference Record, Vol. 1, June 1975, 7.12–7.16.

45. T. Berger, *Rate Distortion Theory: A Mathematical Basis for Data Compression*, Prentice-Hall, Englewood Cliffs, N.J., 1971.

46. H. C. Andrews, "Bibliography on Rate Distortion Theory," *IEEE Trans. Inf. Theory (Correspondence)*, **IT-17**, March 1971, 198–199.

47. J. F. Hayes, A. Habibi, and P. A. Wintz, "Rate Distortion Function for a Gaussian Source Model of images," *IEEE Trans. Inf. Theory (Correspondence)*, **IT-16**, July 1970, 507–508.

48. D. J. Sakrison and V. R. Algazi, "Comparison of Line-by-Line and Two-Dimensional Encoding of Random Images," *IEEE Trans. Inf. Theory*, **IT-17**, July 1971, 386–398.

49. M. Tasto and P. A. Wintz, "A Bound on the Rate-Distortion Function and Application of Images," *IEEE Trans. Inf. Theory*, **IT-18**, January 1972, 150–159.

50. L. D. Davisson, "Rate Distortion Theory and Applications," *Proc. IEEE*, **60**, 7, July 1972, 800–808.

51. T. W. Barnard, "An Image Evaluation Method," *A Symposium on Sampled Images*, Perkin-Elmer Corporation, Norwalk, Connecticut, 1971.

52. E. Landolt, "Tableau d'Optotypes pour la Determination de l'Acuite Visuel," Society François d'Ophthol, 1889, 157.

53. A. Cowan, "Test Cards for Determination of Visual Acuity," *Arch. Ophthol*, **57**, 1928, 283–295.

54. M. Schwartz, W. R. Bennett, and S. Stein, *Communication Systems and Techniques*, McGraw-Hill, New York, 1966, 85.

55. R. B. Arps, et al. "Character Legibility Versus Resolution in Image Processing of Printed Matter," *IEEE Trans. Man-Machine Systems*, **MMS-10**, 3, September 1969, 66–71.

56. R. L. Erdmann and A. S. Neal, "Word Legibility as a Function of Letter Legibility with Word Size, Word Familiarity, and Resolution as Parameters," *J. Appl. Psych.*, **52**, 5, 1968, 403–409.

57. H. L. Snyder, "Image Quality and Observer Performance," in *Perception of Displayed Information*, L. M. Biberman, Ed., Plenum Press, New York, 1973.

3

DISCRETE TWO-DIMENSIONAL LINEAR PROCESSING

Part 3 of the book is concerned with a unified analysis of discrete two-dimensional linear processing operations. Generalized linear operators and pseudoinverse operators are defined. Several forms of discrete two-dimensional superposition and convolution operators are developed and related to one another. Two-dimensional transforms, such as the Fourier, Hadamard, and Karhunen–Loeve transforms, are introduced, and fast computational algorithms are discussed. Consideration is given to the utilization of two-dimensional transforms as an alternative means of achieving convolutional processing more efficiently. Finally, recursive techniques of linear image processing are explored.

8 LINEAR OPERATORS

A large class of image processing operations are linear in nature; an output image field is formed from linear combinations of pixels of an input image field. Such operations include superposition, convolution, unitary transformation, and discrete linear filtering.

8.1. GENERALIZED LINEAR OPERATOR

Consider the $N_1 \times N_2$ element input image array $F(n_1, n_2)$. A generalized linear operation on this image field results in an $M_1 \times M_2$ output image array $P(m_1, m_2)$ as defined by

$$P(m_1, m_2) = \sum_{n_1=1}^{N_1} \sum_{n_2=1}^{N_2} F(n_1, n_2)O(n_1, n_2; m_1, m_2) \qquad (8.1\text{-}1)$$

where the operator kernel $O(n_1, n_2; m_1, m_2)$ represents a weighting constant, which, in general, is a function of both input and output image coordinates.

For the analysis of linear image processing operations it is convenient to adopt the vector-space formulation developed in Chapter 5 (1). Thus let the input image array $F(n_1, n_2)$ be represented as matrix **F** or alternatively as a vector **f** obtained by column scanning **F**. Similarly, let the output image array $P(m_1, m_2)$ be represented by the matrix **P** or the column-scanned vector **p**. For notational simplicity in the subsequent discussions the input and output image arrays are assumed to be square and of dimensions $N_1 = N_2 = N$ and $M_1 = M_2 = M$, respectively. Now, let **T** denote the $M^2 \times N^2$ matrix performing a linear transformation on the $N^2 \times 1$ input image vector **f** yielding the $M^2 \times 1$ output image vector

$$\mathbf{p} = \mathbf{Tf} \qquad (8.1\text{-}2)$$

The matrix $\mathbf{T}$ may be partitioned into $M \times N$ submatrices $\mathbf{T}_{mn}$ and written as

$$\mathbf{T} = \begin{bmatrix} \mathbf{T}_{11} & \mathbf{T}_{12} & \cdots & \mathbf{T}_{1N} \\ \mathbf{T}_{21} & \mathbf{T}_{22} & \cdots & \mathbf{T}_{2N} \\ \vdots & \vdots & & \vdots \\ \mathbf{T}_{M1} & \mathbf{T}_{M2} & \cdots & \mathbf{T}_{MN} \end{bmatrix} \tag{8.1-3}$$

From Eq. 5.3-3 it is possible to relate the output image vector $\mathbf{p}$ to the input image matrix $\mathbf{F}$ by the equation

$$\mathbf{p} = \sum_{n=1}^{N} \mathbf{TN}_n \mathbf{Fv}_n \tag{8.1-4}$$

Furthermore, from Eq. 5.3-4 the output image matrix $\mathbf{P}$ is related to the input image vector $\mathbf{p}$ by

$$\mathbf{P} = \sum_{m=1}^{M} \mathbf{M}_m^T \mathbf{pu}_m^T \tag{8.1-5}$$

Combining the above yields the relation between the input and output matrices,

$$\mathbf{P} = \sum_{m=1}^{M} \sum_{n=1}^{N} (\mathbf{M}_m^T \mathbf{TN}_n) \mathbf{F}(\mathbf{v}_n \mathbf{u}_m^T) \tag{8.1-6}$$

where it is observed that the operators $\mathbf{M}_m$ and $\mathbf{N}_n$ simply extract the partition $\mathbf{T}_{mn}$ from $\mathbf{T}$. Hence

$$\mathbf{P} = \sum_{m=1}^{M} \sum_{n=1}^{N} \mathbf{T}_{mn} \mathbf{F}(\mathbf{v}_n \mathbf{u}_m^T) \tag{8.1-7}$$

If the linear transformation is separable such that $\mathbf{T}$ may be expressed in the direct product form

$$\mathbf{T} = \mathbf{T}_C \otimes \mathbf{T}_R \tag{8.1-8}$$

where $\mathbf{T}_R$ and $\mathbf{T}_C$ are row and column operators on $\mathbf{F}$, then

$$\mathbf{T}_{mn} = T_R(m, n)\mathbf{T}_C \tag{8.1-9}$$

As a consequence

$$\mathbf{P} = \mathbf{T}_C \mathbf{F} \sum_{m=1}^{M} \sum_{n=1}^{N} T_R(m, n)\mathbf{v}_n \mathbf{u}_m^T = \mathbf{T}_C \mathbf{F} \mathbf{T}_R^T \tag{8.1-10}$$

Hence the output image $\mathbf{P}$ can be produced by sequential row and column operations.

In many image processing applications the linear transformation operator $\mathbf{T}$ is highly structured and computational simplifications are possible. Special cases of interest are listed below and illustrated in Figure 8.1-1 for the case in which the input and output images are of the same dimension, $M = N$.

(a) Column processing of F:

$$\mathbf{T} = \text{diag}\,[\mathbf{T}_{C1}, \mathbf{T}_{C2}, \ldots, \mathbf{T}_{CN}] \qquad (8.1\text{-}11)$$

where $\mathbf{T}_{Cj}$ is the transformation matrix for the jth column.

(b) Identical column processing of $\mathbf{F}$:

$$\mathbf{T} = \text{diag}\,[\mathbf{T}_{C}, \mathbf{T}_{C}, \ldots, \mathbf{T}_{C}] = \mathbf{T}_{C} \otimes \mathbf{I}_{N} \qquad (8.1\text{-}12)$$

(c) Row processing of $\mathbf{F}$:

$$\mathbf{T}_{mn} = \text{diag}\,[T_{R1}(m, n), \ldots, T_{RN}(m, n)] \qquad (8.1\text{-}13)$$

where $\mathbf{T}_{Rj}$ is the transformation matrix for the jth row.

(d) Identical row processing of $\mathbf{F}$:

$$\mathbf{T}_{mn} = \text{diag}\,[T_{R}(m, n), T_{R}(m, n), \ldots; T_{R}(m, n)] \qquad (8.1\text{-}14a)$$

$$\mathbf{T} = \mathbf{I}_{N} \otimes \mathbf{T}_{R} \qquad (8.1\text{-}14b)$$

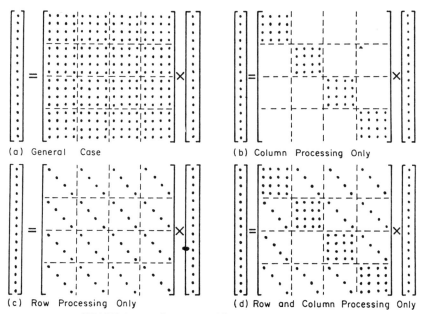

(a) General Case
(b) Column Processing Only
(c) Row Processing Only
(d) Row and Column Processing Only

FIGURE 8.1-1. Structure of linear operator matrices.

(e) Identical row and identical column processing of **F**:

$$\mathbf{T} = \mathbf{T}_C \otimes \mathbf{I}_N + \mathbf{I}_N \otimes \mathbf{T}_R \qquad (8.1\text{-}15)$$

The number of computational operations for each of these cases is tabulated in Table 8.1-1.

TABLE 8.1-1. Computation requirements for linear transform operator

Case	Operations (Multiply and Add)
General	N^4
Column processing	N^3
Row processing	N^3
Row and column processing	$2N^3 - N^2$
Separable row and column processing matrix form	$2N^3$

Equation 8.1-10 indicates that separable two-dimensional linear transforms can be computed by sequential one-dimensional row and column operations on a data array. As indicated by Table 8.1-1, a considerable savings in computations is possible for such transforms: computation by Eq. 8.1-2 in the general case requires $M^2 N^2$ operations; computation by Eq. 8.1-10, when it applies, requires only $MN^2 + M^2 N$ operations. Furthermore, **F** may be stored in a serial memory such as a disc or drum and fetched line by line, thereby obviating the requirement of storing **F** in a random-access memory that is usually more expensive than a serial memory. With this technique, however, it is necessary to transpose the result of the column transforms in order to perform the row transforms. References 2 and 3 describe algorithms for line storage matrix transposition.

8.2. STATISTICAL REPRESENTATION OF LINEAR OPERATORS

If the input image array is considered to be a sample of a random process with known first- and second-order moments, then the first- and second-order moments of the output image array can be determined for a given linear transformation. First, the mean of the output image array is

$$E\{P(m_1, m_2)\} = E\left\{ \sum_{n_1=1}^{N_1} \sum_{n_2=1}^{N_2} F(n_1, n_2)O(n_1, n_2; m_1, m_2) \right\}$$

$$(8.2\text{-}1a)$$

Since, however, the expectation operator is linear,

$$E\{P(m_1, m_2)\} = \sum_{n_1=1}^{N_1} \sum_{n_2=1}^{N_2} E\{F(n_1, n_2)\} O(n_1, n_2; m_1, m_2)$$

$$(8.2\text{-}1b)$$

The correlation function of the output image array is

$$R_P(m_1, m_2; m_3, m_4) = E\{P(m_1, m_2)P^*(m_3, m_4)\}$$

$$= E\left\{ \left[\sum_{n_1=1}^{N_1} \sum_{n_2=1}^{N_2} F(n_1, n_2)O(n_1, n_2; m_1, m_2) \sum_{n_3=1}^{N_1} \sum_{n_4=1}^{N_2} F^*(n_3, n_4) \right. \right.$$

$$\left. \left. \cdot O^*(n_3, n_4; m_3, m_4) \right] \right\}$$

$$(8.2\text{-}2a)$$

After multiplication of the series and performance of the expectation operation one obtains

$$R_P(m_1, m_2; m_3, m_4)$$

$$= \sum_{n_1=1}^{N_1} \sum_{n_2=1}^{N_2} \sum_{n_3=1}^{N_1} \sum_{n_4=1}^{N_2} R_F(n_1, n_2; n_3, n_4)O(n_1, n_2; m_1, m_2)$$

$$\cdot O^*(n_3, n_4; m_3, m_4)$$

$$(8.2\text{-}2b)$$

where $R_F(n_1, n_2; n_3, n_4)$ represents the correlation function of the input image array. In a similar manner the covariance function of the output image is found to be

$$K_P(m_1, m_2; m_3, m_4)$$

$$= \sum_{n_1=1}^{N_1} \sum_{n_2=1}^{N_2} \sum_{n_3=1}^{N_1} \sum_{n_4=1}^{N_2} K_F(n_1, n_2; n_3, n_4)O(n_1, n_2; m_1, m_2)$$

$$\cdot O^*(n_3, n_4; m_3, m_4)$$

$$(8.2\text{-}3)$$

If the input and output image arrays are expressed in vector form, the formulation of the moments of the transformed image becomes much more compact. The mean of the output vector $\mathbf{p}$ is

$$\boldsymbol{\eta}_p = E\{\mathbf{p}\} = E\{\mathbf{Tf}\} = \mathbf{T}E\{\mathbf{f}\} = \mathbf{T}\boldsymbol{\eta}_f \qquad (8.2\text{-}4)$$

and the correlation matrix of $\mathbf{p}$ is

$$\mathbf{R}_p = E\{\mathbf{pp}^{*T}\} = E\{\mathbf{Tff}^{*T}\mathbf{T}^{*T}\} = \mathbf{TR}_f\mathbf{T}^{*T} \qquad (8.2\text{-}5)$$

Finally, the covariance matrix of $\mathbf{p}$ is

$$\mathbf{K}_p = \mathbf{T}\mathbf{K}_f\mathbf{T}^{*T} \tag{8.2-6}$$

Applications of this theory to superposition and unitary transform operators are given in the following chapters.

8.3. PSEUDOINVERSE OPERATORS

A common task in linear signal processing is to "invert" the transformation equation

$$\mathbf{p} = \mathbf{T}\mathbf{f} \tag{8.3-1}$$

to obtain the value of the $Q \times 1$ input data vector $\mathbf{f}$, or some estimate $\hat{\mathbf{f}}$ of the data vector, in terms of the $P \times 1$ output vector $\mathbf{p}$. If $\mathbf{T}$ is a square matrix, obviously

$$\hat{\mathbf{f}} = (\mathbf{T})^{-1}\mathbf{p} \tag{8.3-2}$$

provided that the matrix inverse exists. If $\mathbf{T}$ is not square, a $Q \times P$ matrix pseudoinverse operator $\mathbf{T}^+$ may be used to determine a solution by the operation

$$\hat{\mathbf{f}} = \mathbf{T}^+\mathbf{p} \tag{8.3-3}$$

If a unique solution does indeed exist, the proper pseudoinverse operator will provide a perfect estimate in the sense that $\hat{\mathbf{f}} = \mathbf{f}$. That is, it will be possible to extract the vector $\mathbf{f}$ from the observation $\mathbf{p}$ without error. If multiple solutions exist, a pseudoinverse operator may be utilized to determine a minimum norm choice of solution. Finally, if there are no exact solutions, a pseudoinverse operator can provide a best approximate solution. This subject is explored further in the following sections. References 4–6 provide background and proofs of many of the following statements regarding pseudoinverse operators.

The first type of pseudoinverse operator to be introduced is the generalized inverse $\mathbf{T}^-$, which satisfies the following relations:

$$\mathbf{T}\mathbf{T}^- = (\mathbf{T}\mathbf{T}^-)^T \tag{8.3-4a}$$

$$\mathbf{T}^-\mathbf{T} = (\mathbf{T}^-\mathbf{T})^T \tag{8.3-4b}$$

$$\mathbf{T}\mathbf{T}^-\mathbf{T} = \mathbf{T} \tag{8.3-4c}$$

$$\mathbf{T}^-\mathbf{T}\mathbf{T}^- = \mathbf{T}^- \tag{8.3-4d}$$

The generalized inverse is unique, and it may be expressed explicitly under certain circumstances. If $P > Q$, the system of equations of Eq. 8.3-1 is said to be overdetermined, that is, there are more observations $\mathbf{p}$ than points $\mathbf{f}$ to be estimated. In this case if $\mathbf{T}$ is of rank Q, the generalized inverse may be expressed as

$$\mathbf{T}^- = (\mathbf{T}^T \mathbf{T})^{-1} \mathbf{T}^T \qquad (8.3\text{-}5)$$

At the other extreme, if $P < Q$, Eq. 8.3-1 is said to be underdetermined. In this case if $\mathbf{T}$ is of rank P, the generalized inverse is equal to

$$\mathbf{T}^- = \mathbf{T}^T (\mathbf{T}\mathbf{T}^T)^{-1} \qquad (8.3\text{-}6)$$

It can easily be shown that Eqs. 8.3-5 and 8.3-6 satisfy the defining relations of Eq. 8.3-4. A special case of the generalized inverse operator of computational interest occurs when $\mathbf{T}$ is direct product separable. Under this condition

$$\mathbf{T}^- = \mathbf{T}_C^- \otimes \mathbf{T}_R^- \qquad (8.3\text{-}7)$$

where $\mathbf{T}_R^-$ and $\mathbf{T}_C^-$ are the generalized inverses of the row and column linear operators.

Another type of pseudoinverse operator is the least-squares inverse $\mathbf{T}^\$$, which satisfies the defining relations

$$\mathbf{T}\mathbf{T}^\$ \mathbf{T} = \mathbf{T} \qquad (8.3\text{-}8a)$$

$$\mathbf{T}\mathbf{T}^\$ = (\mathbf{T}\mathbf{T}^\$)^T \qquad (8.3\text{-}8b)$$

Finally, a conditional inverse $\mathbf{T}^\#$ is defined by the relation

$$\mathbf{T}\mathbf{T}^\# \mathbf{T} = \mathbf{T} \qquad (8.3\text{-}9)$$

Examination of the defining relations for the three types of pseudoinverse operators reveals that the generalized inverse is also a least-squares inverse, which in turn is also a conditional inverse. Least-squares and conditional inverses exist for a given linear operator $\mathbf{T}$, however, they may not be unique. Futhermore, it is usually not possible to explicitly express these operators in closed form.

The following is a list of useful relationships for the generalized inverse operator of a $P \times Q$ matrix $\mathbf{T}$.

Generalized Inverse of Matrix Transpose

$$[\mathbf{T}^T]^- = [\mathbf{T}^-]^T \qquad (8.3\text{-}10)$$

Generalized Inverse of Generalized Inverse

$$[\mathbf{T}^-]^- = \mathbf{T} \qquad (8.3\text{-}11)$$

Rank

$$\text{rank}\,[\mathbf{T}^-] = \text{rank}\,[\mathbf{T}] \qquad (8.3\text{-}12)$$

Generalized Inverse of Matrix Product

$$[\mathbf{T}^T\mathbf{T}]^- = (\mathbf{T})^-(\mathbf{T}^T)^- \qquad (8.3\text{-}13)$$

$$[\mathbf{AB}]^- = \mathbf{B}^-\mathbf{A}^- \qquad (8.3\text{-}14)$$

where $\mathbf{A}$ is a $P \times R$ matrix of rank R, and $\mathbf{B}$ is an $R \times P$ matrix of rank R.

Generalized Inverse of Orthogonal Matrix Product

$$[\mathbf{ATB}]^- = \mathbf{B}^T\mathbf{T}^-\mathbf{A}^T \qquad (8.3\text{-}15)$$

where $\mathbf{A}$ is a $P \times P$ orthogonal matrix, and $\mathbf{B}$ is a $Q \times Q$ orthogonal matrix.

8.4. SOLUTIONS TO LINEAR SYSTEMS

The general system of linear equations specified by

$$\mathbf{p} = \mathbf{Tf} \qquad (8.4\text{-}1)$$

where $\mathbf{T}$ is a $P \times Q$ matrix may be considered to represent a system of P equations in Q unknowns. Three possibilities exist:

1. The system of equations has a unique solution $\hat{\mathbf{f}}$ for which $\mathbf{T}\hat{\mathbf{f}} = \mathbf{p}$.
2. The system of equations is satisfied by multiple solutions.
3. The system of equations does not possess an exact solution.

If the system of equations possesses at least one solution, the system is called consistent; otherwise it is inconsistent. The lack of a solution to the set of equations often occurs in physical systems in which the vector $\mathbf{p}$ represents a sequence of physical measurements of observations that are assumed to be generated by some nonobservable driving force represented by the vector $\mathbf{f}$. The matrix $\mathbf{T}$ is formed by mathematically modeling the physical system whose output is $\mathbf{p}$. For image restoration $\mathbf{f}$ often denotes an ideal image vector, $\mathbf{p}$ is a blurred image vector, and $\mathbf{T}$ models the discrete superposition effect causing the blur. Since the modeling process is subject to uncertainty, it is possible that the vector observations $\mathbf{p}$ may not correspond to any possible driving function $\mathbf{f}$. Thus, whenever Eq. 8.4-1 is stated, either explicitly or implicitly, its validity should be tested.

Consideration is now given to the existence of solutions to the set of equations $\mathbf{p} = \mathbf{Tf}$. It is clear from the formation of the set of equations that a solution will exist if and only if the vector $\mathbf{p}$ can be formed by a linear combination of the columns of $\mathbf{T}$. In this case $\mathbf{p}$ is said to be in the column space of $\mathbf{T}$. A more systematic condition for the existence of a solution is given by (4):

A solution to $\mathbf{p} = \mathbf{Tf}$ exists if and only if there is a conditional inverse $\mathbf{T}^{\#}$ of $\mathbf{T}$ for which $\mathbf{TT}^{\#}\mathbf{p} = \mathbf{p}$.

This condition simply states that the conditional inverse mapping $\mathbf{T}^{\#}$ from observation to image space, followed by the reverse mapping $\mathbf{T}$ from image to observation space, must yield the same observation vector $\mathbf{p}$ for a solution to exist. In the case of an underdetermined set of equations ($P < Q$) when $\mathbf{T}$ is of full row rank P, a solution exists; in all other cases, including the overdetermined system, the existence of a solution must be tested.

8.5. SOLUTIONS TO CONSISTENT LINEAR SYSTEMS

On establishment of the existence of a solution of the set of equations

$$\mathbf{p} = \mathbf{Tf} \qquad (8.5\text{-}1)$$

investigation should be directed toward the character of the solution: is the solution unique; are there multiple solutions; what is the form of the solution? The latter question is answered by the following fundamental theorem of linear equations (4).

If a solution to the set of equations $\mathbf{p} = \mathbf{Tf}$ exists, it is of the general form

$$\hat{\mathbf{f}} = \mathbf{T}^{\#}\mathbf{p} + (\mathbf{I} - \mathbf{T}^{\#}\mathbf{T})\mathbf{v} \qquad (8.5\text{-}2)$$

where $\mathbf{T}^{\#}$ is the conditional inverse of $\mathbf{T}$ and $\mathbf{v}$ is an arbitrary $Q \times 1$ vector.

For proof, multiply each side of Eq. 8.5-2 by $\mathbf{T}$ giving

$$\mathbf{T}\hat{\mathbf{f}} = \mathbf{TT}^{\#}\mathbf{p} + \mathbf{T}(\mathbf{I} - \mathbf{T}^{\#}\mathbf{T})\mathbf{v} \qquad (8.5\text{-}3)$$

However, from the test for the existence of a solution, $\mathbf{TT}^{\#}\mathbf{p} = \mathbf{p}$. Also, $\mathbf{T}(\mathbf{I} - \mathbf{T}^{\#}\mathbf{T}) = \mathbf{0}$ from the definition of the conditional inverse. Hence $\mathbf{T}\hat{\mathbf{f}} = \mathbf{p}$ and $\hat{\mathbf{f}}$ is a solution. Since $\mathbf{T}\hat{\mathbf{f}} = \mathbf{p}$, multiply both sides by $\mathbf{T}^{\#}$ to obtain

$$\mathbf{T}^{\#}\mathbf{T}\hat{\mathbf{f}} = \mathbf{T}^{\#}\mathbf{p} \qquad (8.5\text{-}4a)$$

or

$$\mathbf{0} = \mathbf{T}^{\#}\mathbf{p} - \mathbf{T}^{\#}\mathbf{T}\hat{\mathbf{f}} \qquad (8.5\text{-}4b)$$

Adding $\hat{\mathbf{f}}$ to both sides gives

$$\hat{\mathbf{f}} = \mathbf{T}^{\#}\mathbf{p} - \mathbf{T}^{\#}\mathbf{T}\hat{\mathbf{f}} + \hat{\mathbf{f}} = \mathbf{T}^{\#}\mathbf{p} + (\mathbf{I} - \mathbf{T}^{\#}\mathbf{T})\hat{\mathbf{f}} \qquad (8.5\text{-}5)$$

This is the form of Eq. 8.5-2 with $\hat{\mathbf{f}}$ on the right side of Eq. 8.5-5 set equal to the arbitrary vector $\mathbf{v}$.

Since the generalized inverse $\mathbf{T}^{-}$ and the least-squares inverse $\mathbf{T}^{\$}$ are also conditional inverses, the general solution may also be stated as

$$\hat{\mathbf{f}} = \mathbf{T}^{\$}\mathbf{p} + (\mathbf{I} - \mathbf{T}^{\$}\mathbf{T})\mathbf{v} \qquad (8.5\text{-}6a)$$

$$\hat{\mathbf{f}} = \mathbf{T}^{-}\mathbf{p} + (\mathbf{I} - \mathbf{T}^{-}\mathbf{T})\mathbf{v} \qquad (8.5\text{-}6b)$$

Clearly, the solution will be unique if $\mathbf{T}^{\#}\mathbf{T} = \mathbf{I}$. In all such cases $\mathbf{T}^{-}\mathbf{T} = \mathbf{I}$. By examination of the rank of $\mathbf{T}^{-}\mathbf{T}$ it is found that (4)

> If a solution to $\mathbf{p} = \mathbf{T}\mathbf{f}$ exists, the solution is unique if and only if the rank of the $P \times Q$ matrix $\mathbf{T}$ is equal to Q.

As a result, it can be immediately deduced that if a solution exists to an underdetermined set of equations, the solution is of multiple form. Furthermore, the only solution that can exist for an overdetermined set of equations is a unique solution.

If Eq. 8.5-1 is satisfied exactly, the resulting pseudoinverse estimate

$$\hat{\mathbf{f}} = \mathbf{T}^{+}\mathbf{p} = \mathbf{T}^{+}\mathbf{T}\mathbf{f} \qquad (8.5\text{-}7)$$

where $\mathbf{T}^{+}$ represents one of the pseudoinverses of $\mathbf{T}$, may not necessarily be perfect since the matrix product $\mathbf{T}^{+}\mathbf{T}$ may not equate to an identity matrix. The residual estimation error between $\mathbf{f}$ and $\hat{\mathbf{f}}$ is commonly expressed as the least-squares difference of the vectors written as

$$\mathscr{E}_E = (\mathbf{f} - \hat{\mathbf{f}})^{T}(\mathbf{f} - \hat{\mathbf{f}}) \qquad (8.5\text{-}8a)$$

or equivalently

$$\mathscr{E}_E = \text{tr}\left\{(\mathbf{f} - \hat{\mathbf{f}})(\mathbf{f} - \hat{\mathbf{f}})^{T}\right\} \qquad (8.5\text{-}8b)$$

Substitution of Eq. 8.5-7 into Eq. 8.5-8a yields

$$\mathscr{E}_E = \mathbf{f}^{T}[\mathbf{I} - (\mathbf{T}^{+}\mathbf{T})^{T}][\mathbf{I} - (\mathbf{T}^{+}\mathbf{T})]\mathbf{f} \qquad (8.5\text{-}9)$$

The choice of $\mathbf{T}^{+}$ that minimizes the estimation error of Eq. 8.5-8 can be determined by setting the derivative of $\mathscr{E}_E$, with respect to $\mathbf{f}$, to zero. From Eq. 5.1-34

$$\frac{\partial \mathscr{E}_E}{\partial \mathbf{f}} = \mathbf{0} = 2[\mathbf{I} - (\mathbf{T}^{+}\mathbf{T})^{T}][\mathbf{I} - (\mathbf{T}^{+}\mathbf{T})]\mathbf{f} \qquad (8.5\text{-}10)$$

Equation 8.5-10 is satisfied if $(\mathbf{T}^{+} = \mathbf{T}^{-})$ is the generalized inverse of $\mathbf{T}$.

Under this condition the residual least-squares estimation error reduces to

$$\mathscr{E}_E = \mathbf{f}^T[\mathbf{I} - (\mathbf{T}^-\mathbf{T})]\mathbf{f} \qquad (8.5\text{-}11\text{a})$$

or

$$\mathscr{E}_E = \text{tr}\,\{\mathbf{f}\mathbf{f}^T[\mathbf{I} - \mathbf{T}^-\mathbf{T}]\} \qquad (8.5\text{-}11\text{b})$$

The estimation error becomes zero, as expected, if $\mathbf{T}^-\mathbf{T} = \mathbf{I}$. This will occur, for example, if $\mathbf{T}^-$ is a rank-Q generalized inverse as defined in Eq. 8.3-5.

8.6. APPROXIMATE SOLUTIONS TO INCONSISTENT LINEAR SYSTEMS

Inconsistency of the system of equations $\mathbf{p} = \mathbf{T}\mathbf{f}$ means simply that the set of equations does not form an equality for any potential estimate $\mathbf{f} = \hat{\mathbf{f}}$. In such cases the system of equations can be reformulated as

$$\mathbf{p} = \mathbf{T}\mathbf{f} + \mathbf{e}(\mathbf{f}) \qquad (8.6\text{-}1)$$

where $\mathbf{e}(\mathbf{f})$ is an error vector dependent on $\mathbf{f}$. Now, consideration turns toward the determination of an estimate $\hat{\mathbf{f}}$ that minimizes the least-squares modeling error expressed in the equivalent forms

$$\mathscr{E}_M = [\mathbf{e}(\hat{\mathbf{f}})]^T[\mathbf{e}(\hat{\mathbf{f}})] = [\mathbf{p} - \mathbf{T}\hat{\mathbf{f}}]^T[\mathbf{p} - \mathbf{T}\hat{\mathbf{f}}] \qquad (8.6\text{-}2\text{a})$$

$$\mathscr{E}_M = \text{tr}\,\{[\mathbf{e}(\hat{\mathbf{f}})][\mathbf{e}(\hat{\mathbf{f}})]^T\} = \text{tr}\,\{[\mathbf{p} - \mathbf{T}\hat{\mathbf{f}}][\mathbf{p} - \mathbf{T}\hat{\mathbf{f}}]^T\} \qquad (8.6\text{-}2\text{b})$$

Let the matrix $\mathbf{T}^+$ denote the pseudoinverse that gives the estimate

$$\hat{\mathbf{f}} = \mathbf{T}^+\mathbf{p} \qquad (8.6\text{-}3)$$

Then, adding and subtracting the quantity $\mathbf{T}\mathbf{T}^+\mathbf{p}$ inside the brackets of Eq. 8.6-2a yields

$$\mathscr{E}_M = [(\mathbf{I} - \mathbf{T}\mathbf{T}^+)\mathbf{p} + \mathbf{T}(\mathbf{T}^+\mathbf{p} - \hat{\mathbf{f}})]^T[(\mathbf{I} - \mathbf{T}\mathbf{T}^+)\mathbf{p} + \mathbf{T}(\mathbf{T}^+\mathbf{p} - \hat{\mathbf{f}})] \quad (8.6\text{-}4)$$

Expansion then gives

$$\mathscr{E}_M = [(\mathbf{I} - \mathbf{T}\mathbf{T}^+)\mathbf{p}]^T[(\mathbf{I} - \mathbf{T}\mathbf{T}^+)\mathbf{p}] + [\mathbf{T}(\mathbf{T}^+\mathbf{p} - \hat{\mathbf{f}})]^T[\mathbf{T}(\mathbf{T}^+\mathbf{p} - \hat{\mathbf{f}})]$$
$$+ [(\mathbf{I} - \mathbf{T}\mathbf{T}^+)\mathbf{p}]^T[\mathbf{T}(\mathbf{T}^+\mathbf{p} - \hat{\mathbf{f}})] + [\mathbf{T}(\mathbf{T}^+\mathbf{p} - \hat{\mathbf{f}})]^T[(\mathbf{I} - \mathbf{T}\mathbf{T}^+)\mathbf{p}]$$
$$(8.6\text{-}5)$$

The two cross-product terms will equal zero if $\mathbf{T}\mathbf{T}^+\mathbf{T} = \mathbf{T}$ and $(\mathbf{T}\mathbf{T}^+) = (\mathbf{T}\mathbf{T}^+)^T$. These are the defining conditions for $\mathbf{T}^+$ to be a least-squares inverse of $\mathbf{T}$ $(\mathbf{T}^+ = \mathbf{T}^\$)$. Under these circumstances the residual error becomes equal to the sum of two positive terms

$$\mathscr{E}_M = [(\mathbf{I} - \mathbf{T}\mathbf{T}^\$)\mathbf{p}]^T [(\mathbf{I} - \mathbf{T}\mathbf{T}^\$)\mathbf{p}] + [\mathbf{T}(\mathbf{T}^\$\mathbf{p} - \hat{\mathbf{f}})]^T [\mathbf{T}(\mathbf{T}^\$\mathbf{p} - \hat{\mathbf{f}})]$$

(8.6-6)

The second term of Eq. 8.6-6 goes to zero when $\hat{\mathbf{f}}$ equals the least-squares pseudoinverse estimate $(\hat{\mathbf{f}} = \mathbf{T}^\$\mathbf{p})$ and the residual error reduces to

$$\mathscr{E}_M = \mathbf{p}^T [\mathbf{I} - \mathbf{T}\mathbf{T}^\$]\mathbf{p}$$

(8.6-7a)

or equivalently

$$\mathscr{E}_M = \mathrm{tr}\,[\mathbf{p}\mathbf{p}^T (\mathbf{I} - \mathbf{T}\mathbf{T}^\$)]$$

(8.6-7b)

If $\mathbf{T}\mathbf{T}^\$ = \mathbf{I}$ the residual error goes to zero as expected.

The least-squares pseudoinverse solution is not necessarily unique. If the pseudoinverse is further restricted such that $\mathbf{T}^+\mathbf{T}\mathbf{T}^+ = \mathbf{T}$ and $\mathbf{T}^+\mathbf{T} = (\mathbf{T}^+\mathbf{T})^T$ so that $\mathbf{T}^+$ is a generalized inverse $(\mathbf{T}^+ = \mathbf{T}^-)$, then it can be shown that the generalized inverse estimate $(\hat{\mathbf{f}} = \mathbf{T}^-\mathbf{g})$ is a minimum norm solution in the sense that

$$\hat{\mathbf{f}}^T\hat{\mathbf{f}} \le \tilde{\mathbf{f}}^T\tilde{\mathbf{f}}$$

(8.6-8)

for any least-squares estimate $\tilde{\mathbf{f}}$. That is, the sum of the squares of the elements of the estimate is a minimum for all possible least-squares estimates. If $\mathbf{T}^-$ is a rank-Q generalized inverse, as defined in Eq. 8.3-5, $\mathbf{T}\mathbf{T}^-$ is not necessarily an identity matrix, and the least-squares modeling error can be evaluated by Eq. 8.6-7. In the case for which $\mathbf{T}^-$ is a rank-P generalized inverse, as defined in Eq. 8.3-6, $\mathbf{T}\mathbf{T}^- = \mathbf{I}$, and the least-squares modeling error is zero.

Several applications of this theory to image restoration, analysis, and coding are presented in subsequent chapters.

REFERENCES

1. W. K. Pratt, "Vector Formulation of Two Dimensional Signal Processing Operations," *J. Computer Graphics and Image Processing*, **4**, 1, March 1975, 1–24, Academic Press, New York.
2. J. O. Eklundh, "A Fast Computer Method for Matrix Transposing," *IEEE Trans. Computers*, **C-21**, 7, July 1972, 801–803.
3. R. E. Twogood and M. P. Ekstrom, "An Extension of Eklundh's Matrix Transposition Algorithm and Its Applications in Digital Image Processing," *IEEE Trans. Computers*, **C-25**, 9, September 1976, 950–952.

4. F. A. Graybill, *Introduction to Matrices with Applications in Statistics*, Wadsworth, Belmont, Cal., 1969.

5. C. R. Rao and S. K. Mitra, *Generalized Inverse of Matrices and Its Applications*, Wiley, New York, 1971.

6. A. Albert, *Regression and the Moore–Penrose Pseudoinverse*, Academic Press, New York, 1972.

9 SUPERPOSITION OPERATOR

The discrete two-dimensional superposition operator has been defined in the literature in two basic ways: as a discrete linear filtering process to be performed on a data array, and as a discrete model of a continuous filtering process. The two definitions are usually not equivalent. Both definitions are considered in the following. A discrete circulant area superposition operator is also defined, and relations are given between the three operators.

9.1. FINITE AREA SUPERPOSITION OPERATOR

Consider first the discrete superposition of a spatially truncated data array* $F(n_1, n_2)$ for $n_1, n_2 = 1, 2, \ldots, N$ with a spatially truncated impulse response operator $H(l_1, l_2; m_1, m_2)$ for $l_1, l_2 = 1, 2, \ldots, L$. In the general case the impulse response array changes form for each point (m_1, m_2) in the processed array Q. The finite area superposition operation is defined as

$$Q(m_1, m_2) = \sum_{n_1=1}^{m_1} \sum_{n_2=1}^{m_2} F(n_1, n_2) H(m_1 - n_1 + 1, m_2 - n_2 + 1; m_1, m_2)$$

(9.1-1)

for $m_1, m_2 = 1, 2, \ldots, M$, where H and F are assumed to be zero outside their range of indices. Examination of the indices of the impulse response array at its extremal positions indicates that $M = N + L - 1$, and hence the processed array Q is of larger dimension than the data array F. Figure 9.1-1 illustrates the geometry of finite area superposition.

If the arrays F and Q are represented in vector form by the $N^2 \times 1$ vector $\mathbf{f}$ and the $M^2 \times 1$ vector $\mathbf{q}$, respectively, then the finite area superposition operation can be written as (1)

$$\mathbf{q} = \mathbf{Df}$$

(9.1-2)

where $\mathbf{D}$ is an $M^2 \times N^2$ matrix containing the elements of the impulse response. It is convenient to partition the superposition operator matrix $\mathbf{D}$

---

* For notational simplicity all data arrays are assumed square.

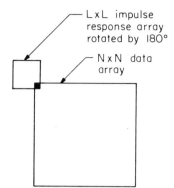

L x L impulse
response array
rotated by 180°

N x N data
array

FIGURE 9.1-1. Relationships between input data array and impulse response array for finite area superposition.

into submatrices of dimension $M \times N$. Observing the summation limits of Eq. 9.1-1, it is seen that

$$
\mathbf{D} =
\begin{bmatrix}
\mathbf{D}_{1,1} & 0 & & & 0 \\
\mathbf{D}_{2,1} & \mathbf{D}_{2,2} & & & \vdots \\
\vdots & \vdots & \ddots & & 0 \\
\mathbf{D}_{L,1} & \mathbf{D}_{L,2} & & \mathbf{D}_{M-L+1,N} & \\
0 & \mathbf{D}_{L+1,2} & & & \vdots \\
0 & 0 & & & \vdots \\
\vdots & \vdots & & & \vdots \\
0 & 0 & \cdots & 0 & \mathbf{D}_{M,N}
\end{bmatrix}
\tag{9.1-3}
$$

The general nonzero term of $\mathbf{D}$ is then given by

$$
D_{m_2,n_2}(m_1, n_1) = H(m_1 - n_1 + 1, m_2 - n_2 + 1; m_1, m_2) \tag{9.1-4}
$$

where $1 \le n_i \le N$ and $n_i \le m_i \le n_i + L - 1$. Thus it is observed that $\mathbf{D}$ is highly structured and quite sparse, with the center band of submatrices containing stripes of zero elements.

If the impulse response is position invariant, then the structure of $\mathbf{D}$ does not explicitly depend on the output array coordinate (m_1, m_2). Also

$$
\mathbf{D}_{m_2,n_2} = \mathbf{D}_{m_2+1,n_2+1} \tag{9.1-5}
$$

As a result, the columns of $\mathbf{D}$ are shifted versions of the first column.

Under these conditions the finite area superposition operator is known as the finite area convolution operator. Figure 9.1-2a contains a computer printout of the finite area convolution operator for a 2×2 ($N = 2$) data array, a 4×4 ($M = 4$) filtered data array, and a 3×3 ($L = 3$) impulse response array. The integer pairs (i, j) at each element of $\mathbf{D}$ represent the element (i, j) of $H(i, j)$. The basic structure of $\mathbf{D}$ can be seen more clearly in the larger size matrix depicted in the photograph of Figure 9.1-2b. In this example $M = 16$, $N = 8$, $L = 9$, and the impulse response has a symmetrical Gaussian shape. Note that $\mathbf{D}$ is a 256×64 matrix in this example.

Following the same technique leading to Eq. 8.1-7, the matrix form of the superposition operation may be written as

$$\mathbf{Q} = \sum_{m=1}^{M} \sum_{n=1}^{N} \mathbf{D}_{m,n} \mathbf{F} \mathbf{v}_n \mathbf{u}_m^T \tag{9.1-6}$$

If the impulse response is spatially invariant and is of separable form such that

$$\mathbf{H} = \mathbf{h}_C \mathbf{h}_R^T \tag{9.1-7}$$

where $\mathbf{h}_R$ and $\mathbf{h}_C$ are column vectors representing row and column impulse responses, respectively, then

$$\mathbf{D} = \mathbf{D}_C \otimes \mathbf{D}_R \tag{9.1-8}$$

$$H = \begin{bmatrix} 11 & 12 & 13 \\ 21 & 22 & 23 \\ 31 & 32 & 33 \end{bmatrix} \qquad D = \left[\begin{array}{cc|cc} 11 & 0 & 0 & 0 \\ 21 & 11 & 0 & 0 \\ 31 & 21 & 0 & 0 \\ 0 & 31 & 0 & 0 \\ \hline 12 & 0 & 11 & 0 \\ 22 & 12 & 21 & 11 \\ 32 & 22 & 31 & 21 \\ 0 & 32 & 0 & 31 \\ \hline 13 & 0 & 12 & 0 \\ 23 & 13 & 22 & 12 \\ 33 & 23 & 32 & 22 \\ 0 & 33 & 0 & 32 \\ \hline 0 & 0 & 13 & 0 \\ 0 & 0 & 23 & 13 \\ 0 & 0 & 33 & 23 \\ 0 & 0 & 0 & 33 \end{array} \right]$$

(a)   (b)

FIGURE 9.1-2. Examples of finite area convolution operators. (a) General impulse array $M = 4$, $N = 2$, $L = 3$. (b) Gaussian-shaped impulse array $M = 16$, $N = 8$, $L = 9$.

The matrices $\mathbf{D}_R$ and $\mathbf{D}_C$ are $M \times N$ matrices of the form

$$\mathbf{D}_R = \begin{bmatrix} h_R(1) & 0 & \cdots & 0 \\ h_R(2) & h_R(1) & & \vdots \\ h_R(3) & h_R(2) & & 0 \\ & & h_R(1) & \\ \vdots & & & \vdots \\ h_R(L) & & & \\ 0 & & & \vdots \\ \vdots & & & \vdots \\ 0 & \cdots & 0 & h_R(L) \end{bmatrix} \qquad (9.1\text{-}9)$$

The two-dimensional convolution operation may then be computed by sequential row and column one-dimensional convolutions. Thus

$$\mathbf{Q} = \mathbf{D}_C \mathbf{F} \mathbf{D}_R^T \qquad (9.1\text{-}10)$$

In vector form the finite area superposition or convolution operator requires $N^2 L^2$ operations if the zero multiplications of $\mathbf{D}$ are avoided. The separable operator of Eq. 9.1-10 can be computed with only $NL(M + N)$ operations.

9.2. SAMPLED INFINITE AREA SUPERPOSITION OPERATOR

Many applications in image processing require a discretization of the superposition integral relating the input and output continuous fields of a linear system. For example, image blurring by an optical system, sampling with a finite area aperture, or imaging through atmospheric turbulence, may be modeled by the superposition integral equation

$$\tilde{G}(x, y) = \int\int_{-\infty}^{\infty} \tilde{F}(\alpha, \beta) \tilde{J}(x, y; \alpha, \beta)\, d\alpha\, d\beta \qquad (9.2\text{-}1a)$$

where $\tilde{F}(x, y)$ and $\tilde{G}(x, y)$ denote the input and output fields of a linear system, respectively, and the kernel $\tilde{J}(x, y; \alpha, \beta)$ represents the impulse response of the linear system model.* In this formulation the impulse

* In this chapter the tilde sign ($\tilde{}$) over a variable indicates that the spatial indices of the variable are bipolar, that is, range from negative to positive spatial limits.

response may change form as a function of its four indices: the input and output coordinates. If the linear system is space invariant, then the output image field may be described by the convolution integral

$$\tilde{G}(x, y) = \int\int\limits_{-\infty}^{\infty} \tilde{F}(\alpha, \beta)\tilde{J}(x - \alpha, y - \beta)\, d\alpha\, d\beta \qquad (9.2\text{-}1b)$$

For discrete processing, physical image sampling will be performed on the output image field. Numerical representation of the integral must also be performed in order to relate the physical samples of the output field to points on the input field.

Numerical representation of a superposition or convolution integral is an important topic because improper representations may lead to gross modeling errors or numerical instability in an image processing application. Also, the selection of a numerical representation algorithm usually has a significant impact on digital processing requirements.

As a first step in the discretization of the superposition integral, the output image field is physically sampled by a finite $(2J + 1) \times (2J + 1)$ array of Dirac pulses at a resolution ΔS to obtain an array whose general term is[*]

$$\tilde{G}(j_1\,\Delta S, j_2\,\Delta S) = \tilde{G}(x, y)\delta(x - j_1\,\Delta S, y - j_2\,\Delta S) \qquad (9.2\text{-}2)$$

where $-J \leq j_i \leq J$. The delta function may be brought under the integral sign of the superposition integral of Eq. 9.2-1a to give

$$\tilde{G}(j_1\,\Delta S, j_2\,\Delta S) = \int\int\limits_{-\infty}^{\infty} \tilde{F}(\alpha, \beta)\tilde{J}(j_1\,\Delta S, j_2\,\Delta S; \alpha, \beta)\, d\alpha\, d\beta \qquad (9.2\text{-}3)$$

It should be noted that the physical sampling is performed on the observed image spatial variables (x, y); physical sampling does not affect the dummy variables of integration (α, β).

Next, the impulse response must be truncated to some spatial bounds. Thus let

$$\tilde{J}(x, y; \alpha, \beta) = 0 \qquad (9.2\text{-}4)$$

---

[*] Equal horizontal and vertical spacing of sample pulses is assumed for notational simplicity. The effect of finite area sample pulses can be easily incorporated by replacing the impulse response with $\tilde{J}(x, y; \alpha, \beta) \circledast P(-x, -y)$ where $P(x, y)$ represents the pulse shape of the sampling pulse.

for $|x| > T$ and $|y| > T$. Then

$$\tilde{G}(j_1 \, \Delta S, j_2 \, \Delta S) = \int_{j_1 \Delta S - T}^{j_1 \Delta S + T} \int_{j_2 \Delta S - T}^{j_2 \Delta S + T} \tilde{F}(\alpha, \beta) \tilde{J}(j_1 \, \Delta S, j_2 \, \Delta S; \alpha, \beta) \, d\alpha \, d\beta$$

(9.2-5)

It should be observed that truncation of the impulse response is equivalent to multiplying the impulse response by a window function $V(x, y)$ which is unity for $|x| < T$ and $|y| < T$ and zero elsewhere. By the Fourier convolution theorem, the Fourier spectrum of $G(x, y)$ is equivalently convolved with the Fourier transform of $V(x, y)$, which is a two-dimensional sinc function. This distortion of the Fourier spectrum of $G(x, y)$ results in the introduction of high spatial frequency artifacts (a Gibbs phenomenon) at spatial frequency multiples of $2\pi/T$. Truncation distortion can be reduced by using a shaped window, such as the Bartlett, Blackman, Hamming, or Hanning windows (3), which smooth the sharp cutoff effects of a rectangular window. This step is especially important for image restoration modeling because ill-conditioning of the superposition operator may lead to severe amplification of the truncation artifacts.

In the next step of the discrete representation, the continuous ideal image array $\tilde{F}(\alpha, \beta)$ is represented by mesh points on a rectangular grid of resolution ΔI and dimension $(2K + 1) \times (2K + 1)$. This is not a physical sampling process, but merely an abstract numerical representation whose general term is described by

$$\tilde{F}(k_1 \, \Delta I, k_2 \, \Delta I) = \tilde{F}(\alpha, \beta) \delta(\alpha - k_1 \, \Delta I, \beta - k_2 \, \Delta I)$$

(9.2-6)

where $K_{iL} \le k_i \le K_{iU}$ with K_{iU} and K_{iL} denoting the upper and lower index limits of k_i.

If the ultimate objective is to estimate the continuous ideal image field by processing the physical observation samples, then the mesh spacing ΔI should be fine enough to satisfy the Nyquist criterion for the ideal image. That is, if the spectrum of the ideal image is bandlimited, and the limits are known, then the mesh spacing should be set at the corresponding Nyquist spacing. Ideally, this will permit perfect interpolation of the estimated points $\tilde{F}(k_1 \, \Delta I, k_2 \, \Delta I)$ to reconstruct $\tilde{F}(x, y)$.

The continuous integration of Eq. 9.2-5 can now be approximated by a discrete summation by employing a quadrature integration formula (2). The physical image samples may then be expressed as

$$\tilde{G}(j_1 \, \Delta S, j_2 \, \Delta S) = \sum_{k_1 = K_{1L}}^{K_{1U}} \sum_{k_2 = K_{2L}}^{K_{2U}} \tilde{F}(k_1 \, \Delta I, k_2 \, \Delta I) \tilde{W}(k_1, k_2)$$

$$\cdot \tilde{J}(j_1 \, \Delta S, j_2 \, \Delta S; k_1 \, \Delta I, k_2 \, \Delta I)$$

(9.2-7)

where $\tilde{W}(k_1, k_2)$ is a weighting coefficient for the particular quadrature formula employed. Usually a rectangular quadrature formula is used, and the weighting coefficients are unity. In any case, it is notationally convenient to lump the weighting coefficient and the impulse response function together so that

$$\tilde{H}(j_1 \Delta S, j_2 \Delta S; k_1 \Delta I, k_2 \Delta I) \equiv \tilde{W}(k_1, k_2)\tilde{J}(j_1 \Delta S, j_2 \Delta S; k_1 \Delta I, k_2 \Delta I)$$
(9.2-8)

Then

$$\tilde{G}(j_1 \Delta S, j_2 \Delta S) = \sum_{k_1=K_{1L}}^{K_{1U}} \sum_{k_2=K_{2L}}^{K_{2U}} \tilde{F}(k_1 \Delta I, k_2 \Delta I)$$
$$\cdot \tilde{H}(j_1 \Delta S, j_2 \Delta S; k_1 \Delta I, k_2 \Delta I) \quad (9.2-9)$$

It should be noted that $\tilde{H}$ is not spatially discretized; the function is simply evaluated at its appropriate spatial argument. The limits of summation of Eq. 9.2-9 are

$$K_{iL} = \left[j_i \frac{\Delta S}{\Delta I} - \frac{T}{\Delta I} \right]_N \qquad K_{iU} = \left[j_i \frac{\Delta S}{\Delta I} + \frac{T}{\Delta I} \right]_N \quad (9.2-10)$$

where $[\cdot]_N$ denotes the nearest integer value of the argument.

Figure 9.2-1 provides an example relating actual physical sample values $\tilde{G}(j_1 \Delta S, j_2 \Delta S)$ to mesh points $\tilde{F}(k_1 \Delta I, k_2 \Delta I)$ on the ideal image field. In this example the mesh spacing is twice as large as the physical sample spacing. In the figure the values of the impulse response function that are utilized in the summation of Eq. 9.2-9 are represented as dots.

An important observation should be made about the discrete model of Eq. 9.2-9 for a sampled superposition integral; the physical area of the ideal image field $\tilde{F}(x, y)$ containing mesh points contributing to physical image samples is larger than the sample image $\tilde{G}(j_1 \Delta S, j_2 \Delta S)$ regardless of the relative number of physical samples and mesh points. The dimensions of the two image fields, as shown in Figure 9.2-2, are related by

$$J \Delta S + T = K \Delta I \quad (9.2-11)$$

to within an accuracy of one sample spacing.

At this point in the discussion, a discrete and finite model for the sampled superposition integral has been obtained in which the physical samples $\tilde{G}(j_1 \Delta S, j_2 \Delta S)$ are related to points on an ideal image field $\tilde{F}(k_1 \Delta I, k_2 \Delta I)$ by a discrete mathematical superposition operation. This discrete superposition is an approximation to continuous superposition because of the truncation of the impulse response function $\tilde{J}(x, y; \alpha, \beta)$ and quadrature integration. The truncation approximation can, of course,

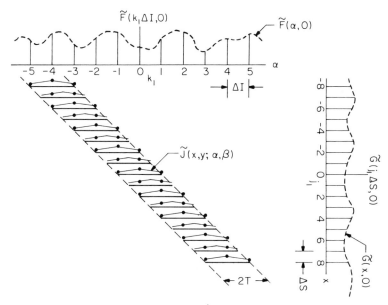

FIGURE 9.2-1. Relationship of physical image samples to mesh points on ideal image field for numerical representation of superposition integral.

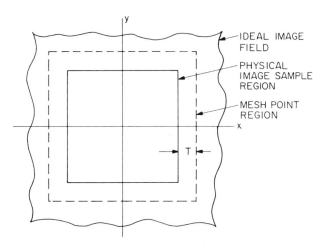

FIGURE 9.2-2. Relationship between regions of physical samples and mesh points for numerical representation of superposition integral.

be made arbitrarily small by extending the bounds of definition of the impulse response, but at the expense of large dimensionality. Also, the quadrature integration approximation can be improved by use of complicated formulas of quadrature, but again the price paid is computational complexity. It should be noted, however, that discrete superposition is a perfect approximation to continuous superposition if the spatial functions of Eq. 9.2-1 are all bandlimited and the physical sampling and numerical representation periods are selected to be the corresponding Nyquist period (4). Representational accuracy and numerical stability are considered in Chapter 14.

It is often convenient to reformulate Eq. 9.2-9 into vector-space form. Toward this end, the arrays $\tilde{G}$ and $\tilde{F}$ are reindexed to $M \times M$ and $N \times N$ arrays, respectively, such that all indices are positive. Let

$$F(n_1 \Delta I, n_2 \Delta I) = \tilde{F}(k_1 \Delta I, k_2 \Delta I) \tag{9.2-12a}$$

where $n_i = k_i + K + 1$ and let

$$G(m_1 \Delta S, m_2 \Delta S) = \tilde{G}(j_1 \Delta S, j_2 \Delta S) \tag{9.2-12b}$$

where $m_i = j_i + J + 1$. Also, let the impulse response be redefined such that

$$H(m_1 \Delta S, m_2 \Delta S; n_1 \Delta I, n_2 \Delta I) = \tilde{H}(j_1 \Delta S, j_2 \Delta S; k_1 \Delta I, k_2 \Delta I) \tag{9.2-12c}$$

Figure 9.2-3 illustrates the geometrical relationship between these functions.

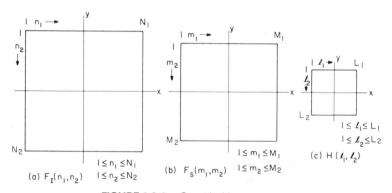

FIGURE 9.2-3. Sampled image arrays.

The discrete superposition relationship of Eq. 9.2-9 for the shifted arrays then becomes

$$G(m_1 \, \Delta S, m_2 \, \Delta S) = \sum_{n_1=N_{1L}}^{N_{1U}} \sum_{n_2=N_{2L}}^{N_{2U}} F(n_1 \, \Delta I, n_2 \, \Delta I)$$

$$\cdot \, H(m_1 \, \Delta S, m_2 \, \Delta S; n_1 \, \Delta I, n_2 \, \Delta I) \qquad (9.2\text{-}13)$$

for $(1 \leq m_i \leq M)$ where

$$N_{iL} = \left[m_i \frac{\Delta S}{\Delta I} \right]_N \qquad N_{iU} = \left[m_i \frac{\Delta S}{\Delta I} + \frac{2T}{\Delta I} \right]_N$$

Following the techniques outlined in Chapter 5, the vectors **g** and **f** may be formed by column scanning the matrices **G** and **F** to obtain (1)

$$\mathbf{g} = \mathbf{Bf} \qquad (9.2\text{-}14)$$

where **B** is an $M^2 \times N^2$ matrix of the form

$$\mathbf{B} = \begin{bmatrix} \mathbf{B}_{1,1} & \mathbf{B}_{1,2} & \cdots & \mathbf{B}_{1,L} & 0 & \cdots & 0 \\ 0 & & & & & & \vdots \\ \vdots & & & & & & 0 \\ 0 & \cdots & 0 & \mathbf{B}_{M,N-L+1} & \cdots & & \mathbf{B}_{M,N} \end{bmatrix} \qquad (9.2\text{-}15)$$

The general term of **B** is defined as

$$B_{m_2,n_2}(m_1, n_1) = H(m_1 \, \Delta S, m_2 \, \Delta S; n_1 \, \Delta I, n_2 \, \Delta I) \qquad (9.2\text{-}16)$$

for $1 \leq m_i \leq M$ and $m_i \leq n_i \leq m_i + L - 1$ where $L = [2T/\Delta I]_N + 1$ represents the nearest odd integer dimension of the impulse response in resolution units ΔI. For descriptional simplicity **B** is called the blur matrix of the superposition integral.

If the impulse response function is translation invariant such that

$$H(j_1 \, \Delta S, j_2 \, \Delta S; k_1 \, \Delta I, k_2 \, \Delta I) = H(j_1 \, \Delta S - k_1 \, \Delta I, j_2 \, \Delta S - k_2 \, \Delta I)$$
$$(9.2\text{-}17)$$

then the discrete superposition operation of Eq. 9.2-13 becomes a discrete convolution operation of the form

$$G(m_1 \, \Delta S, m_2 \, \Delta S) = \sum_{n_1=N_{1L}}^{N_{1U}} \sum_{n_2=N_{2L}}^{N_{2U}} F(n_1 \, \Delta I, n_2 \, \Delta I)$$

$$\cdot \, H(m_1 \, \Delta S - n_1 \, \Delta I + 2T, m_2 \, \Delta S - n_2 \, \Delta I + 2T) \qquad (9.2\text{-}18)$$

A special case of interest occurs when the sampling periods are integer multiples. That is, $\Delta S/\Delta I = k$, where k is an integer. In this case

$$G(m_1 \Delta S, m_2 \Delta S) = \sum_{n_1=m_1k}^{m_1k+L-1} \sum_{n_2=m_2k}^{m_2k+L-1} F(n_1 \Delta I, n_2 \Delta I)$$

$$\cdot H[m_1k \,\Delta I - n_1 \,\Delta I + (L-1)\,\Delta I, m_2k \,\Delta I - n_2 \,\Delta I + (L-1)\,\Delta I] \tag{9.2-19}$$

The general term of the blur matrix then becomes

$$B_{m_2,n_2}(m_1, n_1)$$

$$= H[m_1k \,\Delta I - n_1 \,\Delta I + (L-1)\,\Delta I, m_2k \,\Delta I - n_2 \,\Delta I + (L-1)\,\Delta I] \tag{9.2-20}$$

for $1 \le m_i \le M$ and $m_i \le n_i \le m_i + L - 1$. Continuing further, if the physical sample and quadrature mesh spacings are equal, the general term of the blur matrix assumes the form

$$B_{m_2,n_2}(m_1, n_1) = H(m_1 - n_1 + L, m_2 - n_2 + L) \tag{9.2-21}$$

In Eq. 9.2-21 the mesh spacing variable ΔI is understood. In addition,

$$\mathbf{B}_{m_2,n_2} = \mathbf{B}_{m_2+1, n_2+1} \tag{9.2-22}$$

Consequently, the rows of **B** are shifted versions of the first row. The operator **B** then becomes a sampled infinite area convolution operator and the series form representation of Eq. 9.2-19 reduces to

$$G(m_1, m_2) = \sum_{n_1=m_1}^{m_1+L-1} \sum_{n_2=m_2}^{m_2+L-1} F(n_1, n_2) H(m_1 - n_1 + L, m_2 - n_2 + L) \tag{9.2-23}$$

where the sampling spacing is understood.

$$H = \begin{bmatrix} 11 & 12 & 13 \\ 21 & 22 & 23 \\ 31 & 32 & 33 \end{bmatrix}$$

$$B = \left[\begin{array}{cccc|cccc|cccc|cccc} 33 & 23 & 13 & 0 & 32 & 22 & 12 & 0 & 31 & 21 & 11 & 0 & 0 & 0 & 0 & 0 \\ 0 & 33 & 23 & 13 & 0 & 32 & 22 & 12 & 0 & 31 & 21 & 11 & 0 & 0 & 0 & 0 \\ \hline 0 & 0 & 0 & 0 & 33 & 23 & 13 & 0 & 32 & 22 & 12 & 0 & 31 & 21 & 11 & 0 \\ 0 & 0 & 0 & 0 & 0 & 33 & 23 & 13 & 0 & 32 & 22 & 12 & 0 & 31 & 21 & 11 \end{array}\right]$$

(a)

(b)

FIGURE 9.2-4. Examples of sampled infinite area convolution operators. (a) General impulse array $M = 2$, $N = 4$, $L = 3$. (b) Gaussian-shaped impulse array $M = 8$, $N = 16$, $L = 9$.

Figure 9.2-4*a* contains a computer printout of the sampled infinite area convolution operator for a 4×4 ($N = 4$) data array, a 2×2 ($M = 2$) filtered data array, and a 3×3 ($L = 3$) impulse response array. An extension to larger dimension is shown in Figure 9.2-4*b* for $M = 8$, $N = 16$, $L = 9$ and a Gaussian-shaped impulse response.

When the impulse response is spatially invariant and orthogonally separable

$$\mathbf{B} = \mathbf{B}_C \otimes \mathbf{B}_R \qquad (9.2\text{-}24)$$

where $\mathbf{B}_R$ and $\mathbf{B}_C$ are $M \times N$ matrices of the form

$$\mathbf{B}_R = \begin{bmatrix} h_R(L) & h_R(L-1) & \cdots & h_R(1) & 0 & \cdots & 0 \\ 0 & h_R(L) & \cdots & h_R(2) & h_R(1) & & \vdots \\ \vdots & & & & & & 0 \\ \vdots & & & & & & \\ 0 & & & 0 & h_R(L) & & h_R(1) \end{bmatrix}$$

$$(9.2\text{-}25)$$

The two-dimensional convolution operation then reduces to sequential row and column convolutions of the matrix form of the data array. Thus

$$\mathbf{G} = \mathbf{B}_C \mathbf{F} \mathbf{B}_R^T \qquad (9.2\text{-}26)$$

The superposition or convolution operator expressed in vector form requires $M^2 L^2$ operations if the zero multiplications of $\mathbf{B}$ are avoided. A separable convolution operator can be computed in matrix form with only $ML(M+N)$ operations.

Suppose that both the finite area and the infinite area superposition operations are performed on an $N \times N$ data array for the same $L \times L$ impulse response array with the intention of modeling a continuous superposition process. Then the processed array for finite area computation will be equivalent to the processed array for infinite area computation, surrounded by a boundary of $(L-1)$ superfluous elements.[*] Conversely, if the processed array size is held common for the two superposition operators, the $(L-1)$ boundary elements for the array obtained by the finite area superposition operator will be in error. Thus care must be taken in the application of the finite area superposition operator to model continuous processes.

---

[*] An exception occurs when the data array contains a boundary of $(L-1)/2$ zero elements. A practical example is a blurred photograph of the Moon against the night sky.

9.3. CIRCULANT AREA SUPERPOSITION OPERATOR

In circulant area superposition the input data, the processed output, and the impulse response arrays are all assumed spatially periodic over some common period. In order to unify the presentation, these arrays will be defined in terms of the spatially limited arrays considered previously. First, let the $N \times N$ data array $F(n_1, n_2)$ be imbedded in the upper left corner of a $J \times J$ array $(J > N)$ of zeros giving

$$F_E(n_1, n_2) = F(n_1, n_2) \qquad 1 \le n_i \le N \qquad (9.3\text{-}1a)$$

$$F_E(n_1, n_2) = 0 \qquad N + 1 \le n_i \le J \qquad (9.3\text{-}1b)$$

In a similar manner an extended impulse response array is created by imbedding the spatially limited impulse array in a $J \times J$ matrix of zeros. Thus let

$$H_E(l_1, l_2; m_1, m_2) = H(l_1, l_2; m_1, m_2) \qquad 1 \le l_i \le L \qquad (9.3\text{-}2a)$$

$$H_E(l_1, l_2; m_1, m_2) = 0 \qquad L + 1 \le l_i \le J \qquad (9.3\text{-}2b)$$

Periodic arrays $F_E(n_1, n_2)$ and $H_E(l_1, l_2; m_1, m_2)$ are now formed by replicating the extended arrays over the spatial period J. Then the circular convolution of these functions is defined as

$$K_E(m_1, m_2) = \sum_{n_1=1}^{J} \sum_{n_2=1}^{J} F_P(n_1, n_2) H_P(m_1 - n_1 + 1, m_2 - n_2 + 1; m_1, m_2)$$
$$(9.3\text{-}3)$$

Similarity of this equation with Eq. 9.1-1 describing finite area superposition is evident. In fact, if J is chosen such that $J = N + L - 1$, the terms $F_E(m_1, m_2) = F(m_1, m_2)$ for $1 \le m_i \le M$. The similarity of the circular superposition operation and the sampled infinite area superposition operation should also be noted. These relations become clearer in the vector-space representation of the circular superposition operation.

Let the arrays F_E and K_E be expressed in vector form as the $J^2 \times 1$ vectors $\mathbf{f}_E$ and $\mathbf{k}_E$, respectively. Then the circular superposition operator can be written as

$$\mathbf{k}_E = \mathbf{C}\mathbf{f}_E \qquad (9.3\text{-}4)$$

where $\mathbf{C}$ is a $J^2 \times J^2$ matrix containing elements of the array H_E. The circular superposition operator can then be conveniently expressed in terms of $J \times J$ submatrices $\mathbf{C}_{mn}$ as given by

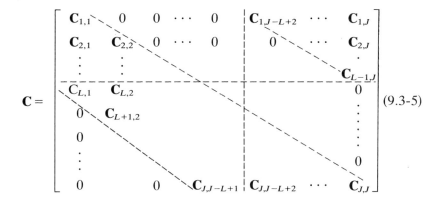

where

$$\mathbf{C}_{m_2, n_2}(m_1, n_1) = H_E(k_1, k_2; m_1, m_2) \qquad (9.3\text{-}6)$$

for $1 \le n_i \le J$ and $1 \le m_i \le J$ with $k_i = (m_i - n_i + 1)$ modulo J and $H_E(0, 0) = 0$. It should be noted that each row and column of $\mathbf{C}$ contains L nonzero submatrices. If the impulse response array is spatially invariant, then

$$\mathbf{C}_{m_2, n_2} = \mathbf{C}_{m_2+1, n_2+1} \qquad (9.3\text{-}7)$$

and the submatrices of the rows (columns) can be obtained by a circular shift of the first row (column). Figure 9.3-1a illustrates the circular area convolution operator for 16×16 $(J = 4)$ data and filtered data arrays and for a 3×3 $(L = 3)$ impulse response array. In Figure 9.3-1b the operator is shown for $J = 16$ and $L = 9$ with a Gaussian-shaped impulse response.

Finally when the impulse response is spatially invariant and orthogonally separable then

$$\mathbf{C} = \mathbf{C}_C \otimes \mathbf{C}_R \qquad (9.3\text{-}8)$$

$$\mathbf{H} = \begin{bmatrix} 11 & 12 & 13 \\ 21 & 22 & 23 \\ 31 & 32 & 33 \end{bmatrix}$$

$$\mathbf{C} =$$

11	0	31	21	0	0	0	0	13	0	33	23	12	0	32	22
21	11	0	31	0	0	0	0	23	13	0	33	22	12	0	32
31	21	11	0	0	0	0	0	33	23	13	0	32	22	12	0
0	31	21	11	0	0	0	0	0	33	23	13	0	32	22	12
12	0	32	22	11	0	31	21	0	0	0	0	13	0	33	23
22	12	0	32	21	11	0	31	0	0	0	0	23	13	0	33
32	22	12	0	31	21	11	0	0	0	0	0	33	23	13	0
0	32	22	12	0	31	21	11	0	0	0	0	0	33	23	13
13	0	33	23	12	0	32	22	11	0	31	21	0	0	0	0
23	13	0	33	22	12	0	32	21	11	0	31	0	0	0	0
33	23	13	0	32	22	12	0	31	21	11	0	0	0	0	0
0	33	23	13	0	32	22	12	0	31	21	11	0	0	0	0
0	0	0	0	13	0	33	23	12	0	32	22	11	0	31	21
0	0	0	0	23	13	0	33	22	12	0	32	21	11	0	31
0	0	0	0	33	23	13	0	32	22	12	0	31	21	11	0
0	0	0	0	0	33	23	13	0	32	22	12	0	31	21	11

(a)

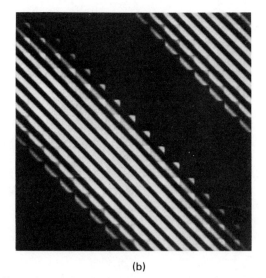

(b)

FIGURE 9.3-1. Examples of circular area convolution operators. (a) General impulse array $J = 4$, $L = 3$. (b) Gaussian-shaped impulse array $J = 16$, $L = 9$.

where $\mathbf{C}_R$ and $\mathbf{C}_C$ are $J \times J$ matrices of the form

$$\mathbf{C}_R = \begin{bmatrix} h_R(1) & 0 & \cdots & 0 & h_R(L) & \cdots & h_R(2) \\ h_R(2) & h_R(1) & \cdots & 0 & 0 & \cdots & h_R(3) \\ \vdots & & & & & & \vdots \\ h_R(L-1) & & & & & & h_R(L) \\ h_R(L) & h_R(L-1) & \cdots & \cdots & \cdots & \cdots & 0 \\ 0 & h_R(L) & & & & & \vdots \\ \vdots & & & & & & 0 \\ 0 & \cdots & \cdots & 0 & h_R(L) & \cdots & \cdots & h_R(1) \end{bmatrix}$$

$$(9.3\text{-}9)$$

Two-dimensional circular convolution may then be computed as

$$\mathbf{K}_E = \mathbf{C}_C \mathbf{E}_F \mathbf{C}_R^T \qquad (9.3\text{-}10)$$

9.4. RELATIONSHIP OF SUPERPOSITION OPERATORS

The elements of the finite area superposition operator $\mathbf{D}$ and the elements of the sampled infinite area superposition operator $\mathbf{B}$ can be extracted from the circular superposition operator $\mathbf{C}$ by use of selection matrices defined as

$$\mathbf{S1}_J^{(K)} = [\,\overbrace{\mathbf{I}_K}^{K} \,\vdots\, \overbrace{\mathbf{0}}^{J-K}\,]\}K \qquad (9.4\text{-}1a)$$

$$\mathbf{S2}_J^{(K)} = [\,\overbrace{\mathbf{0}}^{L-1} \,\vdots\, \overbrace{\mathbf{I}_K}^{K} \,\vdots\, \overbrace{\mathbf{0}}^{J-K-L+1}\,]\}K \qquad (9.4\text{-}1b)$$

where $\mathbf{I}_K$ is a $K \times K$ identity matrix. For future reference it should be noted that the generalized inverses of $\mathbf{S1}$ and $\mathbf{S2}$ and their transposes are

$$[\mathbf{S1}_J^{(K)}]^- = [\mathbf{S1}_J^{(K)}]^T \qquad (9.4\text{-}2a)$$

$$[[\mathbf{S1}_J^{(K)}]^T]^- = \mathbf{S1}_J^{(K)} \qquad (9.4\text{-}2b)$$

$$[\mathbf{S2}_J^{(K)}]^- = [\mathbf{S2}_J^{(K)}]^T \qquad (9.4\text{-}2c)$$

$$[[\mathbf{S2}_J^{(K)}]^T]^- = \mathbf{S2}_J^{(K)} \qquad (9.4\text{-}2d)$$

Examination of the structure of the various superposition operators indicates that

$$\mathbf{D} = [\mathbf{S1}_J^{(M)} \otimes \mathbf{S1}_J^{(M)}]\mathbf{C}[\mathbf{S1}_J^{(N)} \otimes \mathbf{S1}_J^{(N)}]^T \qquad M > N \qquad (9.4\text{-}3a)$$

$$\mathbf{B} = [\mathbf{S2}_J^{(M)} \otimes \mathbf{S2}_J^{(M)}]\mathbf{C}[\mathbf{S1}_J^{(N)} \otimes \mathbf{S1}_J^{(N)}]^T \qquad N > M \qquad (9.4\text{-}3b)$$

That is, the matrix $\mathbf{D}$ is obtained by extracting the first M rows and N columns of submatrices $\mathbf{C}_{mn}$ of $\mathbf{C}$. The first M rows and N columns of each submatrix are also extracted. A similar explanation holds for the extraction of $\mathbf{B}$ from $\mathbf{C}$. In Figure 9.3-1 the elements of $\mathbf{C}$ to be extracted to form $\mathbf{D}$ and $\mathbf{B}$ are indicated by boxes,

   From the definition of the extended input data array of Eq. 9.3-1 it is obvious that the spatially limited input data vector $\mathbf{f}$ can be obtained from the extended data vector $\mathbf{f}_E$ by the selection operation

$$\mathbf{f} = [\mathbf{S1}_J^{(N)} \otimes \mathbf{S1}_J^{(N)}]\mathbf{f}_E \qquad (9.4\text{-}4a)$$

and furthermore

$$\mathbf{f}_E = [\mathbf{S1}_J^{(N)} \otimes \mathbf{S1}_J^{(N)}]^T \mathbf{f} \qquad (9.4\text{-}4b)$$

It can also be shown that the output vector for finite area superposition can be obtained from the output vector for circular superposition by the selection operation

$$\mathbf{q} = [\mathbf{S1}_J^{(M)} \otimes \mathbf{S1}_J^{(M)}]\mathbf{k}_E \qquad (9.4\text{-}5a)$$

The inverse relationship also exists in the form

$$\mathbf{k}_E = [\mathbf{S1}_J^{(M)} \otimes \mathbf{S1}_J^{(M)}]\mathbf{q} \qquad (9.4\text{-}5b)$$

For sampled infinite area superposition

$$\mathbf{g} = [\mathbf{S2}_J^{(M)} \otimes \mathbf{S2}_J^{(M)}]\mathbf{k}_E \qquad (9.4\text{-}6)$$

but it is not possible to obtain $\mathbf{k}_E$ from $\mathbf{g}$ because of the underdeterminacy of the sampled infinite area superposition operator. Expressing both $\mathbf{q}$ and $\mathbf{k}_E$ of Eq. 9.4-5a in matrix form leads to

$$\mathbf{Q} = \sum_{m=1}^{M} \sum_{n=1}^{J} \mathbf{M}_m^T [\mathbf{S1}_J^{(M)} \otimes \mathbf{S1}_J^{(M)}]\mathbf{N}_n \mathbf{K}_E \mathbf{v}_n \mathbf{u}_m^T \qquad (9.4\text{-}7)$$

As a result of the separability of the selection operator, Eq. 9.4-7 reduces to

$$\mathbf{Q} = [\mathbf{S1}_J^{(M)}]\mathbf{K}_E[\mathbf{S1}_J^{(M)}]^T \qquad (9.4\text{-}8)$$

Similarly, for Eq. 9.4-6 describing sampled infinite area superposition

$$\mathbf{G} = [\mathbf{S2}_J^{(M)}]\mathbf{K}_E[\mathbf{S2}_J^{(M)}]^T \tag{9.4-9}$$

Figure 9.4-1 illustrates the locations of the elements of $\mathbf{G}$ and $\mathbf{Q}$ extracted from $\mathbf{K}_E$ for finite area and sampled infinite area superposition.

In summary, it has been shown that the output data vectors for either finite area or sampled infinite area superposition can be obtained by a simple selection operation on the output data vector of circular superposition. Computational advantages that can be realized from this result are considered in Chapter 11.

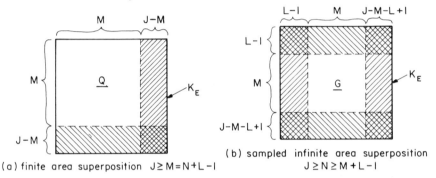

(a) finite area superposition $J \geq M = N + L - 1$

(b) sampled infinite area superposition $J \geq N \geq M + L - 1$

FIGURE 9.4-1.   Location of elements of processed data $\mathbf{Q}$ and $\mathbf{G}$ from $\mathbf{K}_E$.

REFERENCES

1. W. K. Pratt, "Vector Formulation of Two Dimensional Signal Processing Operations, "*J. Computer Graphics and Image Processing*, **4**, 1, March 1975, 1–24, Academic Press, New York.

2. T. R. McCalla, *Introduction to Numerical Methods and FORTRAN Programming*, Wiley, New York, 1967.

3. A. V. Oppenheim and R. W. Schaefer, *Digital Signal Processing*, Prentice-Hall, Englewood Cliffs, N.J., 1975.

4. A. Papoulis, *Systems and Transforms with Applications in Optics*, McGraw-Hill, New York, 1968.

10 TWO-DIMENSIONAL UNITARY TRANSFORMS

Two-dimensional unitary transforms have found three major applications in image processing. Transforms have been utilized to extract features from images. For example, in the Fourier transform the average value or "d.c." term is proportional to the average image brightness, and the high-frequency terms give an indication of the amplitude and orientation of edges within an image. Another application is transform image coding in which a bandwidth reduction is achieved by discarding or grossly quantizing low-magnitude transform coefficients. Dimensionality reduction in computation is a third application. Stated simply, those transform coefficients that are small may be excluded from processing operations such as filtering without much loss in processing performance. These applications are considered in detail in subsequent chapters. This chapter considers the properties of transforms commonly used in image processing.

10.1. UNITARY TRANSFORM OPERATORS

A unitary transformation is a specific type of linear transformation in which the basic linear operation of Eq. 8.1-1 is exactly invertible and the operator kernel satisfies certain orthogonality conditions (1.2). The forward unitary transform of the $N_1 \times N_2$ image array $F(n_1, n_2)$ results in an $N_1 \times N_2$ transformed image array as defined by

$$\mathcal{F}(m_1, m_2) = \sum_{n_1=1}^{N_1} \sum_{n_2=1}^{N_2} F(n_1, n_2)A(n_1, n_2; m_1, m_2) \qquad (10.1\text{-}1)$$

where $A(n_1, n_2; m_1, m_2)$ represents the forward transform kernel. A reverse or inverse transformation provides a mapping from the transform domain to the image space as given by

$$F(n_1, n_2) = \sum_{m_1=1}^{N_1} \sum_{m_2=1}^{N_2} \mathcal{F}(m_1, m_2)B(n_1, n_2; m_1, m_2) \qquad (10.1\text{-}2)$$

where $B(n_1, n_2; m_1, m_2)$ denotes the inverse transform kernel. The transformation is unitary if the following orthonormality conditions are met:

$$\sum_{m_1} \sum_{m_2} A(n_1, n_2; m_1, m_2) A^*(j_1, j_2; m_1, m_2) = \delta(n_1 - j_1, n_2 - j_2) \qquad (10.1\text{-}3a)$$

$$\sum_{m_1} \sum_{m_2} B(n_1, n_2; m_1, m_2) B^*(j_1, j_2; m_1, m_2) = \delta(n_1 - j_1, n_2 - j_2) \qquad (10.1\text{-}3b)$$

$$\sum_{n_1} \sum_{n_2} A(n_1, n_2; m_1, m_2) A^*(n_1, n_2; k_1, k_2) = \delta(m_1 - k_1, m_2 - k_2) \qquad (10.1\text{-}3c)$$

$$\sum_{n_1} \sum_{n_2} B(n_1, n_2; m_1, m_2) B^*(n_1, n_2; k_1, k_2) = \delta(m_1 - k_1, m_2 - k_2) \qquad (10.1\text{-}3d)$$

The transformation is said to be separable if its kernels can be written in the form

$$A(n_1, n_2; m_1, m_2) = A_C(n_1, m_1) A_R(n_2, m_2) \qquad (10.1\text{-}4a)$$

$$B(n_1, n_2; m_1, m_2) = B_C(n_1, m_1) B_R(n_2, m_2) \qquad (10.1\text{-}4b)$$

where the kernel subscripts indicate row and column one-dimensional transform operations. A separable two-dimensional unitary transform can be computed in two steps. First, a one-dimensional transform is taken along each column of the image yielding

$$P(m_1, n_2) = \sum_{n_1=1}^{N_1} F(n_1, n_2) A_C(n_1, m_1) \qquad (10.1\text{-}5)$$

Next, a second one-dimensional unitary transform is taken along each row of $P(m_1, n_2)$ giving

$$\mathscr{F}(m_1, m_2) = \sum_{n_2=1}^{N_2} P(m_1, n_2) A_R(n_2, m_2) \qquad (10.1\text{-}6)$$

Unitary transforms can be conveniently expressed in vector-space form (3). Let $\mathbf{F}$ and $\mathbf{f}$ denote the matrix and vector representations of an image array, and let $\mathscr{F}$ and $\boldsymbol{f}$ be the matrix and vector forms of the transformed image. Then, the two-dimensional unitary transform written in vector form is given by

$$\boldsymbol{f} = \mathbf{A}\mathbf{f} \qquad (10.1\text{-}7)$$

where $\mathbf{A}$ is the forward transformation matrix. The reverse transform is

$$\mathbf{f} = \mathbf{B}\boldsymbol{f} \qquad (10.1\text{-}8)$$

where $\mathbf{B}$ represents the inverse transformation matrix. It is obvious then that

$$\mathbf{B} = \mathbf{A}^{-1} \qquad (10.1\text{-}9)$$

For a unitary transformation the matrix inverse is given by

$$\mathbf{A}^{-1} = \mathbf{A}^{*T} \tag{10.1-10}$$

and $\mathbf{A}$ is said to be a unitary matrix. A real unitary matrix is called an orthogonal matrix. For such a matrix

$$\mathbf{A}^{-1} = \mathbf{A}^{T} \tag{10.1-11}$$

If the transform kernels are separable such that

$$\mathbf{A} = \mathbf{A}_C \otimes \mathbf{A}_R \tag{10.1-12}$$

where $\mathbf{A}_R$ and $\mathbf{A}_C$ are row and column unitary transform matrices, then the transformed image matrix can be obtained from the image matrix by

$$\mathcal{F} = \mathbf{A}_C \mathbf{F} \mathbf{A}_R^T \tag{10.1-13a}$$

The inverse transformation is given by

$$\mathbf{F} = \mathbf{B}_C \mathcal{F} \mathbf{B}_R^T \tag{10.1-13b}$$

where $\mathbf{B}_C = \mathbf{A}_C^{-1}$ and $\mathbf{B}_R = \mathbf{A}_R^{-1}$.

Separable unitary transforms can also be expressed in a hybrid series–vector-space form as a sum of vector outer products. Let $\mathbf{a}_C(n_1)$ and $\mathbf{a}_R(n_2)$ represent columns n_1 and n_2 of the unitary matrices $\mathbf{A}_C^T$ and $\mathbf{A}_R^T$, respectively. Then it is easily verified that

$$\mathcal{F} = \sum_{n_1=1}^{N_1} \sum_{n_2=1}^{N_2} F(n_1, n_2) \mathbf{a}_C(n_1) \mathbf{a}_R^T(n_2) \tag{10.1-14a}$$

Similarly,

$$\mathbf{F} = \sum_{m_1=1}^{M_1} \sum_{m_2=1}^{M_2} \mathcal{F}(m_1, m_2) \mathbf{b}_C(m_1) \mathbf{b}_R^T(m_2) \tag{10.1-14b}$$

where $\mathbf{b}_C(m_1)$ and $\mathbf{b}_R(m_2)$ denote columns m_1 and m_2 of the unitary matrices $\mathbf{B}_C^T$ and $\mathbf{B}_R^T$, respectively. The vector outer products of Eq. 10.1-14 form a series of matrices, called basis matrices, that provide matrix decompositions of the image matrix $\mathbf{F}$ or its unitary transformation $\mathcal{F}$.

There are several ways in which a unitary transformation may be viewed. An image transformation can be interpreted as a decomposition of the image data into a generalized two-dimensional spectrum (4). Each spectral component in the transform domain corresponds to the amount of energy of the spectral function within the original image. In this context the concept of frequency may now be generalized to include transformations of functions other than sine and cosine waveforms. This type of generalized spectral analysis is useful in the investigation of specific decompositions that are best suited for particular classes of images. Another way to visualize an image transformation is to consider the transformation as a multidimensional rotation of coordinates. One of the major properties of a unitary transformation is that measure is preserved. For example, the mean-square difference between two images is equal to the mean-square difference between the transforms of the image. A third approach to the visualization of image transformation is to consider Eq. 10.1-2 as a means of synthesizing an image with a set of two-dimensional mathematical functions $B(n_1, n_2; m_1, m_2)$ for a fixed transform domain coordinate (m_1, m_2). In this interpretation the kernel $B(n_1, n_2; m_1, m_2)$ is called a two-dimensional basis function and the transform coefficient $\mathscr{F}(m_1, m_2)$ is the amplitude of the basis function required in the synthesis of the image.

In the remainder of this chapter, in order to simplify the analysis of two-dimensional unitary transforms, all image arrays are considered square of dimension N. Furthermore, when expressing transformation operations in series form, as in Eqs. 10.1-1 and 10.1-2, the indices are renumbered and renamed. Thus the input image array is denoted by $F(j, k)$ for $j, k = 0, 1, 2, \ldots, N - 1$ and the transformed image array is represented by $\mathscr{F}(u, v)$ for $u, v = 0, 1, 2, \ldots, N - 1$. With these definitions, the forward unitary transform becomes

$$\mathscr{F}(u, v) = \sum_{j=0}^{N-1} \sum_{k=0}^{N-1} F(j, k) A(j, k; u, v) \qquad (10.1\text{-}15a)$$

and the inverse transform is

$$F(j, k) = \sum_{u=0}^{N-1} \sum_{v=0}^{N-1} \mathscr{F}(u, v) B(j, k; u, v) \qquad (10.1\text{-}15b)$$

10.2. FOURIER TRANSFORM

The discrete two-dimensional Fourier transform of an image array is defined in series form as (5–10)

$$\mathscr{F}(u, v) = \frac{1}{N} \sum_{j=0}^{N-1} \sum_{k=0}^{N-1} F(j, k) \exp\left\{ \frac{-2\pi i}{N}(uj + vk) \right\} \qquad (10.2\text{-}1a)$$

where $i = \sqrt{-1}$, and the discrete inverse transform is given by

$$F(j, k) = \frac{1}{N} \sum_{u=0}^{N-1} \sum_{v=0}^{N-1} \mathscr{F}(u, v) \exp\left\{ \frac{2\pi i}{N}(uj + vk) \right\} \qquad (10.2\text{-}1b)$$

The indices (u, v) are called the spatial frequencies of the transformation in analogy with continuous Fourier transforms. It should be noted that Eq. 10.2-1 is not universally accepted by all authors; some prefer to place all scaling constants in the inverse transform equation, while still others employ a reversal in the sign of the kernels.

Since the transform kernels are separable and symmetric, the two-dimensional transforms can be computed as sequential row and column one-dimensional transforms. The basis functions of the transform are complex exponentials that may be decomposed into sine and cosine components. That is,

$$A(j, k; u, v) = \exp\left\{-\frac{2\pi i}{N}(uj + vk)\right\}$$

$$= \cos\left\{\frac{2\pi}{N}(uj + vk)\right\} - i \sin\left\{\frac{2\pi}{N}(uj + vk)\right\} \quad (10.2\text{-}2a)$$

$$B(j, k; u, v) = \exp\left\{\frac{2\pi i}{N}(uj + vk)\right\}$$

$$= \cos\left\{\frac{2\pi}{N}(uj + vk)\right\} + i \sin\left\{\frac{2\pi}{N}(uj + vk)\right\} \quad (10.2\text{-}2b)$$

Figure 10.2-1 contains plots of the sine and cosine components of the one-dimensional Fourier basis functions for $N = 16$. It should be observed that the basis functions are a rough approximation of continuous sinusoids only for low frequencies; in fact, the highest-frequency basis function is a square wave. Also, there are obvious redundancies between the sine and cosine components.

The Fourier transform plane possesses many interesting structural properties. The spectral component at the origin of the Fourier domain

$$\mathscr{F}(0, 0) = \frac{1}{N} \sum_{j=0}^{N-1} \sum_{k=0}^{N-1} F(j, k) \quad (10.2\text{-}3)$$

is equal to N times the spatial average of the image plane. Making the substitutions $u = u + mN, v = v + nN$ in Eq. 10.2-1, where m and n are constants, results in

$$\mathscr{F}(u + mN, v + nN) = \frac{1}{N} \sum_{j=0}^{N-1} \sum_{k=0}^{N-1} F(j, k) \exp\left\{\frac{-2\pi i}{N}(uj + vk)\right\}$$

$$\cdot \exp\left\{-2\pi i(mj + nk)\right\} \quad (10.2\text{-}4)$$

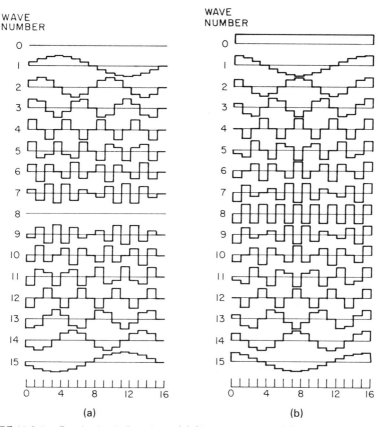

FIGURE 10.2-1. Fourier basis functions. (a) Sine component. (b) Cosine component.

For all integer values of m and n, the second exponential term of Eq. 10.2-4 assumes a value of unity, and the transform domain is found to be periodic. Thus, as shown in Figure 10.2-2a,

$$\mathcal{F}(u + mN, v + nN) = \mathcal{F}(u, v) \qquad (10.2\text{-}5)$$

for $m, n = 0, \pm 1, \pm 2, \ldots$.

The two-dimensional Fourier transform of an image is essentially a Fourier series representation of a two-dimensional field. For the Fourier series representation to be valid, the field must be periodic. Thus, as shown in Figure 10.2-2b, the original image must be considered to be periodic horizontally and vertically. The right side of the image therefore abuts the left side, and the top and bottom of the image are adjacent. Spatial frequencies along the coordinate axes of the transform plane arise from these transitions. Although these are false spatial frequencies from the

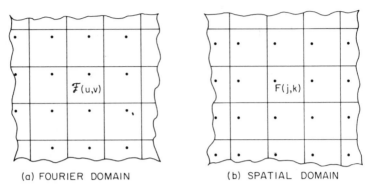

(a) FOURIER DOMAIN   (b) SPATIAL DOMAIN

FIGURE 10.2-2.   Periodic image and Fourier transform arrays.

standpoint of being necessary for representing the image within the image boundary, they do not impair reconstruction. On the contrary, these spatial frequencies are required to reconstruct the sharp boundaries of the image.

If the image array represents a luminance field, $F(j, k)$ will be a real positive function. However, its Fourier transform will, in general, be complex. Since the transform domain contains $2N^2$ components, the real and imaginary, or phase and magnitude components, of each coefficient, it might be thought that the Fourier transformation causes an increase in dimensionality. This, however, is not the case because $\mathcal{F}(u, v)$ exhibits a property of conjugate symmetry. From Eq. 10.2-4 with m and n set to integer values, conjugation yields

$$\mathcal{F}^*(u + mN, v + nN) = \frac{1}{N} \sum_{j=0}^{N-1} \sum_{k=0}^{N-1} F(j, k) \exp\left\{\frac{2\pi i}{N}(uj + vk)\right\}$$

$$(10.2\text{-}6)$$

By the substitution $u = -u$ and $v = -v$ it can be shown that

$$\mathcal{F}(u, v) = \mathcal{F}^*(-u + mN, -v + nN) \qquad (10.2\text{-}7)$$

for $m, n = 0, +1, +2, \dots$. As a result of the conjugate symmetry property, almost one-half of the transform domain samples are redundant, that is, they can be generated from other transform samples. Figure 10.2-3 contains a drawing of the transform plane with a set of redundant components crosshatched. It is possible, of course, to choose the left half-plane samples rather than the upper plane samples as the nonredundant set.

Figure 10.2-4 contains photographs of an image and various versions of its Fourier transform. Since the dynamic range of transform components is much larger than the exposure range of photographic film, it is necessary to compress the coefficient values to produce a useful display. Compression

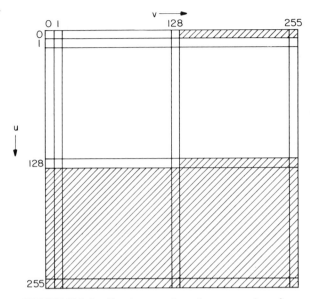

FIGURE 10.2-3.   Fourier transform frequency domain.

can be obtained by clipping large-magnitude values or by taking the logarithm of each magnitude value according to the relation

$$\mathcal{D}(u, v) = \log\left[a + b|\mathcal{F}(u, v)|\right] \tag{10.2-8}$$

where a and b are scaling constants. Figure 10.2-4b is a logarithmic display of the magnitude of the Fourier transform coefficients, as computed by Eq. 10.2-1a, with $a = 1$ and $b = 1$; Figure 10.3-4c contains a display with the upper 25% of the transform coefficients clipped in magnitude. In mathematical operations with continuous signals, the origin of the transform domain is usually at its geometric center. Similarly, the Fraunhofer diffraction pattern of a photographic transparency of transmittance $F(x, y)$ produced by a coherent optical system has its zero-frequency term at the center of its display. A computer-generated two-dimensional discrete Fourier transform with its origin at its center can be produced by a simple reordering of its transform coefficients. Alternatively, the quadrants of the Fourier transform, as computed by Eq. 10.2-1a can be reordered automatically by multiplying the image function by the factor $(-1)^{j+k}$ prior to the Fourier transformation. The proof of this assertion follows from Eq. 10.2-4 with the substitution $m = n = \frac{1}{2}$. Then, by the identity

$$\exp\{i\pi(j + k)\} = (-1)^{j+k} \tag{10.2-9}$$

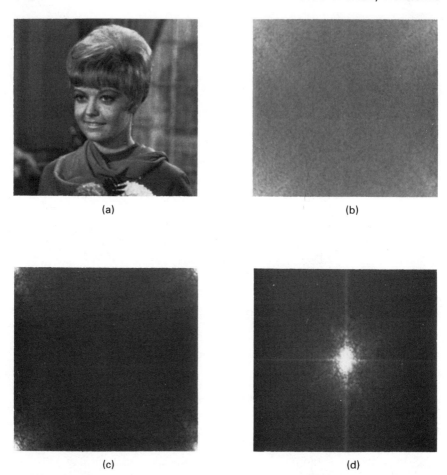

FIGURE 10.2-4. Fourier transform of GIRL image. (a) Original. (b) Log magnitude nonordered. (c) Clipped magnitude nonordered. (d) Clipped magnitude ordered.

Eq. 10.2-4 can be expressed as

$$\mathcal{F}(u + N/2, v + N/2) = \frac{1}{N} \sum_{j=0}^{N-1} \sum_{k=0}^{N-1} F(j, k)(-1)^{j+k} \exp\left\{\frac{-2\pi i}{N}(uj + vk)\right\}$$

$$(10.2\text{-}10)$$

Figure 10.2-4*d* contains a magnitude display of the reordered Fourier components. The conjugate symmetry in the Fourier domain is readily apparent from the photograph.

The Fourier transform written in series form in Eq. 10.2-1 may be redefined in vector space form as

$$\mathcal{f} = \mathbf{A}\mathbf{f} \tag{10.2-11a}$$

and

$$\mathbf{f} = \mathbf{A}^{*T}\mathcal{f} \tag{10.2-11b}$$

where $\mathbf{f}$ and $\mathcal{f}$ are vectors obtained by column scanning the matrices $\mathbf{F}$ and $\mathcal{F}$, respectively. The transformation matrix $\mathbf{A}$ can be written in direct product form as

$$\mathbf{A} = \mathbf{A}_C \otimes \mathbf{A}_R \tag{10.2-12}$$

where

$$\mathbf{A}_R = \mathbf{A}_C = \frac{1}{\sqrt{N}}
\begin{bmatrix}
\mathcal{W}^0 & \mathcal{W}^0 & \mathcal{W}^0 & \cdots & \mathcal{W}^0 \\
\mathcal{W}^0 & \mathcal{W}^1 & \mathcal{W}^2 & \cdots & \mathcal{W}^{N-1} \\
\mathcal{W}^0 & \mathcal{W}^2 & \mathcal{W}^4 & \cdots & \mathcal{W}^{2(N-1)} \\
\vdots & & & & \vdots \\
\mathcal{W}^0 & \cdot & \cdot & \cdots & \mathcal{W}^{(N-1)^2}
\end{bmatrix} \tag{10.2-13}$$

with $\mathcal{W} = \exp\{-2\pi i/N\}$. As a result of the direct product decomposition of $\mathbf{A}$, the image matrix and transformed image matrix are related by

$$\mathcal{F} = \mathbf{A}_C \mathbf{F} \mathbf{A}_R \tag{10.2-14a}$$

and

$$\mathbf{F} = \mathbf{A}_C^* \mathcal{F} \mathbf{A}_R^* \tag{10.2-14b}$$

The properties of the Fourier transform previously proved in series form obviously hold in the matrix formulation.

While the Fourier transform possesses many desirable analytic properties, it has two major drawbacks: complex, rather than real number computations are necessary; and the rate of convergence is low. The latter disadvantage, which is significant in image coding applications, can be explained by rewriting Eq. 10.2-1b in the following form:

$$F(j, k) = \lim_{\substack{U_T \to (N+1)/2 \\ V_T \to (N+1)/2}} \left[\frac{1}{N} \underbrace{\sum_u \sum_v \mathcal{F}(u, v) \exp\left\{\frac{2\pi i}{N}(uj + vk)\right\}}_{u,v \in S(U_T, V_T)} \right] \tag{10.2-15}$$

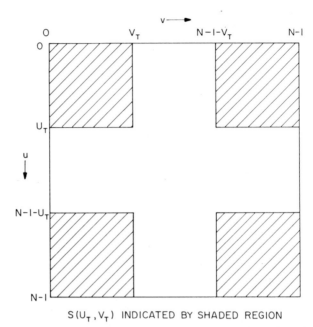

S(U_T, V_T) INDICATED BY SHADED REGION

FIGURE 10.2-5.   Low-pass region in Fourier transform domain.

where $S(U_T, V_T)$ is the geometric zone defined in Figure 10.2-5. For fixed upper limits U_T and V_T, and relatively small dimension N, the bracketed term of Eq. 10.2-15 may differ significantly from $F(j, k)$ unless U_T and V_T are large. In subsequent discussions the question of transform convergence will be approached quantitatively. Qualitatively speaking the poor convergence of the Fourier transform results from the sharp discontinuities between the right and left side, and between the top and bottom of an image. These discontinuities result in large magnitude, high spatial frequency components.

10.3.   COSINE TRANSFORMS

It is known that the Fourier series representation of any continuous real and symmetric function contains only real coefficients corresponding to the cosine terms of the series. This result can be extended to the discrete Fourier transform of images under proper interpretation. There are two ways in which an image field can be made symmetric, as shown in Figure 10.3-1 (11). By the first technique the images are folded about an edge, and in the second method the images are folded and overlapped by one

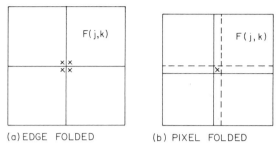

(a) EDGE FOLDED   (b) PIXEL FOLDED

FIGURE 10.3-1.   Cosine transform symmetry.

pixel. Thus, for an $N \times N$ pixel image, the first method, called the even cosine transform, results in a $2N \times 2N$ pixel array, and the second method, called the odd cosine transform, yields a $2N - 1 \times 2N - 1$ pixel array.

Even Symmetrical Cosine Transform

Let a symmetrical image array be formed by reflection of the image array about its edges according to the relation

$$F_s(j, k) = \begin{cases} F(j, k) & j \geq 0, \quad k \geq 0 \\ F(-1-j, k) & j < 0, \quad k \geq 0 \\ F(j, -1-k) & j \geq 0, \quad k < 0 \\ F(-1-j, -1-k) & j < 0, \quad k < 0 \end{cases} \quad (10.3\text{-}1)$$

By this construction $F_s(j, k)$ is symmetrical about the point $j = -\frac{1}{2}, k = -\frac{1}{2}$. Now taking a Fourier transform about the point of symmetry results in

$$\mathcal{F}_s(u, v) = \frac{1}{2N} \sum_{j=-N}^{N-1} \sum_{k=-N}^{N-1} F_s(j, k) \exp \left\{ \frac{-2\pi i}{2N} [u(j + \tfrac{1}{2}) + v(k + \tfrac{1}{2})] \right\}$$

$$(10.3\text{-}2)$$

for $u, v = -N, \ldots, -1, 0, 1, \ldots, N - 1$. Because $F_s(j, k)$ is real and symmetric, Eq. 10.3-2 reduces to

$$\mathcal{F}_s(u, v) = \frac{2}{N} \sum_{j=0}^{N-1} \sum_{k=0}^{N-1} F(j, k) \cos \left[\frac{\pi}{N} u(j + \tfrac{1}{2}) \right] \cos \left[\frac{\pi}{N} v(k + \tfrac{1}{2}) \right] \quad (10.3\text{-}3)$$

Alternatively, the terms of Eq. 10.3-3 can be computed by a Fourier transformation of $F(j, k)$ over $2N$ points from

$$\mathcal{F}_s(u, v) = \frac{2}{N} R_e \left\{ \exp \left[\frac{i\pi u}{2N} \right] \sum_{j=0}^{N-1} \sum_{k=0}^{N-1} F(j, k) \exp \left\{ \frac{-2\pi i}{2N} (uj + vk) \right\} \right\}$$

$$(10.3\text{-}4)$$

The forward even cosine transform is defined to be the normalized version of Eq. 10.3-3 given by (12)

$$\mathcal{F}(u, v) = \frac{2}{N} C(u)C(v) \sum_{j=0}^{N-1} \sum_{k=0}^{N-1} F(j, k) \cos\left(\frac{\pi}{N}[u(j+\tfrac{1}{2})]\right) \cos\left(\frac{\pi}{N}[v(k+\tfrac{1}{2})]\right)$$

$$(10.3\text{-}5a)$$

and its inverse is defined as

$$F(j, k) = \frac{2}{N} \sum_{u=0}^{N-1} \sum_{v=0}^{N-1} C(u)C(v)\mathcal{F}(u, v) \cos\left(\frac{\pi}{N}[u(j+\tfrac{1}{2})]\right) \cos\left(\frac{\pi}{N}[v(k+\tfrac{1}{2})]\right)$$

$$(10.3\text{-}5b)$$

where $C(0) = (2)^{-1/2}$ and $C(w) = 1$ for $w = 1, 2, \ldots, N-1$. It has been observed that the basis functions of the even cosine transform are actually a class of discrete Chebyshev polynomials (12).

Figure 10.3-2 contains plots of the even symmetric cosine transform basis functions for $N = 16$. Photographs of the even symmetric cosine transform of an image are shown in Figure 10.3-3. The origin is placed in the upper left corner of each display, consistent with matrix notation. It should be observed that, as with the Fourier transform, the image energy tends to concentrate toward the lower spatial frequencies.

Odd Symmetrical Cosine Transform

For the odd cosine transform geometry the symmetrical image array may be defined as

$$F_s(j, k) = \begin{cases} F(j, k) & j, k \geq 0 \\ F(-j, k) & j < 0, k \geq 0 \\ F(j, -k) & j \geq 0, k < 0 \\ F(-j, -k) & j, k < 0 \end{cases} \qquad (10.3\text{-}6)$$

Then taking a two-dimensional Fourier transform of this array yields

$$\mathcal{F}_s(u, v) = \frac{1}{2N-1} \sum_{j=-N+1}^{N-1} \sum_{k=-N+1}^{N-1} F_s(j, k) \exp\left\{\frac{-2\pi i}{2N-1}(ju+kv)\right\}$$

$$(10.3\text{-}7)$$

for $u, v = -N+1, \ldots, -1, 0, 1, \ldots, N-1$. As a result of the conjugate symmetry property of the Fourier transform for real image fields,

$$\mathcal{F}_s(u, v) = \mathcal{F}_s^*(-u, -v) \qquad (10.3\text{-}8)$$

Hence it is only necessary to compute $\mathcal{F}_s(u, v)$ for non-negative indices (u, v). Furthermore, since $F_s(j, k)$ is real and symmetric, $\mathcal{F}_s(u, v)$ is also

WAVE
NUMBER

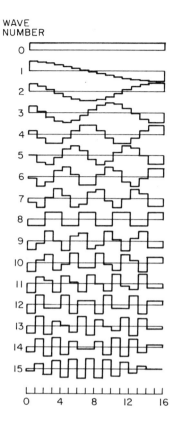

FIGURE 10.3-2. Cosine basis functions.

real. As a consequence, Eq. 10.3-2 may be rewritten as

$$\mathcal{F}_s(u, v) = \frac{4}{2N-1} \sum_{j=0}^{N-1} \sum_{j=0}^{N-1} \tilde{F}(j, k) \cos\left[\frac{2\pi}{2N-1}ju\right] \cos\left[\frac{2\pi}{2N-1}kv\right]$$

$$(10.3\text{-}9)$$

where $\tilde{F}(j, k)$ is obtained by an amplitude weighting of the elements of the image array $F(j, k)$ according to the formula

$$\tilde{F}_s(j, k) = \begin{cases} \frac{1}{4}F(j, k) & j = 0, \quad k = 0 \\ \frac{1}{2}F(j, k) & j = 0, \quad k \neq 0 \\ \frac{1}{2}F(j, k) & j \neq 0, \quad k = 0 \\ F(j, k) & \text{elsewhere} \end{cases} \qquad (10.3\text{-}10)$$

The odd cosine transform is simply a normalized version of Eq. 10.3-9 scaled so that the basis functions are orthonormal. Thus, by definition, the

(a)

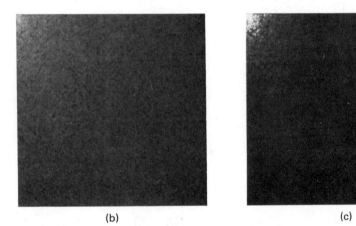

(b)   (c)

FIGURE 10.3-3. Cosine transform of GIRL image. (a) Original. (b) Log magnitude. (c) Clipped magnitude.

odd cosine transform is

$$\mathscr{F}(u, v) = \frac{1}{N} \sum_{j=0}^{N-1} \sum_{k=0}^{N-1} \tilde{F}(j, k) \qquad \text{for } u = 0, \quad v = 0 \quad (10.3\text{-}11a)$$

$$\mathscr{F}(u, v) = \frac{2}{N} \sum_{j=0}^{N-1} \sum_{k=0}^{N-1} \tilde{F}(j, k) \cos\left[\frac{2\pi}{2N-1} ju\right] \cos\left[\frac{2\pi}{2N-1} kv\right]$$

$$\text{for } u, v \neq 0 \quad (10.3\text{-}11b)$$

An identical transformation

$$\tilde{F}(j,k) = \frac{1}{N} \sum_{u=0}^{N-1} \sum_{v=0}^{N-1} \mathcal{F}(u,v) \qquad \text{for } j = 0, \quad k = 0 \quad (10.3\text{-}12a)$$

$$\tilde{F}(j,k) = \frac{2}{N} \sum_{u=0}^{N-1} \sum_{v=0}^{N-1} \mathcal{F}(u,v) \cos\left[\frac{2\pi}{2N-1}ju\right] \cos\left[\frac{2\pi}{2N-1}kv\right]$$

$$\text{for } j, k \neq 0 \qquad (10.3\text{-}12b)$$

yields the amplitude weighted array $\tilde{F}(j,k)$. Then the original image array $F(j,k)$ can be reconstructed from

$$F(j,k) = \begin{cases} 4\tilde{F}(j,k) & j = 0, \quad k = 0 \\ 2\tilde{F}(j,k) & j = 0, k \neq 0 \\ 2\tilde{F}(j,k) & j \neq 0, k = 0 \\ \tilde{F}(j,k) & \text{elsewhere} \end{cases} \qquad (10.3\text{-}13)$$

The basis functions of the odd cosine transform are observed to be orthogonally separable so that a two-dimensional odd cosine transform can be obtained by sequential row and column one-dimensional transforms. Also, it is possible to compute the odd cosine transform with a Fourier transform algorithm of odd length since

$$\mathcal{F}_s(u,v) = \frac{4}{2N-1} R_e \left\{ \sum_{j=0}^{N-1} \sum_{k=0}^{N-1} \tilde{F}(j,k) \exp\left\{ \frac{-2\pi i}{2N-1}(ju+kv) \right\} \right\}$$

$$(10.3\text{-}14)$$

10.4. SINE TRANSFORM

The sine transform, introduced by Jain (13) as a fast algorithmic substitute for the Karhunen–Loeve transform of a Markov Process, is defined in one-dimensional form by the basis functions

$$A(u,j) = \sqrt{\frac{2}{N+1}} \sin\left[\frac{(j+1)(u+1)\pi}{N+1}\right] \qquad (10.4\text{-}1)$$

for $u, j = 0, 1, 2, \ldots, N-1$. Consider the tridiagonal matrix

$$\mathbf{Q} = \begin{bmatrix} 1 & -\alpha & 0 & \cdot\ \cdot & & 0 \\ -\alpha & 1 & -\alpha & & & \vdots \\ & & & & & \vdots \\ \vdots & & & & & \vdots \\ \vdots & & & & & \vdots \\ & & & -\alpha & 1 & -\alpha \\ 0 & & & 0 & -\alpha & 1 \end{bmatrix} \qquad (10.4\text{-}2)$$

where $\alpha = \rho/(1+\rho^2)$ and $(0 \le \rho \le 1)$ is the adjacent element correlation of a Markov process covariance matrix. It can be shown (14) that the basis functions of Eq. 10.4-1, inserted as the elements of the unitary matrix $\mathbf{A}$, diagonalize the matrix $\mathbf{Q}$ in the sense that*

$$\mathbf{AQA}^T = \mathbf{D} \qquad\qquad (10.4\text{-}3)$$

Matrix $\mathbf{D}$ is a diagonal matrix composed of the terms

$$D(k,k) = \frac{1-\rho^2}{1-2\rho \cos[k\pi/(N+1)]+\rho^2} \qquad (10.4\text{-}4)$$

for $k = 1, 2, \ldots, N$.

WAVE
NUMBER

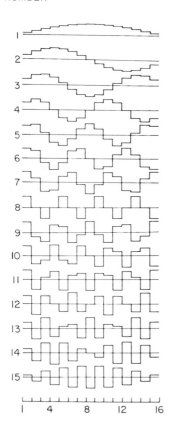

FIGURE 10.4-1. Sine transform basis functions, $N = 15$.

* Jain (15) has shown that the cosine and sine transforms are interrelated in that they diagonalize a family of tridiagonal matrices.

The two-dimensional sine transform is defined as

$$\mathcal{F}(u, v) = \frac{2}{N+1} \sum_{j=0}^{N-1} \sum_{k=0}^{N-1} F(j, k) \sin\left[\frac{(j+1)(u+1)\pi}{N+1}\right] \sin\left[\frac{(k+1)(v+1)\pi}{N+1}\right]$$

(10.4-5)

Its inverse is of identical form. The sine transform can also be computed with a Fourier transform algorithm. Let the $(2N+2) \times (2N+2)$ array $F(m, n)$ be formed according to the formula

$$\tilde{F}(m+1, n+1) = F(m, n) \qquad 0 \le m \le N-1, \quad 0 \le n \le N-1 \quad (10.4\text{-}6a)$$

$$\tilde{F}(m, n) = 0 \qquad \text{otherwise} \qquad (10.4\text{-}6b)$$

(a)

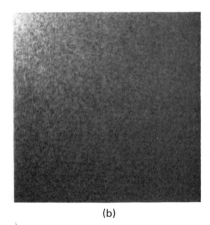

(b)   (c)

FIGURE 10.4-2. Sine transform of GIRL image. (a) Original. (b) Log magnitude. (c) Clipped magnitude.

for $0 \le m, n \le 2N + 1$. Then the sine transform can be computed by extraction of the imaginary part

$$\mathcal{F}(u, v) = \frac{1}{(N + 1)} \sum_{m=0}^{2N+1} \sum_{n=0}^{2N+1} \tilde{F}(m, n) \sin\left[\frac{2(u + 1)m}{2N + 2}\right] \sin\left[\frac{2(v + 1)n}{2N + 2}\right]$$

(10.4-7)

of the $(2N + 2) \times (2N + 2)$ Fourier transform of $F(m, n)$ for $1 \le u, v \le N$.

Sine transform basis functions are plotted in Figure 10.4-1 for $N = 15$. Figure 10.4-2 contains photographs of the sine transform of an image.

10.5. HADAMARD TRANSFORM

The Hadamard transform (16, 17) is based upon the Hadamard matrix (18), which is a square array of plus and minus ones whose rows and columns are orthogonal. A normalized $N \times N$ Hadamard matrix satisfies the relation

$$\mathbf{H}\mathbf{H}^T = \mathbf{I}$$

(10.5-1)

The lowest size orthonormal Hadamard matrix is the 2×2 Hadamard matrix given by

$$\mathbf{H}_2 = \frac{1}{\sqrt{2}}\begin{bmatrix} 1 & 1 \\ 1 & -1 \end{bmatrix}$$

(10.5-2)

It is known that if a Hadamard matrix of size N exists $(N > 2)$, then $N = 0$ modulo 4 (19). The existence of a Hadamard matrix for every value of N satisfying this requirement has not been shown, but constructions are available for nearly all permissible values of N up to 200. The simplest construction is for a Hadamard matrix of size $N = 2^n$ where n is an integer. In this case if $\mathbf{H}_N$ is a Hadamard matrix of size N, the matrix

$$\mathbf{H}_{2N} = \frac{1}{\sqrt{2}}\begin{bmatrix} \mathbf{H}_N & \mathbf{H}_N \\ \mathbf{H}_N & -\mathbf{H}_N \end{bmatrix}$$

(10.5-3)

is a Hadamard matrix of size $2N$. Figure 10.5-1 contains Hadamard matrices of size four and eight obtained by the construction of Eq. 10.5-3.

Harmuth (20) has suggested a frequency interpretation for the Hadamard matrix generated from the core matrix of Eq. 10.5-3; the number of sign changes along each row of the Hadamard matrix divided by two is called the sequency of the row. It is possible to construct a Hadamard matrix of order $N = 2^n$ whose number of sign changes per row increases from 0 to $N - 1$. This attribute is called the sequency property of the unitary matrix.

The rows of the Hadamard matrix of Eq. 10.5-3 can be considered to be samples of rectangular waves with a subperiod of $1/N$ units. These continuous functions, called Walsh functions * (21), are further related to the Rademacher block pulse functions (22). In this context the Hadamard matrix merely performs the decomposition of a function by a set of rectangular waveforms rather than the sine-cosine waveforms associated with the Fourier transform.

For symmetric Hadamard matrices of order $N = 2^n$, the two-dimensional Hadamard transform may be written in series form as

$$\mathscr{F}(u, v) = \frac{1}{N} \sum_{j=0}^{N-1} \sum_{k=0}^{N-1} F(j, k)(-1)^{p(j,k,u,v)} \tag{10.5-4}$$

where

$$p(j, k, u, v) = \sum_{i=0}^{n-1} (u_i j_i + v_i k_i) \tag{10.5-5}$$

The terms u_i, v_i, j_i, and k_i are the bit states of the binary representations of u, v, j, and k, respectively. For example, for $u = 13$, $u_3 = 1$, $u_2 = 1$, $u_1 = 0$,

	Sign Changes
$\mathbf{H}_4 = \dfrac{1}{2}\begin{bmatrix} 1 & 1 & 1 & 1 \\ 1 & -1 & 1 & -1 \\ 1 & 1 & -1 & -1 \\ 1 & -1 & -1 & 1 \end{bmatrix}$	0 3 1 2

	Sign Changes
$\mathbf{H}_8 = \dfrac{1}{2\sqrt{2}}\begin{bmatrix} 1 & 1 & 1 & 1 & 1 & 1 & 1 & 1 \\ 1 & -1 & 1 & -1 & 1 & -1 & 1 & -1 \\ 1 & 1 & -1 & -1 & 1 & 1 & -1 & -1 \\ 1 & -1 & -1 & 1 & 1 & -1 & -1 & 1 \\ 1 & 1 & 1 & 1 & -1 & -1 & -1 & -1 \\ 1 & -1 & 1 & -1 & -1 & 1 & -1 & 1 \\ 1 & 1 & -1 & -1 & -1 & -1 & 1 & 1 \\ 1 & -1 & -1 & 1 & -1 & 1 & 1 & -1 \end{bmatrix}$	0 7 3 4 1 6 2 5

FIGURE 10.5-1. Non-ordered Hadamard matrices of size four and eight.

* The Hadamard transform defined by the matrix construction of Eq. 10.5-3 is also known in the literature as the Walsh transform. It should be noted, however, that there are Hadamard matrices, for example, $N = 12$, for which the rows are not sampled Walsh functions.

252

$u_0 = 1$. Another series representation exists for a Hadamard matrix in "ordered" form in which the sequency of each row is larger than the preceding row. By this representation

$$\mathscr{F}(u, v) = \frac{1}{N} \sum_{j=0}^{N-1} \sum_{k=0}^{N-1} F(j, k)(-1)^{q(j,k,u,v)} \qquad (10.5\text{-}6)$$

where

$$q(j, k, u, v) = \sum_{i=0}^{n-1} [g_i(u)j_i + g_i(v)k_i] \qquad (10.5\text{-}7)$$

WAVE
NUMBER

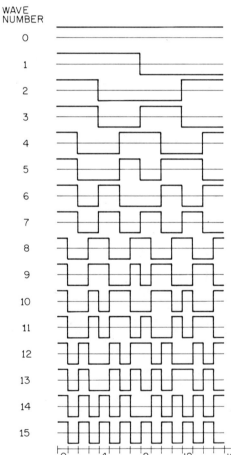

FIGURE 10.5-2. Hadamard transform basis functions, $N = 16$.

and

$$g_0(u) \equiv u_{n-1}$$
$$g_1(u) \equiv u_{n-1} + u_{n-2}$$
$$g_2(u) \equiv u_{n-2} + u_{n-3}$$
$$\vdots$$
$$g_{n-1}(u) \equiv u_1 + u_0$$

(10.5-8)

Hadamard transform basis functions for the ordered transform with $N = 16$ are shown in Figure 10.5-2. Basis planes, formed by the outer products of 8×1 Hadamard basis vectors, are illustrated in Figure 10.5-3. Figure 10.5-4 presents the ordered Hadamard transforms of a scene.

FIGURE 10.5-3.   Hadamard transform basis planes for $N = 8$. Black $= +1$; white $= -1$.

(a)

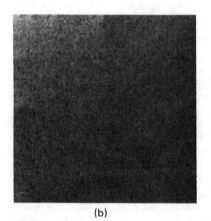

(b)	(c)

FIGURE 10.5-4.   Hadamard transform of GIRL image. (a) Original. (b) Log magnitude. (c) Clipped magnitude.

10.6. HAAR TRANSFORM

The Haar transform (1, 23) is derived from the Haar matrix, which consists of plus and minus ones and zero elements. Examples of 4×4 and 8×8 orthonormal Haar matrices are shown below:

$$\mathbf{H}_4 = \frac{1}{\sqrt{4}} \begin{bmatrix} 1 & 1 & 1 & 1 \\ 1 & 1 & -1 & -1 \\ \sqrt{2} & -\sqrt{2} & 0 & 0 \\ 0 & 0 & \sqrt{2} & -\sqrt{2} \end{bmatrix} \qquad (10.6\text{-}1)$$

$$\mathbf{H}_8 = \frac{1}{\sqrt{8}} \begin{bmatrix} 1 & 1 & 1 & 1 & 1 & 1 & 1 & 1 \\ 1 & 1 & 1 & 1 & -1 & -1 & -1 & -1 \\ \sqrt{2} & \sqrt{2} & -\sqrt{2} & -\sqrt{2} & 0 & 0 & 0 & 0 \\ 0 & 0 & 0 & 0 & \sqrt{2} & \sqrt{2} & -\sqrt{2} & -\sqrt{2} \\ 2 & -2 & 0 & 0 & 0 & 0 & 0 & 0 \\ 0 & 0 & 2 & -2 & 0 & 0 & 0 & 0 \\ 0 & 0 & 0 & 0 & 2 & -2 & 0 & 0 \\ 0 & 0 & 0 & 0 & 0 & 0 & 2 & -2 \end{bmatrix} \qquad (10.6\text{-}2)$$

Extensions to higher-order Haar matrices follow the structure indicated by Eqs. 10.6-1 and 10.6-2. Figure 10.6-1 contains plots of the Haar basis functions for $N = 16$. Haar basis planes for an 8×8 element array are shown in Figure 10.6-2.

The Haar transform can be likened to a sampling process in which rows of the transform matrix sample the input data sequence with finer and finer resolution increasing in powers of two. In image processing applications,

WAVE
NUMBER

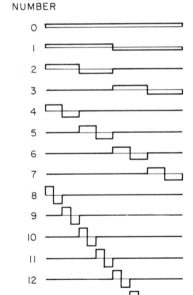

FIGURE 10.6-1. Haar transform basis functions, $N = 16$.

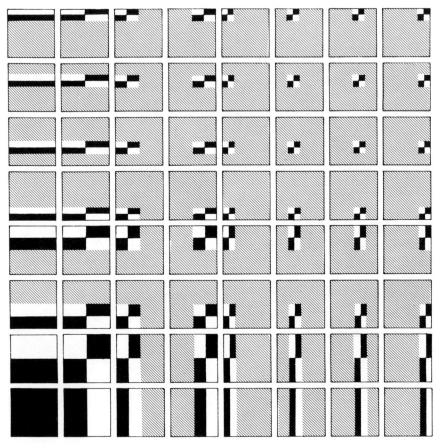

FIGURE 10.6-2. Haar transform basis planes for $N = 8$. Black $= +1$; white $= -1$; cross-hatched $= 0$.

the Haar transform provides a transform domain in which a type of differential energy is concentrated in localized regions. Thus there is an area in which adjacent picture element differential energy is concentrated, an area in which differential energy of adjacent picture elements taken two at a time is concentrated, and in general an area in which difference energy of adjacent picture elements taken a power of two at a time is concentrated.

Figure 10.6-3 presents the Haar transform of an image. The logarithmic presentation vividly displays the derivative energy effect especially in the high-sequency regions of the plane. Note that in the Haar transform there is also a concentration of image energy toward the low-sequency components.

(a)

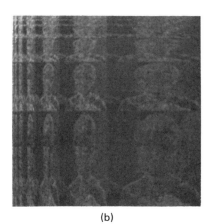

(b)   (c)

FIGURE 10.6-3. Haar transform of GIRL image. (a) Original. (b) Log magnitude.
(c) Clipped magnitude.

10.7. SLANT TRANSFORM

The slant transform (24–26) is an orthogonal transform that is designed to possess the following properties: (1) constant basis vector, (2) slant basis vector (monotonically decreasing in constant size steps from maximum to a minimum amplitude, (3) sequency property, (4) fast computational algorithm, (5) high-energy compaction. For a vector length of $N = 2$ the slant transform is identical to the Hadamard transform of order two. Thus

$$\mathbf{S}_2 = \frac{1}{\sqrt{2}}\begin{bmatrix} 1 & 1 \\ 1 & -1 \end{bmatrix}$$ (10.7-1)

The slant transform matrix of order four is obtained by the operation

$$
S_4 = \frac{1}{2^{1/2}} \left[\begin{array}{cc|cc} 1 & 0 & 1 & 0 \\ a_4 & b_4 & -a_4 & b_4 \\ \hline 0 & 1 & 0 & -1 \\ -b_4 & a_4 & b_4 & a_4 \end{array} \right] \left[\begin{array}{c|c} S_2 & 0 \\ \hline 0 & S_2 \end{array} \right]
\tag{10.7-2a}
$$

or

$$
S_4 = \frac{1}{\sqrt{4}} \left[\begin{array}{cccc} 1 & 1 & 1 & 1 \\ a_4 + b_4 & a_4 - b_4 & -a_4 + b_4 & -a_4 - b_4 \\ 1 & -1 & -1 & 1 \\ a_4 - b_4 & -a_4 - b_4 & a_4 + b_4 & -a_4 + b_4 \end{array} \right]
\tag{10.7-2b}
$$

where a_4 and b_4 are real scaling constants to be determined subject to the conditions that S_4 must be orthogonal and that the step size of the second (slant) basis vector must be the same throughout its length. By setting the step sizes equal it is found that $a_4 = 2b_4$. The orthogonality condition $S_4 S_4^T = I$ leads to $b_4 = 1/\sqrt{5}$. Thus the slant matrix becomes

$$
S_4 = \frac{1}{\sqrt{4}} \left[\begin{array}{cccc} 1 & 1 & 1 & 1 \\ \dfrac{3}{\sqrt{5}} & \dfrac{1}{\sqrt{5}} & \dfrac{-1}{\sqrt{5}} & \dfrac{-3}{\sqrt{5}} \\ 1 & -1 & -1 & 1 \\ \dfrac{1}{\sqrt{5}} & \dfrac{-3}{\sqrt{5}} & \dfrac{3}{\sqrt{5}} & \dfrac{-1}{\sqrt{5}} \end{array} \right]
\tag{10.7-3}
$$

It is easily shown that S_4 is orthonormal. Furthermore, note that S_4 possesses the sequency property; each row has an increasing number of sign reversals from 0 to 3.

An extension of the slant matrix to its next size increment S_8 is given by

$$
S_8 = \frac{1}{2^{1/2}} \left[\begin{array}{cccc|cccc} 1 & 0 & 0 & 0 & 1 & 0 & 0 & 0 \\ a_8 & b_8 & 0 & 0 & -a_8 & b_8 & 0 & 0 \\ 0 & 0 & 1 & 0 & 0 & 0 & 1 & 0 \\ 0 & 0 & 0 & 1 & 0 & 0 & 0 & 1 \\ \hline 0 & 1 & 0 & 0 & 0 & -1 & 0 & 0 \\ -b_8 & a_8 & 0 & 0 & b_8 & a_8 & 0 & 0 \\ 0 & 0 & 1 & 0 & 0 & 0 & -1 & 0 \\ 0 & 0 & 0 & 1 & 0 & 0 & 0 & -1 \end{array} \right] \left[\begin{array}{c|c} S_4 & 0 \\ \hline 0 & S_4 \end{array} \right]
\tag{10.7-4}
$$

In $\mathbf{S}_8$ the slant vector is obtained by a simple scaling operation on $\mathbf{S}_4$. The remaining terms in Eq. 10.7-4 are introduced to obtain the sequency and orthogonality properties.

Equation 10.7-4 can be generalized to give the slant matrix of order N in terms of the slant matrix of order $N - 1$ by the recursive relation

$$
\mathbf{S}_N = \frac{1}{2^{1/2}}
\left[
\begin{array}{cccccc}
1 & 0 & & 1 & 0 & \multirow{2}{*}{$\mathbf{0}$} \\
a_N & b_N & \mathbf{0} & -a_N & b_N & \\
\hline
0 & & \mathbf{I}_{(N/2)-2} & 0 & & \mathbf{I}_{(N/2)-2} \\
0 & 1 & & 0 & -1 & \\
\hline
-b_N & a_N & \mathbf{0} & b_N & a_N & \mathbf{0} \\
\mathbf{0} & & \mathbf{I}_{(N/2)-2} & 0 & & -\mathbf{I}_{(N/2)-2}
\end{array}
\right]
\left[
\begin{array}{cc}
\mathbf{S}_{N/2} & \mathbf{0} \\
\hline
\mathbf{0} & \mathbf{S}_{N/2}
\end{array}
\right]
$$

$$(10.7\text{-}5)$$

where $\mathbf{I}_K$ represents a $K \times K$ identity matrix. The constants a_N and b_N may be computed from the recursive relation (26)

$$a_2 = 1 \tag{10.7-6a}$$

$$b_N = [1 + 4(a_{N/2})^2]^{-1/2} \tag{10.7-6b}$$

$$a_N = 2b_N a_{N/2} \tag{10.7-6c}$$

or by the formulas

$$a_{2N} = \left(\frac{3N^2}{4N^2 - 1}\right)^{1/2} \tag{10.7-7a}$$

$$b_{2N} = \left(\frac{N^2 - 1}{4N^2 - 1}\right)^{1/2} \tag{10.7-7b}$$

Figure 10.7-1 contains drawings of the slant basis functions for $N = 16$. Photographs of the slant transform of an image are shown in Figure 10.7-2.

10.8. KARHUNEN–LOEVE TRANSFORM

Techniques for transforming continuous signals into a set of uncorrelated representational coefficients were originally developed by Karhunen (27) and Loeve (28). Hotelling (29) has been credited (30) with the conversion procedure that transforms discrete signals into a sequence of uncorrelated coefficients. However, most of the literature in the field refers to both discrete and continuous transformations as either Karhunen–Loeve or eigenvector transforms.

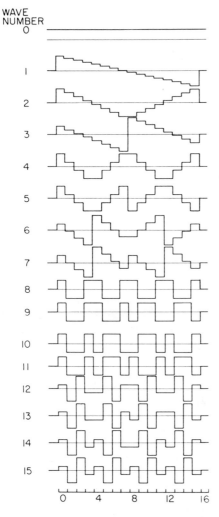

FIGURE 10.7-1. Slant transform basis functions, $N = 16$.

The Karhunen–Loeve transformation is a transformation of the general form

$$\mathcal{F}(u, v) = \sum_{j=0}^{N-1} \sum_{k=0}^{N-1} F(j, k) A(j, k; u, v) \qquad (10.8\text{-}1)$$

for which the kernel $A(j, k; u, v)$ satisfies the equation

$$\lambda(u, v) A(j, k; u, v) = \sum_{j=0}^{N-1} \sum_{k=0}^{N-1} K_F(j, k; j', k') A(j', k'; u, v) \qquad (10.8\text{-}2)$$

(a)

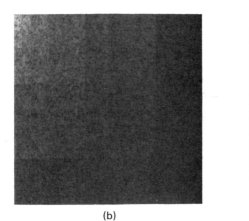

(b)   (c)

FIGURE 10.7-2. Slant transform of GIRL image. (a) Original. (b) Log magnitude. (c) Clipped magnitude.

where $K_F(j, k; j', k')$ denotes the covariance function of the image array and $\lambda(u, v)$ is a constant for fixed (u, v). The set of functions defined by the kernel are the eigenfunctions of the covariance function, and $\lambda(u, v)$ represents the eigenvalues of the covariance function. It is usually not possible to express the kernel in explicit form.

If the covariance function is separable such that

$$K_F(j, k; j', k') = K_C(j, j')K_R(k, k') \qquad (10.8-3)$$

then the Karhunen–Loeve kernel is also separable and

$$A(j, k; u, v) = A_C(j, u)A_R(k, v) \qquad (10.8-4)$$

The row and column kernels satisfy the equations

$$\lambda_R(v)A_R(k, v) = \sum_{k'=0}^{N-1} K_R(k, k')A_R(k', v) \qquad (10.8\text{-}5)$$

$$\lambda_C(u)A_C(j, u) = \sum_{j'=0}^{N-1} K_C(j, j')A_C(j', u) \qquad (10.8\text{-}6)$$

In the special case in which the covariance matrix is of separable first-order Markov process form, the eigenfunctions can be written in explicit form. For a one-dimensional Markov process with correlation factor ρ, the eigenfunctions and eigenvalues are given by (3)

$$A(j, u) = \left[\frac{2}{N + \lambda^2(u)}\right]^{1/2} \sin\left[w(u)\left(j - \frac{N-1}{2}\right) + \frac{(u+1)\pi}{2}\right]$$

$$(10.8\text{-}7)$$

and

$$\lambda(u) = \frac{1 - \rho^2}{1 - 2\rho \cos[w(u)] + \rho^2} \qquad (10.8\text{-}8)$$

for $0 \le j, u \le N - 1$ where $w(u)$ denotes the root of the transcendental equation

$$\tan(Nw) = \frac{(1 - \rho^2)\sin(w)}{\cos(w) - 2\rho + \rho^2\cos(w)} \qquad (10.8\text{-}9)$$

The eigenvectors can also be generated by the recursion formula (32)

$$A(0, u) = \frac{\lambda(u)}{1 - \rho^2}[A(0, u) - \rho A(1, u)] \qquad (10.8\text{-}10a)$$

$$A(j, u) = \frac{\lambda(u)}{1 - \rho^2}[-\rho A(j-1, u) + (1 + \rho^2)A(j, u) - \rho A(j+1, u)]$$

$$0 < j < N - 1 \qquad (10.8\text{-}10b)$$

$$A(N-1, u) = \frac{\lambda(u)}{1 - \rho^2}[-\rho A(N-2, u) + A(N-1, u)]$$

$$(10.8\text{-}10c)$$

by initially setting $A(0, u) = 1$ and subsequently normalizing the eigenvectors.

If the image array and transformed image array are expressed in vector form, the Karhunen–Loeve transform pairs are

$$\boldsymbol{f} = \mathbf{A}\mathbf{f} \qquad (10.8\text{-}11)$$

and

$$\mathbf{f} = \mathbf{A}^T\boldsymbol{f} \qquad (10.8\text{-}12)$$

The transformation matrix $\mathbf{A}$ satisfies the relation

$$\mathbf{A}\mathbf{K}_f = \mathbf{\Lambda}\mathbf{A} \tag{10.8-13}$$

where $\mathbf{K}_f$ is the covariance matrix of $\mathbf{f}$, $\mathbf{A}$ is a matrix whose rows are eigenvectors of $\mathbf{K}_f$, and $\mathbf{\Lambda}$ is a diagonal matrix of the form

$$\mathbf{\Lambda} = \begin{bmatrix} \lambda(1) & & \\ & \lambda(2) & 0 \\ & & \ddots \\ 0 & & \lambda(N^2) \end{bmatrix} \tag{10.8-14}$$

VECTOR NUMBER

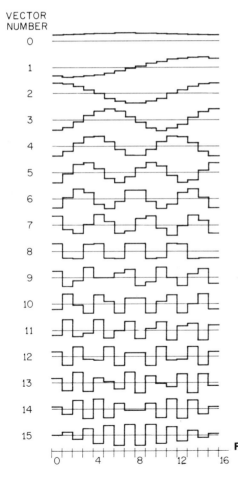

FIGURE 10.8-1. Karhunen–Loeve transform basis functions, $N = 16$.

If $\mathbf{K}_f$ is of separable form then

$$\mathbf{A} = \mathbf{A}_C \otimes \mathbf{A}_R \qquad (10.8\text{-}15)$$

where $\mathbf{A}_R$ and $\mathbf{A}_C$ satisfy the relations

$$\mathbf{A}_R \mathbf{K}_R = \Lambda_R \mathbf{A}_R \qquad (10.8\text{-}16a)$$

$$\mathbf{A}_C \mathbf{K}_C = \Lambda_C \mathbf{A}_C \qquad (10.8\text{-}16b)$$

and $\lambda(k) = \lambda_R(i)\lambda_C(j)$ for $i, j = 1, 2, \ldots, N$ (33, p. 209).

Figure 10.8-1 contains plots of the Karhunen–Loeve basis functions for a one-dimensional Markov process with adjacent element correlation of $\rho = 0.9$.

10.9. SVD TRANSFORM

The SVD transform (34) is a two-dimensional unitary transform based on the singular value decomposition of matrices presented in Chapter 5. The forward transform is defined by

$$\mathscr{F} = \mathbf{A}_C \mathbf{F} \mathbf{A}_R^T \qquad (10.9\text{-}1)$$

and the inverse transform by

$$\mathbf{F} = \mathbf{A}_C^T \mathscr{F} \mathbf{A}_R \qquad (10.9\text{-}2)$$

The row transformation matrix performs the diagonalization operation

$$\mathbf{A}_R [\mathbf{F}^T \mathbf{F}] \mathbf{A}_R^T = \Lambda \qquad (10.9\text{-}3)$$

where Λ is a diagonal matrix whose terms $\lambda(u)$ are the eigenvalues of $\mathbf{F}^T \mathbf{F}$. Similarly,

$$\mathbf{A}_C [\mathbf{F} \mathbf{F}^T] \mathbf{A}_C^T = \Lambda \qquad (10.9\text{-}4)$$

Substitution of Eq. 10.9-2 into Eqs. 10.9-3 and 10.9-4 indicates that

$$\mathscr{F} = \Lambda^{1/2} \qquad (10.9\text{-}5)$$

where $\Lambda^{1/2}$ is a diagonal matrix consisting of the terms $\lambda^{1/2}(u)$, called the singular values of $\mathbf{F}$, which are the respective square roots of the eigenvalues $\lambda(u)$.

The image matrix $\mathbf{F}$ can be expressed in a very compact outer-product form with the SVD expansion. Referring to Eq. 10.1-14b,

$$\mathbf{F} = \sum_{u=1}^{N} \mathscr{F}(u, u) \mathbf{b}_C(u) \mathbf{b}_R^T(u) \qquad (10.9\text{-}6)$$

where $\mathbf{b}_C(u)$ and $\mathbf{b}_R(u)$ represent the uth columns of the matrices $\mathbf{B}_C^T$ and $\mathbf{B}_R^T$, respectively.

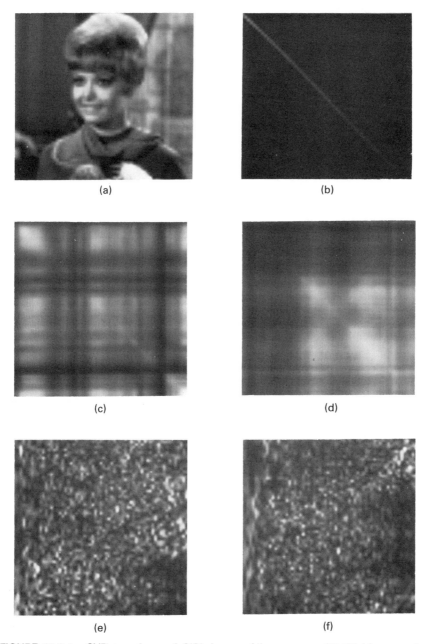

(a)

(b)

(c)

(d)

(e)

(f)

FIGURE 10.9-1. SVD transform of GIRL image. All arrays are 64×64 blown up to 256×256 using bilinear interpolation. (a) Original, **F**. (b) SVD transform, $\mathscr{F}$. (c) **FF**^{T}. (d) **F**^{T}**F**. (e) Magnitude, **U**. (f) Magnitude, **V**.

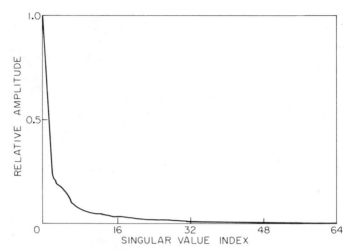

FIGURE 10.9-2.   SVD transform singular values of GIRL image.

With the SVD transform, the $N \times N$ pixel image $\mathbf{F}$ is represented by only N components, the N singular value transform coefficients $\mathcal{F}(u, u)$. However, it must be observed that the row and column transform matrices both depend on the image array.

Figure 10.9-1 provides an example of the SVD transform of an image along with the matrix products $\mathbf{FF}^T$ and $\mathbf{F}^T\mathbf{F}$ plus the corresponding row and column transform matrices $\mathbf{U}$ and $\mathbf{V}$. The singular values for this image are plotted in Figure 10.9-2. Finally, Figure 10.9-3 contains a series of the outer-product matrices $\mathbf{b}_C(u)\mathbf{b}_R^T(u)$.

10.10.   COMPUTATIONAL ALGORITHMS

A unitary transform of an $N \times N$ pixel image into an $N \times N$ array of transform coefficients requires on the order of N^4 computational operations for the general case. A computational operation is defined here to be a multiplication and an addition. For large size image arrays this number of operations may be prohibitively large. Fortunately, efficient computational algorithms exist for many unitary transforms.

The key to efficient or fast computational algorithms is the ability to subdivide the total computational task into a series of computational steps such that partial results from the initial steps can be repeatedly utilized in subsequent steps. As an example, consider computation of the unordered

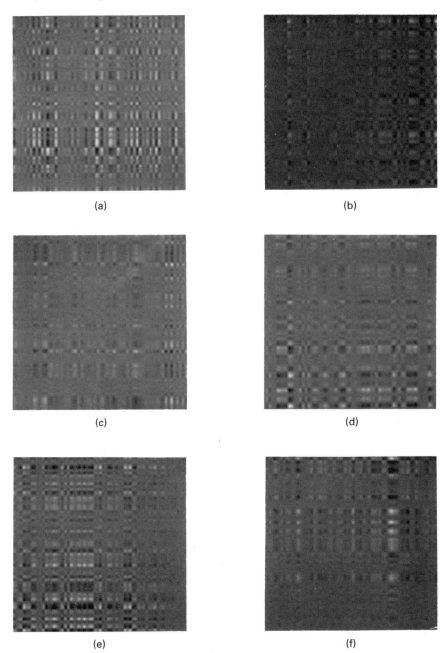

(a)

(b)

(c)

(d)

(e)

(f)

FIGURE 10.9-3. SVD transform basis planes of GIRL image. (a) $b_C(1)b_R^T(1)$. (b) $b_C(4)b_R^T(4)$. (c) $b_C(8)b_R^T(8)$. (d) $b_C(16)b_R^T b(16)$. (e) $b_C(32)b_R^T(32)$. (f) $b_C(64)b_R^T(64)$.

Hadamard transformation of the four-element sequence $f(j)$. Direct computation requires computation of the set of equations

$$f(0) = f(0) + f(1) + f(2) + f(3) \tag{10.10-1a}$$
$$f(1) = f(0) - f(1) + f(2) - f(3) \tag{10.10-1b}$$
$$f(2) = f(0) + f(1) - f(2) - f(3) \tag{10.10-1c}$$
$$f(3) = f(0) - f(1) - f(2) + f(3) \tag{10.10-1d}$$

As formulated, Eq. 10.10-1 requires $[N(N-1)] = 12$ operations.* Alternatively, the Hadamard coefficients can be sequentially computed by the steps

First pass

$$a(0) = f(0) + f(2) \tag{10.10-2a}$$
$$a(1) = f(0) - f(2) \tag{10.10-2b}$$
$$a(2) = f(1) + f(3) \tag{10.10-2c}$$
$$a(3) = f(1) - f(3) \tag{10.10-2d}$$

Second pass

$$f(0) = a(0) + a(2) \tag{10.10-3a}$$
$$f(1) = a(0) - a(2) \tag{10.10-3b}$$
$$f(2) = a(1) + a(3) \tag{10.10-3c}$$
$$f(3) = a(1) - a(3) \tag{10.10-3d}$$

Computation of $\mathbf{H}_4$ by Eqs. 10.10-2 and 10.10-3 requires a total of $[N \log N] = 8$ operations for a savings of four operations.

The operations indicated by the two passes can be described by the flow chart of Figure 10.10-1. The number of operations is equal to one-half the number of lines entering nodes. An alternative representational approach is matrix factorization, in which the Hadamard matrix $\mathbf{H}_4$ is factored into the product of sparse matrices. For example,

$$\mathbf{H}_4 = \begin{bmatrix} 1 & 1 & 0 & 0 \\ 0 & 0 & 1 & 1 \\ 1 & -1 & 0 & 0 \\ 0 & 0 & 1 & -1 \end{bmatrix} \begin{bmatrix} 1 & 1 & 0 & 0 \\ 0 & 0 & 1 & 1 \\ 1 & -1 & 0 & 0 \\ 0 & 0 & 1 & -1 \end{bmatrix} \tag{10.10-4}$$

The required number of operations is equal to one-half the number of nonzero elements in the matrix factors.

* An operation is counted for each plus or minus sign in an expression.

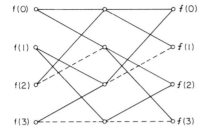

FIGURE 10.10-1. Computational flow chart for Hadamard transform of size four. Solid lines indicate addition, dotted lines indicate subtraction.

The principles outlined above for the fast computation of the Hadamard transform generalize to many other transforms. Fast computational algorithms have been discovered for the Fourier (35), even cosine (12), sine (13), Hadamard (17), Haar (1), and slant (26) transforms. No fast algorithms have been developed for the general Karhunen–Loeve (KL) transform, but approximate KL transform algorithms have been discovered for the Markov process KL transform.

Most one-dimensional unitary transforms require on the order of $N \log_2 N$ operations; an exception is the Haar transform, which can be computed with about $2N$ operations because of its sparseness. There is no systematic method known to determine an efficient computational algorithm for a unitary transform (36). One must simply find some efficient flow-chart decimation or sparse-matrix factorization through inventiveness.

Unitary transforms employing sinusoidal basis vectors (Fourier, cosine, sine) can be computed in an indirect manner by the so-called chirp-Z transform algorithm. In one dimension the Fourier transform of the sequence $f(j)$ is given by

$$\mathcal{F}(u) = \frac{1}{\sqrt{N}} \sum_{j=0}^{N-1} f(j) \exp\left\{\frac{-2\pi i}{N} ju\right\} \qquad (10.10\text{-}5)$$

Making the substitution

$$2ju = j^2 + u^2 - (u - j)^2 \qquad (10.10\text{-}6)$$

one obtains

$$\mathcal{F}(u) = \frac{\exp\left\{-i\pi u^2/N\right\}}{\sqrt{N}} \sum_{j=0}^{N-1} \exp\left\{\frac{i\pi}{N}(u - j)^2\right\} \exp\left\{\frac{-i\pi j^2}{N}\right\} f(j) \qquad (10.10\text{-}7)$$

Equation 10.10-7 can be considered as:

1. Point-by-point multiplication of the sequence $f(j)$ by the quadratic term $\exp\{-i\pi j^2/N\}$;

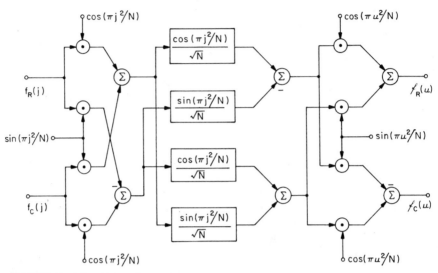

FIGURE 10.10-2.   Chirp-Z transform algorithm implementation of Fourier transform.

2. convolution of the result of step (1) with the kernel $\exp\{i\pi j^2/N\}$;
3. point-by-point multiplication of the result of step (2) with the quadratic term $\exp\{i\pi u^2/N\}$.

Figure 10.10-2 contains a block diagram for computation of the Fourier transform with the chirp-Z transform algorithm. If computation is to be performed on a general-purpose digital computer, utilization of the chirp-Z transform is generally not advisable because the convolution step usually requires more operations than direct transformation with a fast Fourier transform algorithm. However, the chirp-Z transform can be implemented quite easily by analog transversal filters for pipeline computation of the Fourier, cosine, and sine transforms.

10.11.   STATISTICAL ANALYSIS OF IMAGE TRANSFORMS

The development of efficient quantization and coding methods for image transform samples requires an understanding of the statistical properties of the transform domain. This section presents a derivation of the first and second moments of transform samples. The following section contains the development of a stochastic model for the probability density of transform samples.

If the image array $F(j, k)$ is assumed to be a sample of a two-dimensional stochastic process with known mean and covariance function, then its unitary transform

$$\mathcal{F}(u, v) = \sum_{j=0}^{N-1} \sum_{k=0}^{N-1} F(j, k) A(j, k; u, v) \qquad (10.11\text{-}1)$$

will be a stochastic process. From Eq. 8.2-1b, the mean of $\mathcal{F}(u, v)$ is

$$E\{\mathcal{F}(u, v)\} = \sum_{j} \sum_{k} E\{F(j, k)\} A(j, k; u, v) \qquad (10.11\text{-}2)$$

where $E\{F(j, k)\}$ represents the mean of $F(j, k)$. Equation 8.2-3 provides an expression for the covariance function of $\mathcal{F}(u, v)$,

$$K_{\mathcal{F}}(u_1, v_1; u_2, v_2) = \sum_{j_1} \sum_{j_2} \sum_{k_1} \sum_{k_2} K_F(j_1, j_2; k_1, k_2) A(j_1, k_1; u_1, v_1)$$

$$A^*(j_2, k_2; u_2, v_2) \qquad (10.11\text{-}3)$$

where $K_F(j_1, j_2; k_1, k_2)$ denotes the covariance function of $F(j, k)$. Finally, the variance function of $\mathcal{F}(u, v)$ is

$$\sigma_{\mathcal{F}}^2(u, v) = K_{\mathcal{F}}(u, v; u, v) \qquad (10.11\text{-}4)$$

In the vector-space representation of a unitary transform, the vector of column-scanned transform coefficients is given by

$$\mathbf{\mathcal{f}} = \mathbf{Af} \qquad (10.11\text{-}5)$$

The mean vector of transform coefficients is then

$$\mathbf{\eta}_{\mathcal{f}} = \mathbf{A}\mathbf{\eta}_f \qquad (10.11\text{-}6)$$

and the covariance matrix of transform coefficients is

$$\mathbf{K}_{\mathcal{f}} = \mathbf{A}\mathbf{K}_f \mathbf{A}^{*T} \qquad (10.11\text{-}7)$$

The variance matrix $\mathbf{V}_{\mathcal{F}}$ of transform coefficients is obtained by arranging the trace of the transform covariance matrix of Eq. 10.11-7 into matrix form.

Consideration is now given to computation of the first and second moments of the array of transform coefficients for specific unitary transforms. In the general case the moments can, of course, be computed either in series form or vector-space form by brute force computation utilizing the formulas previously stated. however, it is desirable to develop analytic formulations of the moment functions for purposes of design and analysis.

Attention is first given to the KL transform. The general expression for the covariance function of transform coefficients given by Eq. 10.11-3 can be rewritten as

$$K_{\mathscr{F}}(u_1, v_1; u_2, v_2)$$

$$= \sum_{j_2}\sum_{k_2} A^*(j_2, k_2; u_2, v_2)\sum_{j_1}\sum_{k_1} K_F(j_1, j_2; k_1, k_2)A(j_1, k_1; u_1, v_1)$$

$$(10.11\text{-}8)$$

However, from Eq. 10.8-2, the second set of summations is recognized as the defining relationship for the KL transform kernel. Thus

$$K_{\mathscr{F}}(u_1, v_1; u_2, v_2) = \sum_{j_2}\sum_{k_2} A^*(j_2, k_2; u_2, v_2)\lambda(u_1, v_1)A(j_2, k_2; u_1, v_1)$$

$$(10.11\text{-}9)$$

where the function $\lambda(u, v)$ represents the eigenvalues of the image covariance function. Since the KL transform is orthogonal,

$$K_{\mathscr{F}}(u_1, v_1; u_2, v_2) = \lambda(u_1, v_1)\delta(u_1 - u_2, v_1 - v_2) \qquad (10.11\text{-}10)$$

Thus the KL transform coefficients are uncorrelated and the variance function equals the corresponding eigenvalue

$$\sigma_{\mathscr{F}}^2(u, v) = \lambda(u, v) \qquad (10.11\text{-}11)$$

The KL transform is the only unitary transform that performs a complete decorrelation for an arbitrary image process; other transformations result in some residual correlation between transform coefficients. Also, the KL transform provides the best energy compaction of all unitary transforms. Suppose that the variances of transform coefficients for an arbitrary transform are arranged in a sequence such that $\sigma^2(1) > \sigma^2(2) > \cdots > \sigma^2(N^2)$ and suppose that the eigenvalues of the covariance function are similarly arranged in a sequence for which $\lambda(1) > \lambda(2) > \cdots > \lambda(N^2)$. Then it can be shown for any upper limit of summation $W < N^2$ that

$$\sum_{w=0}^{W} \lambda(w) \geq \sum_{w=0}^{W} \sigma^2(w) \qquad (10.11\text{-}12)$$

In order to develop analytic formulations for the moments of other transforms, it is necessary to specify the statistical properties of the image array. If the image array is stationary in the wide sense, then the mean of the array is a constant. As a result

$$E\{\mathscr{F}(u, v)\} = E\{F\}\sum_{j}\sum_{k} A(j, k; u, v) \qquad (10.11\text{-}13)$$

Since, however, the transform kernel is an orthogonal function, the summation yields zero except for the zeroth basis function for an ordered transform. Hence

$$E\{\mathscr{F}(0,0)\} = E\{F\} \sum_j \sum_k A(j,k;0,0) \qquad u, v = 0 \qquad (10.11\text{-}14a)$$

$$E\{\mathscr{F}(u,v)\} = 0 \qquad\qquad\qquad u, v \neq 0 \qquad (10.11\text{-}14b)$$

The double summation equates to N for unitary transforms possessing a constant basis function.

For a wide-sense stationary image array, the covariance function of the image array assumes the functional form $K_F(j_1 - j_2, k_1 - k_2)$. However, the array of transform coefficients will not be wide-sense stationary unless the transform kernel is space invariant. A notable example is the Fourier transform.

Most common image transform are spatially separable. If, in addition, the image covariance function is spatially separable, then

$$K_{\mathscr{F}}(u_1, v_1; u_2, v_2) = K_{\mathscr{F}_C}(u_1, v_1) K_{\mathscr{F}_R}(u_2, v_2) \qquad (10.11\text{-}15)$$

where

$$K_{\mathscr{F}_C}(u_1, u_2) = \sum_{j_1} \sum_{j_2} K_{F_C}(j_1, j_2) A_C(j_1, u_1) A_C^*(j_2, u_2) \qquad (10.11\text{-}16a)$$

$$K_{\mathscr{F}_R}(v_1, v_2) = \sum_{k_1} \sum_{k_2} K_{F_R}(k_1, k_2) A_R(k_1, v_1) A_R^*(k_2, u_2) \qquad (10.11\text{-}16b)$$

Under these conditions the variance function is also separable into the product of row and column variance functions as given by

$$\sigma_{\mathscr{F}}^2(u, v) = \sigma_{\mathscr{F}_R}^2(u) \sigma_{\mathscr{F}_C}^2(v) \qquad (10.11\text{-}17)$$

For the Fourier transform the one-dimensional variance function for a wide-sense stationary image is given by

$$\sigma_{\mathscr{F}_Z}^2(w) = \frac{1}{N} \sum_{z_1} \sum_{z_2} K_{F_Z}(z_1 - z_2) \exp\left\{ -\frac{2\pi i}{N} w(z_1 - z_2) \right\} \qquad (10.11\text{-}18)$$

with $w = u$ or v and $z_i = j_i$ or k_i. The variance function may then be rewritten as

$$\sigma_{\mathscr{F}_Z}^2(w) = \frac{1}{N} \sum_{z_2} \exp\left\{ \frac{2\pi i}{N} w z_2 \right\} \sum_{z_1} K_{F_Z}\{z_1 - z_2\} \exp\left\{ -\frac{2\pi i}{N} w z_1 \right\} \qquad (10.11\text{-}19)$$

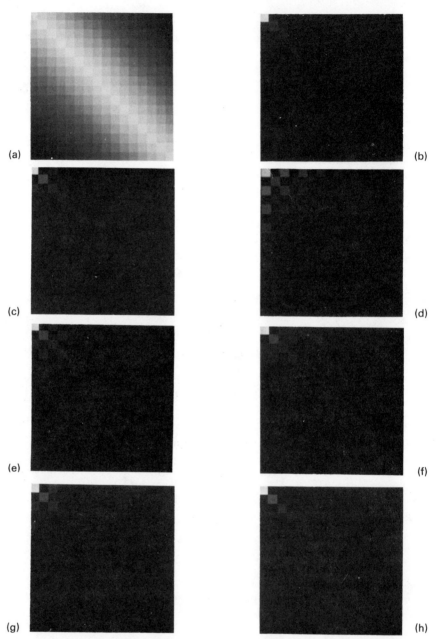

(a)

(b)

(c)

(d)

(e)

(f)

(g)

(h)

FIGURE 10.11-1. Graphics displays of covariance matrices for unitary transforms, $N = 16$, $\rho = 0.9$. (a) Identity. (b) Fourier. (c) cosine. (d) sine. (e) Hadamard. (f) Haar. (g) slant. (h) Karhunen–Loeve.

The second summation is the one-dimensional discrete Fourier transform of the covariance function shifted by z_2. By the Fourier transform translation theorem

$$\sigma^2_{\mathcal{F}_Z}(w) = \frac{1}{N} \sum_{z_2} \exp\left\{\frac{2\pi i}{N} wz_2\right\} \exp\left\{-\frac{2\pi i}{N} wz_2\right\} \mathcal{G}_Z(w) = \mathcal{G}_Z(w) \quad (10.11\text{-}20)$$

where $\mathcal{G}_Z(w)$ and $K_{F_Z}(z)$ are one-dimensional discrete Fourier transform pairs. From Eq. 5.4-16 it is seen that $\mathcal{G}_Z(w)$ is the discrete version of the power-spectral density $\mathcal{W}_{F_Z}(w)$ of the image function along one coordinate minus the average image power. For a zero mean process

$$\sigma^2_{\mathcal{F}_Z}(w) = \mathcal{W}_{F_Z}(w) \quad (10.11\text{-}21)$$

The Hadamard, Haar, and other transforms discussed earlier do not possess the Fourier transform translation property. As a consequence, no closed expressions have been developed for covariance or variance functions for these transforms.

Figure 10.11-1 contains displays of the covariance functions of several unitary transforms for a discrete one-dimensional Markov process of length 16 with an adjacent element correlation factor of $\rho = 0.9$. A plot of the variance of the transform coefficients is presented in Figure 10.11-2.

10.12. PROBABILITY DENSITY MODELS FOR IMAGE TRANSFORMS

It would be desirable to know the probability density of transform samples for an arbitrary image transform. Unfortunately, this result is not easily obtained because the original image probability density is not usually well defined, and, also, the transform operation is usually mathematically complex. However, the transforms considered for image processing applications form a weighted sum over all of the elements in the original image. Therefore, one can evoke qualitative arguments, based upon the central limit theorem of statistics, that the probability density of transform samples tends to be Gaussian with moments as calculated in the previous section.

Fourier transform samples are complex numbers that may be represented in real and imaginary, or magnitude and phase, form. In either case there are two components per transform sample that must be quantized. The real $\mathcal{F}_R(u, v)$ and imaginary $\mathcal{F}_I(u, v)$ components of the Fourier transform samples may be assumed to follow the same Gaussian distribution whose variance $\sigma^2_{\mathcal{F}}(u, v)$ is proportional to the power-spectral

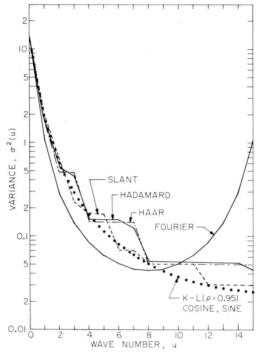

FIGURE 10.11-2. Variances of unitary transform coefficients, $N = 16$, $\rho = 0.9$.

density of the original image. Hence

$$p\{\mathcal{F}_R(u, v)\} = [2\pi\sigma_{\mathcal{F}}^2(u, v)]^{-1/2} \exp\left\{\frac{-\mathcal{F}_R^2(u, v)}{2\sigma_{\mathcal{F}}^2(u, v)}\right\} \quad (10.12\text{-}1a)$$

$$p\{\mathcal{F}_I(u, v)\} = [2\pi\sigma_{\mathcal{F}}^2(u, v)]^{-1/2} \exp\left\{\frac{-\mathcal{F}_I^2(u, v)}{2\sigma_{\mathcal{F}}^2(u, v)}\right\} \quad (10.12\text{-}1b)$$

If the real and imaginary components are Gaussian, the magnitude of the Fourier transform sample $\mathcal{F}_M(u, v)$ is Rayleigh distributed. Thus

$$p\{\mathcal{F}_M(u, v)\} = \frac{\mathcal{F}_M(u, v)}{\sigma_{\mathcal{F}}^2(u, v)} \exp\left\{\frac{-\mathcal{F}_M^2(u, v)}{2\sigma_{\mathcal{F}}^2(u, v)}\right\} \quad (10.12\text{-}2)$$

for $\mathcal{F}_M(u, v) \geq 0$, and its phase $\mathcal{F}_P(u, v)$ is uniformly distributed as specified by

$$P\{\mathcal{F}_P(u, v)\} = \frac{1}{2\pi} \quad (10.12\text{-}3)$$

where $-\pi \leq \mathcal{F}_P(u, v) \leq \pi$. The statistical distribution of transform components for real transforms may be considered to follow a Gaussian distribution of the form

$$p\{\mathcal{F}(u, v)\} = [2\pi\sigma_{\mathcal{F}}^2(u, v)]^{-1/2} \exp\left\{\frac{-\mathcal{F}^2(u, v)}{2\sigma_{\mathcal{F}}^2(u, v)}\right\} \qquad (10.12\text{-}4)$$

The Rayleigh density of Eq. 10.12-2 has often been applied as a probability density model of the "d.c." coefficient $\mathcal{F}(0, 0)$ for luminance images since this coefficient is strictly positive for such images. These probability density models are used extensively in the design of transform image coders.

REFERENCES

1. H. C. Andrews, *Computer Techniques in Image Processing*, Academic Press, New York, 1970.

2. H. C. Andrews, "Two Dimensional Transforms," in *Topics in Applied Physics: Picture Processings and Digital Filtering*, Vol. 6, T. S. Huang, Ed., Springer-Verlag, New York, 1975.

3. R. Bellman, *Introduction to Matrix Analysis*, McGraw-Hill, New York, 1960.

4. H. C. Andrews and K. Caspari, "A Generalized Technique for Spectral Analysis," *IEEE Trans. Computers*, **C-19**, 1, January 1970, 16–25.

5. J. W. Cooley and J. W. Tukey, "An Algorithm for the Machine Calculation of Complex Fourier Series," *Math. Comput.*, **19**, 90, April 1965, 297–301.

6. *IEEE Trans. Audio and Electroacoustics*, Special Issue on Fast Fourier Transforms, **Au-15**, 2, June 1967.

7. W. T. Cochran et al., "What is the Fast Fourier Transform?" *Proc. IEEE*, **55**, 10, 1967, 1664–1674.

8. *IEEE Trans. Audio and Electroacoustics*, Special Issue on Fast Fourier Transforms, **Au-17**, 2, June 1969.

9. J. W. Cooley, P. A. Lewis, and P. D. Welch, "Historical Notes on the Fast Fourier Transform," *Proc. IEEE*, **55**, 10, October 1967, 1675–1677.

10. E. O. Brigham and R. E. Morrow, "The Fast Fourier Transform," *IEEE Spectrum*, **4**, 12, December 1967, 63–70.

11. R. W. Means, H. J. Whitehouse, and J. M. Speiser, "Television Encoding Using a Hybrid Discrete Cosine Transform and a Differential Pulse Code Modulator in Real Time," Proceedings of the National Telecommunications Conference, San Diego, California, December 1974, 61–66.

12. N. Ahmed, T. Natarajan, and K. R. Rao, "On Image Processing and a Discrete Cosine Transform," *IEEE Trans. Computers*, **C-23**, 1, January 1974, 90–93.

13. A. K. Jain, "A Fast Karhunen–Loeve Transform for Finite Discrete Images," Proceedings of the National Electronics conference, Chicago, Illinois, October 1974, 323–328.

14. A. K. Jain and E. Angel, "Image Restoration, Modelling, and Reduction of Dimensionality," *IEEE Trans. Computers*, **C-23**, 5, May 1974, 470–476.

15. A. K. Jain (private communication).

16. J. E. Whelchel Jr. and D. F. Guinn, "The Fast Fourier-Hadamard Transform and Its use in Signal Representation and Classification," EASCON 1968 Convention Record, 1968, 561–573.

17. W. K. Pratt, H. C. Andrews, and J. Kane, "Hadamard Transform Image Coding," *Proc. IEEE*, **57**, 1, January 1969, 58–68.

18. J. Hadamard, "Resolution d'une Question Relative aux Determinants," *Bull. Sci. Math. Ser. 2*, **17**, Part I, 1893, 240–246.

19. H. J. Ryser, *Combinatorial Mathematics*, Wiley, New York, 1963.

20. H. F. Harmuth, *Transmission of Information by Orthogonal Functions*, Springer-Verlag, New York, 1969.

21. J. L. Walsh, "A Closed Set of Orthogonal Functions,"*Am. J. Math.*, **45**, 1923, 5–24.

22. H. Rademacher, "Einige Satze von Allgemeinen Orthogonal-Funktionen," *Math. Annalen*, **87**, 1922, 112–138.

23. A. Haar, "Zur Theorie der Orthogonalen Funktionen-System," Inaugural Dissertation, *Math. Annalen*, **5**, 1955, 17–31.

24. H. Enomoto and K. Shibata, "Orthogonal Transform Coding System for Television Signals," *IEEE Trans. Electromagnetic Compatibility*, **EMC-13**, 3, August 1971, 11–17.

25. W. K. Pratt, L. R. Welch, and W. H. Chen, "Slant Transform for Image Coding," Proceedings Symposium an Applications of Walsh Functions, March 1972.

26. W. K. Pratt, W. H. Chen, and L. R. Welch, "Slant Transform Image Coding," *IEEE Trans. Commun.*, **COM-22**, 8, August 1974, 1075–1093.

27. H. Karhunen, 1947, English translation by I. Selin, "On Linear Methods in Probability Theory," The Rand Corporation, Doc. T-131, August 11, 1960.

28. M. Loeve, *Fonctions Aléatories de Seconde Ordre*, Hermann, Paris, 1948.

29. H. Hotelling, "Analysis of a complex of Statistical Variables into Principal Components," *J. Educ. Psych.*, **24**, 1933, 417–441, 498–520.

30. P. A. Wintz, "Transform Picture coding," *Proc. IEEE*, 60, 7, July 1972, 809–820.

31. W. D. Ray and R. M. Driver, "Further Decomposition of the Karhunen–Loeve Series Representation of a Stationary Random Process," *IEEE Trans. Inf. Theory*, **IT-16**, 6, November 1970, 663–668.

32. W. K. Pratt, "Generalized Wiener Filtering Computation Techniques," *IEEE Trans. Computers*, **C-21**, 7, July 1972, 636–641.

33. B. Friedman, "Eigenvalues of Composite Matrices," *Proc. Cambridge Phil. Soc.*, **57**, Part 1, 1961, 37–49.

34. H. C. Andrews and C. L. Patterson, "Outer product Expansions and their Uses in Digital Image Processing," *Am. Math. Monthly*, **1**, 82, January 1975, 1–13.

35. E. O. Brigham, *The Fast Fourier Transform*, Prentice-Hall, Englewood Cliffs, N.J., 1974.

36. W. M. Gentleman, "Matrix Multiplication and Fast Fourier Transformations," *Bell Syst. Tech. J.*, **47**, July–August 1968, 1099–1103.

11 TWO-DIMENSIONAL LINEAR PROCESSING TECHNIQUES

Most discrete image processing computational algorithms are linear in nature; an output image array is produced by a weighted linear combination of elements of an input array. The popularity of linear operations stems from the relative simplicity of spatial linear processing as opposed to spatial nonlinear processing. However, for image processing operations, conventional linear processing is often computationally infeasible without efficient computational algorithms because of the large size image arrays. This chapter considers indirect computational techniques based on unitary transforms that permit more efficient linear processing than by conventional methods. Two-dimensional recursive filtering methods are also described.

11.1. TRANSFORM DOMAIN PROCESSING

Two-dimensional linear transformations have been defined in series form as

$$P(m_1, m_2) = \sum_{n_1=1}^{N_1} \sum_{n_2=1}^{N_2} F(n_1, n_2) T(n_1, n_2; m_1, m_2) \qquad (11.1\text{-}1)$$

and defined in vector form as

$$\mathbf{p} = \mathbf{T}\mathbf{f} \qquad (11.1\text{-}2)$$

It will now be shown that such linear transformations can often be computed more efficiently by an indirect computational procedure utilizing two-dimensional unitary transforms, than by the direct computation indicated by Eq. 11.1-1 or 11.1-2.

Figure 11.1-1 contains a block diagram of the indirect computation technique called generalized linear filtering (1). In the process the input array $F(n_1, n_2)$ undergoes a two-dimensional unitary transformation resulting in an array of transform coefficients $\mathscr{F}(u_1, u_2)$. Next, a linear

(a) DIRECT PROCESSING

(b) GENERALIZED LINEAR FILTERING

FIGURE 11.1-1.   Direct processing and generalized linear filtering—series formulation.

combination of these coefficients is taken according to the general relation

$$\tilde{\mathscr{F}}(w_1, w_2) = \sum_{m_1=1}^{M_1} \sum_{m_2=1}^{M_2} \mathscr{F}(u_1, u_2) \mathscr{T}(u_1, u_2; m_1, m_2) \qquad (11.1\text{-}3)$$

where $\mathscr{T}(u_1, u_2; m_1, m_2)$ represents the kernel of the linear filtering transformation. Finally, an inverse unitary transformation is performed to reconstruct the processed array $P(m_1, m_2)$. If this computational procedure is to be more efficient than direct computation by Eq. 11.1-1, it is necessary that fast computational algorithms exist for the unitary transformation, and also the kernel $\mathscr{T}(u_1, u_2; m_1, m_2)$ must be reasonably sparse, that is, must contain many zero elements.

The generalized linear filtering process can also be defined in terms of vector-space computations as shown in Figure 11.1-2. For notational simplicity let $N_1 = N_2 = N$ and $M_1 = M_2 = M$. Then the generalized linear

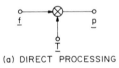

(a) DIRECT PROCESSING

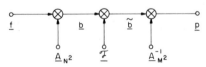

(b) GENERALIZED LINEAR FILTERING

FIGURE 11.1-2.   Direct processing and generalized linear filtering—vector formulation.

filtering process can be described by the equations

$$\not{f} = (\mathbf{A}_{N^2})\mathbf{f} \tag{11.1-4a}$$

$$\tilde{\not{f}} = \mathscr{T}\not{f} \tag{11.1-4b}$$

$$\mathbf{p} = (\mathbf{A}_{M^2})^{-1}\tilde{\not{f}} \tag{11.1-4c}$$

where $\mathbf{A}_{N^2}$ is an $N^2 \times N^2$ unitary transform matrix, $\mathscr{T}$ is an $M^2 \times N^2$ linear filtering transform operation, and $\mathbf{A}_{M^2}$ is an $M^2 \times M^2$ unitary transform matrix. From Eq. 11.1-4 the input and output vectors are related by

$$\mathbf{p} = (\mathbf{A}_{M^2})^{-1}\mathscr{T}(\mathbf{A}_{N^2})\mathbf{f} \tag{11.1-5}$$

Therefore, equating Eqs. 11.1-2 and 11.1-5 yields the relations between $\mathscr{T}$ and $\mathbf{T}$ given by

$$\mathbf{T} = (\mathbf{A}_{M^2})^{-1}\mathscr{T}(\mathbf{A}_{N^2}) \tag{11.1-6a}$$

$$\mathscr{T} = (\mathbf{A}_{M^2})\mathbf{T}(\mathbf{A}_{N^2})^{-1} \tag{11.1-6b}$$

If direct processing is employed, computation by Eq. 11.1-2 requires $k_d(M^2N^2)$ operations, where k_d ($0 \le k_d \le 1$) is a measure of the sparseness of $\mathbf{T}$. With the generalized linear filtering technique the number of operations required for a given operator are

Forward transform: N^4—by direct transformation
                       $2N^2 \log_2 N$—by fast transformation
Filter multiplication $k_g M^2 N^2$
Inverse transform: M^4—by direct transformation
                       $2M^2 \log_2 M$—by fast transformation

where $0 \le k_g \le 1$ is a measure of the sparseness of $\mathscr{T}$. If $k_g = 1$ and direct unitary transform computation is performed, it is obvious that the generalized linear filtering concept is not as efficient as direct computation. However, if fast transform algorithms, similar in structure to the fast Fourier transform, are employed, then generalized linear filtering will be more efficient than direct processing if the sparseness index satisfies the inequality

$$k_g < k_d - \frac{2}{M^2}\log_2 N - \frac{2}{N^2}\log_2 M \tag{11.1-7}$$

In many applications $\mathscr{T}$ will be sufficiently sparse such that the inequality will be satisfied. In fact, unitary transformation tends to "decorrelate" the elements of $\mathbf{T}$ causing $\mathscr{T}$ to be sparse. Also, it is often possible to render the filter matrix sparse by setting small-magnitude elements to zero, without seriously affecting computational accuracy (1).

In subsequent sections the structure of linear processing operators such as superposition, convolution, and pseudoinverse operators is analyzed to determine the feasibility of generalized linear filtering in these applications.

11.2. TRANSFORM DOMAIN SUPERPOSITION

The superposition operations discussed in Chapter 9 can often be performed more efficiently by transform domain processing rather than by direct processing. Figure 11.2-1a illustrates a block diagram of the computational steps involved in direct finite area or sampled infinite area superposition. In Figure 11.2-1b an alternative form of processing is illustrated in which a unitary transformation operation is performed on the data vector $\mathbf{f}$ before multiplication by a finite area filter matrix $\mathcal{D}$ or sampled infinite area filter matrix $\mathcal{B}$. An inverse transform reconstructs the output vector. From Figure 11.2-1, for finite area superposition, because

$$\mathbf{q} = \mathbf{Df} \tag{11.2-1a}$$

and

$$\mathbf{q} = (\mathbf{A}_{M^2})^{-1}\mathcal{D}(\mathbf{A}_{N^2})\mathbf{f} \tag{11.2-1b}$$

then clearly the finite area filter matrix may be expressed as

$$\mathcal{D} = (\mathbf{A}_{M^2})\mathbf{D}(\mathbf{A}_{N^2})^{-1} \tag{11.2-2a}$$

Similarly

$$\mathcal{B} = (\mathbf{A}_{M^2})\mathbf{B}(\mathbf{A}_{N^2})^{-1} \tag{11.2-2b}$$

If direct finite area superposition is performed, the required number of computational operations is approximately $N^2 L^2$ where L is the dimension of the impulse response matrix. In this case the sparseness index of $\mathbf{D}$ is

$$k_D = \left(\frac{L}{N}\right)^2 \tag{11.2-3a}$$

Direct sampled infinite area superposition requires on the order of $M^2 L^2$ operations and the corresponding sparseness index of $\mathbf{B}$ is

$$k_B = \left(\frac{L}{M}\right)^2 \tag{11.2-3b}$$

Figure 11.2-1f contains a block diagram of a system for performing circulant area superposition by transform domain processing. In this case the

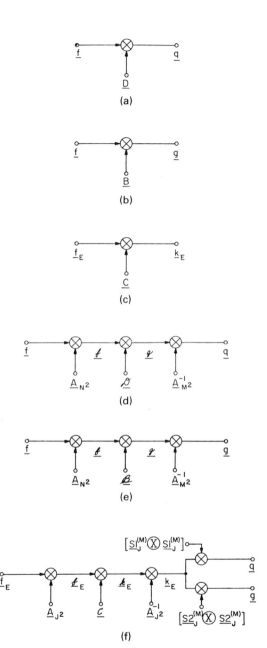

FIGURE 11.2-1. Data and transform domain circular superposition. (a) Finite area superposition. (b) Sampled infinite area superposition. (c) Circular superposition. (d) Transform domain finite area superposition. (e) Transform domain sampled infinite area superposition. (f) Transform domain circular superposition.

input vector $\mathbf{k}_E$ is the so-called extended data vector obtained by imbedding the input image array $F(n_1, n_2)$ in the left corner of a $J \times J$ array of zeros and then column scanning the resultant matrix. Following the same reasoning as above, it is seen that

$$\mathbf{k}_E = \mathbf{C}\mathbf{f}_E = (\mathbf{A}_{J^2})^{-1}\mathscr{C}(\mathbf{A}_{J^2})\mathbf{f}_E \qquad (11.2\text{-}4a)$$

and hence

$$\mathscr{C} = (\mathbf{A}_J{}^2)\mathbf{C}(\mathbf{A}_{J^2})^{-1} \qquad (11.2\text{-}4b)$$

As noted in Chapter 9, the equivalent output vector for either finite area or sampled infinite area superposition can be obtained by an element selection operation of $\mathbf{k}_E$. For finite area superposition

$$\mathbf{q} = [\mathbf{S1}_J^{(M)} \otimes \mathbf{S1}_J^{(M)}]\mathbf{k}_E \qquad (11.2\text{-}5a)$$

and for sampled infinite area superposition

$$\mathbf{q} = [\mathbf{S2}_J^{(M)} \otimes \mathbf{S2}_J^{(M)}]\mathbf{k}_E \qquad (11.2\text{-}5b)$$

Also, the matrix form of the output for finite area superposition is related to the extended image matrix $\mathbf{K}_E$ by

$$\mathbf{Q} = [\mathbf{S1}^{(M)}]\mathbf{K}_E[\mathbf{S1}^{(M)}]^T \qquad (11.2\text{-}6a)$$

For infinite area superposition

$$\mathbf{G} = [\mathbf{S2}_J^{(M)}]\mathbf{K}_E[\mathbf{S2}_J^{(M)}]^T \qquad (11.2\text{-}6b)$$

The number of computational operations required to obtain $\mathbf{k}_E$ by transform domain processing is given by the previous analysis for $M = N = J$:

Direct transformation: $3J^4$
Fast transformation: $J^2 + 4J^2 \log_2 J$

If $\mathscr{C}$ is sparse, many of the J^2 filter multiplication operations can be avoided.

From above it can be seen that the secret to computationally efficient superposition is to select a transformation that possesses a fast computational algorithm and that results in a relatively sparse transform domain superposition filter matrix. As an example, consider finite area convolution performed by Fourier domain processing (2, 3). Referring to Figure 11.2-1, let

$$\mathbf{A}_{K^2} = \mathbf{A}_K \otimes \mathbf{A}_K \qquad (11.2\text{-}7)$$

where

$$\mathbf{A}_K = \left[\frac{1}{\sqrt{K}} \mathcal{W}^{(x-1)(y-1)} \right] \qquad \mathcal{W} \equiv \exp\left\{ \frac{-2\pi i}{K} \right\}$$

for $x, y = 1, 2, \ldots, K$. Also, let $\mathbf{h}_E^{(K)}$ denote the $K^2 \times 1$ vector representation of the extended spatially invariant impulse response array of Eq. 9.3-2 for $J = K$. The Fourier transform of $\mathbf{h}_E^{(K)}$ is denoted as

$$\boldsymbol{\hbar}_E^{(K)} = (\mathbf{A}_{K^2}) \mathbf{h}_E^{(K)} \tag{11.2-8}$$

These transform components are then inserted as the diagonal elements of a $K^2 \times K^2$ matrix

$$\mathcal{H}^{(K)} = \operatorname{diag}\{\boldsymbol{\hbar}_E^{(K)}(1), \ldots, \boldsymbol{\hbar}_E^{(K)}(K^2)\} \tag{11.2-9}$$

Then it can be shown, after considerable manipulation, that the Fourier transform domain superposition matrices for finite area and sampled infinite area convolution can be written as (4)

$$\mathcal{D} = \mathcal{H}^{(M)}[\mathbf{P}_D \otimes \mathbf{P}_D] \tag{11.2-10}$$

for $N = M - L + 1$ and

$$\mathcal{B} = \mathbf{P}_B \otimes \mathbf{P}_B \mathcal{H}^{(N)} \tag{11.2-11}$$

where $N = M + L - 1$ and

$$P_D(u, v) = \frac{1}{\sqrt{M}} \frac{1 - \mathcal{W}_M^{-(u-1)(L-1)}}{1 - \mathcal{W}_M^{(u-1)} \mathcal{W}_N^{-(v-1)}} \tag{11.2-12a}$$

$$P_B(u, v) = \frac{1}{\sqrt{N}} \frac{1 - \mathcal{W}_N^{(v-1)(L-1)}}{1 - \mathcal{W}_M^{(u-1)} \mathcal{W}_N^{-(v-1)}} \tag{11.2-12b}$$

Thus the transform domain convolution operators each consist of a scalar weighting matrix $\mathcal{H}^{(K)}$ and an interpolation matrix $(\mathbf{P} \otimes \mathbf{P})$ that performs the dimensionality conversion between the N^2 element input vector and the M^2 element output vector. Generally, the interpolation matrix $\mathbf{P} \otimes \mathbf{P}$ is relatively sparse, and therefore transform domain superposition is quite efficient.

Now consider circulant area convolution in the transform domain. Following the previous analysis it is found (4) that the circulant area convolution filter matrix reduces to a scalar operator

$$\mathcal{C} = J \mathcal{H}^{(J)} \tag{11.2-13}$$

Thus, as indicated in Eqs. 11.2-12 and 11.2-13, the Fourier domain convolution filter matrices can be expressed in a compact closed form for analysis or operational storage. No closed-form expressions have been found for other unitary transforms.

Fourier domain convolution is computationally efficient because the convolution operator **C** is a circulant matrix, and the corresponding filter matrix $\mathscr{C}$ is of diagonal form. Actually, as can be seen from Eq. 11.1-6, the Fourier transform basis vectors are eigenvectors of **C** (5). This result does not hold true for superposition in general, nor for convolution using other unitary transforms. However, in many instances, the filter matrices $\mathscr{D}$, $\mathscr{B}$, and $\mathscr{C}$ are relatively sparse, and computational savings can often be achieved by transform domain processing.

Figure 11.2-2 contains displays of the Fourier and Hadamard domain filter matrices for the three forms of convolution for a one-dimensional

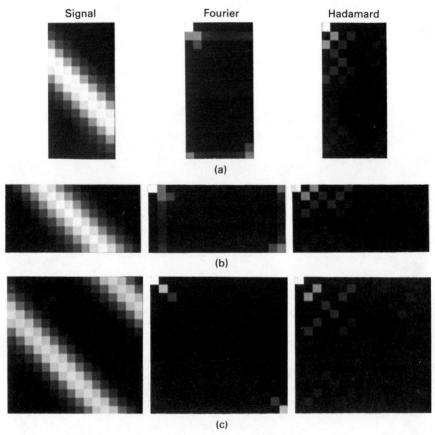

FIGURE 11.2-2. One-dimensional Fourier and Hadamard domain superposition matrices. (a) Finite length convolution. (b) Sampled infinite length convolution. (c) Circular length convolution.

input vector and a Gaussian-shaped impulse response (6). As expected, the transform domain representations are much more sparse than the data domain representations. Also, the Fourier domain circular convolution filter is seen to be of diagonal form. Figure 11.2-3 illustrates the structure of the three convolution matrices for two-dimensional convolution (4).

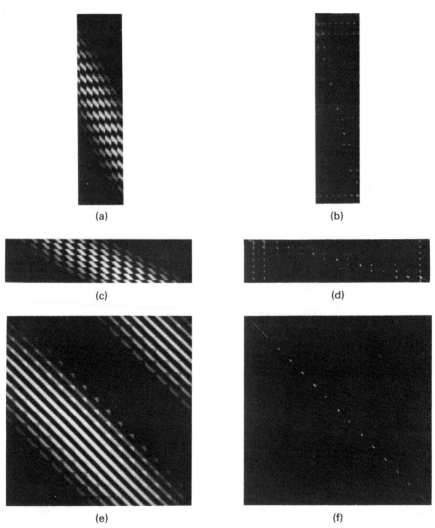

(a)   (b)

(c)   (d)

(e)   (f)

FIGURE 11.2-3. Two-dimensional Fourier domain convolution matrices. Finite area convolution operator: (a) spatial domain; (b) Fourier domain. Sampled infinite area convolution operator: (c) spatial domain; (d) Fourier domain. Circular area convolution operator: (e) spatial domain; (f) Fourier domain.

11.3. FAST FOURIER TRANSFORM CONVOLUTION

As noted previously, the equivalent output vector for either finite area or sampled infinite area convolution can be obtained by an element selection operation on the extended output vector $\mathbf{k}_E$ for circulant area convolution or its matrix counterpart $\mathbf{K}_E$. This result combined with Eq. 11.2-13 leads to a particularly efficient means of convolution computation indicated by the following steps:

1. Imbed the impulse response matrix in the upper left corner of an all zero $J \times J$ matrix, $J \geq M$ for finite area convolution or $J \geq N$ for sampled infinite area convolution, and take the two-dimensional Fourier transform of the extended impulse response matrix giving

$$\mathscr{H}_E = \mathbf{A}_J \mathbf{H}_E \mathbf{A}_J \qquad (11.3\text{-}1)$$

2. Imbed the input data array in the upper left corner of an all zero $J \times J$ matrix, and take the two-dimensional Fourier transform of the extended input data matrix to obtain

$$\mathscr{F}_E = \mathbf{A}_J \mathbf{F}_E \mathbf{A}_J \qquad (11.3\text{-}2)$$

3. Perform the scalar multiplication

$$\mathscr{K}_E(m, n) = J\mathscr{H}_E(m, n)\mathscr{F}_E(m, n) \qquad (11.3\text{-}3)$$

   where $1 \leq m \leq J$ and $1 \leq n \leq J$.

4. Take the inverse Fourier transform

$$\mathbf{K}_E = (\mathbf{A}_J)^{-1}\mathscr{K}_E(\mathbf{A}_J)^{-1} \qquad (11.3\text{-}4)$$

5. Extract the desired output matrix

$$\mathbf{Q} = [\mathbf{S1}_J^{(M)}]\mathbf{K}_E[\mathbf{S1}_J^{(M)}]^T \qquad (11.3\text{-}5a)$$

   or

$$\mathbf{G} = [\mathbf{S2}_J^{(M)}]\mathbf{K}_E[\mathbf{S2}_J^{(M)}]^T \qquad (11.3\text{-}5b)$$

It is important that the size of the extended arrays in steps (1) and (2) be chosen large enough to satisfy the indicated inequalities. If the computational steps are performed with $J = N$, the resulting output array, shown in Figure 11.3-1a and 11.3-1b will contain erroneous terms in a boundary region of width $L - 1$ elements, on the top and left-hand side of the output field. This is the so-called wrap-around error associated with the incorrect usage of the Fourier domain convolution method. In addition, for finite area (D-type) convolution, the bottom and right-hand side strip of

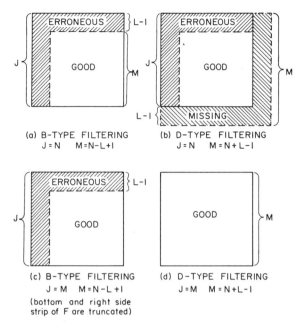

FIGURE 11.3-1. Illustration of wraparound error effects.

output elements will be missing. If the computation is performed with $J = M$, the output array will be completely filled with the correct terms for D-type convolution. In order to force $J = M$ for B-type convolution, it is necessary to truncate the bottom and right-hand side of the input array. As a consequence, the top and left-hand side elements of the output array are erroneous.

In many signal processing applications the same impulse response operator is used on different data, and hence step (1) of the computational algorithm need not be repeated. The filter matrix $\mathcal{H}_E$ may be either stored functionally or indirectly as a computational algorithm. Using a fast Fourier transform algorithm, the forward and inverse transforms require on the order of $2J^2 \log_2 J$ operations each. The scalar multiplication requires J^2 operations, in general, for a total of $J^2(1 + 4 \log_2 J)$ operations. For an $N \times N$ input array, an $M \times M$ output array, and an $L \times L$ impulse response array, finite area convolution requires $N^2 L^2$ operations and sampled infinite area convolution requires $M^2 L^2$ operations. If the dimension of the impulse response L is sufficiently large with respect to the dimension of the input array N, Fourier domain convolution will be more efficient than direct convolution, perhaps by an order of magnitude or more. Figure 11.3-2 provides a plot of L versus N for equality between

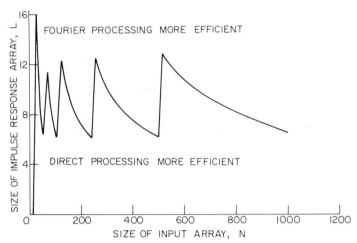

FIGURE 11.3-2. Comparison of direct and Fourier domain processing for finite area convolution.

direct and Fourier domain finite area convolution. The jaggedness of the plot arises from discrete changes in J (64, 128, 256, . . .) as N increases.

Fourier domain processing is more computationally efficient than direct processing for image convolution if the impulse response is sufficiently large. However, if the image to be processed is large, the relative computational advantage of Fourier domain processing diminishes. Also, there are attendant problems of computational accuracy with large size Fourier transforms. Both difficulties can be alleviated by a block-mode filtering technique in which a large size image is separately processed in adjacent overlapped blocks (2, 7-9).

Figure 11.3-3a illustrates the extraction of an $N_B \times N_B$ pixel block from the upper left corner of a large size image array. After convolution with an $L \times L$ impulse response, the resulting $M_B \times M_B$ pixel block is placed in the upper left corner of an output data array as indicated in Figure 11.3-3a. Next, a second block of $N_B \times N_B$ pixels is extracted from the input array to produce a second $M_B \times M_B$ block of output pixels that will lie adjacent to the first block. As indicated in Figure 11.3-3b, this second input block must be overlapped by $(L-1)$ pixels in order to generate an adjacent output block. The computational process then proceeds until all input blocks are filled along the first row. If a partial input block remains along the row, zero-value elements can be added to complete the block. Next, an input block, overlapped by $(L-1)$ pixels with the first row blocks, is extracted to produce the first block of the second output row. The algorithm continues in this fashion until all output points are computed.

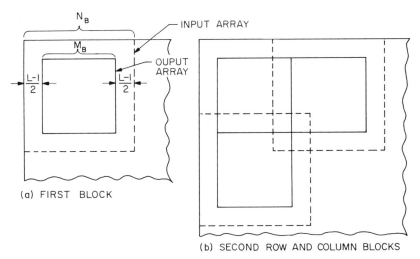

(b) SECOND ROW AND COLUMN BLOCKS

FIGURE 11.3-3.   Geometric arrangement of blocks for block-mode filtering.

A total of

$$O_F = N^2 + 2N^2 \log_2 N \qquad (11.3\text{-}6)$$

operations is required for Fourier domain convolution over the full size image array. With block-mode filtering with $N_B \times N_B$ input pixel blocks, the required number of operations is

$$O_B = R^2 [N_B^2 + 2N_B^2 \log_2 N_B] \qquad (11.3\text{-}7)$$

where R represents the largest integer value of the ratio $N/[N_B + L - 1]$. Hunt (9) has determined the optimum block size as a function of the original image size and impulse response size.

11.4. FOURIER TRANSFORM FILTER DESIGN

The discrete fast Fourier transform convolutional processing algorithm of the previous section is often utilized for computer simulation of continuous Fourier domain linear filtering. This section considers modeling errors inherent in the simulation process and design techniques for determining the sample values of the discrete Fourier domain filter function in terms of a desired continuous Fourier domain transfer function. For simplicity the discussion is limited to one-dimensional signals.

Consider a one-dimensional continuous signal $f_C(x)$ of wide extent which is bandlimited such that its Fourier transform $\mathcal{f}_C(\omega)$ is zero for $|\omega|$

greater than the cutoff frequency ω_0. This signal is to be convolved with a continuous impulse function $h_C(x)$ whose transfer function $\hbar_C(\omega)$ is also bandlimited to ω_0. From Chapter 1 it is known that the convolution can be performed either in the spatial domain by the operation

$$g_C(x) = \int_{-\infty}^{\infty} f_C(\alpha) h_C(x - \alpha)\, d\alpha \qquad (11.4\text{-}1a)$$

or in the continuous Fourier domain by

$$g_C(x) = \frac{1}{2\pi} \int_{-\infty}^{\infty} f_C(\omega) \hbar_C(\omega) \exp\{i\omega x\}\, d\omega \qquad (11.4\text{-}1b).$$

Chapter 9 has presented techniques for the discretization of the convolution integral of Eq. 11.4-1. In this process the continuous impulse response function $h_C(x)$ must be truncated by spatial multiplication of a window function $y(x)$ to produce the windowed impulse response

$$b_C(x) = h_C(x) y(x) \qquad (11.4\text{-}2)$$

where $y(x) = 0$ for $|x| > T$. The window function is designed to smooth the truncation effect. The resulting convolution integral is then approximated as

$$g_C(x) = \int_{x-T}^{x+T} f_C(\alpha) b_C(x - \alpha)\, d\alpha \qquad (11.4\text{-}3)$$

Next, the output signal $g_C(x)$ is sampled over $2J + 1$ points at a resolution $\Delta = \pi/\omega_0$ and the continuous integration is replaced by a quadrature summation at the same resolution Δ yielding the discrete representation

$$g_C(j\Delta) = \sum_{k=j-K}^{j+K} f_C(k\Delta) b_C[(j - k)\Delta] \qquad (11.4\text{-}4)$$

where K is the nearest integer value of the ratio T/Δ.

Computation of Eq. 11.4-4 by discrete Fourier transform processing can be accomplished according to the computational algorithm of Section 11.3. As a first step in the algorithm, the samples of the windowed impulse response function are inserted as the first $L = 2K + 1$ elements of a J-element sequence and the remaining $J - L$ elements are zet to zero. Thus let

$$b_D(\ell) = \underbrace{b_C(-K), \ldots, b_C(0), \ldots, b_C(K)}_{L \text{ terms}}, 0, \ldots, 0 \qquad (11.4\text{-}5)$$

where $0 \le \ell \le P - 1$. The terms of $b_D(\ell)$ can be extracted from the continuous impulse response function $h_C(x)$ and the window function $y(x)$ by the sampling operation

$$b_D(\ell) = y(x)h_C(x)\delta(x + K\Delta - \ell\Delta) \qquad (11.4\text{-}6)$$

The next step in the discrete Fourier transform convolution algorithm is to perform a discrete Fourier transform of $b_D(\ell)$ over P points to obtain

$$\mathcal{b}_D(u) = \frac{1}{\sqrt{P}} \sum_{\ell=0}^{P-1} b_D(\ell) \exp\left\{-\frac{2\pi i}{P}\ell u\right\} \qquad (11.4\text{-}7)$$

where $0 \le u \le P - 1$. Upon substitution of Eq. 11.4-6 into Eq. 11.4-7 and considerable manipulation, the discrete Fourier transform filter function is found to be related to the continuous Fourier transform transfer functions $\mathcal{h}_C(\omega)$ and $\mathcal{y}(\omega)$ by the relation

$$\mathcal{b}_D(u) = \frac{1}{4\pi^2}\frac{1}{\sqrt{P}}\exp\left\{-i\pi\left(\frac{L-1}{P}\right)u\right\}\mathcal{b}_C\left(\frac{2\omega_0}{P}u\right) \qquad (11.4\text{-}8a)$$

$$\mathcal{b}_D(P - u) = \mathcal{b}_D^*(u) \qquad (11.4\text{-}8b)$$

for $u = 0, 1, \ldots, P/2$ where $\mathcal{b}_C(\omega) = \mathcal{h}_C(\omega) \circledast \mathcal{y}(\omega)$.

Equation 11.4-8 provides the desired link between the continuous and discrete Fourier domains. If the continuous transfer function $\mathcal{h}_C(\omega)$ and window function $\mathcal{y}(\omega)$ are known analytic transfer functions, then, in principle, elements of the discrete filter function $\mathcal{b}_C(\omega)$ can be obtained by analytically performing the indicated convolution operations of Eq. 11.4-8 and evaluating the resulting function at points $(2\pi u/P\Delta)$ for each value of u. In practice, the analytic convolution is often difficult to perform, especially in two dimensions. An easier alternative is to perform an analytic inverse Fourier transformation of the transfer function $\mathcal{h}_C(\omega)$ to obtain its impulse response and then extract samples of $b_D(\ell)$ according to Eq. 11.4-6. Another approach is to form the discrete inverse Fourier transform of $\mathcal{h}_C(2\pi u/P\Delta)$ according to Eq. 11.4-8, window the resulting extended impulse response sequence, and then perform a discrete Fourier transform to obtain $\mathcal{b}_D(u)$.

The windowing operation performed explicitly in the spatial domain according to Eq. 11.4-6 or implicitly in the Fourier domain by Eq. 11.4-8 is absolutely imperative if the wrap-around error effect described in Chapter 9 is to be avoided. A common mistake in image filtering is to arbitrarily set the values of the discrete impulse response function equal to samples of the continuous impulse response function. The corresponding extended discrete impulse response function will generally possess nonzero elements in each of its J elements. That is, the length L of the discrete impulse response imbedded in the extended vector of Eq. 11.4-5 will be implicitly

TABLE 11.4-1. Window functions

Function	Definition
Rectangular	$w(n) = 1 \quad 0 \leq n \leq L - 1$
Bartlett (triangular)	$w(n) = \begin{cases} \dfrac{2n}{L-1} & 0 \leq n < \dfrac{L-1}{2} \\ 2 - \dfrac{2n}{L-1} & \dfrac{L-1}{2} \leq n \leq L-1 \end{cases}$
Hanning	$w(n) = \dfrac{1}{2}\left[1 - \cos\left(\dfrac{2\pi n}{L-1}\right)\right] \quad 0 \leq n \leq L-1$
Hamming	$w(n) = 0.54 - 0.46 \cos\left(\dfrac{2\pi n}{L-1}\right) \quad 0 \leq n \leq L-1$
Blackman	$w(n) = 0.42 - 0.5\cos\left(\dfrac{2\pi n}{L-1}\right) + 0.08\cos\left(\dfrac{4\pi n}{L-1}\right) \quad 0 \leq n \leq L-1$
Kaiser	$\dfrac{I_0\{\omega_a[((L-1)/2)^2 - [n - ((L-1)/2)]^2]^{1/2}\}}{I_0\{\omega_a((L-1)/2)\}} \quad 0 \leq n \leq L-1$

where $I_0\{\,\cdot\,\}$ is the modified zeroth-order Bessel function of the first kind and ω_a is a design parameter.

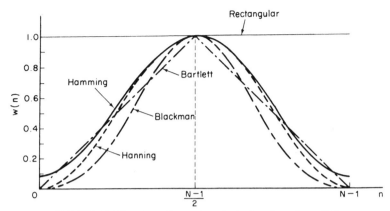

FIGURE 11.4-1. One-dimensional window functions (10).

set equal to J. Therefore all elements of the output filtering operation will be subject to wrap-around error.

A variety of window functions have been proposed for discrete linear filtering (10–12). Several of the most common are listed in Table 11.4-1 and sketched in Figure 11.4-1. Figure 11.4-2 contains plots of the transfer functions of these window functions. The window transfer functions consist of a main lobe and side lobes whose peaks decrease in magnitude with increasing frequency. Examination of the structure of Eq. 11.4-8 indicates that the main lobe causes a loss in frequency response over the signal passband from 0 to ω_0, while the side lobes are responsible for an aliasing error since the windowed impulse response function $\ell_C(\omega)$ is not bandlimited. A tapered window function reduces the magnitude of the side lobes and consequently attenuates the aliasing error, but the main lobe becomes wider, causing the signal frequency response within the passband to be reduced. A design tradeoff must be made between these complementary sources of error. Both sources of degradation can be reduced by increasing the truncation length of the windowed impulse response, but this strategy will either result in a shorter length output sequence or an increased number of computational operations.

11.5.   TRANSFORM DOMAIN PSEUDOINVERSE

Transform domain processing can be applied to advantage in generalized inverse computations. From Eq. 11.1-6b the transform domain operator $\mathcal{T}$ is related to the general $M^2 \times N^2$ matrix $\mathbf{T}$ by

$$\mathcal{T} = (\mathbf{A}_{M^2})\mathbf{T}(\mathbf{A}_{N^2})^{-1} \qquad (11.5\text{-}1)$$

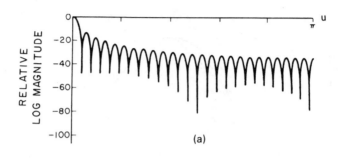

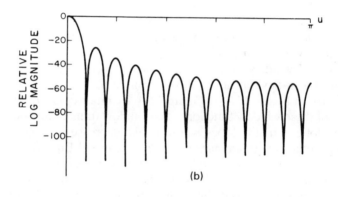

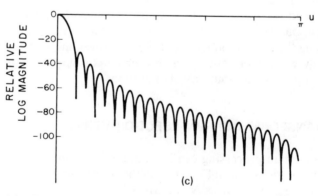

FIGURE 11.4-2. Transfer functions of one dimensional window functions (10). (a) Rectangular. (b) Triangular. (c) Hanning. (d) Hamming. (e) Blackman.

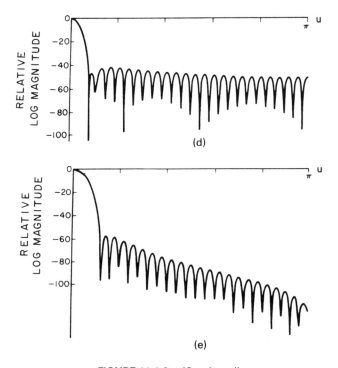

FIGURE 11.4-2. (Continued).

Following the same definition, the transform domain generalized inverse assumes the form

$$\mathcal{T}^- = (\mathbf{A}_{N^2})\mathbf{T}^-(\mathbf{A}_{M}{}^2)^{-1} \tag{11.5-2}$$

where it is noted that $\mathbf{T}^-$ is an $N^2 \times M^2$ matrix. Equations 11.5-1 and 11.5-2 are self-consistent since for any matrix $\mathbf{Z}$ and unitary matrices $\mathbf{P}$ and $\mathbf{R}$ it is known that $(\mathbf{P} \ \mathbf{Z} \ \mathbf{R})^- = \mathbf{R}^{*T} \ \mathbf{Z}^- \mathbf{P}^{*T}$ (13, p. 100).

If $\mathbf{T}$ is of rank N^2, then from Eq. 8.3-5

$$\mathbf{T}^- = (\mathbf{T}^T\mathbf{T})^{-1}\mathbf{T}^T \tag{11.5-3}$$

and it can be easily shown that

$$\mathcal{T}^- = (\mathcal{T}^{*T}\mathcal{T})^{-1}\mathcal{T}^{*T} \tag{11.5-4}$$

In the opposite case, if $\mathbf{T}$ is of rank M^2, then from Eq. 8.3-6

$$\mathbf{T}^- = \mathbf{T}^T(\mathbf{T}\mathbf{T}^T)^{-1} \tag{11.5-5}$$

and the transform domain generalized inverse is of the form

$$\mathcal{T}^- = \mathcal{T}^{*T}(\mathcal{T}\mathcal{T}^{*T})^{-1} \tag{11.5-6}$$

As an example, the transform domain generalized inverses of the super-position operators $\mathcal{D}$, $\mathcal{B}$, and $\mathcal{C}$ of full rank are given by

$$\mathcal{D}^- = (\mathcal{D}^{*T}\mathcal{D})^{-1}\mathcal{D}^{*T} \qquad (11.5\text{-}7a)$$

$$\mathcal{B}^- = \mathcal{B}^{*T}(\mathcal{B}\mathcal{B}^{*T})^{-1} \qquad (11.5\text{-}7b)$$

$$\mathcal{C}^- = \mathcal{C}^{-1} \qquad (11.5\text{-}7c)$$

Figure 11.5-1 contains computer graphics plots of the convolution generalized inverse matrices in the Fourier and Hadamard domains for a

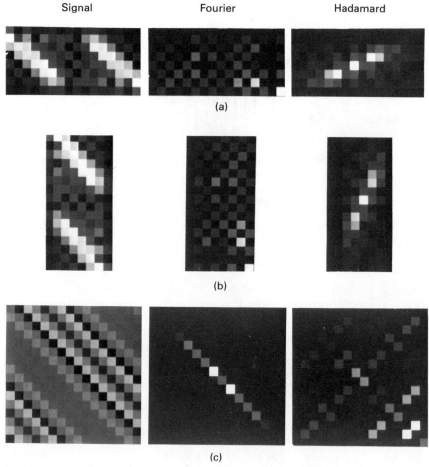

FIGURE 11.5-1. One-dimensional Fourier and Hadamard domain generalized inverse convolution matrices. (a) Finite length convolution. (b) Sampled infinite length convolution. (c) Circular length convolution.

one-dimensional signal. The relative sparseness of the transform domain representations in comparison to the signal domain representations is apparent from the figure. In fact, the Fourier domain circulant area convolution generalized inverse is a diagonal matrix since, as indicated by Eq. 11.2-13, $\mathscr{C}$ is diagonal.

11.6. RECURSIVE FILTERING

In the previous sections of this chapter, transform domain processing techniques have been explored as an alternative means of performing two-dimensional linear processing. It has been found that transform domain processing can often be much more efficient than direct processing in terms of the number of arithmetic operations required. Attention is now directed to another method for performing linear processing called recursive filtering (14–16). In some cases recursive filtering is even more computationally efficient than transform domain processing. A further advantage is a reduction of data storage requirements as compared to transform processing.

Recursive filtering is based on a recursion relationship between input and output system variables. The one-dimensional recursive relation is defined as (14)

$$r(m) = \sum_{j=1}^{J} a(j)f(m - j + 1) - \sum_{k=2}^{K} b(k)r(m - k + 1) \qquad (11.6\text{-}1)$$

where $f(n)$ for $n = 1, 2, \ldots, N$ is an input sequence, $r(m)$ for $m = 1, 2, \ldots, M$ is an output sequence, and $a(j)$ and $b(k)$ are weighting constants. The key concept in the definition is that, proceeding from left to right, the mth element in the sequence is dependent not only on the present input sample and $J - 1$ past input samples, but also on the $K - 1$ previously computed elements of the output sequence.

Most design and analysis procedures for recursive filters are based upon Z-transform techniques. The Z transform of an N-element sequence $f(n)$ is defined as (17, 18)

$$\mathscr{f}(z) = \sum_{n=1}^{N} f(n)z^{1-n} \qquad (11.6\text{-}2)$$

It can be easily shown that the Z transform of Eq. 11.6-1 yields the relation

$$\mathscr{r}(z) = \frac{\mathscr{a}(z)}{\mathscr{b}(z)} \mathscr{f}(z) \qquad (11.6\text{-}3)$$

where $\mathscr{a}(z)$, $\mathscr{b}(z)$, and $\mathscr{f}(z)$ are one-dimensional Z transforms of the corresponding sequences

The two-dimensional recursive filtering recursion relation is defined as (19, 20)

$$R(m_1, m_2) = \sum_{j_1=1}^{J_1} \sum_{j_2=1}^{J_2} A(j_1, j_2) F(m_1 - j_1 + 1, m_2 - j_2 + 1)$$

$$- \sum_{k_1=1}^{K_1} \sum_{k_2=2}^{K_2} B(k_1, k_2) R(m_1 - k_1 + 1, m_2 - k_2 + 1)$$

$$(11.6\text{-}4)$$

where $F(n_1, n_2)$ is an $N_1 \times N_2$ input array, $R(m_1, m_2)$ is an $M_1 \times M_2$ output array, and $A(j_1, j_2)$ and $B(k_1, k_2)$ are weighting constants. The formulation of Eq. 11.6-4 assumes that the recursion proceeds from the upper left corner of the input image. The two-dimensional Z transform of Eq. 11.6-4. yields

$$\mathcal{R}(z_1, z_2) = \frac{\mathcal{A}(z_1, z_2)}{\mathcal{B}(z_1, z_2)} \mathcal{F}(z_1, z_2) \qquad (11.6\text{-}5)$$

where $\mathcal{A}(z_1, z_2)$, $\mathcal{B}(z_1, z_2)$ and $\mathcal{F}(z_1, z_2)$ are two-dimensional Z transforms of the corresponding arrays. For example,

$$\mathcal{A}(z_1, z_2) = \sum_{n_1=1}^{N} \sum_{n_2=1}^{N} A(n_1, n_2) z_1^{-n_1+1} z_2^{-n_2+1} \qquad (11.6\text{-}6)$$

Equation 11.6-4 provides the basic relationship for linear processing by recursive filtering. Synthesis of a recursive filter entails determination of the weighting coefficient arrays A and B that will produce an output array $R(m_1, m_2)$ which is equivalent to the output obtained by direct convolution of the input image array $F(n_1, n_2)$ and a specified impulse response array $H(\ell_1, \ell_2)$. Generally, an exact correspondence cannot be achieved, and approximate design procedures must be invoked (21, 22). An associated problem is the stability of the resultant recursive filter. If the filter is unstable, roundoff errors or noise in the input array may propagate through the computation and be amplified to extremely high levels. A recursive filter will be stable (20) if the Z transform expansion coefficients $K(j_1, j_2)$ obtained from

$$\frac{\mathcal{A}(z_1, z_2)}{\mathcal{B}(z_1, z_2)} \equiv \mathcal{K}(z_1, z_2) = \sum_{j_1=1}^{\infty} \sum_{j_2=1}^{\infty} K(j_1, j_2) z_1^{1-j_1} z_2^{1-j_2} \qquad (11.6\text{-}7)$$

are absolutely summable in the sense that

$$\sum_{j_1=1}^{\infty} \sum_{j_2=1}^{\infty} |K(j_1, j_2)| < \infty \qquad (11.6\text{-}8)$$

Several tests (23–25) have been developed to assess the stability of recursive filters.

The number of computational operations required to implement the recursion relation of Eq. 11.6-4 is

$$N_R = (J_1 J_2 + K_1 K_2) N_1 N_2 \qquad (11.6\text{-}9)$$

where J_i is the dimension of the input domain processing window, K_i is the size of the output domain window, and N_i is the input image dimension. With square images and square windows ($J_1 = J_2 = J$, $K_1 = K_2 = K$, $N_1 = N_2 = N$), the number of operations required for recursive filtering becomes

$$N_R = (J^2 + K^2) N^2 \qquad (11.6\text{-}10)$$

For purposes of comparison, the number of operations required for finite area convolution, as determined in Section 9.3, is

$$N_C = L^2 N^2 \qquad (11.6\text{-}11)$$

where L is the dimension of the impulse response. From Section 11.2, the number of operations required for fast Fourier transform convolution is approximately

$$N_F = N^2 [1 + 4 \log_2 N] \qquad (11.6\text{-}12)$$

The relative computational efficiencies of the three types of processing are dependent on the impulse response size (27). For a small impulse response, direct convolution and recursive filtering require about the same number of computations. In this case Figure 11.3-2 provides a comparison with these methods and FFT convolution. For a large size impulse response, FFT convolution has been shown to be much more efficient than direct convolution. Equating the number of operations specified by Eqs. 11.6-10 and 11.6-12 indicates that recursive filtering is much more efficient than FFT convolution for a large impulse size if the recursive filter window area satisfies the inequality

$$J^2 + K^2 \leq c \log_2 N \qquad (11.6\text{-}13)$$

where c is a constant in the range of 1 to 20 that depends on the type of FFT algorithm employed and the relative computational importance of complex number versus real number arithmetic.

REFERENCES

1. W. K. Pratt, "Generalized Wiener Filtering Computation Techniques," *IEEE Trans. Computers*, **C-21**, 7, July 1972, 636–641.

2. T. G. Stockham, Jr., "High Speed Convolution and Correlation," Proceedings Spring Joint Computer Conference, 1966, 229–233.

3. W. M. Gentleman and G. Sande, "Fast Fourier Transforms—for Fun and Profit," Proceedings Fall Joint Computer Conference, 1966, 563–578.

4. W. K. Pratt, "Vector Formulation of Two-Dimensional Signal Processing Operations," *J. Computer Graphics and Image Processing*, March 1975, Academic Press, New York.

5. B. R. Hunt, "A Matrix Theory Proof of the Discrete Convolution Theorem," *IEEE Trans. Audio and Electroacoustics*, **AU-19**, 4, December 1973, 285–288.

6. W. K. Pratt, "Transform Domain Signal Processing Techniques," Proceedings National Electronics Conference, Chicago, Illinois, 1974.

7. H. D. Helms, "Fast Fourier Transform Method of Computing Difference Equations and Simulating Filters," *IEEE Trans. Audio and Electroacoustics*, **AU-15**, 2, June 1967, 85–90.

8. M. P. Ekstrom and V. R. Algazi, "Optimum Design of Two-Dimensional Nonrecursive Digital Filters," Proceedings 4th Asilomar Conference on Circuits and Systems, Pacific Grove, California, November 1970.

9. B. R. Hunt, "Computational Considerations in Digital Image Enhancement," Proceedings Conference on Two-Dimensional Signal Processing, University of Missouri, Columbia, Missouri, October 1971.

10. A. V. Oppenheim and R. W. Schafer, *Digital Signal Processing*, Prentice-Hall, Englewood Cliffs, N.J., 1975.

11. R. B. Blackman and J. W. Tukey, *The Measurement of Power Spectra*, Dover, New York, 1958.

12. J. F. Kaiser, "Digital Filters," Chapter 7 in *Systems Analysis by Digital Computer*, F. F. Kuo and J. F. Kaiser, Eds., Wiley, New York, 1966.

13. F. A. Graybill, *Introduction to Matrices with Applications in Statistics*, Wadsworth Publishing, Belmont, Calif., 1969.

14. D. G. Childers and A. Durling, *Digital Filtering and Signal Processing*, West Publishing, St. Paul, Minn., 1975.

15. A. V. Oppenheim and R. W. Schafer, *Digital Signal Processing*, Prentice-Hall, Englewood Cliffs, N.J., 1975.

16. L. R. Rabiner and B. Gold, *Theory and Application of Digital Signal Processing*, Prentice-Hall, Englewood Cliffs, N.J., 1975.

17. J. R. Ragazzini and G. F. Franklin, *Sampled Data Control Systems*, McGraw-Hill, New York, 1958.

18. E. I. Jury, *Theory and Applications of the Z-Transform Method*, Wiley, New York, 1964.

19. J. L. Shanks, "Two-Dimensional Recursive Filters," SWIEECO Record, Vol. 21, 19E1, 1969.

20. C. H. Farmer and D. S. Gooden, "Rotation and Stability of a Recursive Digital Filter," Proceedings Two Dimensional Signal Processing Conference, University of Missouri, Columbia, Missouri, October 1971.

21. J. V. Hu and L. R. Rabiner, "Design Techniques for Two-Dimensional Digital Filters," *IEEE Trans. Audio and Electroacoustics*, **AU-20**, 4, October 1972, 249–257.

22. D. E. Dudgeon, "Two-Dimensional Recursive Filter Design Using Differential Correction," *IEEE Trans. Acoustics, Speech, and Signal Processing*, **ASSP-23**, 3, June 1975, 264–267.

23. J. L. Shanks, S. Treitel, and J. H. Justice, "Stability and Synthesis of Two-Dimensional Recursive Filters," *IEEE Trans. Audio and Electroacoustics*, **AU-20**, 2, June 1972, 115–128.

24. T. S. Huang, "Stability of Two-Dimensional Recursive Filters," *IEEE Trans. Audio and Electroacoustics*, **AU-20**, 2, June 1972, 158–163.

25. B. D. Anderson and E. I. Jury, "Stability Test for Two-Dimensional Recursive Filters," *IEEE Trans. Audio and Electroacoustics*, **AU-21**, 4, August 1973, 366–372.

26. P. Pistor, "Stability Criterion for Recursive Filters," *IBM J. Res. Devel.*, **18**, 1, January 1974, 59–71.

27. E. L. Hall, "A Comparison of Computations for Spatial Frequency Filtering," *Proc. IEEE*, **60**, 7, July 1972, 887–891.

4 IMAGE RESTORATION AND ENHANCEMENT

The use of electronic, digital, and optical processing techniques for image "improvement" has received much interest during the past few years with the publicity given to applications in space imagery and biomedical research. Other applications include image improvement for photographic surveys and industrial radiographic analysis.

Image improvement is a term coined to denote two types of image manipulation processes: image restoration and image enhancement. Image restoration has commonly been defined as the reconstruction or estimation of an image field to correct for image degradation and approximate an ideal degradation-free image field as closely as possible. Image enhancement entails operations that improve the appearance of an image to a human viewer, or operations to convert an image to a format better suited to machine processing, but still recognizable as an image.

Chapter 12 describes several techniques of monochrome and color image enhancement. The four chapters that follow describe models for image restoration, present methods of spatial image restoration, and discuss techniques of point, spectral, and color image restoration.

12 IMAGE ENHANCEMENT

Image enhancement processes consist of a collection of techniques that seek to improve the visual appearance of an image, or to convert the image to a form better suited to human or machine analysis. In an image enhancement system there is no conscious effort to improve the fidelity of a reproduced image with regard to some ideal form of the image, as is done in image restoration. Actually, there is some evidence to indicate that often a distorted image, for example, an image with edge overshoot, is actually more subjectively pleasing than a perfectly reproduced original.

For machine processing the definition of image enhancement stops short of information extraction. As an example, an image enhancement system might emphasize the edge outline of an image by high-frequency filtering. This edge-enhanced image would then serve as an input to a machine that would trace the outline of the edges, and perhaps make measurements of the shape and size of the outline. In this application the image enhancement processor would emphasize salient features of the original image and simplify the processing task of the data-extraction machine.

There is no general unifying theory of image enhancement at present because there is no general standard of image quality that can serve as a design criterion for an image enhancement processor. Consideration is given here to a variety of techniques that have proved useful for human observation improvement and for machine analysis.

12.1. CONTRAST MANIPULATION

One of the most common defects of photographic or electronic images is poor contrast resulting from a reduced, and perhaps nonlinear, image brightness range. Image contrast can often be improved by amplitude rescaling of each pixel (1, 2). Figure 12.1-1a illustrates a desired transfer function for contrast enhancement of a typical continuous low-contrast image. For continuous images the transfer function operator can be implemented by photographic techniques, but it is usually difficult to realize an arbitrary transfer function accurately. For digital images implementation of the transfer function is a relatively simple task. However, in the design of the transfer function operator, consideration must be given to the

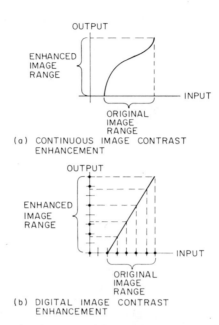

FIGURE 12.1-1. Continuous and discrete image contrast enhancement.

effects of brightness quantization. Suppose that an original image is quantized to J levels, but occupies a smaller range, as shown in Figure 12.1-1b. The output image is also assumed to be restricted to J levels and the mapping is linear. In the mapping strategy indicated in Figure 12.1-1b, the output level chosen is that level closest to the exact mapping of an input level. It is obvious from the diagram that the output image will have unoccupied levels within its range, and some of the gray scale jumps will be larger than in the original image. The latter effect may result in noticeable gray scale contouring between certain gray levels. If the output image is quantized to more levels than the input image, then it is possible to approach a linear placement of output levels, and hence decrease the gray scale contouring effect.

A digitally processed image may occupy a range different from the range of the original image. In fact, the numerical range of the processed image may encompass negative values, which cannot be mapped directly into an intensity range. Figure 12.1-2 illustrates two possibilities of scaling the output image back into the domain of values occupied by the original image. By the first technique the processed image is linearly mapped over its entire range, while by the second technique, the extreme brightness values of the processed image are clipped to maximum and minimum

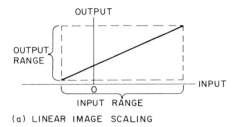

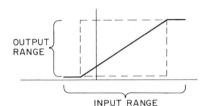

FIGURE 12.1-2.   Example of image scaling.

limits. The second technique is often subjectively preferable, especially for images in which a relatively small number of points exceed the limits. Contrast-enhancement programs and systems often possess an option to clip a fixed percentage of the brightness values on each end of the luminance scale.

Figure 12.1-3 contains examples of contrast enhancement of an ERTS satellite picture along with gray scale histograms of the original and enhanced pictures. In Figure 12.1-3c the clip levels are set at the histogram limits of the original, while in Figure 12.1-3e, the clip levels truncate 5% of the original image upper and lower luminance levels.

The examples of contrast enhancement previously considered have all employed a monotonically increasing transfer function. There are applications in image processing in which monotonically decreasing and nonmonotonic transfer functions are useful. For example, if a display is highly nonlinear toward the dark end of the display range, a contrast reversal transfer function, as indicated in Figure 12.1-4a, could be performed to transfer low-luminance regions of the input image to the brighter and presumably more linear portion of the display range. Figure 12.1-4b contains a plot of the transfer function for sawtooth contrast scaling. This type of scaling is often employed to produce a wide dynamic range image on a small dynamic range display. An example of sawtooth scaling is given in Figure 12.1-5c. The level slicing contrast-enhancement transfer function of Figure 12.1-4c permits isolation of a band of input

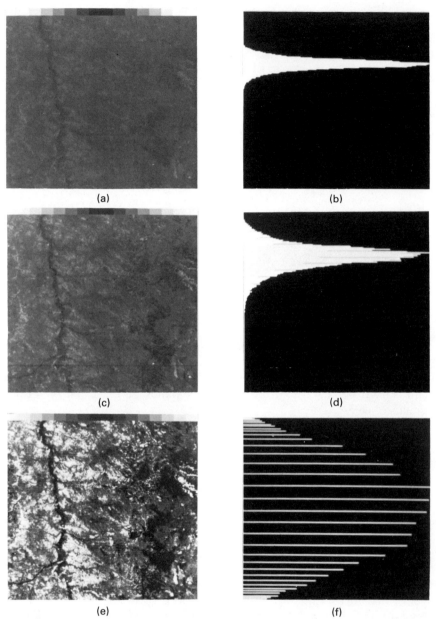

FIGURE 12.1-3. Example of contrast enhancement. (a) Original. (b) Original histogram. (c) Contrast enhancement; min clip = 43, max clip = 163. (d) Enhancement histogram. (e) Contrast enhancement; min clip = 62, max clip = 88. (f) Enhancement histogram.

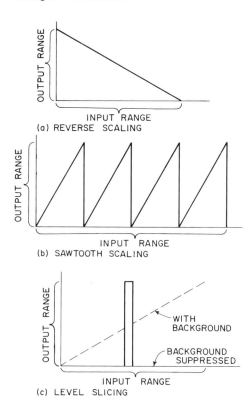

(a) REVERSE SCALING

(b) SAWTOOTH SCALING

(c) LEVEL SLICING

FIGURE **12.1-4**. Reverse-scaling, sawtooth scaling, and level slicing.

gray levels. Figure 12.1-5*d* illustrates level slicing of a monochromatic image. With a color display it is possible to display a monochrome image in normal form except for some narrow band of gray levels that can be mapped into some brilliant color such as red. Figure 12.1-6 contains examples of bit plane level slicing in which only those luminance values corresponding to certain bits of the luminance code are displayed. The level slicing process has proved to be a highly effective technique for human analysis of imagery when implemented in an interactive display.

12.2. HISTOGRAM MODIFICATION

The luminance histogram of a typical natural image that has been linearly quantized is usually highly skewed toward the darker levels; a majority of the pixels possess a luminance less than the average. In such images detail in the darker regions is often not perceptible. One means of enhancing

(a)

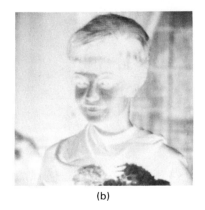

(b)

(c)

(d)

FIGURE 12.1-5. Examples of sawtooth scaling and level slicing. (a) Original. (b) Reverse scaling. (c) 4-cycle sawtooth scaling. (d) Level slicing white: $(16 \leq F(j, k) \leq 40)$.

these types of images is a technique called histogram modification in which the original image is rescaled so that the histogram of the enhanced image follows some desired form. Andrews, Hall, and others (3–5) have produced enhanced imagery by a histogram equalization process for which the histogram of the enhanced image is forced to be uniform. Frei (6) has explored the use of histogram modification procedures that produce enhanced images possessing exponential or hyperbolic shaped histograms. Ketcham (7) has obtained improved results by a local area histogram modification procedure.

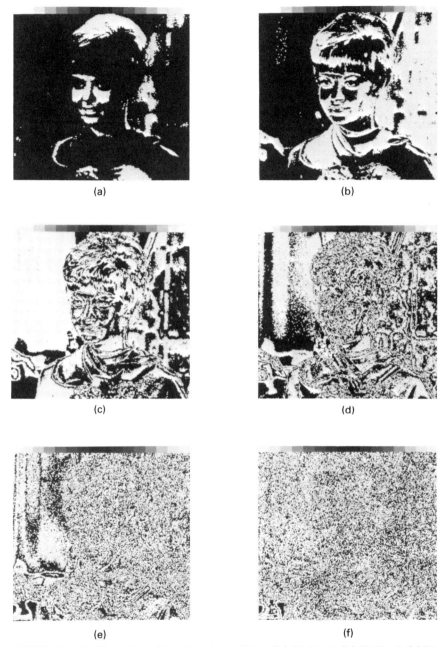

FIGURE 12.1-6. Examples of bit-plane level slicing. (a) Bit No. 1. (b) Bit No. 2. (c) Bit No. 3. (d) Bit No. 4. (e) Bit No. 5. (f) Bit No. 6.

Figure 12.2-1 gives an example of histogram equalization in which the number of output levels is one-half the number of input levels. In Figure 12.2-1 let $H_F(j)$ for $j = 1, 2, \ldots, J$ represent the fractional number of pixels in an input image whose brightness is quantized to the jth reconstruction level. Histogram equalization then seeks to produce an output image field G by point rescaling such that the normalized gray level histogram $H_G(k) = 1/K$ for $k = 1, 2, \ldots, K$. The scaling algorithm is developed as follows. The average value of the histogram levels is computed. Then starting at the lowest gray level of the original, the pixels in the quantization bands are combined until the sum is closest to the average. All of these pixels are then rescaled to the new first reconstruction level at the midpoint of the enhanced image first quantization band. The process is repeated for higher value gray levels. If the number of reconstruction levels of the original image is large, it is possible to rescale the gray levels so that the enhanced image histogram is almost constant. It should be noted that the number of reconstruction levels of the enhanced image must be less than the number of levels of the original image to provide proper gray scale redistribution if all pixels in each quantization level are to be treated similarly. This process results in a somewhat larger quantization error. It is possible to perform the gray scale histogram equalization process with the same number of gray levels for the original and enhanced images, and still achieve a constant histogram of the enhanced image, by randomly redistributing pixels from input to output quantization bands.

The histogram modification process can be considered to be a monotonic point transformation $g_k = T\{f_j\}$ for which the input intensity variable $f_0 \le f_j \le f_J$ is mapped into an output variable $g_0 \le g_k \le g_K$ such that the output probability distribution $P_R\{g_k = b_k\}$ follows some desired form for a given input probability distribution $P_R\{f_j = a_j\}$ where a_j and b_j are reconstruction

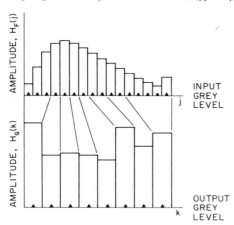

FIGURE 12.2-1. Example of approximate gray level histogram equalization with unequal number of quantization levels.

values of the jth and kth levels. Clearly, the input and output probability distributions must each sum to unity. Thus

$$\sum_{j=0}^{J} P_R\{f_j = a_j\} = 1 \qquad (12.2\text{-}1a)$$

$$\sum_{k=0}^{K} P_R\{g_k = b_k\} = 1 \qquad (12.2\text{-}1b)$$

Furthermore, the cumulative distributions must equate for any input index j. That is, the probability that pixels in the input image have a luminance less than or equal to a_j must be equal to the probability that pixels in the output image have luminance less than or equal to b_k where $b_k = T\{a_j\}$ since the transformation is monotonic. Hence,

$$\sum_{n=0}^{k} P_R\{g_n = b_n\} = \sum_{m=0}^{j} P_R\{f_m = a_m\} \qquad (12.2\text{-}2)$$

The summation on the right is the cumulative probability distribution of the input image. For a given picture the cumulative distribution is replaced by the cumulative histogram to yield the relationship

$$\sum_{n=0}^{k} P_R\{g_n = b_n\} = \sum_{m=0}^{j} H_F(m) \qquad (12.2\text{-}3)$$

Equation 12.2-3 now must be inverted to obtain a solution for g_k in terms of f_j. In general, this is a difficult or impossible task to perform analytically, but certainly easily accomplished by numerical methods. The resulting solution is simply a table that indicates the output image level for each input level.

The histogram transformation can be obtained in approximate form by replacing the discrete probability distributions of Eq. 12.2-2 by continuous probability densities. The resulting approximation is

$$\int_{g_{\min}}^{g} p_g(g)\,dg = \int_{f_{\min}}^{f} p_f(f)\,df \qquad (12.2\text{-}4)$$

where $p_f(f)$ and $p_g(g)$ are the probability densities of f and g, respectively.

The integral on the right is the cumulative distribution function $P_f(f)$ of the input variable f. Hence

$$\int_{g_{min}}^{g} p_g(g)\, dg = P_f(f) \qquad (12.2\text{-}5)$$

In the special case for which the output density is forced to be the uniform density,

$$p_g(g) = \frac{1}{g_{max} - g_{min}} \qquad (12.2\text{-}6)$$

for $g_{min} \le g \le g_{max}$, the histogram equalization transfer function becomes

$$g = [g_{max} - g_{min}]P_f(f) + g_{min} \qquad (12.2\text{-}7)$$

Table 12.2-1 lists several output image histograms and their corresponding transfer functions.

Frei (6) has suggested the histogram hyperbolization procedure listed in Table 12.2-1 and described in Figure 12.2-2. With this method the input image histogram is modified by a transfer function such that the output image probability density will be of hyperbolic form. Then the resulting gray scale probability density following as assumed logarithmic or cube root response of the photoreceptors of the eye model will be uniform. In essence, histogram equalization is performed after the rods and cones of the retina.

Figure 12.2-3 contains several examples of histogram modification image enhancement. As can be seen from these pictures, the subjective performance is image dependent.

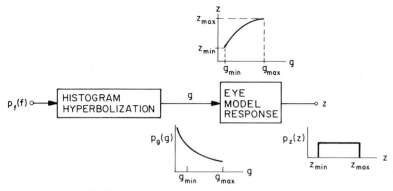

FIGURE 12.2-2. Histogram hyperbolization.

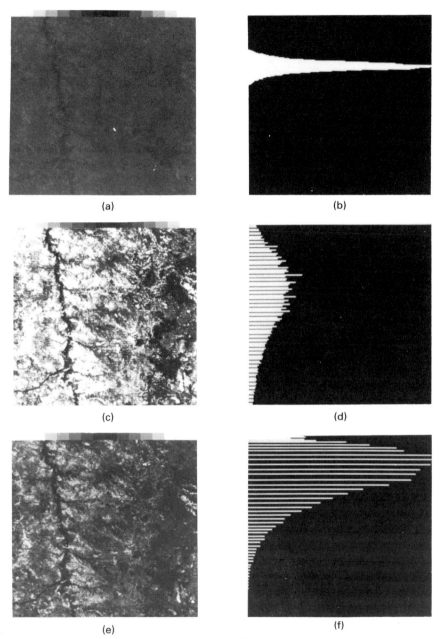

(a)

(b)

(c)

(d)

(e)

(f)

FIGURE 12.2-3. Examples of histogram modification. (a) Original. (b) Original histogram. (c) Histogram equalization. (d) Enhancement histogram. (e) Histogram hyperpolization. (f) Enhancement histogram.

TABLE 12.2-1. Histogram modification transfer functions

Output Probability Density Model		Transfer Function[a]
Uniform	$p_g(g) = \dfrac{1}{g_{max} - g_{min}}$ $\quad g_{min} \leq g \leq g_{max}$	$g = [g_{max} - g_{min}]P_f(f) + g_{min}$
Exponential	$p_g(g) = \alpha \exp\{-\alpha(g - g_{min})\}$ $\quad g \geq g_{min}$	$g = g_{min} - \dfrac{1}{\alpha}\ln[1 - P_f(f)]$
Rayleigh	$p_g(g) = \dfrac{g - g_{min}}{\alpha^2}\exp\left\{-\dfrac{(g - g_{min})^2}{2\alpha^2}\right\}$ $\quad g \geq g_{min}$	$g = g_{min} + \left[2\alpha^2 \ln\left(\dfrac{1}{1 - P_f(f)}\right)\right]^{1/2}$
Hyperbolic (Cube Root)	$p_g(g) = \dfrac{1}{3}\dfrac{g^{-2/3}}{g_{max}^{1/3} - g_{min}^{1/3}}$	$g = ([g_{max}^{1/3} - g_{min}^{1/3}][P_f(f)] + g_{min}^{1/3})^3$
Hyperbolic (Logarithmic)	$p_g(g) = \dfrac{1}{g[\ln(g_{max}) - \ln(g_{min})]}$	$g = g_{min}\left[\dfrac{g_{max}}{g_{min}}\right]^{P_f(f)}$

[a] The cumulative probability distribution, $P_f(f)$, of the input image is approximated by its cumulative histogram

$$P_f(f) \approx \sum_{m=0}^{j} H_F(m)$$

12.3. NOISE CLEANING

An image may be subject to noise and interference from several sources including electrical sensor noise, photographic grain noise, and channel errors. These noise effects can be minimized by classical statistical filtering techniques to be discussed in Chapter 14. Another approach is the application of spatial ad hoc processing techniques.

Image noise arising from a noisy sensor or channel transmission errors usually appears as discrete isolated pixel variations that are not spatially correlated. Pixels that are in error often appear markedly different from their neighbors. This observation is the basis of many noise-cleaning algorithms (8–11). Figure 12.3-1 describes a simple "out-range" noise-cleaning method. With this technique, each pixel is sequentially examined, and if the magnitude of a pixel is greater than the average brightness of its immediate neighbors by some threshold level, it is replaced by the average value. Figure 12.3-2 provides examples of this noise-cleaning algorithm for PCM pictures subjected to simulated binary symmetric channel errors with an error rate of 10^{-2}.

Noise in an image generally has a higher spatial frequency spectrum than the normal image components because of its spatial decorrelatedness. Hence simple low-pass spatial filtering can be effective for noise smoothing. Following the techniques outlined in Part 3, an output $M \times M$ image array Q is formed by discrete convolution of the input $N \times N$ image array F with the $L \times L$ convolution array H according to the relation

$$Q(m_1, m_2) = \sum_{n_1} \sum_{n_2} F(n_1, n_2) H(m_1 - n_1 + 1, m_2 - n_2 + 1) \qquad (12.3\text{-}1)$$

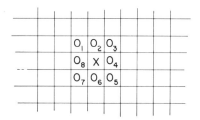

IF $\left[x - \dfrac{1}{8} \displaystyle\sum_{i=1}^{8} O_i \right] > \epsilon$ THEN

$x = \dfrac{1}{8} \displaystyle\sum_{i=1}^{8} O_i$

FIGURE 12.3-1. Example of noise-cleaning algorithm.

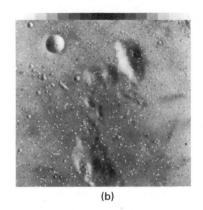

(a)   (b)

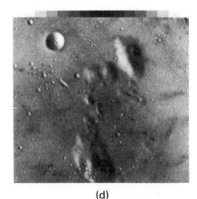

(c)   (d)

FIGURE 12.3-2. Examples of noise cleaning with out-range algorithm with $\varepsilon = 49$. (a) Noisy GIRL. (b) Noisy MOON. (c) Cleaned GIRL. (d) Cleaned MOON.

For noise smoothing H should be of low-pass form with all positive components. Several convolution arrays of low-pass form are listed below.

Mask 1

$$\mathbf{H} = \frac{1}{9}\begin{bmatrix} 1 & 1 & 1 \\ 1 & 1 & 1 \\ 1 & 1 & 1 \end{bmatrix} \qquad (12.3\text{-}2a)$$

Mask 2

$$\mathbf{H} = \frac{1}{10}\begin{bmatrix} 1 & 1 & 1 \\ 1 & 2 & 1 \\ 1 & 1 & 1 \end{bmatrix} \qquad (12.3\text{-}2b)$$

Mask 3

$$\mathbf{H} = \frac{1}{16}\begin{bmatrix} 1 & 2 & 1 \\ 2 & 4 & 2 \\ 1 & 2 & 1 \end{bmatrix} \qquad (12.3\text{-}2c)$$

These arrays, which are often called noise-cleaning masks, are normalized to unit weighting so that the noise-cleaning process does not introduce a brightness bias in the processed image. The effect of noise cleaning with these arrays is shown in Figure 12.3-3. If the required noise mask becomes large in order to achieve adequate noise cleaning, it is usually more computationally efficient to perform the convolution operation indirectly by the Fourier filtering techniques outlined in Chapter 11.

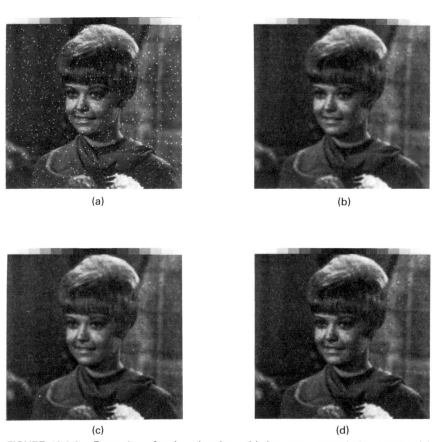

(a)

(b)

(c)

(d)

FIGURE 12.3-3. Examples of noise cleaning with low-pass convolution masks. (a) Noisy original. (b) With mask No. 1. (c) With mask No. 2. (d) With mask No. 3.

12.4. EDGE CRISPENING

Psychophysical experiments indicate that a photograph or visual signal with accentuated edges is often more subjectively pleasing than an exact photometric reproduction. Edge enhancement or crispening can be accomplished in a variety of ways.

For electronically scanned images the scanner signal can be passed through an electrical filter with a high-frequency bandpass characteristic. Another possibility for scanned images is the technique of unsharp masking (12). In this process the image is effectively scanned by two overlapping apertures, one at normal resolution and the other at a lower resolution, producing normal and low-resolution images $F(j, k)$ and $F_L(j, k)$, respectively. A masked image

$$F_M(j, k) = cF(j, k) - (1 - c)F_L(j, k) \tag{12.4-1}$$

is then formed electronically where c is a proportionality constant. Typically, c is in the range of $\frac{3}{5}$ to $\frac{5}{6}$ so that the ratio of normal to low-resolution components in the masked image is from $1.5:1$ to $5:1$. Figure 12.4-1 illustrates typical scan signals for scanning over a sharp edge. The masked signal has a longer duration edge gradient as well as an overshoot compared to the original high-resolution signal. Subjectively, the apparent sharpness of the image is improved.

Edge crispening can also be accomplished by discrete convolutional filtering, as defined by Eq. 12.3-1, in which the impulse response array H is

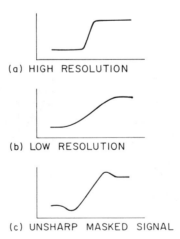

(a) HIGH RESOLUTION

(b) LOW RESOLUTION

(c) UNSHARP MASKED SIGNAL

FIGURE 12.4-1. Waveforms in an unsharp masking image enhancement system.

of high-pass form (13–15). Several typical high-pass masks are listed below.

Mask 1

$$\mathbf{H} = \begin{bmatrix} 0 & -1 & 0 \\ -1 & 5 & -1 \\ 0 & -1 & 0 \end{bmatrix} \qquad (12.4\text{-}2)$$

Mask 2

$$\mathbf{H} = \begin{bmatrix} -1 & -1 & -1 \\ -1 & 9 & -1 \\ -1 & -1 & -1 \end{bmatrix} \qquad (12.4\text{-}3)$$

Mask 3

$$\mathbf{H} = \begin{bmatrix} 1 & -2 & 1 \\ -2 & 5 & -2 \\ 1 & -2 & 1 \end{bmatrix} \qquad (12.4\text{-}4)$$

These masks possess the property that the sum of their elements is unity. Figure 12.4-2 provides examples of edge crispening with unsharp masking and with high-pass masks.

Another form of edge enhancement called statistical differencing (7, 16, p. 100) involves the generation of an image by dividing each pixel value by its measured statistical standard deviation $\sigma(j, k)$ according to the relation

$$G(j, k) = \frac{F(j, k)}{\sigma(j, k)} \qquad (12.4\text{-}5)$$

where the standard deviation

$$\sigma^2(j, k) = \underbrace{\sum_j \sum_k \, [F(j, k) - \bar{F}(j, k)]^2}_{j,k \in N(j,k)} \qquad (12.4\text{-}6)$$

is computed over some neighborhood $N(j, k)$ of the pixel at coordinate (j, k). The function $\bar{F}(j, k)$ is the mean value of the original image at point (j, k), which is approximated by blurring or smoothing the original image by a smoothing operator of low-pass form as described by Eq. 12.3-1. The enhanced image $G(j, k)$ will be increased in amplitude with respect to the original image $F(j, k)$ at edge points that deviate from their neighbors, and decreased in relative amplitude elsewhere. It should be stressed that noise components may be accentuated as well as valid edge structure.

(a)

(b)

(c)

(d)

(e)

FIGURE 12.4-2. Examples of edge crispening with unsharp masking and with high pass masks. (a) Original. (b) Unsharp masking $c = \frac{3}{4}$. (c) Mask No. 1. (d) Mask No. 2. (e) Mask No. 3.

(a)

(b)   (c)

(d)   (e)

FIGURE 12.4-3. Example of statistical differencing (17). Photographs provided by R. H. Wallis, Stanford Technology Corp., Sunnyvale, California. (a) Original. (b) Neighborhood average. (c) Neighborhood standard deviation. (d) Enhancement $\alpha = 0.8$, $m_d = 128$, $\alpha_d = 85$, $A = 6$. (e) Enhancement $\alpha = 0.1$, $m_d = 128$, $\alpha_d = 85$, $A = 6$.

Wallis (17) has suggested a generalization of the statistical differencing operator in which the enhanced image is forced to a form with desired first- and second-order moments. The operator is defined by

$$G(j, k) = [F(j, k) - \bar{F}(j, k)] \left[\frac{A\sigma_d}{A\sigma(j, k) + \sigma_d} \right] + [\alpha m_d + (1 - \alpha)\bar{F}(j, k)]$$

(12.4-7)

where m_d and σ_d represent desired mean and standard deviation factors, A is a gain factor that prevents overly large output values when $\sigma(j, k)$ is small, and α is a proportionality factor controlling the ratio of edge to background composition of the enhanced image. Figure 12.4-3 illustrates the effect of statistical differencing on a scene with deep sun shadows. In this example the experimental mean and standard deviation factors are computed in nonoverlapping 20×20 pixel blocks. Bilinear interpolation of the four nearest block values is used to compute the mean and standard deviation at each point.

12.5. TRANSFORM PROCESSING

Unitary image transforms such as the Fourier and Hadamard transforms provide a spectral decomposition of an image into coefficients that tend to isolate certain features of an image. For example, the first or d.c. spectral component is proportional to the average image brightness, and the higher spatial frequency or sequency components are measures of the image edge content. This inherent property of many image transforms can be exploited for image enhancement. Let $\mathcal{F}(u, v)$ represent the discrete two-dimensional unitary transform of a sampled image $F(j, k)$ as given by the transform pairs

$$\mathcal{F}(u, v) = \sum_{j=0}^{N-1} \sum_{k=0}^{N-1} F(j, k) A(j, k; u, v) \qquad (12.5\text{-}1a)$$

$$F(j, k) = \sum_{u=0}^{N-1} \sum_{v=0}^{N-1} \mathcal{F}(u, v) B(j, k; u, v) \qquad (12.5\text{-}1b)$$

where $A(j, k; u, v)$ and $B(j, k; u, v)$ are the forward and inverse transform kernels, respectively.

Coefficient Rooting (3)

In the coefficient rooting process the magnitude of each transform domain coefficient is raised to a power and the sign or phase portion of the coefficient is retained. The modified transform coefficient is given by

$$\tilde{\mathscr{F}}(u, v) = \frac{\mathscr{F}(u, v)}{|\mathscr{F}(u, v)|} |\mathscr{F}(u, v)|^{\alpha} = \mathscr{F}(u, v)|\mathscr{F}(u, v)|^{\alpha - 1} \qquad (12.5\text{-}2)$$

For a Fourier transform in which

$$\mathscr{F}(u, v) = \mathcal{M}(u, v) \exp\{i\Phi(u, v)\} \qquad (12.5\text{-}3)$$

where $\mathcal{M}(u, v)$ and $\Phi(u, v)$ are the magnitude and phase components of the transform coefficient, respectively, the modified coefficient becomes

$$\tilde{\mathscr{F}}(u, v) = [\mathcal{M}(u, v)]^{\alpha} \exp\{i\Phi(u, v)\} \qquad (12.5\text{-}4)$$

In the limiting case for which $\alpha = 0$, the modified transform coefficient is simply the phase component of the image. If the rooting factor α is chosen to be less than unity, the coefficient rooting operation tends to reduce the magnitude of high-amplitude transform coefficients and increase the amplitude of low-magnitude coefficients. The result of this energy redistribution in the transform domain is often a better utilization of the image dynamic range, and a more subjectively pleasing reproduction. Figure 12.5-1 contains examples of the coefficient rooting process.

Generalized Cepstrum

Another method of nonlinear transform image enhancement consists of taking the logarithm of each transform coefficient. Qualitatively, this operation tends to reduce the dynamic range of samples in the transform domain and increase the dynamic range in the image domain upon reconstruction. Bogert, Healy, and Tukey (18) have introduced a similar transformation for speech processing as a means of detecting echoes. In their transformation, called the cepstrum,* the power spectrum is taken of the logarithm of the power spectrum of a signal. This concept has been extended by Oppenheim, Schafer, and Stockham (19), who defined the complex cepstrum as the Fourier transform of the logarithm of the Fourier transform. For an arbitrary transform a generalized logarithmic transform cepstrum is defined as (20)

$$\tilde{F}(j, k) = K \sum_{u=0}^{N-1} \sum_{v=0}^{N-1} [\ln\{a + b|\mathscr{F}(u, v)|\}] \frac{\mathscr{F}(u, v)}{|\mathscr{F}(u, v)|} B(j, k; u, v)$$

$$(12.5\text{-}5)$$

---

* Cepstrum is a juxtaposition of letters of the word Spectrum.

FIGURE 12.5-1. Examples of Fourier transform coefficient rooting. (a) Original $\alpha = 1$. (b) Square root $\alpha = \frac{1}{2}$. (c) Cube root $\alpha = \frac{1}{3}$. (d) Phase only $\alpha = 0$.

where K is a scaling constant and a and b are constants that control the shape of the logarithmic transfer function. The generalized logarithmic transform can be rewritten as

$$F(j, k) = \sum_{u=0}^{N-1} \sum_{v=0}^{N-1} \mathcal{G}(u, v)\mathcal{F}(u, v)B(j, k; u, v) \qquad (12.5\text{-}6)$$

where

$$\mathcal{G}(u, v) = \frac{K \ln\{a + b|\mathcal{F}(u, v)|\}}{|\mathcal{F}(u, v)|} \qquad (12.5\text{-}7)$$

is a nonlinear filter function dependent on the input image to be filtered.

Qualitatively, logarithmic transform processing reduces the dynamic range within the transform domain and provides a stretching of the resultant dynamic range in the reconstructed image. Since natural images tend to have large-magnitude low spatial frequencies and small high spatial frequencies, the logarithmic transform operation provides a certain amount of inherent edge enhancement. Figure 12.5-2 contains examples of Fourier and Hadamard transform cepstrum operations.

(a)

(b)   (c)

FIGURE 12.5-2. Examples of Fourier and Hadamard cepstrum processing. (a) Original. (b) Fourier cepstrum. (c) Hadamard cepstrum.

12.6. MEDIAN FILTER

Median filtering is a nonlinear signal processing technique developed by Tukey (21) that is useful for noise suppression in images. In one-dimensional form the median filter consists of a sliding window encompassing an odd number of pixels. The center pixel in the window is replaced by the median of the pixels within the window. The median of a discrete sequence $a_1, a_2, \ldots, a_N$ for N odd is that member of the sequence for which $(N-1)/2$ elements are smaller or equal in value, and $(N-1)/2$ elements are larger or equal in value. For example, if the values of the pixels within a window are 80, 90, 200, 110, 120, the center pixel would be replaced by the value 110, which is the median value of the sorted sequence 80, 90, 110, 120, 200. In this example if the value 200 were a noise spike in a monotonically increasing sequence, the median filter would result in considerable improvement. On the other hand, the value 200 might represent a valid signal pulse for a wide-bandwidth sensor, and the resultant image would suffer some loss of resolution. Thus in some cases the median filter will provide noise suppression, and in other cases it will cause signal suppression.

Figure 12.6-1 illustrates some examples of the operation of a median filter and a mean (smoothing) filter for a discrete step function, ramp function, pulse function, and triangle function with a window of five pixels. It is seen from these examples that the median filter has the usually desirable property of not affecting step functions or ramp functions. Pulse functions whose periods are less than one-half the window width are suppressed. Also, the peak of the triangle function is flattened.

Operation of the median filter can be analyzed to a limited extent. It can be shown that the median of the product of a constant K and a sequence $f(j)$ is

$$\text{med}\,\{Kf(j)\} = K\,\text{med}\,\{f(j)\} \qquad (12.6\text{-}1)$$

Furthermore,

$$\text{med}\,\{K + f(j)\} = K + \text{med}\,\{f(j)\} \qquad (12.6\text{-}2)$$

However, for two arbitrary sequences $f(j)$ and $g(j)$ it does not follow that the median of the sum of the sequences is equal to the sum of their medians. That is, in general,

$$\text{med}\,\{f(j) + g(j)\} \neq \text{med}\,\{f(j)\} + \text{med}\,\{g(j)\} \qquad (12.6\text{-}3)$$

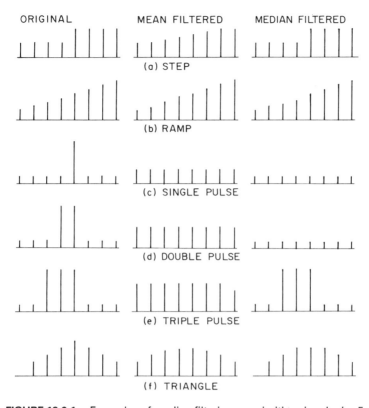

FIGURE 12.6-1. Examples of median filtering on primitive signals, $L = 5$.

The sequences 80, 90, 100, 110, 120 and 80, 90, 100, 90, 80 are examples for which the additive linearity property does not hold.

There are various strategies for application of the median filter for noise suppression. One method would be to try a median filter with a window of length three. If there is no significant signal loss, the window length could be increased to five for median filtering of the original. The process would be terminated when the median filter begins to do more harm than good. It is also possible to perform cascaded median filtering on a signal using a fixed or variable length window. In general, regions that are unchanged by a single pass of the filter will remain unchanged in subsequent passes. Regions in which the signal period is lower than one-half the window width will be continually altered by each successive pass. Usually, the process will continue until the resultant period is greater than one-half the window width, but it can be shown that some sequences will never converge.

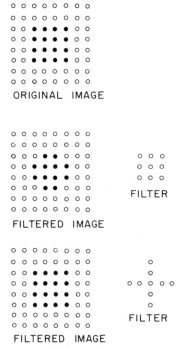

ORIGINAL IMAGE

FILTERED IMAGE

FILTER

FILTERED IMAGE

FILTER

FIGURE 12.6-2. Example of two-dimensional median filtering.

The concept of the median filter can be easily extended to two dimensions by utilizing a two-dimensional window of some desired shape such as a rectangle or a discrete approximation to a circle. It is obvious that a two-dimensional $L \times L$ median filter will provide a greater degree of noise suppression than sequential horizontal and vertical processing with $L \times 1$ median filters, but two-dimensional processing also results in greater signal suppression. Figure 12.6-2 illustrates the effect of two-dimensional median filtering of a spatial pulse signal with a 3×3 square filter and a 5×5 plus-sign-shaped filter. In this example the square median has deleted the corners, while the plus median filter has not affected the signal function.

Figures 12.6-3 and 12.6-4 contain several examples of the application of median filtering for noise suppression in an image. These examples indicate that the median filter is much more effective in reducing the effect of discrete impulse noise than smoothly generated noise. For image enhancement applications the median filter should simply be considered to be an ad hoc tool for noise suppression. It should not be used blindly, but rather its performance should be monitored to determine if its application is beneficial.

(a)   (b)

(c)   (d)

FIGURE 12.6-3. Examples of one-dimensional median filtering for images corrupted by impulse noise. (a) Image with impulse noise, 15 errors per line. (b) Median filtering of (a) with $L = 3$. (c) Median filtering of (a) with $L = 5$. (d) Median filtering of (a) with $L = 7$.

12.7. FALSE COLOR

False color is a point-by-point mapping of an original color image, described by three primary colors, or of a set of multispectral image planes of the same scene, to a color space defined by display tristimulus values that are linear or nonlinear functions of the original image pixel values (22, 23). A common intent is to provide a displayed image with objects possessing different or false colors from what might be expected. For example, blue

FIGURE 12.6-4. Examples of one-dimensional median filtering for images corrupted by Gaussian noise. (a) Image with Gaussian noise $\sigma_n = 25$. (b) Median filtering of (a) with $L = 3$. (c) Median filtering of (a) with $L = 5$. (d) Median filtering of (a) with $L = 7$.

sky in a normal scene might be converted to appear red, and green grass transformed to blue. One possible reason for such a color mapping is to place normal objects in a strange color world so that a human observer will pay more attention to the objects than if they were colored normally. By slowly changing the mapping, the observer could be prevented from totally adapting to the new color world. The usefulness of false color for this application involves rather deep psychological questions.

Another reason for false color mappings that has been explored is the attempt to color a normal scene to match the color sensitivity of a human viewer. For example, it is known that the luminance response of rods and cones in the retina peaks in the green region of the visible spectrum. Thus if a normally red object is false colored to appear green, it may become more easily detectable. Another psychophysical property of color vision that can be exploited is the contrast sensitivity of the eye to changes in blue light. In some situations it may be worthwhile to map the normal colors of objects with fine detail into shades of blue.

A third application of false color is to produce a natural color representation of a set of multispectral images of a scene. Some of the multispectral images may even be obtained from sensors whose wavelength response extends outside the visible wavelength range, for example, infrared or ultraviolet.

In a false color mapping the red, green, and blue display tristimulus values are related to natural color or multispectral image planes F_i by

$$R_D = \mathcal{O}_R\{F_1, F_2, \ldots\} \tag{12.7-1a}$$

$$G_D = \mathcal{O}_G\{F_1, F_2. \ldots\} \tag{12.7-1b}$$

$$B_D = \mathcal{O}_B\{F_1, F_2, \ldots\} \tag{12.7-1c}$$

where $\mathcal{O}_R(\cdot)$, $\mathcal{O}_G(\cdot)$, $\mathcal{O}_B(\cdot)$ are general functional operators. As a simple example, the set of red, green, and blue sensor tristimulus values ($R_S = F_1$, $G_S = F_2$, $B_S = F_3$) may be interchanged according to the relation

$$\begin{bmatrix} R_D \\ G_D \\ B_D \end{bmatrix} = \begin{bmatrix} 0 & 1 & 0 \\ 0 & 0 & 1 \\ 1 & 0 & 0 \end{bmatrix} \begin{bmatrix} R_S \\ G_S \\ B_S \end{bmatrix} \tag{12.7-2}$$

Thus green objects in the original would appear red in the display, blue objects would appear green, and red objects would appear blue. A general linear false color mapping of natural color images may be defined as

$$\begin{bmatrix} R_D \\ G_D \\ B_D \end{bmatrix} = \begin{bmatrix} m_{11} & m_{12} & m_{13} \\ m_{21} & m_{22} & m_{23} \\ m_{31} & m_{32} & m_{33} \end{bmatrix} \begin{bmatrix} R_S \\ G_S \\ B_S \end{bmatrix} \tag{12.7-3}$$

This mapping should be recognized as a linear coordinate conversion of colors reproduced by the primaries of the original image to a new set of primaries.

12.8. PSEUDOCOLOR

Pseudocolor is another color mapping, like false color, that is designed to enhance the detectability of objects within an image by a human observer. However, in a pseudocolor mapping the original image is not a color image, but rather a two-dimensional array of values that is converted to a color plane (24–26). In general terms the pseudocolor mapping for a data plane $F(j, k)$ is defined as

$$R(j, k) = \mathscr{O}_R\{F(j, k)\} \tag{12.8-1a}$$

$$G(j, k) = \mathscr{O}_G\{F(j, k)\} \tag{12.8-1b}$$

$$B(j, k) = \mathscr{O}_B\{F(j, k)\} \tag{12.8-1c}$$

where $R(j, k)$, $G(j, k)$, $B(j, k)$ are display tristimulus values and $\mathscr{O}_R(\cdot)$. $\mathscr{O}_G(\cdot)$, $\mathscr{O}_B(\cdot)$ are linear or nonlinear functional operators. This mapping defines a path in three-dimensional color space parametrically in terms of the data plane value $F(j, k)$. Figure 12.8-1 contains a drawing of the *RGB* color space and two pseudocolor mappings that begin at black and end at white. Mapping *A* represents the achromatic path through all shades of gray, and is the normal representation of a monochrome image. Mapping *B* is a spiral path through color space.

Another class of pseudocolor mappings includes those mappings that exclude all shades of gray. Mapping *C*, which follows the edges of the *RGB* color cube, is an example of such a mapping. This mapping follows the perimeter of the gamut of reproducible colors as depicted by the uniform chromaticity scale (UCS) chromaticity chart shown in Figure 12.8-2. The luminances of the colors red, green, blue, cyan, magenta, and yellow that lie along the perimeter of reproducible colors are noted in the figure. It is

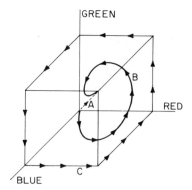

FIGURE 12.8-1. Black to white pseudocolor mappings and *RGB* perimeter mapping.

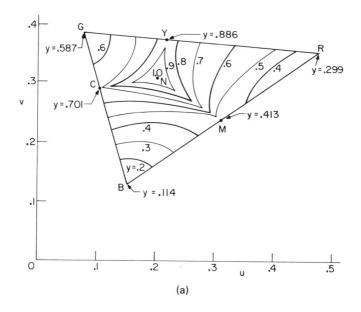

(a)

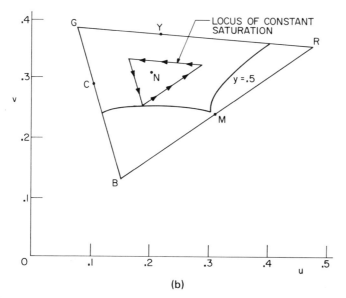

(b)

FIGURE 12.8-2. Luminance loci for N.T.S.C. colors. (a) Loci of maximum luminance. (b) Locus of luminance, $Y = 0.5$.

seen that the luminance of the pseudocolor scale varies between a minimum of 0.114 for blue to a maximum of 0.886 for yellow. A maximum luminance of unity is reached only for white. In some applications it may be desirable to set the luminance of all displayed colors so that discrimination along the pseudocolor scale is by hue and saturation attributes of a color only. Loci of constant luminance are plotted in Figure 12.8-2.

Figure 12.8-2 also includes bounds for displayed colors of constant luminance. For example, if the *RGB* perimeter path is to be followed, the maximum luminance of any color must be limited to 0.114, the luminance of blue. At a luminance of 0.2 the *RGB* perimeter path can be followed except for the region around saturated blue. At higher luminance levels the gamut of constant luminance colors that can be included in the pseudocolor scale becomes severely limited. Figure 12.8-2*b* contains a plot of the 0.5 luminance locus. Inscribed within this locus is the locus of those colors of largest constant saturation. A pseudocolor scale along this path would have the property that all points differ only in hue.

With a given pseudocolor path in color space it is necessary to choose the scaling between the data plane variable and the incremental path distance. On the UCS chromaticity chart, incremental distances are subjectively almost equally noticeable. Therefore it is reasonable to geometrically subdivide the path length into equal increments.

12.9. MULTISPECTRAL IMAGE ENHANCEMENT

Enhancement procedures are often performed on multispectral images of a scene in order to accentuate salient features to assist in subsequent human interpretation or machine analysis (22, 27). These procedures include individual image plane enhancement techniques such as contrast stretching, histogram modification, and edge crispening, as described in previous sections. Other methods, considered in this section, involve the joint processing of multispectral image planes.

Multispectral images are often subtracted in pairs according to the relation

$$D_{m,n}(j, k) = F_m(j, k) - F_n(j, k) \qquad (12.9\text{-}1)$$

in order to accentuate reflectivity variations between the multispectral planes. An associated advantage is the removal of any unknown but common luminance bias components that may exist. Another simple, but highly effective, means of multispectral image enhancement is the formation of ratios of the image planes. The ratio plane between the mth and

nth multispectral planes is defined as

$$R_{m,n}(j, k) = \frac{F_m(j, k)}{F_n(j, k)} \qquad (12.9\text{-}2)$$

It is assumed that the image planes are adjusted to be nonzero. In many multispectral imaging systems the image plane $F_n(j, k)$ can be modeled by the product of an object reflectivity function $R_n(j, k)$ and an illumination function $E(j, k)$ that is nearly identical for all multispectral planes. Ratioing of such imagery provides an automatic normalization or compensation of the illumination factor. One problem with the ratioing method is the accentuation of the gray scale quantization error associated with each plane. The ratio $[F_m(j, k)/F_n(j, k) \pm \Delta(j, k)]$, for which $\Delta(j, k)$ represents a quantization uncertainty, can vary considerably if $F_n(j, k)$ is small. This variation can be reduced significantly by forming the logarithm of the ratios defined by (26)

$$L_{m,n}(j, k) = \log[R_{m,n}(j, k)] = \log[F_m(j, k)] - \log[F_n(j, k)] \tag{12.9-3}$$

There are a total of $N(N-1)$ different difference or ratio pairs that may be formed from N multispectral planes. To reduce the number of combinations, the differences or ratios are often formed with respect to an average image field

$$A(j, k) = \frac{1}{N} \sum_{n=1}^{N} F_n(j, k) \qquad (12.9\text{-}4)$$

Unitary transforms between multispectral planes have also been employed as a means of enhancement. For N image planes an $N \times 1$ vector

$$\mathbf{x} = \begin{bmatrix} F_1(j, k) \\ F_2(j, k) \\ \vdots \\ F_N(j, k) \end{bmatrix} \qquad (12.9\text{-}5)$$

is formed at each coordinate (j, k). Then a transformation

$$\mathbf{y} = \mathbf{A}\mathbf{x} \qquad (12.9\text{-}6)$$

is formed where $\mathbf{A}$ is an $N \times N$ unitary matrix. A common transformation is the principal components decomposition in which the rows of the matrix $\mathbf{A}$ are composed of the eigenvectors of the covariance matrix $\mathbf{K}_x$ between the planes. The matrix **A** performs a diagonalization of the covariance matrix $\mathbf{K}_x$ such that the covariance matrix of the transformed imagery

$$\mathbf{K}_y = \mathbf{A}\mathbf{K}_x\mathbf{A}^T = \Lambda \qquad (12.9\text{-}7)$$

is a diagonal matrix Λ whose elements are the eigenvalues of $\mathbf{K}_x$ arranged in descending value. The principal components decomposition therefore results in a set of decorrelated data planes whose energies can be ranged in value. This process, of course, requires knowledge of the covariance matrix between the multispectral planes. The covariance matrix must either be modeled, estimated, or measured. If the covariance matrix is highly non-stationary, the principal components method becomes difficult to utilize.

Figure 12.9-1 contains a set of four multispectral images and Figure 12.9-2 exhibits their corresponding log ratios. Principal components planes of these multispectral pictures are illustrated in Figure 12.9-3.

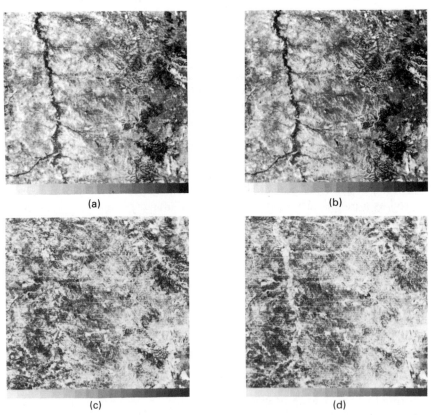

(a)   (b)

(c)   (d)

FIGURE 12.9-1.   Multispectral images (27). (a) Band 4 (green). (b) Band 5 (red). (c) Band 6 (infrared 1). (d) Band 7 (infrared 2).

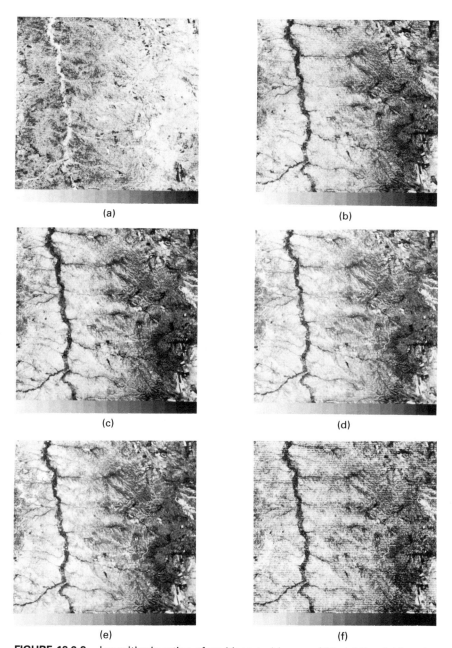

FIGURE 12.9-2. Logarithmic ratios of multispectral images (27). (a) Band 4/band 5. (b) Band 4/band 6. (c) Band 4/band 7. (d) Band 5/band 6. (e) Band 5/band 7. (f) Band 6/band 7.

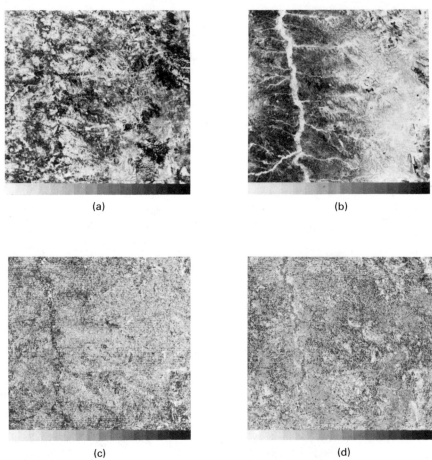

(a)   (b)

(c)   (d)

FIGURE 12.9-3. Principal components of multispectral images (27). (a) λ_1 plane. (b) λ_2 plane. (c) λ_3 plane. (d) λ_4 plane.

REFERENCES

1. R. Nathan, "Picture Enhancement for the Moon, Mars, and Man" *Pictorial Pattern Recognition*, G. C. Cheng, Ed., Thompson, Washington D.C., 1968, 239–266.

2. F. Billingsley, "Applications of Digital Image Processing," *Appl. Opt.*, **9**, 2, February 1970, 289–299.

3. H. C. Andrews, A. G. Tescher, and R. P. Kruger, "Image Processing by Digital Computer," *IEEE Spectrum*, **9**, 7, July 1972, 20–32.

4. E. L. Hall et al., "A Survey of Preprocessing and Feature Extraction Techniques for Radiographic Images," *IEEE Trans. Computers*, **C-20**, 9, September 1971, 1032–1044.

5. E. L. Hall, "Almost Uniform Distribution for Computer Image Enhancement," *IEEE Trans. Computers*, **C-23**, 2, February 1974, 207–208.

6. W. Frei (private communication).

7. D. J. Ketcham, "Real Time Image Enhancement Technique," Proceedings SPIE/OSA Conference on Image Processing, Pacific Grove, California, Vol. 74, February 1976, 120–125.

8. G. P. Dinneen, "Programming Pattern Recognition," Proceedings Western Joint Computer Conference, March 1955, 94–100.

9. R. E. Graham, "Snow-Removal: A Noise-Stripping Process for Picture Signals," *IRE Trans. Inf. Theory*, **IT-8**, 1, February 1962, 129–144.

10. A. Rosenfeld, C. M. Park, and J. P. Strong, "Noise Cleaning in Digital Pictures," Proceedings EASCON Convention Record, October 1969, 264–273.

11. R. Nathan, "Spatial Frequency Filtering," in *Picture Processing and Psychopictorics*, B. S. Lipkin and A. Rosenfeld, Eds., Academic Press, New York, 1970, 151–164.

12. W. F. Schreiber, "Wirephoto Quality Improvement by Unsharp Masking," *J. Pattern Recognition*, **2**, 1970, 171–121, Pergamon Press, London.

13. L. G. Roberts, "Machine Perception of Three-Dimensional Solids," in *Optical and Electro-Optical Information Processing*, J. T. Tippett et al., Eds., MIT Press, Cambridge, Mass., 1965.

14. J. M. S. Prewitt, "Object Enhancement and Extraction," in *Picture Processing and Psychopictorics*, B. S. Lipkin and A. Rosenfeld, Eds., Academic Press, New York, 1970, 75–150.

15. A. Arcese, P. H. Mengert, and E. W. Trombini, "Image Detection Through Bipolar Correlation," *IEEE Trans. Inf. Theory*, **IT-16**, 5, September 1970, 534–541.

16. A. Rosenfeld, *Picture Processing by Computer*, Academic Press, New York, 1969.

17. R. H. Wallis, "An Approach for the Space Variant Restoration and Enhancement of Images," Proceedings Symposium on Current Mathematical Problems in Image Science, Monterey, California, November 1976.

18. B. P. Bogert, M. J. R. Healy, and J. W. Tukey, "The Quefrency Alanysis of Time Series for Echoes: Cepstrum and Saphe Cracking," in *Proceedings of the Symposium held at Brown University, July 11–14, 1962*, M. Rosenblatt, Ed., Wiley, New York, 1963, Chapter 15, 209–243.

19. A. V. Oppenheim, R. W. Schafer, and T. G. Stockham, "Nonlinear Filtering of Multiplied and Convolved Signals," *Proc. IEEE*, **56**, 8, August 1968, 1264–1292.

20. H. C. Andrews and W. K. Pratt, "Digital Image Transform Processing," Proceedings Applications of Walsh Functions, Washington D.C., 1970, 183–194.

21. J. W. Tukey, *Exploratory Data Analysis*, Addison-Wesley, Reading, Mass., 1971.

22. A. F. H. Goetz et al., "Application of ERTS Images and Image Processing to Regional Geologic Problems and Geologic Mapping in Northern Arizona," Jet Propulsion Laboratory, Technical Report 32-1597, Pasadena, California, May 1975.

23. W. Fink, "Image Coloration as an Interpretation Aid," Proceedings SPIE/OSA Conference on Image Processing, Pacific Grove, California, Vol. 74, February 1976, 209–215.

24. C. Gazley, J. E. Reiber, and R. H. Stratton, "Computer Works a New Trick in Seeing Pseudo Color Processing," *Aeronautics and Astronautics*, **4**, April 1967, 56.

25. L. W. Nichols and J. Lamar, "Conversion of Infrared Images to Visible in Color," *Appl. Opt.*, **7**, 9, September 1968, 1757.

26. E. R. Kreins and L. J. Allison, "Color Enhancement of Nimbus High Resolution Infrared Radiometer Data," *Appl. Opt.*, **9**, 3, March 1970, 681.

27. G. S. Robinson and W. Frei, "Final Research Report on Computer Processing of ERTS Images," University of Southern California, Image Processing Institute, Report USCIPI 640, September 1975.

13 IMAGE RESTORATION MODELS

Image restoration may be viewed as an estimation process in which operations are performed on an observed or measured field to estimate the ideal image field that would be observed if no image degradation were present in an imaging system. Mathematical models are described in this chapter for image degradation in general classes of imaging systems. These models are then utilized in subsequent chapters as a basis for the development of image restoration techniques.

13.1. GENERAL IMAGE RESTORATION MODELS

In order effectively to design a digital image restoration system it is necessary quantitatively to characterize the image degradation effects of the physical imaging system, the image digitizer, and the image display. Basically, the procedure is to model the image degradation effects and then perform operations to "undo" the model to obtain a restored image. It should be emphasized that accurate image modeling is often the key to effective image restoration.

There are two basic approaches to the modelling of image degradation effects: a priori modeling and a posteriori modeling. In the former case, measurements are made on the physical imaging system, digitizer, and display to determine their response for an arbitrary image field. In some instances it will be possible to model the system response deterministically, while in other situations it will only be possible to determine the system response in a stochastic sense. The a posteriori modeling approach is to develop the model for the image degradations based on measurements of a particular image to be restored. Basically, these two approaches differ only in the manner in which information is gathered to describe the character of the image degradation.

Figure 13.1-1 contains a general model of a digital imaging system and restoration process. In the model a continuous image light distribution $C(x, y, t, \lambda)$ dependent on spatial coordinates (x, y), time (t), and spectral wavelength (λ) is assumed to exist as the driving force of a physical imaging system subject to point and spatial degradation effects and corrupted by deterministic and stochastic disturbances. Potential degradations include

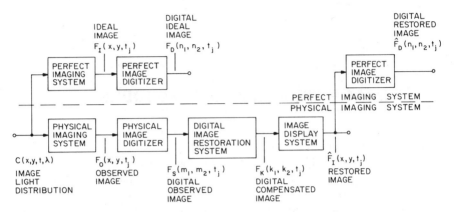

FIGURE 13.1-1. Digital image restoration model.

diffraction in the optical system, sensor nonlinearities, optical system aberrations, film nonlinearities, atmospheric turbulence effects, image motion blur, and geometric distortion. Noise disturbances may be caused by electronic imaging sensors or film granularity. The physical imaging system produces a set of output image fields $F_O^{(i)}(x, y, t)$ at time instant t described by the general relation*

$$F_O^{(i)}(x, y, t) = \mathcal{O}_P\{C, x, y, t, \lambda ; C(x, y, t, \lambda)\} \qquad (13.1\text{-}1)$$

where $\mathcal{O}_P\{\cdot\}$ represents a general operator that is dependent on the space coordinates (x, y), the time history (t), the wavelength (λ), and the amplitude of the light distribution (C). For a monochrome imaging system there will only be a single output field, while for a natural color imaging system, $F_O^{(i)}(\cdot)$ may denote the red, green, and blue tristimulus planes for $i = 1, 2, 3$, respectively. Multispectral imagery may also involve several output planes of data.

The general physical imaging system operator of Eq. 13.1-1 may be characterized by its structure. For example, the operator may possess a time memory or may be memoryless. Time response, as considered here, results directly from the interaction of observed pixel values at the same coordinates (x, y) but at different frame times. In this context spatial smearing caused by the limited electronic response of a raster scanning

---

* Notationally, the variables before the semicolon indicate the functional dependency, that is, t indicates $\mathcal{O}\{\cdot\}$ is time dependent while the term after the semicolon is the function to be operated on.

sensor is not considered a time response effect. A noninstantaneous time response may arise, for example, from the stored charge of a vidicon camera operated at too high a frame rate. If the imaging system is memoryless, then the observed image may be characterized by

$$F_O^{(i)}(x, y, t) = \mathcal{O}_P\{C, x, y, \lambda ; C(x, y, t, \lambda)\} \qquad (13.1\text{-}2)$$

Another special case occurs when the time response is given by a finite length weighted time integration of the image light distribution as modeled by

$$F_O^{(i)}(x, y, t) = \mathcal{O}_P\left\{C, x, y, \lambda ; \int_{t-T}^{t} C(x, y, t, \lambda)L_i(t)\, dt\right\} \qquad (13.1\text{-}3)$$

where T is the integration period and $L_i(t)$ represents the time response weighting factor.

In many imaging systems the point wavelength response assumes the form of a wavelength weighted integration of the input light distribution. That is,

$$F_O^{(i)}(x, y, t) = \mathcal{O}_P\left\{C, x, y, t ; \int_{0}^{\infty} C(x, y, t, \lambda)S_i(\lambda)\, d\lambda\right\} \qquad (13.1\text{-}4)$$

where $S_i(\lambda)$ is the sensor wavelength response.

Image degradations can be often modeled as a cascade of spatial and point intensity effects. For example, if the intensity effects $\mathcal{O}_c\{\cdot\}$ occur first, followed by the spatial effects $\mathcal{O}_s\{\cdot\}$, then

$$F_O^{(i)}(x, y, t) = \mathcal{O}_S\{x, y, t, \lambda ; \mathcal{O}_C\{C, t, \lambda ; C(x, y, t, \lambda)\}\} \qquad (13.1\text{-}5)$$

For the opposite situation

$$F_O^{(i)}(x, y, t) = \mathcal{O}_C\{C, t, \lambda ; \mathcal{O}_S\{x, y, t, \lambda ; C(x, y, t, \lambda)\}\} \qquad (13.1\text{-}6)$$

In both cases the spatial and point effects are each permitted to be wavelength and time dependent.

If the spatial image degradation is linear, it may be expressed by a superposition operation. For an imaging system that is memoryless with separable point and spatial degradation, the observed image is

$$F_O^{(i)}(x, y, t) = \mathcal{O}_C\left\{C, \lambda ; \int\int_{-\infty}^{\infty} C(\alpha, \beta, t, \lambda)J(x, y, \alpha, \beta, t, \lambda)\, d\alpha\, d\beta\right\}$$

$$(13.1\text{-}7)$$

where $J(\cdot)$ is the impulse response of the spatial image degradation. In general, the impulse response may be dependent on each of the four spatial variables x, y, α, β and wavelength. Such a system is called linear space variant. As a special case the spatial degradation may be modeled by a linear-space-invariant image degradation for which the observed image is related to the image light distribution by a convolution integral

$$F_O^{(i)}(x, y, t) = \mathcal{O}_C \left\{ C, \lambda ; \int\int_{-\infty}^{\infty} C(\alpha, \beta, t, \lambda) J(x - \alpha ; y - \beta ; t, \lambda) \, d\alpha \, d\beta \right\}$$

(13.1-8)

In the general model of Figure 13.1-1 each observed image field $F_O^{(i)}(x, y, t)$ is digitized, following the techniques outlined in Part 3, to produce an array of image samples $F_S^{(i)}(m_1, m_2, t)$ at each time instant t. The output samples of the digitizer are related to the input observed field by

$$F_S^{(i)}(m_1, m_2, t) = \mathcal{O}_G\{F_O, x, y; F_O^{(i)}(x, y, t)\}$$

(13.1-9)

where $\mathcal{O}_G\{\cdot\}$ is an operator modeling the image digitization process.

A digital image restoration system that follows produces an output array $F_K^{(i)}(n_1, n_2, t)$ by the transformation

$$F_K^{(i)}(n_1, n_2, t) = \mathcal{O}_K\{F_S^{(i)}(m_1, m_2, t)\}$$

(13.1-10)

where $\mathcal{O}_K\{\cdot\}$ represents the designed restoration operator. Next, the output samples of the digital restoration system are interpolated by the image display system to produce a continuous image estimate $\hat{F}_I^{(i)}(x, y, t)$. This operation is governed by the relation

$$\hat{F}_I^{(i)}(x, y, t) = \mathcal{O}_D\{F_S; x, y; F_K^{(i)}(m_1, m_2, t)\}$$

(13.1-11)

where $\mathcal{O}_D\{\cdot\}$ models the display transformation.

The function of the digital image restoration system is to compensate for degradations of the physical imaging system, the digitizer, and the image display system to produce an estimate of a hypothetical ideal image field $F_I^{(i)}(x, y, t)$ that would be displayed if all physical elements were perfect. The perfect imaging system would produce an ideal image field modeled by

$$F_I^{(i)}(x, y, t) = \int_0^\infty \int_{t-T}^t C(x, y, t, \lambda) U_i(\lambda) \, dt \, d\lambda$$

(13.1-12)

where $U_i(\lambda)$ is a desired spectral response and T is the observation period.

Usually, it will not be possible to restore perfectly the observed image such that the output image field is identical to the ideal image field. The design objective of the image restoration processor is to minimize some error measure between $F_I^{(i)}(x, y, t)$ and $\hat{F}_I^{(i)}(x, y, t)$. The discussion here is limited, for the most part, to a consideration of techniques that minimize the mean-square error between the ideal and estimated image fields as defined by

$$\mathscr{E}_i = E\{[F_I^{(i)}(x, y, t) - \hat{F}_I^{(i)}(x, y, t)]^2\} \qquad (13.1\text{-}13)$$

Often, it will be desirable to place side constraints on the error minimization, for example, to require that the image estimate be strictly positive if it is to represent light intensities that are positive.

Since the restoration process is to be performed digitally, it is often more convenient to restrict the error measure to discrete points on the ideal and estimated image fields. These discrete arrays are obtained by mathematical models of perfect image digitizers that produce the arrays

$$F_D^{(i)}(n_1, n_2, t) = F_I^{(i)}(x, y, t)\delta(x - n_1\Delta I, y - n_2\Delta I) \qquad (13.1\text{-}14a)$$

and

$$\hat{F}_D^{(i)}(n_1, n_2, t) = \hat{F}_I^{(i)}(x, y, t)\delta(x - n_1\Delta I, y - n_2\Delta I) \qquad (13.1\text{-}14b)$$

It is assumed that continuous image fields are sampled at a spatial period ΔI satisfying the Nyquist criterion. Also, quantization error is assumed negligible. It should be noted that the processes indicated by the blocks of Figure 13.1-1 above the dotted division line represent mathematical modeling, and are not physical operations performed on physical image fields and arrays. With this descretization of the continuous ideal and estimated image fields, the corresponding mean-square restoration error becomes

$$\mathscr{E}_i = E\{[F_D^{(i)}(n_1, n_2, t) - \hat{F}_D^{(i)}(n_1, n_2, t)]^2\} \qquad (13.1\text{-}15)$$

With the relationships of Figure 13.1-1 quantitatively established, the restoration problem may be formulated as follows:

Given the sampled observation $F_S^{(i)}(m_1, m_2, t)$ expressed in terms of the image light distribution $C(x, y, t, \lambda)$, determine the transfer function $\mathcal{O}_K\{\cdot\}$ that minimizes the error measure between $F_I^{(i)}(n_1, n_2, t)$ and $\hat{F}_I^{(i)}(n_1, n_2, t)$ subject to desired constraints.

There are no general solutions for the restoration problem as formulated above because of its complexity. To proceed further it is necessary to be more specific about the type of degradation and the method of restoration. The following sections describe models for the elements of the generalized imaging system of Figure 13.1-1.

13.2. OPTICAL SYSTEMS MODELS

One of the major advances in the field of optics during the past 20 years
has been the application of system concepts to optical imaging. Imaging
devices consisting of lenses, mirrors, prisms, and so on can be considered to
provide a deterministic transformation of an input spatial light distribution
to some output spatial light distribution. Also, the systems concept can be
extended to encompass the spatial propagation of light through free space
or some dielectric medium.

In the study of geometric optics it is assumed that light rays always travel
in a straight-line path in a homogeneous medium. By this assumption a
bundle of rays passing through a clear aperture onto a screen produces a
geometric light projection of the aperture. However, if the light distribution at the region between the light and dark areas on the screen is
examined in detail, it is found that the boundary is not sharp. This effect is
more pronounced as the aperture size is decreased. For a pinhole aperture
the entire screen appears diffusely illuminated. From a simplistic viewpoint
the aperture causes a bending of rays called diffraction. Diffraction of light
can be quantitatively characterized by considering light as electromagnetic
radiation that satisfies Maxwell's equations. The formulation of a complete
theory of optical imaging from the basic electromagnetic principles of
diffraction theory is a complex and lengthy task. In the following, only the
key points of the formulation are presented; details may be found in
References 1–3.

Figure 13.2-1 contains a diagram of a generalized optical imaging system. A point in the object plane at coordinate (x_o, y_o) of intensity $I_o(x_o, y_o)$
radiates energy toward an imaging system characterized by an entrance
pupil, exit pupil, and intervening system transformation. Electromagnetic
waves emanating from the optical system are focused to a point (x_i, y_i) on
the image plane producing an intensity $I_i(x_i, y_i)$. The imaging system is said
to be diffraction limited if the light distribution at the image plane

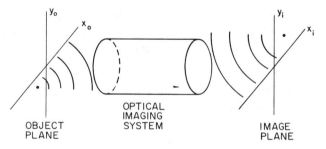

FIGURE 13.2-1. Generalized optical imaging system.

produced by a point-source object consists of a converging spherical wave whose extent is limited only by the exit pupil. If the wavefront of the electromagnetic radiation emanating from the exit pupil is not spherical, the optical system is said to possess aberrations.

In most optical image formation systems the optical radiation emitted by an object arises from transmitted or reflected light from an incoherent light source. The image radiation can often be regarded as quasimonochromatic in the sense that the spectral bandwidth of the image radiation detected at the image plane is small with respect to the center wavelength of the radiation. Under these joint assumptions the imaging system of Figure 13.2-1 will respond as a linear system in terms of the intensity of its input and output fields. The relationship between the image intensity and object intensity for the optical system can then be represented by the superposition integral equation

$$I_i(x_i, y_i) = \int\limits_{-\infty}^{\infty}\!\!\int H(x_i, y_i; x_o, y_o) I_o(x_o, y_o)\, dx_o\, dy_o \qquad (13.2\text{-}1)$$

where $H(x_i, y_i; x_o, y_o)$ represents the image intensity response to a point source of light. Often, the intensity impulse response is space invariant and the input-output relationship is given by the convolution equation

$$I_i(x_i, y_i) = \int\limits_{-\infty}^{\infty}\!\!\int H(x_i - x_o, y_i - y_o) I_o(x_o, y_o)\, dx_o\, dy_o \qquad (13.2\text{-}2)$$

In this case the normalized Fourier transforms

$$\mathcal{I}_0(\omega_x, \omega_y) = \frac{\displaystyle\int\limits_{-\infty}^{\infty}\!\!\int I_0(x_o, y_o) \exp\left[-i(\omega_x x_o + \omega_y y_o)\right] dx_0\, dy_0}{\displaystyle\int\limits_{-\infty}^{\infty}\!\!\int I_0(x_o, y_o)\, dx_o\, dy_o}$$

$$(13\text{-}2\text{-}3a)$$

$$\mathcal{I}_i(\omega_x, \omega_y) = \frac{\displaystyle\int\limits_{-\infty}^{\infty}\!\!\int I_i(x_i, y_i) \exp\left[-i(\omega_x x_i + \omega_y y_i)\right] dx_i\, dy_i}{\displaystyle\int\limits_{-\infty}^{\infty}\!\!\int I_i(x_i, y_i)\, dx_i\, dy_i}$$

$$(13.2\text{-}3b)$$

of the object and image intensity fields are related by

$$\mathcal{I}_o(\omega_x, \omega_y) = \mathcal{H}(\omega_x, \omega_y)\mathcal{I}_i(\omega_x, \omega_y) \qquad (13.2\text{-}4)$$

where $\mathcal{H}(\omega_x, \omega_y)$, which is called the optical transfer function (OTF), is defined by

$$\mathcal{H}(\omega_x, \omega_y) = \frac{\displaystyle\iint_{-\infty}^{\infty} H(x, y) \exp\left[-i(\omega_x x + \omega_y y)\right] dx \, dy}{\displaystyle\iint_{-\infty}^{\infty} H(x, y) \, dx \, dy} \qquad (13.2\text{-}5)$$

The absolute value $|\mathcal{H}(\omega_x, \omega_y)|$ of the OTF is known as the modulation transfer function (MTF) of the optical system.

The most common optical image formation system is a circular thin lens. Figure 13.2-2 illustrates the OTF for such a lens as a function of its degree of misfocus (1, p. 486, 4). For extreme misfocus the OTF will actually become negative at some spatial frequencies. In this state the lens will cause a contrast reversal, dark objects will appear light and vice versa.

The Earth's atmosphere acts as an imaging system for optical radiation transversing a path through the atmosphere. Normally, the index of refraction of the atmosphere remains relatively constant over the optical extent of an object, but in some instances atmospheric turbulence can produce a spatially variable index of refraction that leads to an effective blurring of any imaged object. An equivalent impulse response

$$H(x, y) = K_1 \exp\left[-(K_2 x^2 + K_3 y^2)^{5/6}\right] \qquad (13.2\text{-}6)$$

where the K_i are constants, has been mathematically predicted and verified by experimentation (5) for long-exposure image formation. For convenience in analysis, the function $\frac{5}{6}$ is often replaced by unity to obtain a

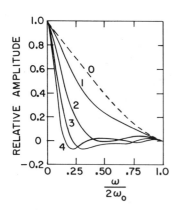

FIGURE 13.2-2. Cross section of transfer function of a lens. Numbers indicate degree of misfocus.

Gaussian-shaped impulse response model of the form

$$H(x, y) = K \, \exp\left\{-\left(\frac{x^2}{2b_x^2} + \frac{y^2}{2b_y^2}\right)\right\}$$ (13.2-7)

where K is an amplitude scaling constant and b_x and b_y are blur spread factors.

13.3. PHOTOGRAPHIC PROCESS MODEL

There are many different types of materials and chemical processes that have been utilized for photographic image recording. No attempt is made here either to survey the field of photography, nor to deeply investigate the physics of photography. References 6–8 contain such discussions. Rather, the attempt here is to develop mathematical models of the photographic process in order quantitatively to characterize the photographic components of an imaging system.

13.3.1. Monochromatic Photography

The most common material for photographic image recording is silver halide emulsion, depicted in Figure 13.3-1. In this material silver halide grains are suspended in a transparent layer of gelatin that is deposited on a glass, acetate, or paper backing. If the backing is transparent, a transparency can be produced, and if the backing is a white paper, a reflection print can be obtained. When light strikes a grain, an electrochemical conversion process occurs, and part of the grain is converted to metallic silver. A development center is then said to exist in the grain. In the development process a chemical developing agent causes grains with partial silver content to be entirely converted to metallic silver. Next, the film is fixed by chemically removing unexposed grains.

The photographic process described above is called a nonreversal process. It produces a negative image in the sense that the silver density is

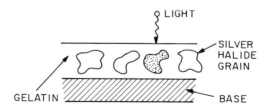

FIGURE 13.3-1.   Cross section of silver halide emulsion.

inversely proportional to the exposing light. A positive reflection print of an image can be obtained in a two-stage process with nonreversal materials. First, a negative transparency is produced, and then the negative transparency is illuminated to expose negative reflection print paper. The resultant silver density on the developed paper is then proportional to the light intensity that exposed the negative transparency.

A positive transparency of an image can be obtained with a reversal type of film. This film is exposed and undergoes a first development similar to that of a nonreversal film. At this stage in the photographic process all grains that have been exposed to light are completely converted to metalic silver. In the next step the metallic silver grains are chemically removed. The film is then uniformly exposed to light, or, alternatively, a chemical process is performed to expose the remaining silver halide grains. Then the exposed grains are developed and fixed to produce a positive transparency whose density is proportional to the original light exposure.

The relationships between light intensity exposing a film and the density of silver grains in a transparency or print can be quantitatively described by sensitometric measurements. Through sensitometry a model is sought that will predict the spectral light distribution passing through an illuminated transparency or reflected from a print as a function of the spectral light distribution of the exposing light and certain physical parameters of the photographic process. The first stage of the photographic process, that of exposing the silver halide grains, can be modeled to a first-order approximation by the integral equation

$$X(C) = k_x \int C(\lambda) L(\lambda) \, d\lambda \qquad (13.3-1)$$

where $X(C)$ is the integrated exposure, $C(\lambda)$ represents the spectral energy distribution of the exposing light, $L(\lambda)$ denotes the spectral sensitivity of the film or paper, plus any spectral losses resulting from filters or optical elements, and k_x is an exposure constant that is controllable by an aperture or exposure time setting. Equation 13.3-1 assumes a fixed exposure time. Ideally, if the exposure time were to be increased by a certain factor, the exposure would be increased by the same factor. Unfortunately, this relationship does not hold exactly. The departure from linearity is called a reciprocity failure of the film. Another anomoly in exposure prediction is the intermittency effect in which the exposures for a constant intensity light and for an intermittently flashed light differ, even though the incident energy is the same for both sources. Thus, if Eq. 13.3-1 is to be utilized as an exposure model, it is necessary to observe its limitations: the equation is strictly valid only for a fixed exposure time and constant intensity illumination.

The transmittance $\tau(\lambda)$ of a developed reversal or nonreversal transparency as a function of wavelength can be ideally related to the density of silver grains by the exponential law of absorption as given by

$$\tau(\lambda) = \exp\{-d_e D(\lambda)\} \qquad (13.3\text{-}2)$$

where $D(\lambda)$ represents the characteristic density as a function of wavelength for a reference exposure value, and d_e is a variable proportional to the actual exposure. For monochrome transparencies the characteristic density function $D(\lambda)$ is reasonably constant over the visible region. As Eq. 13.3-2 indicates, high silver densities result in low transmittances and vice versa. It is common practice to change the proportionality constant of Eq. 13.3-2 so that measurements are made in exponent ten units. Thus the transparency transmittance can be equivalently written as

$$\tau(\lambda) = 10^{-\{d_x D(\lambda)\}} \qquad (13.3\text{-}3)$$

where d_x is the density variable, inversely proportional to exposure, for exponent ten units. From Eq. 13.3-3 it is seen that the photographic density is logarithmically related to the transmittance. Thus

$$d_x D(\lambda) = -\log_{10}\{\tau(\lambda)\} \qquad (13.3\text{-}4)$$

The reflectivity $r_o(\lambda)$ of a photographic print as a function of wavelength is also inversely proportional to its silver density, and follows the exponential law of absorption of Eq. 13.3-2. thus from Eqs. 13.3-3 and 13.3-4 one obtains directly

$$r_o(\lambda) = 10^{-\{d_x D(\lambda)\}} \qquad (13.3\text{-}5)$$

and

$$d_x D(\lambda) = \log_{10}\{r_o(\lambda)\} \qquad (13.3\text{-}6)$$

where d_x is an appropriately evaluated variable proportional to the exposure of the photographic paper.

The relational model between photographic density and transmittance or reflectivity is straighforward and reasonably accurate. The major problem is the next step of modeling the relationship between the exposure $X(C)$ and the density variable d_x. Figure 13.3-2a contains a typical curve of the transmittance of a nonreversal transparency as a function of exposure. It is to be noted that the curve is highly nonlinear except for a relatively narrow region in the lower exposure range. In Figure 13.3-2b the curve of Figure 13.3-2a has been replotted as transmittance versus the logarithm of exposure. An approximate linear relationship is found to exist between transmittance and the logarithm of exposure, but operation in this exposure region is usually of little use in imaging systems. The parameter

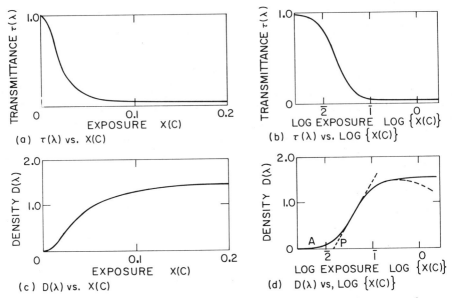

FIGURE 13.3-2. Relationships between transmittance, density, and exposure for a nonreversal film.

of interest in photography is the photographic density variable d_x, which is plotted as a function of exposure and logarithm of exposure in Figures 13.3-2c and 13.3-2d. The plot of density versus logarithm of exposure is known as the H & D curve after Hurter and Driffield, who performed fundamental investigations of the relationships between density and exposure. Figure 13.3-3 is a plot of the H & D curve for a reversal type of film. In Figure 13.3-2d the central portion of the curve, which is approximately linear, has been approximated by the line defined by

$$d_x = \gamma[\log_{10}\{X(C)\} - K_F] \tag{13.3-7}$$

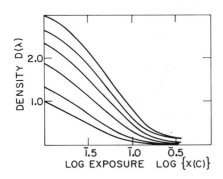

FIGURE 13.3-3. H & D curves for reversal film as a function of development time.

where γ represents the slope of the line and K_F denotes the intercept of the line with the log exposure axis. The slope of the curve γ, pronounced "gamma," is a measure of the contrast of the film, while the factor K_F is a measure of the film speed; that is, a measure of the base exposure required to produce a negative in the linear region of the H & D curve. If the exposure is restricted to the linear portion of the H & D curve, then substitution of Eq. 13.3-7 into Eq. 13.3-3 yields a transmittance function

$$\tau(\lambda) = K_\tau(\lambda)[X(C)]^{-\gamma D(\lambda)} \qquad (13.3\text{-}8)$$

where

$$K_\tau(\lambda) \equiv 10^{\gamma K_F D(\lambda)}$$

With the exposure model of Eq. 13.3-1 the transmissivity or reflectivity models of Eqs. 13.3-3 and 13.3-5, and the H & D curve, or its linearized model of Eq. 13.3-7, it is possible mathematically to model the monochrome photographic process. As an application of the model, consider the production of a positive monochrome transparency in which it is desired perfectly to reproduce the luminance of a light with spectral energy distribution $C(\lambda)$. The luminance of this light is

$$L(C) = \int C(\lambda) V(\lambda)\, d\lambda \qquad (13.3\text{-}9)$$

The positive transparency when illuminated by a white light source with energy distribution $E(\lambda)$ will produce a light with spectral energy distribution $C_T(\lambda) = E(\lambda)\tau_T(\lambda)$ and luminance

$$L(C_T) = \int \tau_T(\lambda) E(\lambda) V(\lambda)\, d\lambda \qquad (13.3\text{-}10)$$

Substitution for the transparency transmittance from Eq. 13.3-3 yields

$$L(C_T) = \int 10^{-\{d_x D(\lambda)\}} E(\lambda) V(\lambda)\, d\lambda \qquad (13.3\text{-}11)$$

where the density parameter d_x is related to the film exposure $X(C)$ by an H & D curve. If the exposure range and position permits the linear approximation of Eq. 13.3-7, then the luminance of the transparency becomes

$$L(C_T) = \int K_\tau(\lambda)[X(C)]^{-\gamma D(\lambda)} D(\lambda) V(\lambda)\, d\lambda \qquad (13.3\text{-}12)$$

For monochrome transparencies the characteristic density function usually is reasonably constant over visible wavelengths. Hence, setting $D(\lambda) = 1$ and $K_\tau(\lambda) = K_\tau$ gives

$$L(C_T) = K_\tau[X(C)]^{-\gamma} L(E) \qquad (13.3\text{-}13)$$

where $L(E)$ represents the luminance of the transparency illumination. If the film is selected and processed such that the gamma is unity with a negative slope, that is, $\gamma = -1$, then the luminance of the transparency will be linearly proportional to the exposure. Under this condition, Eq. 13.3-1 yields

$$L(C_T) = K_\tau L(E)k_x \int C(\lambda)L(\lambda)\, d\lambda \qquad (13.3\text{-}14)$$

where $L(\lambda)$ represents the spectral sensitivity of the emulsion. Comparison of Eqs. 13.3-9 and 13.3-14 indicates that the luminance of the exposing light and the luminance of the transparency will be linearly proportional if the emulsion sensitivity is identical to the relative luminous efficiency at all wavelengths. In practice, emulsion sensitivity curves depart radically from the relative luminous efficiency curve, and therefore exact luminance reproduction is usually not obtained even under the idealized photographic conditions imposed on the model. Additional photographic degradation effects result from nonunity film gammas, exposures that extend beyond the linear regions of the H & D curve, and from other effects that have not even been considered in the simple model.

13.3.2. Color Photography

Modern color photography systems utilize an integral tripack film, as illustrated in Figure 13.3-4, to produce positive or negative transparencies. In a cross section of this film the first layer is a silver halide emulsion sensitive to blue light. A yellow filter following the blue emulsion prevents blue light from passing through to the green and red silver emulsions that follow in consecutive layers, and are naturally sensitive to blue light. A transparent base supports the emulsion layers. Upon development the blue emulsion layer is converted into a yellow dye transparency whose dye concentration is proportional to the blue exposure for a negative transparency, and inversely proportional for a positive transparency. Similarly,

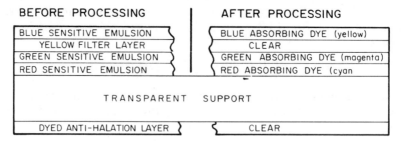

FIGURE 13.3-4. Color film integral tripack.

the green and blue emulsion layers become magenta and cyan dye layers, respectively. Color prints can be obtained by a variety of processes (7). The most common technique is to produce a positive print from a color negative transparency onto nonreversal color paper.

In the establishment of a mathematical model of the color photographic process, each emulsion layer can be considered to react to light as does an emulsion layer of a monochrome photographic material. To a first approximation this assumption is correct. However, there are often significant interactions between the emulsion and dye layer. Each emulsion layer possesses a characteristic spectral sensitivity as shown by the typical curves of Figure 13.3-5. The integrated exposures of the layers are given by

$$X_R(C) = d_R \int C(\lambda) L_R(\lambda)\, d\lambda \qquad (13.3\text{-}15a)$$

$$X_G(C) = d_G \int C(\lambda) L_G(\lambda)\, d\lambda \qquad (13.3\text{-}15b)$$

$$X_B(C) = d_B \int C(\lambda) L_B(\lambda)\, d\lambda \qquad (13.3\text{-}15c)$$

where d_R, d_G, d_B are proportionality constants whose values are adjusted so that the exposures are equal for a reference white illumination, and so that the film is not saturated. In the chemical development process of the film, a positive transparency is produced with three absorptive dye layers of cyan, magenta, and yellow dyes.

The transmittance $\tau_T(\lambda)$ of the developed transparency is the product of the transmittances of the cyan $\tau_{TC}(\lambda)$, the magenta $\tau_{TM}(\lambda)$, and the yellow $\tau_{TY}(\lambda)$ dyes. Hence

$$\tau_T(\lambda) = \tau_{TC}(\lambda)\tau_{TM}(\lambda)\tau_{TY}(\lambda) \qquad (13.3\text{-}16)$$

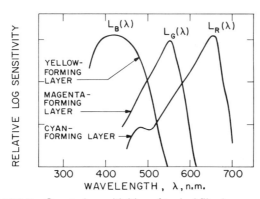

FIGURE 13.3-5. Spectral sensitivities of typical film layer emulsions.

the transmittance of each dye is a function of its spectral absorption characteristic and its concentration. This functional dependence is conveniently expressed in terms of the relative density of each dye as

$$\tau_{TC}(\lambda) = 10^{\{-cD_{NC}(\lambda)\}} \qquad (13.3\text{-}17a)$$

$$\tau_{TM}(\lambda) = 10^{\{-mD_{NM}(\lambda)\}} \qquad (13.3\text{-}17b)$$

$$\tau_{TY}(\lambda) = 10^{\{-yD_{NY}(\lambda)\}} \qquad (13.3\text{-}17c)$$

where c, m, y represent the relative amounts of the cyan, magenta, and yellow dyes, and $D_{NC}(\lambda)$, $D_{NM}(\lambda)$, $D_{NY}(\lambda)$ denote the spectral densities of unit amounts of the dyes. For unit amounts of the dyes the transparency transmittance is

$$\tau_{TN}(\lambda) = 10^{\{-D_{TN}(\lambda)\}} \qquad (13.3\text{-}18)$$

where

$$D_{TN}(\lambda) = D_{NC}(\lambda) + D_{NM}(\lambda) + D_{NY}(\lambda)$$

Such a transparency appears to be a neutral gray when illuminated by a reference white light. Figure 13.3-6 illustrates the typical dye densities and neutral density for a reversal film.

The relationship between the exposure values and dye layer densities is, in general, quite complex. For example, the amount of cyan dye produced is a nonlinear function not only of the red exposure, but is also dependent

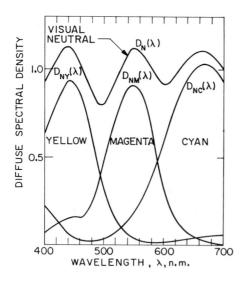

FIGURE 13.3-6. Spectral dye densities and neutral density of a typical reversal color film.

to a smaller extent on the green and blue exposures. Similar relationships hold for the amounts of magenta and yellow dyes produced by their exposures. Often, these so-called interimage effects can be neglected, and it can be assumed that the cyan dye is produced only by the red exposure, the magenta dye by the green exposure, and the blue dye by the yellow exposure. For this assumption, the dye density-exposure relationship can be characterized by the Hurter-Driffield plot of equivalent neutral density versus the logarithm of exposure for each dye. Figure 13.3-7 shows a typical H & D curve for a reversal film. In the central portion of each H & D curve the density versus exposure characteristic can be modeled as

$$c = K_{FC} + \gamma_C \log_{10}(X_R) \qquad (13.3\text{-}19a)$$

$$m = K_{FM} + \gamma_M \log_{10}(X_G) \qquad (13.3\text{-}19b)$$

$$y = K_{FY} + \gamma_Y \log_{10}(X_B) \qquad (13.3\text{-}19c)$$

where γ_C, γ_M, γ_Y, representing the slopes of the curves in the linear region, are called the gammas of the dye layers.

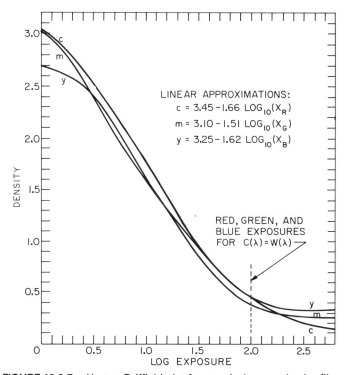

FIGURE 13.3-7. Hurter–Driffield plot for a typical reversal color film.

The spectral energy distribution of light passing through a developed transparency is the product of the transparency transmittance and the incident illumination spectral energy distribution $E(\lambda)$ as given by

$$C_T(\lambda) = E(\lambda) 10^{-\{cD_{NC}(\lambda) + mD_{NM}(\lambda) + yD_{NY}(\lambda)\}} \qquad (13.3\text{-}20)$$

Figure 13.3-8 contains a block diagram of the complete color film recording and reproduction process. The original light with distribution $C(\lambda)$ and the light passing through the transparency $C_T(\lambda)$ at a given resolution element are rarely identical. That is, a spectral match is usually not achieved in the photographic process. Furthermore, the lights $[C]$ and $[C_T]$ usually do not even provide a colorimetric match, since, in general, the tristimulus values of $[C_T]$ given by

$$U(C_T) = \int C_T(\lambda) U_S(\lambda) \, d\lambda \qquad (13.3\text{-}21a)$$

$$V(C_T) = \int C_T(\lambda) V_S(\lambda) \, d\lambda \qquad (13.3\text{-}21b)$$

$$W(C_T) = \int C_T(\lambda) W_S(\lambda) \, d\lambda \qquad (13.3\text{-}21c)$$

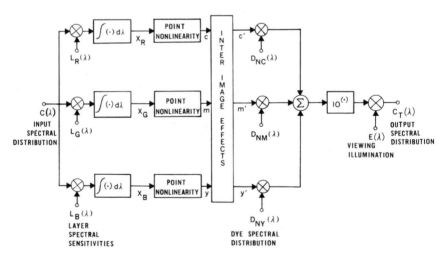

FIGURE 13.3-8.   Color film model.

are not equal to the tristimulus values of $[C]$, which are

$$U(C) = \int C(\lambda) U_S(\lambda) \, d\lambda \qquad (13.3\text{-}22a)$$

$$V(C) = \int C(\lambda) V_S(\lambda) \, d\lambda \qquad (13.3\text{-}22b)$$

$$W(C) = \int C(\lambda) W_S(\lambda) \, d\lambda \qquad (13.3\text{-}22c)$$

In Eqs. 13.3-21 and 13.3-22 the functions $U_S(\lambda)$, $V_S(\lambda)$, $W_S(\lambda)$ represent the spectral tristimulus values for the Uniform Chromaticity Scale (UCS) color coordinate system. The subject of color image restoration is covered in Chapter 16.

13.4. DIGITIZATION SYSTEM MODELS

In Chapter 6 it was noted that a physical digitizer may introduce error in a digital imaging system in the sense that the continuous image reconstructed from the physical samples may not be identical to the image field that was sampled. A major potential source of error is aliasing error resulting from undersampling. Restoration for aliasing error is considered as a separate topic in Chapter 15. In the remaining discussion it is assumed that the sampling rate satisfies the Nyquist criterion. Another error contributor is the limited array size, which causes a truncation of the interpolation functions at the image boundary. This error is usually only significant in a border region of about 5–10 pixels from the edge of a picture.

Sampling with a finite width sampling pulse effectively results in a blurring of the sampled image. As indicated in Eq. 4.2-10, the array of samples $F_S(m_1, m_2, t)$ is related to the observed image by the convolution integral

$$F_S(m_1, m_2, t) = \int\limits_{-\infty}^{\infty}\!\!\int F_O(\alpha, \beta, t) P(\alpha - m_1 \, \Delta x, \beta - m_2 \, \Delta y) \, d\alpha \, d\beta$$

$$(13.4\text{-}1)$$

where $P(x, y)$ is the pulse shape of the sampling pulse and Δx and Δy are the sampling periods. The effect of sampling with finite extent pulses can be modeled as a continuous image field convolution of the image to be sampled with an impulse response $P(-x, -y)$ before ideal sampling with Dirac delta functions.

Image quantization errors can be a serious source of image degradation if an insufficient number of quantization levels is employed in the quantizer. Restoration methods designed to compensate for quantization errors for PCM, DPCM, and transform image coding are presented in Part 6.

13.5. DISPLAY SYSTEM MODEL

The image display system of Figure 13.1-1 produces a continuous image field estimate $\hat{F}_x(x, y, t)$ by interpolating the output array of the digital restoration processor $F_K(k_1, k_2, t)$ with a two-dimensional interpolation function $R(x, y)$. A display system is often subject to a point nonlinearity dependent on the magnitude of F_K. In some display systems the point nonlinearity is also dependent on the display coordinate (x, y). Thus according to Eq. 13.1-11, the general model for the display system is

$$\hat{F}_I(x, y, t) = \mathcal{O}_D\{F_S, x, y; F_K(m_1, m_2, t)\} \qquad (13.5\text{-}1)$$

where $\mathcal{O}_D\{\cdot\}$ models the overall display transformation.

Often, the point nonlinearity and interpolation operations can be considered to be separable with the point nonlinearity modeled as

$$F_G(k_1, k_2, t) = \mathcal{O}_P\{F_K, x, y; F_K(k_1, k_2, t)\} \qquad (13.5\text{-}2)$$

where $\mathcal{O}_P\{\cdot\}$ is the point nonlinearity operator, followed by the spatial interpolation operation described by

$$\hat{F}_I(x, y, t) = \sum_{k_1=-K_1}^{K_1} \sum_{k_2=-K_2}^{K_2} F_G(k_1, k_2, t) R(x - k_1 \Delta x, y - k_2 \Delta y) \qquad (13.5\text{-}3)$$

where the displayed image is produced over an area of $(2K_1 + 1)\Delta x$ by $(2K_2 + 1)\Delta y$.

Ideally, the spatial interpolation function $R(x, y)$ should consist of two-dimensional sinc or Bessel functions, or similar functions, as defined in Section 4.1. Unfortunately, such interpolation functions usually possess negative lobes, and hence cannot be exactly implemented by the summation of positive light quantities. The effect of utilizing nonoptimal interpolation functions can be determined by comparing points on the displayed image $\hat{F}_I(x, y, t)$ and an ideal version of the displayed image $F_I(x, y, t)$ by idealized mathematical sampling of these fields with an array of Dirac delta functions $\delta(x - n_1 \Delta I, y - n_2 \Delta I)$ arranged over a grid of spacing ΔI. Let these arrays be denoted as $\hat{F}_D(n_1, n_2, t)$ and $\tilde{F}_o(n_1, n_2, t)$, respectively. Then it is possible to relate points on the displayed image to the image samples to be displayed $F_G(k_1, k_2, t)$ by the vector-space equation

$$\hat{\mathbf{f}}_D = \mathbf{R}\mathbf{f}_G \tag{13.5-4}$$

where $\hat{\mathbf{f}}_D$ is an $N^2 \times 1$ vector, $\mathbf{f}_K$ is a $K^2 \times 1$ vector, and $\mathbf{R}$ is an $N^2 \times K^2$ matrix of samples of the display interpolation waveforms. Similarly, an image produced by optimal interpolation functions would be modeled as

$$\tilde{\mathbf{f}}_D = \mathbf{R}_O\mathbf{f}_G \tag{13.5-5}$$

where $\mathbf{R}_O$ is an $N^2 \times K^2$ matrix of samples of optimal display interpolation waveforms.

In summary, it is possible linearly to model the image display interpolation process by the pair of matrix equations 13.5-4 and 13.5-5. In Chapter 15 techniques are described for modifying the elements of $\mathbf{f}_G$ in Eq. 13.5-5 in order to improve display fidelity.

13.6. IMAGE NOISE MODELS

Observations of an image field are subject to measurement error or uncertainty arising from such sources as sensor noise, film grain irregularities, and atmospheric light fluctuations. For semantic convenience all such effects are referred to as noise.

13.6.1. Photodetector Noise

Figure 13.6-1a contains a simple model of a photodetector imaging sensor and an associated electrical filter that will serve as a basis for the discussion of sensor noise sources. Ideally, the photodetector acts as a converter of optical intensity to detector current, or, equivalently, as a converter of incident photons to electrons emitted by the detector. The detector produces a signal current that passes through an electrical filter and creates a signal voltage across a load resistor.

Perhaps the most common noise source associated with electronic imaging systems is thermal noise resulting from random electron fluctuations in resistive elements of photodetectors or resistors within sensor amplifiers (9, 10). Thermal noise can be modeled as an additive Gaussian stochastic process independent of the sensed image field. A detailed analysis, although straightforward, requires knowledge of the sensor circuitry. As an illustration of thermal noise calculations, consider the photodetector model of Figure 13.6-1 in which the load resistor is assumed to be the only

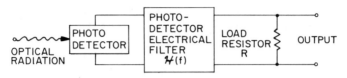

(a) PHOTODETECTOR

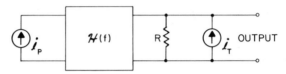

(b) PHOTODETECTOR SIGNAL AND THERMAL NOISE MODEL

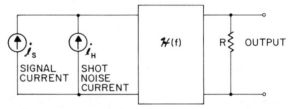

(c) PHOTODETECTOR SIGNAL AND SHOT NOISE MODEL

FIGURE 13.6-1.   Photodetector noise models.

significant resistive element in the unit. In Figure 13.6-1*b* the photodetector is replaced by an ideal current generator i_P whose current is linearly proportional to the incident light intensity at some image point. The thermal noise contribution can be modeled as a thermal noise current source of value i_T in parallel with the noise resistor. This thermal noise current represents a zero-mean Gaussian random process with variance $\sigma_{i_T}^2 = N_T/R$ where N_T is the thermal noise power at the system output. It is easily shown (11, p. 147) that

$$N_T = 2kT \int_{-\infty}^{\infty} |\mathcal{H}_E(f)|^2 \, df \qquad (13.6\text{-}1)$$

where k is the Boltzmann's constant (1.38×10^{-23} joules/degree Kelvin), T is the temperature in degrees Kelvin, and $\mathcal{H}_E(f)$ is the equivalent transfer function of the photodetector electrical filter and load resistor. In the simple case in which the filter is a capacitor of value C placed in parallel with the detector and load resistor, the thermal noise power becomes $N_T = kT/RC$. If the detector current is constant and the equivalent filter is linear, the probability density of the current output of the detector can be written directly as

$$p(i) = [2\pi\sigma_{i_T}^2]^{-1/2} \exp\left\{-\frac{[i-i_S]^2}{2\sigma_{i_T}^2}\right\} \qquad (13.6\text{-}2)$$

where i_S is the equivalent average signal current at the output produced by the photodetector current i_P passing through the filter.

Photodetector current is not truly constant valued even when the incident light intensity is constant. Photoelectric sensors exhibit a measurement uncertainty resulting from the quantum-mechanical nature of light. At low light levels the number of electrons emitted by a photodetector is governed by a Poisson probability density (12). In an observation time period τ the probability distribution of detector current pulses is given by

$$P_R\left(i_P = \frac{jq}{\tau}\right) = \frac{(u_S + u_H)^j \exp\{-(u_S + u_H)\}}{j!} \qquad (13.6\text{-}3)$$

where j is a positive integer, q is the charge of an electron (1.6×10^{-19} Cs), u_S denotes the average number of electrons emitted from the detector as a result of the incident illumination, and u_H represents the average number of electron emissions caused by detector dark current and extraneous background radiation. The resultant uncertainty in knowledge of the detector current is called shot noise in photoemissive detectors and generation-recombination noise in photoconductive and photovoltaic detectors (13). If the photodetector possesses sufficient internal amplification, for example, a photomultiplier tube, the shot noise will normally dominate any subsequent thermal noise sources; otherwise, thermal noise generally dominates and the photodetector current may be considered constant. In either case, if the average number of signal electron emissions becomes large, the Poisson distribution of Eq. 13.6-3 can be well approximated by the Gaussian distribution (11, p. 162)

$$p(i_p) = \left[\frac{2\pi q^2 u_S}{\tau^2}\right]^{-1/2} \exp\left\{\frac{-(i_p - qu_S/\tau)^2}{2q^2 u_S/\tau^2}\right\} \qquad (13.6\text{-}4)$$

In summary, for most imaging sensors, the associated sensor noise can be modeled either as a Gaussian- or Poisson-distributed random process. Poisson-distributed noise only occurs when the image light level is extremely small and the photodetector possesses a large internal electron amplification. Other practical detector circuits are usually well modeled as additive Gaussian noise dominated. Calculation of the exact noise variance often entails analysis of complex electrical circuits, and consequently indirect measurement techniques are usually invoked.

13.6.2. Film-Grain Noise

In the exposure and development of a photographic film, silver halide grains that are exposed to a sufficient quantity of light are converted to grains of metallic silver. This process is not entirely deterministic; silver halide grains experiencing an equivalent exposure are not necessarily converted to the same size and shape silver grains; furthermore, silver grains are randomly distributed over the surface of the film. This inherent randomness in silver grain formation, called film-grain noise, leads to a randomness or uncertainty in the amount of light passing through a transparency or reflected from a print (8, 14).

The classical model (15, 16) for film-grain noise fluctuations assumes a Gaussian distribution

$$p[D(x, y)] = [2\pi\sigma_D^2(x, y)]^{-1/2} \exp\left\{ -\frac{[D(x, y) - u_D(x, y)]^2}{2\sigma_D^2(x, y)} \right\}$$

$$(13.6\text{-}5)$$

of the exposed film density $D(x, y)$ about a mean density $u_D(x, y)$ with a variance $\sigma_D^2(x, y)$. The mean density is determined by a spatial average about the point (x, y) over some window including many individual grains, and the standard deviation is modeled as (17)

$$\sigma_D(x, y) = \alpha[u_D(x, y)]^\beta \qquad (13.6\text{-}6)$$

where β is a constant, α is empirically set at

$$\alpha = 0.66\left[\frac{a}{A}\right]^{1/2} \qquad (13.6\text{-}7)$$

and a is the average film-grain area, and A is the examination area of the film. Falconer (17) has suggested $\beta = \frac{1}{2}$ while Huang (18) has proposed setting $\beta = \frac{1}{3}$. Experimental analysis indicates that the the spatial correlation of the film-grain fluctuations is quite small, and consequently film-grain noise may be considered to be a white noise process. The Gaussian density $D(x, y)$ described by Eq. 13.6-5 can be expressed as the sum of a mean density component $u_D(x, y)$ and a zero mean Gaussian random process component $N(x, y)$ according to the relation (18).

$$D(x, y) = u_D(x, y) + \sigma_D(x, y)N(x, y) \qquad (13.6\text{-}8a)$$

or

$$D(x, y) = u_D(x, y) + \alpha[u_D(x, y)]^\beta N(x, y) \qquad (13.6\text{-}8b)$$

In this form it is readily apparent that although film-grain noise is signal dependent, it is additive in the density domain (19). From Eq. 13.3-3 the transmittance of the exposed film at a fixed wavelength may be written as

$$\tau(x, y) = 10^{-\{D(x,y)D(\lambda)\}} \qquad (13.6\text{-}9)$$

where $D(\lambda)$ represents the characteristic density of the film as a function of wavelength. Then it is easily seen that the transmittance function

$$\tau(x, y) = \tau_o(x, y)10^{-\{\sigma_D(x,y)N(x,y)D(\lambda)\}} \qquad (13.6\text{-}10)$$

may be expressed as the product of the average transmittance without grain noise $\tau_o(x, y)$ and a noise factor proportional to $\sigma_D(x, y)$. Thus, in the intensity domain, film-grain noise is a multiplicative noise process (19).

Naderi and Sawchuk (20) have developed a model for photographic film image recording based upon an earlier model of Kelly (21). This model, shown in Figure 13.6-2, incorporates spatial blur effects resulting from the imaging system, photographic process, and image scanner as well as the film nonlinearities. Applications of this model to film-grain noise restoration are presented in Chapter 15.

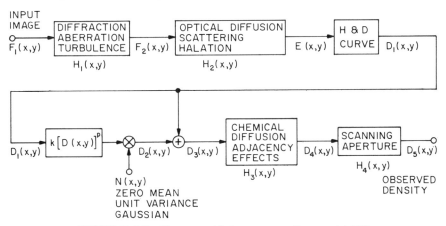

FIGURE 13.6-2. Photographic image recording model (20).

13.7. DISCRETE RESTORATION MODELS

This chapter began with the introduction of a general model of an imaging system and a digital restoration processor. Next, typical components of the imaging system were described and modeled within the context of the general model. Now the discussion turns to the construction of several discrete image restoration models. The following chapters describe restoration techniques for these models.

After each element of the digital image restoration system of Figure 13.1-1 is modeled, following the techniques previously described, the restoration system may be conceptually distilled to three equations:

$$F_S(m_1, m_2) = \mathcal{O}_M\{F_I(n_1, n_2), N_1(m_1, m_2), \ldots, N_N(m_1, m_2)\} \quad (13.7\text{-}1a)$$

$$F_K(k_1, k_2) = \mathcal{O}_R\{F_S(m_1, m_2)\} \quad\quad\quad\quad\quad\quad (13.7\text{-}1b)$$

$$\hat{F}_I(n_1, n_2) = \mathcal{O}_D\{F_K(k_1, k_2)\} \quad\quad\quad\quad\quad\quad (13.7\text{-}1c)$$

where F_S represents an array of observed image samples, F_I and $\hat{F}_I$ are arrays of ideal image points and estimates, respectively, F_K is an array of compensated image points from the digital restoration system, N_i denotes arrays of noise samples from various system elements, and $\mathcal{O}_M(\cdot)$, $\mathcal{O}_R(\cdot)$, $\mathcal{O}_D(\cdot)$ represent general transfer functions of the imaging system, restoration processor, and display system, respectively. Vector-space equivalents of Eq. 13.7-1 can be formed for purposes of analysis by column scanning of the arrays of Eq. 13.7-1. These relationships are given by

$$\mathbf{f}_S = \mathcal{O}_M\{\mathbf{f}_I, \mathbf{n}_1, \ldots, \mathbf{n}_N\} \quad\quad\quad (13.7\text{-}2a)$$

$$\mathbf{f}_K = \mathcal{O}_R\{\mathbf{f}_S\} \quad\quad\quad\quad\quad\quad (13.7\text{-}2b)$$

$$\hat{\mathbf{f}}_I = \mathcal{O}_D\{\mathbf{f}_K\} \quad\quad\quad\quad\quad\quad (13.7\text{-}2c)$$

Several estimation approaches to the solution of Eq. 13.7-1 or Eq. 13.7-2 are described in the following chapters. Unfortunately, general solutions have not been found; recourse must be made to specific solutions for less general models.

The most common digital restoration model is that of Figure 13.7-1 in which a continuous image field is subjected to a linear blur, the electrical sensor responds nonlinearly to its input intensity, and the sensor amplifier introduces additive Gaussian noise independent of the image field. The physical image digitizer that follows may also introduce an effective blurring of the sampled image as the result of sampling with extended pulses.

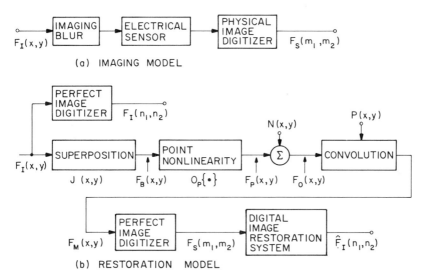

FIGURE 13.7-1. Imaging and restoration models for a sampled blurred image with additive noise.

Figure 13.7-1*b* contains a restoration model for the imaging system. It is assumed that the imaging blur can be modeled as a superposition operation with an impulse response $J(x, y)$ that may be space variant. The sensor is assumed to respond nonlinearly to the input field $F_B(x, y)$ on a point-by-point basis, and its output is subject to an additive noise field $N(x, y)$. The effect of sampling with extended sampling pulses, which are assumed symmetric, can be modeled as a convolution of $F_D(x, y)$ with each pulse $P(x, y)$ followed by perfect sampling.

The objective of the restoration is to produce an array of samples $\hat{F}_I(n_1, n_2)$ that are estimates of points on the ideal input image field $F_I(x, y)$ obtained by a perfect image digitizer sampling at a spatial period ΔI. To produce a digital restoration model it is necessary quantitatively to relate the physical image samples $F_S(m_1, m_2)$ to the ideal image points $F_I(n_1, n_2)$ following the techniques outlined in Section 9.2. This is accomplished by truncating the sampling pulse equivalent impulse response $P(x, y)$ to some spatial limits $\pm T_P$, and then extracting points from the continuous observed field $F_O(x, y)$ at a grid spacing ΔP. The discrete representation must then be carried one step further by relating points on the observed image field $F_O(x, y)$ to points on the image field $F_P(x, y)$ and the noise field $N(x, y)$. The final step in the development of the discrete restoration model involves discretization of the superposition operation with $J(x, y)$. There are two potential sources of error in this modeling process: truncation of the impulse responses $J(x, y)$ and $P(x, y)$, and quadrature integration errors.

Both sources of error can be made negligibly small by choosing the truncation limits T_B and T_P large, and by choosing the quadrature spacings ΔI and ΔP small. This, of course, increases the sizes of the arrays, and eventually the amount of storage and processing required. Actually, as is subsequently shown, the numerical stability of the restoration estimate may be impaired by improving the accuracy of the discretization process!

The relative dimensions of the various arrays of the restoration model are important. Figure 13.7-2 shows the nested nature of the arrays. The blurred image array $F_B(k_1, k_2)$ is smaller than the ideal image array $F_I(n_1, n_2)$ by the half-width of the truncated impulse response $J(x, y)$. Similarly, the array of physical sample points $F_S(m_1, m_2)$ is smaller than the array of observed image points $F_O(k_1, k_2)$ by the half-width of the truncated impulse response $P(x, y)$.

It is convenient to form vector equivalents of the various arrays of the restoration model in order to utilize the formal structure of vector algebra in the subsequent restoration analysis. Again, following the techniques of Section 9.2, the arrays are reindexed so that the first element appears in the upper-left corner of each array. Next, the vector relationships between the stages of the model are obtained by column scanning of the arrays to give

$$\mathbf{f}_S = \mathbf{B}_P \mathbf{f}_O \qquad (13.7\text{-}3a)$$

$$\mathbf{f}_O = \mathbf{f}_P + \mathbf{n} \qquad (13.7\text{-}3b)$$

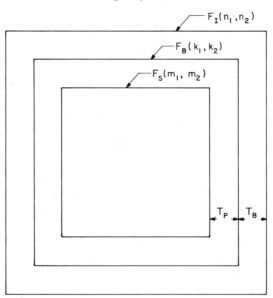

FIGURE 13.7-2. Relationship of sampled image arrays.

$$\mathbf{f}_P = \mathcal{O}_P\{\mathbf{f}_B\} \tag{13.7-3c}$$

$$\mathbf{f}_B = \mathbf{B}_B \mathbf{f}_I \tag{13.7-3d}$$

where the blur matrix $\mathbf{B}_P$ contains samples of $P(x, y)$ and $\mathbf{B}_B$ contains samples of $J(x, y)$. The nonlinear operation of Eq. 13.7-3c is defined as a point-by-point nonlinear transformation. That is,

$$f_P(i) = \mathcal{O}_P\{f_B(i)\} \tag{13.7-4}$$

Equations 13.7-3a to 13.7-3d can be combined to yield a single equation for the observed physical image samples in terms of points on the ideal image

$$\mathbf{f}_S = \mathbf{B}_P \mathcal{O}_P\{\mathbf{B}_B \mathbf{f}_I\} + \mathbf{B}_P \mathbf{n} \tag{13.7-5}$$

Several special cases of Eq. 13.7-5 will now be defined. First, if the point nonlinearity is absent,

$$\mathbf{f}_S = \mathbf{B}\mathbf{f}_I + \mathbf{n}_B \tag{13.7-6}$$

where $\mathbf{B} = \mathbf{B}_P \mathbf{B}_B$ and $\mathbf{n}_B = \mathbf{B}_P \mathbf{n}$. This is the classical discrete model consisting of a set of linear equations with measurement uncertainty. Another case that will be defined for later discussion occurs when the spatial blur of the physical image digitizer is negligible. In this case

$$\mathbf{f}_S = \mathcal{O}_P\{\mathbf{B}\mathbf{f}_I\} + \mathbf{n} \tag{13.7-7}$$

where $\mathbf{B} = \mathbf{B}_B$. If the quadrature grid spacing ΔI is chosen to be the same as the physical sample spacing ΔS, the blur matrices of Eqs. 13.7-6 and 13.7-7 assume the special form

$$\mathbf{B} = \begin{bmatrix} \mathbf{B}_{1,1} & \mathbf{B}_{1,2} & \cdots & \mathbf{B}_{1,L} & 0 & \cdots & 0 \\ 0 & \mathbf{B}_{2,2} & \cdots & \mathbf{B}_{2,L} & \mathbf{B}_{2,L+1} & & 0 \\ \cdot & \cdot & & & & & \cdot \\ \cdot & \cdot & & & & & \cdot \\ \cdot & \cdot & & & & & 0 \\ 0 & 0 & \cdots & \mathbf{B}_{M,N-L+1} & \cdot & \cdots & \mathbf{B}_{M,N} \end{bmatrix} \tag{13.7-8}$$

where

$$B_{m_2,n_2}(m_1, n_1) = H(m_1 - n_1 + L, m_2 - n_2 + L) \tag{13.7-9}$$

for $1 \le m_i \le M$ and $m_i \le n_i \le m_i + L - 1$.

Chapter 14 contains results for several image restoration experiments based upon the restoration models defined by Eqs. 13.7-6 and 13.7-7. Two artificial pictures have been generated for these computer simulation experiments (22). The original image used for the analysis of underdetermined restoration techniques, shown in Figure 13.7-3a, consists of a 4×4 pixel square of intensity 245 placed against an extended background of intensity 10 referenced to a 0 to 255 intensity scale. All images are "blown up" for display purposes. The Gaussian-shaped point-spread function,

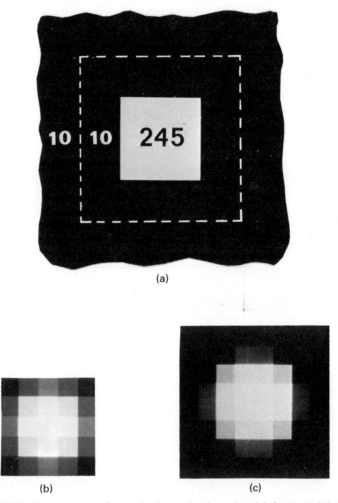

(a)

(b)   (c)

FIGURE 13.7-3.   Image arrays for underdetermined model. (a) Original. (b) Impulse response. (c) Observation.

illustrated in Figure 13.7-3b, is defined as

$$H(l_1, l_2) = K \exp\left\{ -\left(\frac{l_1^2}{2b_C^2} + \frac{l_2^2}{2b_R^2} \right) \right\} \qquad (13.7\text{-}10)$$

over a 5×5 point array where K is an amplitude scaling constant and b_C and b_R are blur-spread constants. The original picture for the analysis of overdetermined restoration techniques is shown in Figure 13.7-4a. This

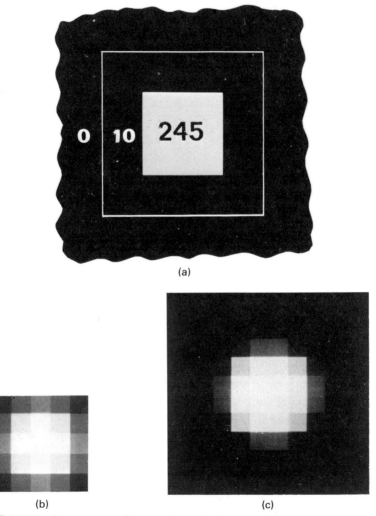

(a)

(b)   (c)

FIGURE 13.7-4. Image arrays for overdetermined model. (a) Original. (b) Impulse response. (c) Observation.

picture consists of a 4×4 pixel region of intensity 245 on an 8×8 pixel region of intesity 10, which is in turn surrounded by an area of zero intensity. A physical example of such an original image would be the moon viewed against a dark sky background. This original image is then blurred by the 5×5 point impulse response of Figure 13.7-4b resulting in the 12×12 pixel blurred image. It is assumed that all 12×12 pixel points are observed, and that it is known a priori that the original image size is limited to an 8×8 pixel array. Hence many of the entries of the blur matrix of Eq. 13.7-8 are identically zero. In ·fact, letting **f** denote the column scanned 8×8 pixel $(M = 8)$ original image, it can be shown that the physical observation of 12×12 pixel points $(N = 2)$ can be modeled in vector-space form as

$$\mathbf{g} = \mathbf{D}\mathbf{f} + \mathbf{n} \qquad (13.7\text{-}11)$$

where **D** is an $M^2 \times N^2$ matrix of the form

$$\mathbf{D} = \begin{bmatrix} \mathbf{D}_{1,1} & 0 & \cdots & & 0 \\ \mathbf{D}_{2,1} & \mathbf{D}_{2,2} & & & \vdots \\ \vdots & \vdots & & & \\ & & & & 0 \\ & & & \mathbf{D}_{M,N-L+1} & \\ \mathbf{D}_{L,1} & \mathbf{D}_{L,2} & & & \vdots \\ 0 & \mathbf{D}_{L+1,2} & & & \vdots \\ \vdots & & & & \vdots \\ 0 & & \vdots & \cdots 0 & \mathbf{D}_{M,N} \end{bmatrix} \qquad (13.7\text{-}12)$$

with

$$D_{m_2,n_2}(m_1, n_1) = H(m_1 - n_1 + 1, m_2 - n_2 + 1) \qquad (13.7\text{-}13)$$

for $1 \le n_i \le N$ and $n_i \le m_i \le n_i + L - 1$. Equation 13.1-12 is identical to the D-type finite area convolution operator introduced in Chapter 9. Comparison of the structure of the blur matrices for the underdetermined model given in Eq. 13.7-8 and the overdetermined model of Eq. 13.7-12 indicates that they are transpose pairs. That is, $\mathbf{B} = \mathbf{D}^T$, and for the special case of row and column separability $\mathbf{B}_R = \mathbf{D}_R^T$ and $\mathbf{B}_C = \mathbf{D}_C^T$. These relations are utilized later in computation of the condition numbers of the blur matrices.

In the computer simulation restoration experiments the observed blurred images for the underdetermined and overdetermined models have been obtained by multiplying the column-scanned original images of Figure 13.7-3a and 13.7-4a by the blur matrices **B** and **D**, respectively.

Next, additive white, Gaussian observation noise has been simulated by adding output variables from an appropriate random number generator to the blurred images. For display all restored image points are clipped to the intensity range 0 to 255.

REFERENCES

1. M. Born and E. Wolf, *Principles of Optics*, Pergamon Press, New York, 1970.
2. J. W. Goodman, *Introduction to Fourier Optics*, McGraw-Hill, New York, 1968.
3. E. L. O'Neill, *Introduction to Statistical Optics*, Addison-Wesley, Reading, Mass., 1963.
4. H. H. Hopkins, *Proc. Roy. Soc.*, series A, **231**, 1184, July 1955, 98.
5. R. E. Hufnagel and N. R. Stanley, "Modulation Transfer Function Associated with Image Transmission through Turbulent Media," *J. Opt. Soc. Am.*, **54**, 1, January 1964, 52–61.
6. K. Henney and B. Dudley, *Handbook of Photography*, McGraw-Hill, New York, 1939.
7. R. M. Evans, W. T. Hanson, and W. L. Brewer, *Principles of Color Photography*, Wiley, New York, 1953.
8. C. E. Mees, *The Theory of Photographic Process*, MacMillan, New York, 1966.
9. J. B. Johnson, "Thermal Agitation of Electricity in Conductors," *Phys. Rev.*, **32**, July 1928, 97–109.
10. H. Nyquist, "Thermal Agitation of Electric Charge in Conductors," *Phys. Rev.* **32**, July 1928, 110–113.
11. W. K. Pratt, *Laser Communication Systems*, Wiley, New York, 1969.
12. M. Gadsen, "Some Statistical Properties of Pulses from Photomultipliers," *Appl. Opt.*, **4**, 11, November 1965, 1446–1452.
13. J. A. Jamieson et al., *Infrared Physics and Engineering*, McGraw-Hill, New York, 1963.
14. W. Thomas, Ed., *SPSE Handbook of Photographic Science and Engineering*, Wiley-Interscience, New York, 1973.
15. E. W. H. Selwyn, "A Theory of Graininess," *Phot. J.*, **73**, 1935, 571.
16. E. W. H. Selwyn, "Experiments on the Nature of Graininess," *Phot. J.*, **79**, 1939, 513.
17. D. G. Falconer, "Noise and Distortion in Photographic Data Storage," *IBM J. Res. Dev.* September 1970, 521–526.
18. T. S. Huang, "Some Notes on Film Grain Noise," Appendix 14 in Restoration of Degraded Images, NSF Summer Study Report, Woods Hole, Mass., 1966, 105–109.
19. B. R. Hunt, "Digital Image Processing," *Proc. IEEE*, 63, 4, April 1975, 693–708.
20. F. Naderi and A. A. Sawchuk, "Nonlinear Detection and Estimation of Images Degraded by Film-Grain Noise," In Proceedings SPIE/OSA Conference on Image Processing, J. C. Urbach, Ed., Pacific Grove, California, Vol. 74, February 1976, 17–24.
21. D. H. Kelly, "Systems Analysis of Photographic Process-I: A Three Stage Model," *J. Opt. Soc. Am.*, **50**, 1960, 269.
22. N. D. A. Mascarenhas and W. K. Pratt, "Digital Image Restoration Under a Regression Model," *IEEE Trans. Circuits and Systems*, **CAS-22**, 3, March 1975, 252–266.

14 ALGEBRAIC SPATIAL
IMAGE RESTORATION TECHNIQUES

One of the most common image restoration tasks is that of spatial image restoration to remove geometric distortion, compensate for image blur, and diminish noise effects. Algebraic methods of spatial image restoration are analyzed in this chapter. The following chapter considers specialized applications of spatial image restoration. References 1–5 contain surveys of spatial image restoration methods.

14.1. CONTINUOUS IMAGE SPATIAL FILTERING TECHNIQUES

For the class of imaging systems in which the spatial degradation can be modeled by a linear-shift-invariant impulse response and the noise is additive, restoration of continuous images can be performed by linear filtering techniques. These methods are described below and the techniques are extended to the restoration of discrete images.

14.1.1. Inverse Filter

The earliest attempts toward image restoration were based on the concept of inverse filtering in which the degrading transfer function is inverted to yield a restored image (6–10). Figure 14.1-1 contains a block diagram for the analysis of inverse filtering of a continuous image field. An ideal image $F_I(x, y)$ passes through a linear degrading system with an impulse response $H_0(x, y)$ and is combined with noise $N(x, y)$. The noise is assumed to be

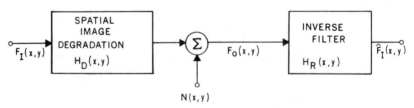

FIGURE 14.1-1. Inverse filtering image restoration.

378

uncorrelated with the ideal image. The observed image field can be represented by the convolution operation as

$$F_O(x, y) = \int\!\!\!\int_{-\infty}^{\infty} F_I(\alpha, \beta) H_D(x - \alpha, y - \beta) \, d\alpha \, d\beta + N(x, y) \qquad (14.1\text{-}1a)$$

or

$$F_O(x, y) = F_I(x, y) \circledast H_D(x, y) + N(x, y) \qquad (14.1\text{-}1b)$$

The restoration system consists of a linear-shift-invariant filter described by the impulse response $H_R(x, y)$. With this filter the reconstructed image becomes

$$\hat{F}_I(x, y) = [F_I(x, y) \circledast H_D(x, y) + N(x, y)] \circledast H_R(x, y) \qquad (14.1\text{-}2)$$

By the Fourier transform convolution theorem,

$$\hat{\mathcal{F}}_I(\omega_x, \omega_y) = [\mathcal{F}_I(\omega_x, \omega_y) \mathcal{H}_D(\omega_x, \omega_y) + \mathcal{N}(\omega_x, \omega_y)] \mathcal{H}_R(\omega_x, \omega_y)$$
$$(14.1\text{-}3)$$

where $\mathcal{F}_I(\omega_x, \omega_y)$, $\hat{\mathcal{F}}_I(\omega_x, \omega_y)$, $\mathcal{N}(\omega_x, \omega_y)$, $\mathcal{H}_D(\omega_x, \omega_y)$, $\mathcal{H}_R(\omega_x, \omega_y)$ are the two-dimensional Fourier transforms of $F_I(x, y)$, $\hat{F}_I(x, y)$, $N(x, y)$, $H_D(x, y)$, $H_R(x, y)$, respectively. Now if the restoration filter transfer function $\mathcal{H}_R(\omega_x, \omega_y)$ is chosen so that

$$\mathcal{H}_R(\omega_x, \omega_y) = \frac{1}{\mathcal{H}_D(\omega_x, \omega_y)} \qquad (14.1\text{-}4)$$

then the spectrum of the reconstructed image becomes

$$\hat{\mathcal{F}}_I(\omega_x, \omega_y) = \mathcal{F}_I(\omega_x, \omega_y) + \frac{\mathcal{N}(\omega_x, \omega_y)}{\mathcal{H}_D(\omega_x, \omega_y)} \qquad (14.1\text{-}5)$$

Upon inverse Fourier transformation, the restored image field

$$\hat{F}_I(x, y) = F_I(x, y) + \frac{1}{4\pi^2} \int\!\!\!\int_{-\infty}^{\infty} \frac{\mathcal{N}(\omega_x, \omega_y)}{\mathcal{H}_D(\omega_x, \omega_y)} \exp\{i[\omega_x x, \omega_y y]\} \, d\omega_x \, d\omega_y$$
$$(14.1\text{-}6)$$

is obtained. In the absence of source noise, a perfect reconstruction results, but if source noise is present there will be an additive reconstruction error whose value can become quite large at spatial frequencies for which $\mathcal{H}_D(\omega_x, \omega_y)$ is small. Typically, both $\mathcal{H}_D(\omega_x, \omega_y)$ and $\mathcal{F}_I(\omega_x, \omega_y)$ are small at high spatial frequencies, and hence image quality becomes severely degraded in high detail regions of the image. Figure 14.1-2 contains sketches of typical frequency spectra involved in inverse filtering.

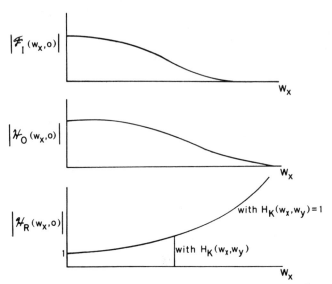

FIGURE 14.1-2. Typical spectra of inverse filtering image restoration system.

The presence of noise may severely affect the uniqueness of the estimate. That is, small changes in $N(x, y)$ may radically change the value of the estimate $\hat{F}_I(x, y)$. For example, consider the dither function $Z(x, y)$ added to the ideal image field $F_I(x, y)$ to produce a perturbed image field

$$F_Z(x, y) = F_I(x, y) + Z(x, y) \tag{14.1-7}$$

There may be many dither functions for which

$$\left| \int\int_{-\infty}^{\infty} Z(\alpha, \beta) H_D(x - \alpha, y - \beta) \, d\alpha \, d\beta \right| < |N(x, y)| \tag{14.1-8}$$

For such functions the perturbed image field $F_Z(x, y)$ may satisfy the convolution integral of Eq. 14.1-1 to within the measurement accuracy of the observed image field. Specifically, it can be shown that if the dither function is a high-frequency sinusoid of arbitrary amplitude, then in the limit

$$\lim_{n \to \infty} \left[\int\int_{-\infty}^{\infty} \sin\left[n(\alpha + \beta)\right] H_D(x - \alpha, y - \beta) \, d\alpha \, d\beta \right] = 0 \tag{14.1-9}$$

For image restoration problems this fact is particularly disturbing for two reasons. High-frequency signal components may be present in an ideal image field, yet their presence may be masked by observation noise. Conversely, a small amount of observation noise may lead to a reconstruction of $F_I(x, y)$ which contains very large amplitude, high-frequency components. If relatively small perturbations $N(x, y)$ in the observation result in large dither functions for a particular impulse response, the superposition integral equation is said to be unstable or poorly conditioned. This potential instability is dependent on the structure of the continuous impulse response function.

There have been several ad hoc proposals to alleviate noise problems inherent to inverse filtering. One approach (8) is to choose a restoration filter with a transfer function

$$\mathcal{H}_R(\omega_x, \omega_y) = \frac{\mathcal{H}_K(\omega_x, \omega_y)}{\mathcal{H}_D(\omega_x, \omega_y)} \tag{14.1-10}$$

where $\mathcal{H}_K(\omega_x, \omega_y)$ has a value near unity at spatial frequencies for which the expected magnitude of the ideal spectrum is greater than the expected magnitude of the noise spectrum, and near zero elsewhere. The reconstructed image spectrum is then

$$\hat{\mathcal{F}}_I(\omega_x, \omega_y) = \mathcal{F}_I(\omega_x, \omega_y)\mathcal{H}_K(\omega_x, \omega_y) + \frac{\mathcal{H}_K(\omega_x, \omega_y)\mathcal{N}(\omega_x, \omega_y)}{\mathcal{H}_D(\omega_x, \omega_y)} \tag{14.1-11}$$

The result is a compromise between noise suppression and loss in high-frequency image detail.

Another fundamental difficulty with inverse filtering is that the transfer function of the degradation may have zeros in its passband. At such points in the frequency spectrum, the inverse filter is not physically realizable, and therefore the filter must be approximated by a large value response.

14.1.2. Wiener Filter—Additive Noise

It should not be surprising that inverse filtering performs poorly in the presence of noise since the filter design ignores the noise process. Improved restoration quality is possible with Wiener filtering techniques, which incorporate a priori statistical knowledge of the noise field (11–15). Extensions of the Wiener filter process based on statistical models of the ideal image field and blur impulse response are presented in subsequent sections. Here consideration is limited to the restoration model of Figure 14.1-1 in which the blurred image is subject to additive noise. It is assumed that the noise is zero mean, independent of the image, and that its power spectral density $W_N(\omega_x, \omega_y)$ is known.

In a continuous image Wiener filtering system the impulse response of the restoration filter is chosen to minimize the mean-square restoration error

$$\mathscr{E} = E\{[F_I(x, y) - \hat{F}_I(x, y)]^2\} \qquad (14.1\text{-}12)$$

The transfer function of the resultant restoration filter has been found to be (11)

$$\mathscr{H}_R(\omega_x, \omega_y) = \frac{\mathscr{H}_D^*(\omega_x, \omega_y)}{|\mathscr{H}_D(\omega_x, \omega_y)|^2 + W_N(\omega_x, \omega_y)} \qquad (14.1\text{-}13)$$

where $\mathscr{H}_D(\omega_x, \omega_y)$ is the transfer function of the spatial degradation.* In the limit for no noise the Wiener filter reduces to the inverse filter. Figure 14.1-3 contains sketches of a typical image spectrum, blur transfer func-

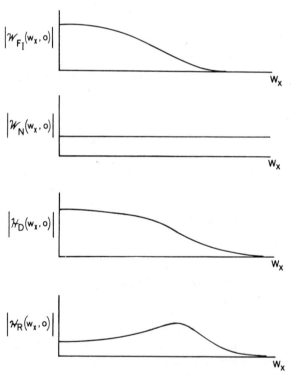

FIGURE 14.1-3.   Typical spectra of Wiener filtering image restoration system.

* Complete derivations of the discrete image Wiener estimators are presented in the following sections.

tion, and the resultant Wiener filter transfer function. The inclusion of the noise power-spectral density term in the transfer function for the inverse filter provides a smooth, natural rolloff of the transfer function.

14.1.3 Wiener Filter—Stochastic Image Field

The Wiener filter for the additive noise case of Eq. 14.1-13 essentially ignores the inherent spatial correlation of the ideal image field. Considerable restoration improvement can often be realized by incorporating a priori statistical knowledge of the spatial correlation. In this extension of the Wiener filter, the ideal image is assumed to be a sample of a two-dimensional stochastic process with known power-spectral density $\mathcal{W}_{F_I}(\omega_x, \omega_y)$. For analytical convenience the image process will also be considered zero mean. Under these assumptions the transfer function for the restoration filter for minimum mean-square error estimation becomes (11)

$$\mathcal{H}_R(\omega_x, \omega_y) = \frac{\mathcal{H}_D^*(\omega_x, \omega_y)\mathcal{W}_{F_I}(\omega_x, \omega_y)}{|\mathcal{H}_D(\omega_x, \omega_y)|^2 \mathcal{W}_{F_I}(\omega_x, \omega_y) + \mathcal{W}_N(\omega_x, \omega_y)}$$

$$(14.1\text{-}14a)$$

or

$$\mathcal{H}_R(\omega_x, \omega_y) = \frac{\mathcal{H}_D^*(\omega_x, \omega_y)}{|\mathcal{H}_D(\omega_x, \omega_y)|^2 + \mathcal{W}_N(\omega_x, \omega_y)/\mathcal{W}_{F_I}(\omega_x, \omega_y)}$$

$$(14.1\text{-}14b)$$

In this latter formulation the transfer function of the restoration filter is expressed in terms of the signal-to-noise power ratio

$$\text{SNR}(\omega_x, \omega_y) \equiv \frac{\mathcal{W}_{F_I}(\omega_x, \omega_y)}{\mathcal{W}_N(\omega_x, \omega_y)} \qquad (14.1\text{-}15)$$.

at each spatial frequency. If the image field is assumed uncorrelated, the ideal image field power-spectral density assumes a unit value for all spatial frequencies, and Eq. 14.1-14 becomes equivalent to Eq. 14.1-13, which ignored the spatial image correlation.

14.1.4. Wiener Filter—Stochastic Blur

In many imaging systems the impulse response of the blur may not be fixed; rather, it changes shape in a random manner. A practical example is the blur caused by imaging through a turbulent atmosphere. Obviously, the Wiener filter would perform better if it could dynamically adapt to the changing blur impulse response. If this is not possible, a design improvement in the Wiener filter can be obtained by considering the impulse response to be a sample of a two-dimensional stochastic process with a known mean shape and with a random perturbation about the mean described by a known power spectral density. Transfer functions for this type of restoration filter have been developed by Slepian (16) for several error measures.

14.1.5. Parametric Estimation Filters

Several variations of the Wiener filter have been developed for image restoration. Some techniques are ad hoc, while others have a quantitative basis.

Stockham and Cole (17) have proposed a restoration filter with a transfer function

$$\mathcal{H}_R(\omega_x, \omega_y) = \left[\frac{W_{F_I}(\omega_x, \omega_y)}{|\mathcal{H}_D(\omega_x, \omega_y)|^2 W_{F_I}(\omega_x, \omega_y) + W_N(\omega_x, \omega_y)} \right]^{1/2} \tag{14.1-16}$$

The power spectrum of the filter output is

$$W_{\hat{F}_I}(\omega_x, \omega_y) = |\mathcal{H}_R(\omega_x, \omega_y)|^2 W_{F_O}(\omega_x, \omega_y) \tag{14.1-17}$$

where $W_{F_O}(\omega_x, \omega_y)$ represents the power spectrum of the observation, which is related to the power spectrum of the ideal image by

$$W_{F_O}(\omega_x, \omega_y) = |\mathcal{H}_D(\omega_x, \omega_y)|^2 W_{F_I}(\omega_x, \omega_y) + W_N(\omega_x, \omega_y) \tag{14.1-18}$$

Thus it is easily seen that the power spectrum of the reconstructed image is identical to the power spectrum of the ideal image field. That is,

$$W_{\hat{F}_I}(\omega_x, \omega_y) = W_{F_I}(\omega_x, \omega_y) \tag{14.1-19}$$

For this reason the restoration filter defined by Eq. 14.1-16 will be called the image power-spectrum filter. In contrast, the power spectrum for the reconstructed image as obtained by the Wiener filter of Eq. 14.1-14 is

$$W_{\hat{F}_I}(\omega_x, \omega_y) = \frac{|\mathcal{H}_D(\omega_x, \omega_y)|^2 [W_{F_I}(\omega_x, \omega_y)]^2}{[|\mathcal{H}_D(\omega_x, \omega_y)|^2 W_{F_I}(\omega_x, \omega_y) + W_N(\omega_x, \omega_y)]} \tag{14.1-20}$$

In this case the power spectra of the reconstructed and ideal images become identical only for a noise-free observation. While equivalence of the power spectra of the ideal and reconstructed images appears to be an attractive feature of the image power-spectrum filter, it should be realized that it is more important that the Fourier spectra (Fourier transforms) of the ideal and reconstructed images be identical since the ideal image field is deterministic and Fourier transform pairs are unique, but power-spectra pairs are not necessarily unique. Furthermore, the Wiener filter provides a minimum mean-square error estimate, while the image power-spectrum filter may result in a large residual mean-square error.

Stockham and Cole (17) have also introduced a geometrical mean filter defined by the transfer function

$$\mathcal{H}_R(\omega_x, \omega_y) = [\mathcal{H}_D(\omega_x, \omega_y)]^{-S} \left[\frac{\mathcal{H}_D^*(\omega_x, \omega_y) W_{F_I}(\omega_x, \omega_y)}{|\mathcal{H}_D(\omega_x, \omega_y)|^2 W_{F_I}(\omega_x, \omega_y) + W_N(\omega_x, \omega_y)} \right]^{1-S}$$

$$(14.1-21)$$

where $0 \le S \le 1$ is a design parameter. If $S = \frac{1}{2}$ and $\mathcal{H}_D = \mathcal{H}_D^*$ the geometrical mean filter reduces to the image power-spectrum filter as given in Eq. 14.1-16.

Hunt (18) has developed another parametric restoration filter called the constrained least-squares filter, whose transfer function is of the form

$$\mathcal{H}_R(\omega_x, \omega_y) = \frac{\mathcal{H}_D^*(\omega_x, \omega_y)}{|\mathcal{H}_D(\omega_x, \omega_y)|^2 + \gamma |\mathcal{C}(\omega_x, \omega_y)|^2} \qquad (14.1-22)$$

where γ is a design constant and $\mathcal{C}(\omega_x, \omega_y)$ is a design spectral variable. If $\gamma = 1$ and $|\mathcal{C}(\omega_x, \omega_y)|^2$ is set equal to the spectral signal-to-noise power ratio of Eq. 14.1-15, the constrained least-squares filter becomes equivalent to the Wiener filter of Eq. 14.1-14b. The spectral variable can also be used to minimize higher-order derivatives of the estimate.

14.1.6. Application to Discrete Images

The inverse filtering, Wiener filtering, and parametric estimation filtering techniques developed for continuous image fields are often applied to the restoration of discrete images. The common procedure has been to replace each of the continuous spectral functions involved in the filtering operation by its discrete two-dimensional Fourier transform counterpart. However, care must be taken in this conversion process so that the discrete filtering operation is an accurate representation of the continuous convolution process described by

$$\hat{F}_I(x, y) = F_O(x, y) \circledast H_R(x, y) \qquad (14.1\text{-}23)$$

and so that the discrete form of the restoration filter impulse response accurately models the appropriate continuous filter impulse response. Both considerations are discussed below.

Following the principles outlined in Chapter 11, it will be assumed that all continuous functions are represented over square grids at a sample spacing Δ, which is the Nyquist sample spacing of the ideal image. The restoration filter impulse response is then spatially truncated to a region $L\Delta$ and sampled to produce the $L \times L$ array $H_R(j, k)$. Similarly, the observed image field $F_O(x, y)$ is truncated to size $N\Delta$ to produce the $N \times N$ array $F_O(j, k)$. Actually, the discretization of $H_R(x, y)$ is a mathematical modeling process, while the discretization of $F_O(x, y)$ results from physical sampling of the observed image. The discrete convolution will produce an $M \times M$ array $\hat{F}_I(j, k)$. Figure 9.2-3 illustrates the relative sizes of the arrays. Next, discrete two-dimensional Fourier transforms are performed on the arrays $F_O(j, k)$ and $H_R(j, k)$ to produce

$$\mathscr{F}_O(u, v) = \frac{1}{N} \sum_{j=0}^{N-1} \sum_{j=0}^{N-1} F_O(j, k) \exp\left\{-\frac{2\pi i}{J}(uj + vk)\right\} \quad (14.1\text{-}24)$$

and

$$\mathscr{H}_R(u, v) = \frac{1}{N} \sum_{j=0}^{L-1} \sum_{k=0}^{L-1} H_R(j, k) \exp\left\{-\frac{2\pi i}{J}(uj + vk)\right\} \quad (14.1\text{-}25)$$

where $u, v = 0, 1, 2, \ldots, J - 1$. The value of J is chosen such that $J \geq N$ and $J = 2^n$ where n is an integer so that a fast Fourier transform algorithm may be utilized. The Fourier domain observed image and the Fourier domain representation of the restoration filter are then scalar multiplied, and the product is inverse Fourier transformed to yield the $J \times J$ array

$$K_E(j, k) = \frac{1}{N} \sum_{u=0}^{J-1} \sum_{v=0}^{J-1} \mathscr{F}_O(u, v)\mathscr{H}_R(u, v) \exp\left\{\frac{2\pi i}{J}(uj + vk)\right\}$$

$$(14.1\text{-}26)$$

The $M \times M$ center section of the array $K_E(j, k)$ indicated in Figure 9.4-1 is the desired restored discrete image $\hat{F}_I(j, k)$. Thus far the only approximation that has been made is the spatial truncation of the impulse response of the restoration filter. This error can be made as small as desired at the expense of dimensionality and processing complexity. The Nyquist sample spacing ensures that $\hat{F}_I(x, y)$ can be perfectly reconstructed, in theory, by interpolation of the samples of $F_I(j, k)$ over the $M \times M$ array of samples. The major problem that remains is to accurately determine the values of the discrete samples of the restoration filter impulse response in terms of the formulas for the appropriate restoration filter transfer function. Theoretically, this procedure is straightforward; given the desired continuous field transfer function $\mathcal{H}_R(\omega_x, \omega_y)$, the continuous field impulse response $H_R(x, y)$ is determined by analytically performing an inverse Fourier transform, and then the discrete impulse response $H_R(j, k)$ is obtained by sampling $H_R(x, y)$ over an $L \times L$ grid at a sample spacing Δ. In practice, however, it is often difficult to obtain $H_R(x, y)$ by analytic inversion of $\mathcal{H}_R(\omega_x, \omega_y)$. An alternative procedure is to convert the continuous field transfer function $\mathcal{H}_R(\omega_x, \omega_y)$ directly to the discrete Fourier transform domain to obtain $\mathcal{H}_R(u, v)$ according to Eq. 11.4-8. However, this procedure is also analytically difficult for complicated window functions. If an analytical conversion is not feasible, then the only alternative is to form the discrete inverse Fourier transform of $\mathcal{H}_R(\omega_x, \omega_y)$ with $\omega_x = 2\pi u/J\Delta$ and $\omega_y = 2\pi v/J\Delta$. The resulting spatial domain impulse response array must then be windowed to produce an $L \times L$ array, which is then Fourier transformed to produce the desired discrete Fourier domain array $\mathcal{H}_R(u, v)$. Failure to perform the windowing operation will subject the restored image to wraparound error.

The continuous image field restoration techniques derived in this section are advantageous in that they are relatively simple to understand and to implement using Fourier domain processing. However, these techniques face several important limitations. First, there is no provision for aliasing error effects caused by physical undersampling of the observed image. Second, the formulation inherently assumes that the quadrature spacing of the convolution integral is the same as the physical sampling. Third, the methods only permit restoration for linear, space-invariant degradation. Fourth, and perhaps most importantly, it is difficult to analyze the effects of numerical errors in the restoration process and to develop methods of combatting such errors. For these reasons it is necessary to return to the discrete model of a sampled blurred image developed in Section 9.2, and then reformulate the restoration problem on a firm numeric basis. This is the subject of the remaining sections of the chapter.

14.2. PSEUDOINVERSE SPATIAL IMAGE RESTORATION

The matrix pseudoinverse defined in Chapter 8 can be used for spatial image restoration of digital images when it is possible to model the spatial degradation as a vector-space operation on a vector of ideal image points yielding a vector of physical observed samples obtained from the degraded image (19–21).

14.2.1. Pseudoinverse—Image Blur

The first application of the pseudoinverse to be considered is that of the restoration of a blurred image. The observed image is modeled by the superposition integral

$$F_O(x, y) = \int_{-\infty}^{\infty} F_I(x, y) J(x, y; \alpha, \beta) \, d\alpha \, d\beta \qquad (14.2\text{-}1)$$

where $F_I(x, y)$ and $F_O(x, y)$ represent the ideal and blurred image fields, respectively, and $J(x, y; \alpha, \beta)$ is the impulse response of the imaging system causing the blur, which may be spatially variant. Complete discretization of Eq. 14-2-1 results in the general vector-space model

$$\mathbf{g} = \mathbf{B}\mathbf{f} \qquad (14.2\text{-}2)$$

as derived in Eq. 13.7-6 where $\mathbf{g}$ is a $P \times 1$ vector $(P = M^2)$ containing the $M \times M$ physical samples of the blurred image, $\mathbf{f}$ is a $Q \times 1$ vector $(Q = N^2)$ containing $N \times N$ points of the ideal image, and $\mathbf{B}$ is the $P \times Q$ matrix whose elements are points on the impulse function. If the physical sample period and the quadrature representation period are identical, P will be smaller than Q, and the system of equations will be underdetermined. By oversampling the blurred image it is possible to force $P > Q$ or even $P = Q$. In either case the system of equations is called overdetermined. An overdetermined set of equations can also be obtained if some of the elements of the ideal image vector can be specified through a priori knowledge. For example, if the ideal image is known to contain a limited size object against a black background (zero luminance), the elements of $\mathbf{f}$ beyond the limits may be set to zero.

In discrete form the restoration problem reduces to finding a solution $\hat{\mathbf{f}}$ to Eq. 14.2-2 in the sense that

$$\mathbf{B}\hat{\mathbf{f}} = \mathbf{g} \qquad (14.2\text{-}3)$$

Since the vector $\mathbf{g}$ is determined by physical sampling, and the elements of $\mathbf{B}$ are specified independently by system modeling, there is no guarantee that an $\hat{\mathbf{f}}$ even exists to satisfy Eq. 14.2-3. If there is a solution, the system of equations is said to be consistent; otherwise the system of equations is inconsistent.

In Chapter 8 it has been shown that inconsistency in the set of equations of Eq. 14.2-2 can be characterized as

$$\mathbf{g} = \mathbf{Bf} + \mathbf{e(f)} \tag{14.2-4}$$

where $\mathbf{e(f)}$ is a vector of remainder elements whose value depends on $\mathbf{f}$. If the set of equations is inconsistent, a solution of the form

$$\hat{\mathbf{f}} = \mathbf{Wg} \tag{14.2-5}$$

is sought for which the linear operator $\mathbf{W}$ minimizes the least-squares modeling error

$$\mathscr{E}_M = [\mathbf{e}(\hat{\mathbf{f}})]^T [\mathbf{e}(\hat{\mathbf{f}})] = [\mathbf{g} - \mathbf{B}\hat{\mathbf{f}}]^T [\mathbf{g} - \mathbf{B}\hat{\mathbf{f}}] \tag{14.2-6}$$

This error has been shown, in chapter 8, to be minimized when the operator $\mathbf{W} = \mathbf{B}^{\$}$ is set equal to the least-squares inverse of $\mathbf{B}$. The least-squares inverse is not necessarily unique. It has also been proved in chapter 8 that the generalized inverse operator $\mathbf{W} = \mathbf{B}^-$, which is a special case of the least-squares inverse, is unique, minimizes the least-squares modeling error, and simultaneously provides a minimum norm estimate. That is, the sum of the squares of $\hat{\mathbf{f}}$ is a minimum for all possible minimum least-square error estimates. For the restoration of image blur the generalized inverse provides a lowest-intensity restored image.

If Eq. 14.2-2 represents a consistent set of equations, one or more solutions may exist for Eq. 14.2-3. The solution commonly chosen is the estimate that minimizes the least-square estimation error defined in the equivalent forms

$$\mathscr{E}_E = (\mathbf{f} - \hat{\mathbf{f}})^T (\mathbf{f} - \hat{\mathbf{f}}) \tag{14.2-7a}$$

$$\mathscr{E}_E = \mathrm{tr}\,\{(\mathbf{f} - \hat{\mathbf{f}})(\mathbf{f} - \hat{\mathbf{f}})^T\} \tag{14.2-7b}$$

It has been proved that the estimation error is minimum for a generalized inverse ($\mathbf{W} = \mathbf{B}^-$) estimate. The resultant residual estimation error then becomes

$$\mathscr{E}_E = \mathbf{f}^T [\mathbf{I} - (\mathbf{B}^-\mathbf{B})]\mathbf{f} \tag{14.2-8a}$$

or

$$\mathscr{E}_E = \mathrm{tr}\,\{\mathbf{f}\mathbf{f}^T [\mathbf{I} - \mathbf{B}^-\mathbf{B}]\} \tag{14.2-8b}$$

The estimate is perfect, of course, if $\mathbf{B}^-\mathbf{B} = \mathbf{I}$.

Thus it is seen that the generalized inverse is an optimal solution, in the sense previously defined, both for consistent and inconsistent sets of equations modeling image blur. From Eq. 8.3-5 the generalized inverse has been found to be algebraically equivalent to

$$\mathbf{B}^- = (\mathbf{B}^T \mathbf{B})^{-1} \mathbf{B}^T \tag{14.2-9a}$$

if the $P \times Q$ matrix $\mathbf{B}$ is of rank Q. If $\mathbf{B}$ is of rank P, then

$$\mathbf{B}^- = \mathbf{B}^T (\mathbf{B}\mathbf{B}^T)^{-1} \tag{14.2-9b}$$

For a consistent set of equations and a rank Q generalized inverse, the estimate

$$\hat{\mathbf{f}} = \mathbf{B}^- \mathbf{g} = \mathbf{B}^- \mathbf{B}\mathbf{f} = [(\mathbf{B}^T \mathbf{B})^{-1} \mathbf{B}^T] \mathbf{B}\mathbf{f} = \mathbf{f} \tag{14.2-10}$$

is obviously perfect. However, in all other cases a residual estimation error may occur. Clearly, it would be desirable to deal with an overdetermined blur matrix of rank Q in order to achieve a perfect estimate. Unfortunately, this situation is rarely achieved in image restoration. Oversampling the blurred image can produce an overdetermined set of equations ($P > Q$), but the rank of the blur matrix is likely to be much less than Q because the rows of the blur matrix will become more linearly dependent with finer sampling. The only practical case in which a rank Q generalized inverse can be utilized for image restoration is when the object to be restored is of known limited spatial extent.

A major problem in the application of the generalized inverse to image restoration is dimensionality. The generalized inverse is a $Q \times P$ matrix where P is equal to the number of pixel observations and Q is equal to the number of pixels to be estimated in an image. It is usually not computationally feasible to use the generalized inverse operator, defined by Eq. 14.2-9, over large size images because of difficulties in reliably computing the generalized inverse, and the large number of vector multiplications associated with Eq. 14.2-5. Computational savings can be realized if the blur matrix $\mathbf{B}$ is separable such that

$$\mathbf{B} = \mathbf{B}_C \otimes \mathbf{B}_R \tag{14.2-11}$$

where $\mathbf{B}_C$ and $\mathbf{B}_R$ are row and column blur operators. In this case the generalized inverse is separable in the sense that

$$\mathbf{B}^- = \mathbf{B}_C^- \otimes \mathbf{B}_R^- \tag{14.2-12}$$

where $\mathbf{B}_C^-$ and $\mathbf{B}_R^-$ are generalized inverses of $\mathbf{B}_C$ and $\mathbf{B}_R$, respectively. Thus when the blur matrix is of separable form, it becomes possible to form the estimate of the image by sequentially applying the generalized inverse of the row blur matrix to each row of the observed image array, and then using the column generalized inverse operator on each column of the array.

Pseudoinverse restoration of large size images can be accomplished in an approximate fashion by a block mode restoration process, similar to the block mode filtering technique of Section 11.3, in which the blurred image is partitioned into small blocks that are individually restored. It is wise to overlap the blocks and only accept the pixel estimates in the center of each ⁻estored block since these pixels exhibit the least uncertainty. Section 14.3 describes an efficient computational algorithm for pseudoinverse restoration for space-invariant blur.

Figure 14.2-1 contains blurred and restored pictures using generalized inverse restoration for the image restoration models of Figures 13.7-3 and 13.7-4. In these examples the observation is noise free and the blur

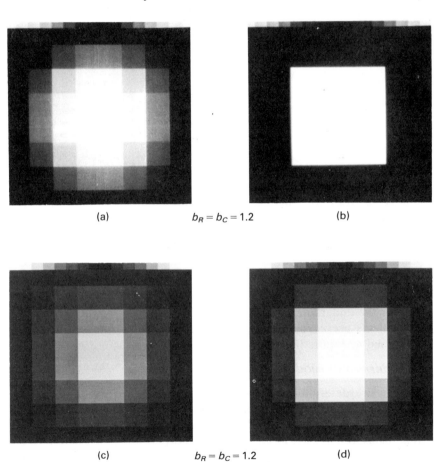

(a) $b_R = b_C = 1.2$ (b)

(c) $b_R = b_C = 1.2$ (d)

FIGURE 14.2-1. Examples of pseudoinverse restoration for test image blurred with Gaussian shaped impulse response. Noise-free observation. Overdetermined model, $M = 12, N = 8, L = 5$: (a) blurred; (b) restored. Undetermined model, $M = 8, N = 12, L = 5$: (c) blurred, PMSE = 4.97%; (d) restored, PMSE = 1.41%.

impulse response is Gaussian shaped, as defined in Eq. 13.7-10 with $b_R = b_C = 1.2$. For the overdetermined case only the center 8×8 region of the 12×12 blurred picture is displayed, blown up to 256×256 points. Visually, the restoration is equivalent to the original picture, but inspection of the numerical results reveals some round-off errors in the computation. In the underdetermined case only the center 8×8 region of the estimate is displayed. The restored image appear to be an "improved" version of the blurred image, but the restoration is not identical to the original image.

14.2.2. Pseudoinverse—Image Blur Plus Additive Noise

In many imaging systems an ideal image is subject both to blur and additive noise. the resultant vector-space model, derived in Eq. 13.7-6, is repeated here in the simplified notational form

$$\mathbf{g} = \mathbf{Bf} + \mathbf{n} \tag{14.2-13}$$

where $\mathbf{g}$ and $\mathbf{n}$ are $P \times 1$ vectors of the observed image field and noise field, respectively, $\mathbf{f}$ is a $Q \times 1$ vector of ideal image points, and $\mathbf{B}$ is a $P \times Q$ blur matrix. The vector $\mathbf{n}$ is composed of two additive components: samples of an additive external noise process, and elements of the vector difference $(\mathbf{g} - \mathbf{Bf})$ arising from modeling errors in the formulation of $\mathbf{B}$. As a result of the noise contribution, there may be no vector solutions $\hat{\mathbf{f}}$ that satisfy Eq. 14.2-13. However, as indicated in Chapter 8, the generalized inverse $\mathbf{B}^-$ can be utilized to determine a least-squares error, minimum norm estimate. In the absence of modeling error the estimate

$$\hat{\mathbf{f}} = \mathbf{B}^- \mathbf{g} = \mathbf{B}^- \mathbf{Bf} + \mathbf{B}^- \mathbf{n} \tag{14.2-14}$$

differs from the ideal image because of the additive noise contribution $\mathbf{B}^- \mathbf{n}$. Also, for the underdetermined model, $\mathbf{B}^- \mathbf{B}$ will not be an identity matrix. Noise effects are considered below for the overdetermined and underdetermined restoration models.

Overdetermined Model

If $\mathbf{B}$ is an overdetermined rank Q matrix, as defined in Eq. 14.2-9a, then $\mathbf{B}^- \mathbf{B} = \mathbf{I}$ and the resulting estimate is equal to the original image vector $\mathbf{f}$ plus a perturbation vector $\Delta \mathbf{f} = \mathbf{B}^- \mathbf{n}$. The perturbation error in the estimate can be measured as the ratio of the vector norm of the perturbation to the vector norm of the estimate. It can be shown (22, p. 52) that the relative error is subject to the bound

$$\frac{\|\Delta \mathbf{f}\|}{\|\mathbf{f}\|} < \|\mathbf{B}^-\| \cdot \|\mathbf{B}\| \frac{\|\mathbf{n}\|}{\|\mathbf{g}\|} \tag{14.2-15}$$

The product $\|\mathbf{B}^-\| \cdot \|\mathbf{B}\|$, which is called the condition number $C\{\mathbf{B}\}$ of $\mathbf{B}$, determines the relative error in the estimate in terms of the ratio of the vector norm of the noise to the vector norm of the observation. The condition number can be computed directly or found in terms of the ratio

$$C\{\mathbf{B}\} = \|\mathbf{B}^-\| \cdot \|\mathbf{B}\| = \frac{W_1}{W_N} \qquad (14.2\text{-}16)$$

of the largest W_1 to smallest W_N singular values of $\mathbf{B}$. Obviously, the larger the condition number of the blur matrix, the greater will be the sensitivity to noise perturbations.

Figure 14.2-2 contains image restoration examples for the overdetermined model of Figure 13.7-4 for a Gaussian-shape blur function for several values of the blur standard deviation and a noise variance of 10 on an amplitude scale of 0 to 255. As expected, observation noise degrades the restoration. Also as expected, the restoration for a moderate degree of blur is worse than the restoration for less blur. However, this trend does not continue; the restoration for severe blur is actually better in a subjective sense than for moderate blur. This seemingly anomolous behavior, which results from spatial truncation of the point-spread function, can be explained in terms of the condition number of the blur matrix. Figure 14.2-3 contains a plot of the condition number of the blur matrix of the previous examples as a function of the blur coefficient (19). For small amounts of blur the condition number is low. A maximum is attained for moderate blur, followed by a decrease in the curve for increasing values of the blur coefficient. The curve tends to stabilize as the blur coefficient approaches infinity. This curve provides an explanation for the previous experimental results. In the restoration operation the PSF is spatially truncated over a square region of 5×5 quadrature points. As the blur coefficient increases, for fixed M and N, the PSF becomes increasingly wider and its tails become truncated to a greater extent. In the limit the nonzero elements in the blur matrix become constant values and the condition number assumes a constant level. For small values of the blur coefficient, the truncation effect is negligible, and the condition number curve follows an ascending path toward infinity with the asymptotic value obtained for a smoothly represented PSF. As the blur factor increases, the number of nonzero elements in the blur matrix increases, and the condition number stabilizes to a constant value. In effect, a tradeoff exists between numerical errors caused by ill-conditioning and modeling accuracy. Although this conclusion is formulated on the basis of a particular degradation model, the inference seems to be more general since the inverse of the integral operator that describes the blur is unbounded. Therefore, the

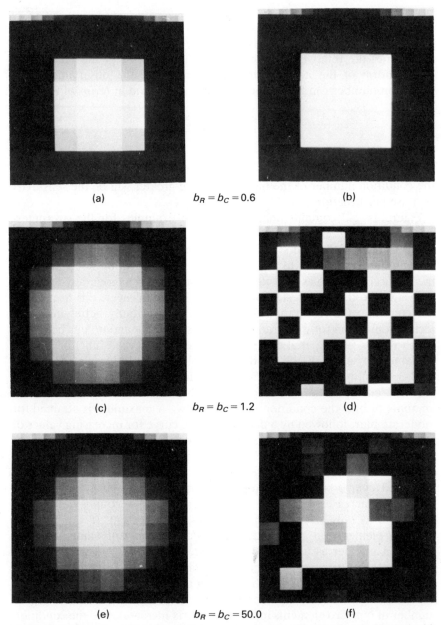

(a) $b_R = b_C = 0.6$ (b)

(c) $b_R = b_C = 1.2$ (d)

(e) $b_R = b_C = 50.0$ (f)

FIGURE 14.2-2. Examples of pseudoinverse restoration for test image blurred with Gaussian-shaped impulse response. Overdetermined model $M = 12$, $N = 8$, $L = 5$; noisy observation, Var = 10.0. (a) Blurred; (b) restored. (c) Blurred; (d) restored. (e) Blurred; (f) restored.

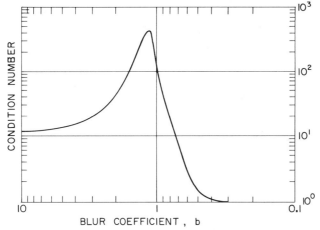

FIGURE 14.2-3. Condition number curve.

closer the discrete model follows the continuous model, the greater the degree of ill-conditioning. A move in the opposite direction reduces singularity, but imposes modeling errors. This inevitable dilemma can only be broken with the intervention of correct a priori knowledge about the original image.

Undetermined Model

Figure 14.2-4 contains restoration examples for the underdetermined model of Figure 13.7-3 for Gaussian blur for several values of the blur standard deviation and a noise variance of 10. The restorations show the same pattern as for the overdetermined model. Perturbations in the solution appear to be worst for moderate values of the blur spread coefficient. This result cannot be explained by the condition number, which is infinite in the underdetermined case ($W_N = 0$). However, since the blur matrix $\mathbf{B}$ is the transpose of the matrix in the overdetermined case, and since the nonzero eigenvalues of $\mathbf{B}^T\mathbf{B}$ and $\mathbf{B}\mathbf{B}^T$ are the same (23, p. 41), it follows that the ratio of the largest to the smallest nonzero eigenvalues of $\mathbf{B}^T\mathbf{B}$ follows the curve given by Figure 14.2-3.

14.3. PSEUDOINVERSE COMPUTATIONAL ALGORITHMS

Efficient computational algorithms have been developed by Pratt and Davarian (20) for pseudoinverse image restoration with space-invariant blur. These algorithms are described for overdetermined and underdetermined imaging models.

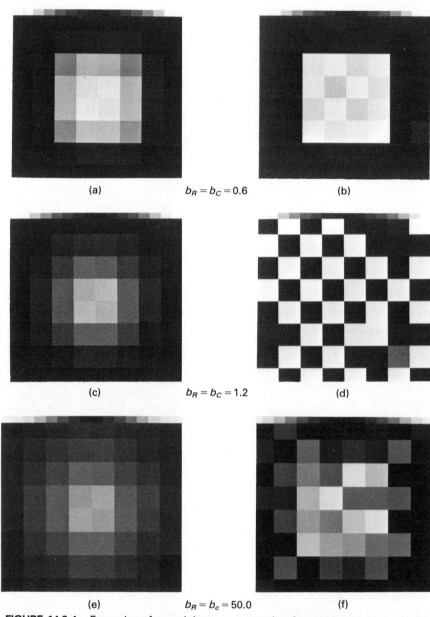

(a) $b_R = b_C = 0.6$ (b)

(c) $b_R = b_C = 1.2$ (d)

(e) $b_R = b_c = 50.0$ (f)

FIGURE 14.2-4. Examples of pseudoinverse restoration for test image blurred with Gaussian shaped impulse response. Underdetermined model, $M = 8$, $N = 12$, $L = 5$; noisy observation, Var = 10.0. (a) Blurred, PMSE = 1.30%; (b) restored, PMSE = 0.21%. (c) Blurred, PMSE = 4.91%; (d) restored, PMSE = 2695.81%. (e) Blurred, PMSE = 7.99%, (f) restored, PMSE = 7.29%.

14.3.1.   Overdetermined Model Algorithm

The pseudoinverse computational algorithm for the overdetermined imaging model is based on the circular convolution vector-space relationship of Eq. 9.3-4 in which

$$\mathbf{k}_E = \mathbf{C}\mathbf{g}_E \qquad (14.3\text{-}1)$$

where $\mathbf{C}$ is a circulant area convolution matrix, $\mathbf{f}_E$ is a $J^2 \times 1$ extended image vector obtained by padding the $N^2 \times 1$ ideal image vector $\mathbf{f}$ with zeros, and $\mathbf{k}_E$ is the corresponding $J^2 \times 1$ output vector. The generalized inverse estimate can be obtained directly as

$$\hat{\mathbf{f}}_E = \mathbf{C}^{-1}\mathbf{k}_E \qquad (14.3\text{-}2)$$

where $\mathbf{C}^{-1}$ is the inverse of $\mathbf{C}$. From Eqs. 9.4-4a and 9.4-5b it is easily found that

$$\hat{\mathbf{f}} = [\mathbf{S1}_J^{(N)} \otimes \mathbf{S1}_J^{(N)}]\mathbf{C}^{-1}[\mathbf{S1}_J^{(M)} \otimes \mathbf{S1}_J^{(M)}]^T \mathbf{g} \qquad (14.3\text{-}3)$$

where $\mathbf{g} = \mathbf{Bf}$ for the overdetermined model and $\mathbf{S1}^{(K)}$ is a selection matrix as defined in Eq. 9.4-1. Then by the substitution of the Fourier transform operators $\mathbf{A}_J$, Eq. 14.3-3 may be rewritten as

$$\hat{\mathbf{f}} = [\mathbf{S1}_J^{(N)} \otimes \mathbf{S1}_J^{(N)}][\mathbf{A}_J^{-1} \otimes \mathbf{A}_J^{-1}]\boldsymbol{\mathscr{C}}^{-1}[\mathbf{A}_J \otimes \mathbf{A}_J][\mathbf{S1}_J^{(M)} \otimes \mathbf{S1}_J^{(M)}]\mathbf{g} \qquad (14.3\text{-}4)$$

where $\boldsymbol{\mathscr{C}}$ is the Fourier domain convolution filter matrix defined by Eq. 11.2-13.

Equation 14.3-4 combined with Eq. 11.2-13 forms the basis of the following efficient computational algorithm for pseudoinverse restoration of the overdetermined model:

(a) Imbed the impulse response matrix $\mathbf{H}$ in the upper left corner of an all zero $J \times J$ matrix to obtain an extended impulse response matrix where $J \geq M$ and take the two-dimensional Fourier transform of the extended impulse response matrix yielding

$$\boldsymbol{\mathscr{H}}_E = \mathbf{A}_J \mathbf{H}_E \mathbf{A}_J \qquad (14.3\text{-}5)$$

(b) Imbed the observation matrix $\mathbf{G}$ in the upper left corner of an all zero $J \times J$ matrix to obtain the matrix $\mathbf{K}_E$ and take its two-dimensional Fourier transform, which gives

$$\boldsymbol{\mathscr{K}}_E = \mathbf{A}_J \mathbf{K}_E \mathbf{A}_J \qquad (14.3\text{-}6)$$

(c) Perform the scalar division

$$\hat{\mathcal{F}}_E(m, n) = \frac{\mathcal{H}_E(m, n)}{J\mathcal{H}_E(m, n)} \qquad (14.3\text{-}7)$$

where $1 \le m \le J$ and $1 \le n \le J$.

(d) Take the inverse Fourier transform

$$\hat{\mathbf{F}}_E = \mathbf{A}_J^{-1} \hat{\mathcal{F}}_E \mathbf{A}_J^{-1} \qquad (14.3\text{-}8)$$

(e) Extract the desired output matrix

$$\hat{\mathbf{F}} = [\mathbf{S1}_J^{(N)}] \hat{\mathbf{F}}_E [\mathbf{S1}_J^{(N)}]^T \qquad (14.3\text{-}9)$$

Computation of the finite area convolution pseudoinverse requires on the order of $J^2(1 + 4 \log_2 J)$ operations using the above algorithm, while direct computation requires about $M^2 N^2$ operations. As an example, for $M = 256$ and $L = 17$, the computational savings are nearly $1750:1$!

It should be observed that the discrete pseudoinverse algorithm avoids one of the major problems plaguing continuous image inverse filtering: division by zeros of the continuous transfer function. The elements of the discrete transfer function obtained from Eq. 14.3-5 will never be identically zero provided that the impulse response size L is set at an odd integer and the processing dimension J is an even integer of binary form. As an example consider the extreme case in which the impulse response $\mathbf{H}$ is constant. The resultant discrete transfer function then becomes

$$\mathcal{H}_E(u, v) = \frac{1}{J} \exp\left\{\frac{-i\pi(L-1)}{J}[u+v]\right\} \frac{\sin[\pi L u/J]}{\sin[\pi u/J]} \frac{\sin[\pi L v/J]}{\sin[\pi v/J]} \qquad (14.3\text{-}10)$$

for $0 \le u, v \le J - 1$. The discrete transfer function $\mathcal{H}_E(u, v)$ assumes zero value only at noninteger spatial frequencies $u = J/L$ and $v = J/L$ because J is even and L is odd.

14.3.2. Underdetermined Model Algorithm

Unfortunately, there is no direct counterpart to the pseudoinverse relationship of Eq. 14.3-4 for the underdetermined model because, as noted in Section 9.4, $\hat{\mathbf{f}}$ cannot be extracted from $\mathbf{k}_E$ when $\mathbf{g} = \mathbf{Bf}$ represents an underdetermined set of equations. However, it is possible to modify the blurred image observation $\mathbf{g}$ and achieve the computational advantages of the overdetermined model. To simplify the explanation consideration will be initially limited to a one-dimensional example.

Let the $N \times 1$ vector $\mathbf{f}_T$ and the $M \times 1$ vector $\mathbf{g}_T$ be formed by selecting the center portions of $\mathbf{f}$ and $\mathbf{g}$, respectively. The truncated vectors are obtained by dropping $L - 1$ elements at each end of the appropriate vector by the selection operations

$$\mathbf{f}_T = \mathbf{S2}_N^{(K)'}\mathbf{f} \qquad (14.3\text{-}11)$$

where $K = N - 2(L - 1)$ and

$$\mathbf{g}_T = \mathbf{S2}_M^{(R)'}\mathbf{g} \qquad (14.3\text{-}12)$$

where $R = M - 2(L - 1)$. Figure 14.3-1a illustrates the relationships of all vectors for $N = 9$ original vector points, $M = 7$ observations, and an impulse response of length $L = 3$.

The elements $\mathbf{f}_T$ and $\mathbf{g}_T$ are entries in the adjoint model

$$\mathbf{q}_E = \mathbf{C}\mathbf{f}_E + \mathbf{n}_E \qquad (14.3\text{-}13a)$$

where the extended vectors $\mathbf{q}_E$, $\mathbf{f}_E$, and $\mathbf{n}_E$ are defined in correspondence with

$$\begin{matrix} M \left\{ \\ J - M \left\{ \right. \end{matrix} \left[-\frac{\mathbf{q}}{\mathbf{0}} - \right] = \left[\ \mathbf{C} \ \right] \left[-\frac{\mathbf{f}_T}{\mathbf{0}} - \right] \begin{matrix} \} K \\ \} J - K \end{matrix} + \left[-\frac{\mathbf{n}_T}{\mathbf{0}} - \right] \qquad (14.3\text{-}13b)$$

As noted in Figure 14.3-1b, the vector $\mathbf{q}$ is identical to the image observation $\mathbf{g}$ over its R center elements where $R = M - 2(L - 1)$. The outer elements of $\mathbf{q}$ can be approximated by

$$\mathbf{q} \approx \tilde{\mathbf{q}} = \mathbf{E}\mathbf{g} \qquad (14.3\text{-}14)$$

where $\mathbf{E}$, called an extraction weighting matrix, is defined later. Combining Eqs. 14.2-13 and 14.3-14 an estimate of $\mathbf{f}_T$ can be obtained from

$$\hat{\mathbf{f}}_E = \mathbf{C}^{-1}\hat{\mathbf{q}}_E \qquad (14.3\text{-}15a)$$

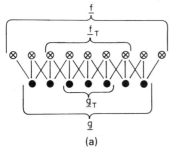
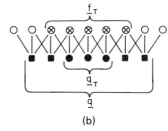

(a)   (b)

FIGURE 14.3-1. Examples of one-dimensional sampled continuous convolution and discrete convolution. (a) Sampled continuous convolution. (b) Discrete convolution.

in correspondence with

$$
\begin{matrix}
K & \left\{ \begin{bmatrix} \hat{\mathbf{f}}_T \\ --- \\ \vdots \\ \vdots \end{bmatrix} \right. \\
J - K & \left\{ \phantom{\begin{bmatrix} \vdots \end{bmatrix}} \right.
\end{matrix}
=
\begin{bmatrix} \mathbf{C}^{-1} \end{bmatrix}
\begin{bmatrix} \tilde{\mathbf{q}} \\ --- \\ \mathbf{0} \end{bmatrix}
\qquad (14.3\text{-}15b)
$$

Comparison of the algebraic similarity of Eqs. 14.3-2 and 14.3-15 leads directly to the estimate

$$
\hat{\mathbf{f}}_E = [\mathbf{A}_J^{-1} \otimes \mathbf{A}_J^{-1}] \mathscr{C}^{-1} [\mathbf{A}_J \otimes \mathbf{A}_J] \tilde{\mathbf{q}}_E \qquad (14.3\text{-}16)
$$

The underdetermined model computational algorithm is then seen to be the same as the algorithm for the overdetermined model of Eqs. 14.3-5 to 14.3-9 with the matrix $\tilde{\mathbf{Q}} = (\mathbf{E} \otimes \mathbf{E})\mathbf{G}$ substituted for the observation of step (b) in Eq. 14.3-6.

The function of the extraction weighting matrix $\mathbf{E}$ is to modify the elements of the physical observation $\mathbf{g}$ such that they approximate the elements of $\mathbf{q}$. For the one-dimensional example of Figure 14.3-1 the sequences are related by

$$
q(1) = g(1) - h(3)f(1) - h(2)f(2)
$$
$$
q(2) = g(2) - h(3)f(2)
$$
$$
q(m) = g(m) \qquad 2 < m < M - 2 \qquad (14.3\text{-}17)
$$
$$
q(M - 1) = g(M - 1) - h(1)f(N - 1)
$$
$$
q(M) = g(M) - h(2)f(N - 1) - h(1)f(N)
$$

Since the values of $\mathbf{f}$ are not known, the correspondence of Eq. 14.3-17 cannot be made directly. However, by making an assumption of continuity of the original data vector that

$$
f(1) = f(2) = f(3) \qquad (14.3\text{-}18a)
$$

and

$$
f(N - 2) = f(N - 1) = f(N) \qquad (14.3\text{-}18b)
$$

then it is found that

$$
q(1) = \frac{g(1)h(1)}{S} \qquad (14.3\text{-}19a)
$$

$$
q(2) = g(2)\frac{[h(1) + h(2)]}{S} \qquad (14.3\text{-}19b)
$$

FIGURE 14.3-2. Examples of pseudoinverse restoration for small degree of blur, $b_R = 1.5$. (a) Original image vectors, **f**. (b) Truncated image vectors, $\mathbf{f}_T$. (c) Observation vectors, **g**. (d) Windowed observation vectors, **q**. (e) Restoration $\hat{\mathbf{f}}_T$ without windowing. (f) Restoration $\hat{\mathbf{f}}_T$ with windowing.

where $S = h(1) + h(2) + h(3)$. Similar equations exist for $q(M-1)$ and $q(M)$. The resultant extraction weighting matrix assumes the simple form

$$\mathbf{E} = \begin{bmatrix} \boldsymbol{\alpha} & 0 & 0 \\ \hline 0 & \mathbf{I} & 0 \\ \hline 0 & 0 & \boldsymbol{\beta} \end{bmatrix} \qquad (14.3\text{-}20)$$

where $\boldsymbol{\alpha}$ and $\boldsymbol{\beta}$ are $L \times L$ submatrices obtained from Eq. 14.3-17 or its generalization (20).

Figure 14.3-2 contains a computer simulation example of the operation of the underdetermined model pseudoinverse image restoration algorithm for one-dimensional blur. In the first step of the simulation the center K pixels of the original image are extraced to form the set of truncated image vectors $\mathbf{f}_T$ shown in Figure 14.3-2b. Next, the truncated image vectors are subjected to a simulated blur with a Gaussian-shaped impulse response with $b_R = 1.5$ to produce the observation of Figure 14.3-2c. Figure 14.3-2d contains the result of the extraction operation on the observation. Restoration results without and with the extraction weighting operator $\mathbf{E}$ are presented in Figures 14.3-2e and 14.3-2f, respectively. These results graphically illustrate the importance of the extraction operation. Without weighting, errors at the observation boundary completely destroy the estimate in the boundary region, but with weighting the restoration is subjectively satisfying, and the restoration error is significantly reduced. Figure 14.3-3 contains simulation results for the experiment of Figure 14.3-2 when the degree of blur is increased by setting $b_R = 2.0$. The higher degree of blur greatly increases the ill-conditioning of the blur matrix, and the residual error in formation of the modified observation after weighting leads to the disappointing estimate of Figure 14.3-3b. Figures 14.3-3c and 14.3-3d illustrate the restoration improvement obtained with the pseudoinverse algorithm for horizontal image motion blur. In this example the blur impulse response is constant, and the corresponding blur matrix is better conditioned than the blur matrix for Gaussian image blur.

14.4. SVD PSEUDOINVERSE SPATIAL IMAGE RESTORATION

In Chapter 5 it was demonstrated that any discrete image in matrix form can be decomposed into a series of eigenimages by the technique of singular value decomposition. For image restoration this concept has been extended (24–27) to the eigen-decomposition of blur matrices in the imaging model

$$\mathbf{g} = \mathbf{Bf} + \mathbf{n} \qquad (14.4\text{-}1)$$

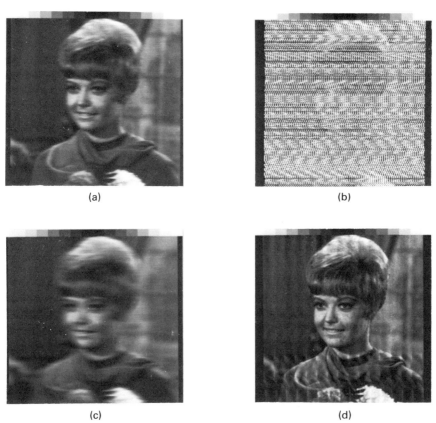

(a) (b)

(c) (d)

FIGURE 14.3-3. Example of pseudoinverse image restoration for moderate and high degrees of blur. Gaussian blur $b_R = 2$: (a) observation **g**; (b) restoration $\mathbf{f}_T$. Uniform motion blur L=15: (c) observation **g**; (d) restoration $\hat{\mathbf{f}}_T$.

From Eq. 5.2-3, the blur matrix **B** may be expressed as

$$\mathbf{B} = \mathbf{U}\boldsymbol{\Lambda}^{1/2}\mathbf{V}^T \qquad (14.4\text{-}2)$$

where the $P \times P$ matrix **U** and the $Q \times Q$ matrix **V** are unitary matrices composed of the eigenvectors of $\mathbf{BB}^T$ and $\mathbf{B}^T\mathbf{B}$, respectively, and $\boldsymbol{\Lambda}$ is a $P \times Q$ matrix whose diagonal terms $\lambda(i)$ contain the eigenvalues of $\mathbf{BB}^T$ and $\mathbf{B}^T\mathbf{B}$. As a consequence of the orthogonality of **U** and **V** it is possible to express the blur matrix in the series form

$$\mathbf{B} = \sum_{i=1}^{R} \lambda^{1/2}(i)\mathbf{u}_i\mathbf{v}_i^T \qquad (14.4\text{-}3)$$

where $\mathbf{u}_i$ and $\mathbf{v}_i$ are the ith columns of $\mathbf{U}$ and $\mathbf{V}$, respectively, and R is the rank of the matrix $\mathbf{B}$.

From Eq. 14.4-2, since $\mathbf{U}$ and $\mathbf{V}$ are unitary matrices, the generalized inverse of $\mathbf{B}$ is

$$\mathbf{B}^- = \mathbf{V}\Lambda^{-1/2}\mathbf{U}^T = \sum_{i=1}^{R} \lambda^{-1/2}(i)\mathbf{v}_i\mathbf{u}_i^T \qquad (14.4\text{-}4)$$

Figure 14.4-1 contains an example of the SVD decomposition of a blur matrix. The generalized inverse estimate can then be expressed as

$$\hat{\mathbf{f}} = \mathbf{B}^-\mathbf{g} = \mathbf{V}\Lambda^{-1/2}\mathbf{U}^T\mathbf{g} \qquad (14.4\text{-}5a)$$

or equivalently

$$\hat{\mathbf{f}} = \sum_{i=1}^{R} [\lambda(i)]^{-1/2}\mathbf{v}_i\mathbf{u}_i^T\mathbf{g} = \sum_{i=1}^{R} \lambda^{-1/2}(i)(\mathbf{u}_i^T\mathbf{g})\mathbf{v}_i \qquad (14.4\text{-}5b)$$

recognizing the fact that the inner product $\mathbf{u}_i^T\mathbf{g}$ is a scalar. Equation 14.4-5 provides the basis for sequential estimation; the kth estimate is equal to

$$\hat{\mathbf{f}}_k = \hat{\mathbf{f}}_{k-1} + [\lambda(k)]^{-1/2}(\mathbf{u}_k^T\mathbf{g})\mathbf{v}_k \qquad (14.4\text{-}6)$$

One of the principal advantages of the sequential formulation is that problems of ill-conditioning generally occur only for higher-order singular values. Thus it is possible interactively to terminate the expansion before numerical problems occur.

Figure 14.4-2 illustrates an example of sequential SVD restoration for the underdetermined model example of Figure 13.7-3 with a poorly conditioned Gaussian blur matrix. A one-step pseudoinverse would have resulted in the final image estimate that is totally overwhelmed by numerical errors. The sixth step, which is the best subjective restoration, offers a considerable improvement over the blurred original, but the lowest least-square error occurs for three singular values.

The major limitation of the SVD image restoration method formulation in Eqs. 14.4-5 and 14.4-6 is computational. The eigenvectors $\mathbf{u}_i$ and $\mathbf{v}_i$ must first be determined for the matrix $\mathbf{BB}^T$ and its transpose. Then the vector computations of Eqs. 14.4-5 or 14.4-6 must be performed. Even if $\mathbf{B}$ is direct-product separable, permitting separable row and column SVD pseudoinversion, the computational task is staggering in the general case.

The pseudoinverse computational algorithm described in the previous section can be adapted for SVD image restoration in the special case of space-invariant blur (21). From the adjoint model of Eq. 14.3-13 given by

$$\mathbf{q}_E = \mathbf{Cf}_E + \mathbf{n}_E \qquad (14.4\text{-}7)$$

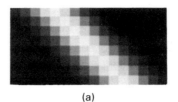

(a)

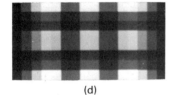

(b)

(c)

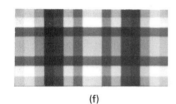

(d)

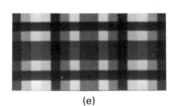

(e)

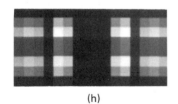

(f)

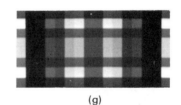

(g)

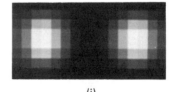

(h)

(i)

FIGURE 14.4-1. SVD decomposition of blur matrix for $b_R = 2.0$, $M = 8$, $N = 16$, $L = 9$. (a) **B**. (b) $\mathbf{u}_1\mathbf{v}_1^T$, $\lambda(1) = 0.871$. (c) $\mathbf{u}_2\mathbf{v}_2^T$, $\lambda(2) = 0.573$. (d) $\mathbf{u}_3\mathbf{v}_3^T$, $\lambda(3) = 0.285$. (e) $\mathbf{u}_4\mathbf{v}_4^T$, $\lambda(4) = 0.108$. (f) $\mathbf{u}_5\mathbf{v}_5^T$, $\lambda(5) = 0.034$. (g) $\mathbf{u}_6\mathbf{v}_6^T$, $\lambda(6) = 0.014$. (h) $\mathbf{u}_7\mathbf{v}_7^T$, $\lambda(7) = 0.011$. (i) $\mathbf{u}_8\mathbf{v}_8^T$, $\lambda(8) = 0.010$.

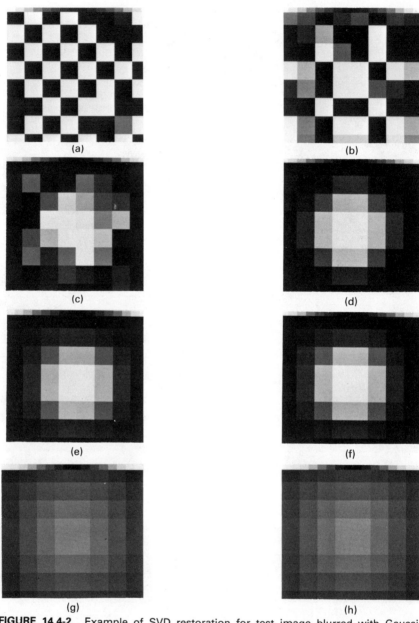

FIGURE 14.4-2. Example of SVD restoration for test image blurred with Gaussian-shaped impulse response, $b_R = b_C = 1.2$. Underdetermined model, $M = 8$, $N = 12$, $L = 5$; noisy observation, Var = 10.0. (a) 8 singular values, PMSE = 2695.81%. (b) 7 singular values, PMSE = 148.93%. (c) 6 singular values, PMSE = 6.88%. (d) 5 singular values, PMSE = 3.31%. (e) 4 singular values, PMSE = 3.06%. (f) 3 singular values, PMSE = 3.05%. (g) 2 singular values, PMSE = 9.52%. (h) 1 singular value, PMSE = 9.52%.

the circulant matrix $\mathbf{C}$ can be expanded in SVD form as

$$\mathbf{C} = \mathbf{X}\boldsymbol{\Delta}^{1/2}\mathbf{Y}^{*T} \qquad (14.4\text{-}8)$$

where $\mathbf{X}$ and $\mathbf{Y}$ are unitary matrices defined by

$$\mathbf{X}[\mathbf{CC}^{T}]\mathbf{X}^{*T} = \boldsymbol{\Delta} \qquad (14.4\text{-}9a)$$

$$\mathbf{Y}[\mathbf{C}^{T}\mathbf{C}]\mathbf{Y}^{*T} = \boldsymbol{\Delta} \qquad (14.4\text{-}9b)$$

Since $\mathbf{C}$ is circulant, $\mathbf{CC}^{T}$ is also circulant. Therefore $\mathbf{X}$ and $\mathbf{Y}$ must be equivalent to the Fourier transform matrix $\mathbf{A}$ (or $\mathbf{A}^{-1}$) because the Fourier matrix produces a diagonalization of a circulant matrix. For purposes of standardization let $\mathbf{X} = \mathbf{Y} = \mathbf{A}^{-1}$. As a consequence the eigenvectors $\mathbf{x}_i = \mathbf{y}_i$, which are rows of $\mathbf{X}$ and $\mathbf{Y}$, are actually the complex exponential basis functions

$$x_k^*(j) = \exp\left\{\frac{2\pi i}{J}(k-1)(j-1)\right\} \qquad (14.4\text{-}10)$$

of a Fourier transform for $1 \le j, k \le J$. Furthermore

$$\boldsymbol{\Delta} = \mathscr{C}\mathscr{C}^{*T} \qquad (14.4\text{-}11)$$

where $\mathscr{C}$ is the Fourier domain circular area convolution matrix.

Then in correspondence with Eq. 14.4-5

$$\hat{\mathbf{f}}_E = \mathbf{A}^{-1}\boldsymbol{\Delta}^{-1/2}\mathbf{A}\tilde{\mathbf{q}}_E \qquad (14.4\text{-}12)$$

where $\tilde{\mathbf{q}}_E$ is the modified blurred image observation of Eqs. 14.3-14 and 14.3-15. Equation 14.4-12 should be recognized as being exactly equivalent to the Fourier domain pseudoinverse estimate of Eq. 14.3-16. Sequential SVD restoration, analogous to the procedure of Eq. 14.4-6, can be obtained by replacing the SVD pseudoinverse matrix $\boldsymbol{\Delta}^{-1/2}$ of Eq. 14.4-12 by the operator

$$\boldsymbol{\Delta}_T^{-1/2} = \begin{bmatrix} [\Delta_T(1)]^{-1/2} & & & & \\ & [\Delta_T(2)]^{-1/2} & & 0 & \\ & & [\Delta_T(T)]^{-1/2} & & \\ & 0 & & 0 \cdot & \\ & & & & \cdot \cdot 0 \end{bmatrix} \qquad (14.4\text{-}13)$$

Complete truncation of the high-frequency terms to avoid ill-conditioning effects may not be necessary in all situations. As an alternative to truncation, the diagonal zero elements can be replaced by $[\Delta(T)]^{-1/2}$ or perhaps by some sequence that declines in value as a function of frequency. This concept is actually analogous to the truncated inverse filtering technique defined by Eq. 14.1-11 for continuous image fields.

Figure 14.4-3 contains an example of SVD pseudoinverse image restoration for one-dimensional Gaussian image blur with $b_R = 3.0$. It should be noted that the restoration attempt with the standard pseudoinverse shown in Figure 14.3-3b was subject to severe ill-conditioning errors at a blur spread of $b_R = 2.0$.

(a)

(b)

(c)

FIGURE 14.4-3. Examples of sequential SVD pseudoinverse image restoration for horizontal Gaussian blur with $b_R = 3$, $L = 23$, $J = 256$. (a) Blurred observation. (b) Restoration $T = 58$. (c) Restoration $T = 60$.

14.5. REGRESSION SPATIAL IMAGE RESTORATION

A fundamental limitation of pseudoinverse image restoration techniques is that observation noise may lead to severe numerical instability and render the image estimate unusable. This problem can be alleviated in some applications by regression restoration methods which incorporate some a priori statistical knowledge of the observation noise (19).

Consider the vector-space model

$$\mathbf{g} = \mathbf{Bf} + \mathbf{n} \tag{14.5-1}$$

for a blurred image plus additive noise in which $\mathbf{B}$ is a $P \times Q$ blur matrix and the noise is assumed to be zero mean with known covariance matrix $\mathbf{K}_n$. The regression method seeks to form an estimate

$$\hat{\mathbf{f}} = \mathbf{Wg} \tag{14.5-2}$$

where $\mathbf{W}$ is a restoration matrix that minimizes the weighted error measure

$$\theta(\hat{\mathbf{f}}) = (\mathbf{g} - \mathbf{B}\hat{\mathbf{f}})^T \mathbf{K}_n^{-1}(\mathbf{g} - \mathbf{B}\hat{\mathbf{f}}) \tag{14.5-3}$$

Minimization of the restoration error can be accomplished by the classical method of setting the partial derivative of $\theta(\hat{\mathbf{f}})$ with respect to $\hat{\mathbf{f}}$ to zero. Thus

$$\frac{\partial \theta(\hat{\mathbf{f}})}{\partial \hat{\mathbf{f}}} = 0 = -2\mathbf{B}^T \mathbf{K}_n^{-1}(\mathbf{g} - \mathbf{B}\hat{\mathbf{f}}) \tag{14.5-4}$$

If $P > Q$, the inverse of matrix $\mathbf{B}^T \mathbf{K}_n^{-1}\mathbf{B}$ can exist, and the resulting restoration matrix assumes the form

$$\mathbf{W} = (\mathbf{B}^T \mathbf{K}_n^{-1}\mathbf{B})^{-1}\mathbf{B}^T \mathbf{K}_n^{-1} \tag{14.5-5}$$

This restoration operator is applicable to an overdetermined observation. If the noise is white with variance σ_n^2, then $\mathbf{K}_n = \sigma_n^2\mathbf{I}$ and the regression matrix reduces to the rank Q generalized inverse for an overdetermined system given by Eq. 14.2-9a.

In the underdetermined case for which $P < Q$, it can be shown (25) that the regression solution is

$$\hat{\mathbf{f}} = (\mathbf{K}^{-1}\mathbf{B})^- \mathbf{K}^{-1}\mathbf{g} + [\mathbf{I} - (\mathbf{K}^{-1}\mathbf{B})^- \mathbf{K}^{-1}\mathbf{B}]\mathbf{v} \tag{14.5-6}$$

where $\mathbf{v}$ is an arbitrary vector and $\mathbf{K}$ is a matrix obtained from the spectral factorization

$$\mathbf{K}_n = \mathbf{KK}^T \tag{14.5-7}$$

of the noise covariance matrix. Thus if the restoration model is under-determined, the estimate is not unique. The minimum norm estimate is simply

$$\hat{\mathbf{f}} = (\mathbf{K}^{-1}\mathbf{B})^{-}\mathbf{K}^{-1}\mathbf{g} \qquad (14.5\text{-}8)$$

and the resulting regression operator becomes

$$\mathbf{W} = (\mathbf{K}^{-1}\mathbf{B})^{-}\mathbf{K}^{-1} \qquad (14.5\text{-}9)$$

For white noise, $\mathbf{K} = \sigma_n^2\mathbf{I}$, and the regression operator assumes the form of a rank P generalized inverse for an underdetermined system as given by Eq. 14.2-9b.

14.6. WIENER ESTIMATION SPATIAL IMAGE RESTORATION

With the regression technique of spatial image restoration the noise field is modeled as a sample of a two-dimensional random process with a known mean and covariance function. Wiener estimation techniques assume, in addition, that the ideal image is also a sample of a two-dimensional random process with known first and second moments (19, 20, 29).

14.6.1. Wiener Estimation—General Case

Consider the general discrete model of Figure 14.6-1 in which a $Q \times 1$ image vector $\mathbf{f}$ is subject to some unspecified type of point and spatial degradation resulting in the $P \times 1$ vector of observations $\mathbf{g}$. An estimate of $\mathbf{f}$ is formed by the linear operation

$$\hat{\mathbf{f}} = \mathbf{W}\mathbf{g} + \mathbf{b} \qquad (14.6\text{-}1)$$

where $\mathbf{W}$ is a $Q \times P$ restoration matrix and $\mathbf{b}$ is a $Q \times 1$ bias vector. The objective of Wiener estimation is to choose $\mathbf{W}$ and $\mathbf{b}$ to minimize the

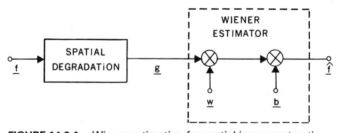

FIGURE 14.6-1. Wiener estimation for spatial image restoration.

mean-square restoration error, which may be defined as

$$\mathcal{E} = E\{(\mathbf{f} - \hat{\mathbf{f}})^T (\mathbf{f} - \hat{\mathbf{f}})\} \qquad (14.6\text{-}2a)$$

or

$$\mathcal{E} = \text{tr}\,[E\{(\mathbf{f} - \hat{\mathbf{f}})(\mathbf{f} - \hat{\mathbf{f}})^T\}] \qquad (14.6\text{-}2b)$$

Equation 14.6-2a expresses the error in inner-product form as the sum of the squares of the elements of the error vector $(\mathbf{f} - \hat{\mathbf{f}})$, while Eq. 14.6-2b forms the covariance matrix of the error vector and then sums together its variance terms (diagonal elements) by the trace operation. Minimization of Eq. 14.6-2 in either of its forms can be accomplished by differentiation of $\mathcal{E}$ with respect to $\hat{\mathbf{f}}$. An alternative approach, which is of quite general utility, is to employ the orthogonality principle (30, p. 219) to determine the values of $\mathbf{W}$ and $\mathbf{b}$ that minimize the mean-square error. In the context of image restoration the orthogonality principle specifies two necessary and sufficient conditions for the minimization of the mean-square restoration error:

1. The expected value of the image estimate must equal the expected value of the image

$$E\{\hat{\mathbf{f}}\} = E\{\mathbf{f}\} \qquad (14.6\text{-}3)$$

2. The restoration error must be orthogonal to the observation about its mean

$$E\{(\hat{\mathbf{f}} - \mathbf{f})(\mathbf{g} - E\{\mathbf{g}\})^T\} = \mathbf{0} \qquad (14.6\text{-}4)$$

From condition 1 one obtains

$$\mathbf{b} = E\{\mathbf{f}\} - \mathbf{W}E\{\mathbf{g}\} \qquad (14.6\text{-}5)$$

and from condition 2

$$E\{(\mathbf{W}\mathbf{g} + \mathbf{b} - \mathbf{f})(\mathbf{g} - E\{\mathbf{g}\})^T\} = \mathbf{0} \qquad (14.6\text{-}6)$$

On substitution for the bias vector $\mathbf{b}$ from Eq. 14.6-5 and simplification, Eq. 14-6-6 reduces to

$$\mathbf{W} = \mathbf{K}_{fg}(\mathbf{K}_{gg})^{-1} \qquad (14.6\text{-}7)$$

where $\mathbf{K}_{gg}$ is the $P \times P$ covariance matrix of the observation vector (assumed nonsingular) and $\mathbf{K}_{fg}$ is the $Q \times P$ cross-covariance matrix between the image and observation vectors. Thus the optimal bias vector $\mathbf{b}$ and restoration matrix $\mathbf{W}$ may be directly determined in terms of the first and second joint moments of the ideal image and observation vectors. It should be noted that these solutions apply for nonlinear and space-variant degradations. Subsequent sections describe applications of Wiener estimation to specific restoration models.

14.5.2. Wiener Estimation—Image Blur with Additive Noise

In the discrete model for a blurred image subject to additive noise the observation vector is given by

$$\mathbf{g} = \mathbf{Bf} + \mathbf{n} \tag{14.6-8}$$

The Wiener estimation for this model is composed of a bias term

$$\mathbf{b} = E\{\mathbf{f}\} - \mathbf{W}E\{\mathbf{g}\} = E\{\mathbf{f}\} - \mathbf{W}\mathbf{B}E\{\mathbf{f}\} + \mathbf{W}E\{\mathbf{n}\} \tag{14.6-9}$$

and a matrix operator

$$\mathbf{W} = \mathbf{K}_{fg}(\mathbf{K}_{gg})^{-1} = \mathbf{K}_f\mathbf{B}^T(\mathbf{B}\mathbf{K}_f\mathbf{B}^T + \mathbf{K}_n)^{-1} \tag{14.6-10}$$

or by the matrix identity of Eq. 5.1-11

$$\mathbf{W} = (\mathbf{B}^T\mathbf{K}_n^{-1}\mathbf{B} + \mathbf{K}_f^{-1})^{-1}\mathbf{B}^T\mathbf{K}_n^{-1} \tag{14.6-11}$$

Although Eqs. 14.6-10 and 14.6-11 are equivalent, Eq. 14.6-10 should be utilized for underdetermined systems and Eq. 14.6-12 for overdetermined systems, because the matrix inverses are of smallest dimension in such cases.

If the ideal image field is assumed uncorrelated, $\mathbf{K}_f = \sigma_f^2\mathbf{I}$ where σ_f^2 represents the image energy. Equation 14.6-10 then reduces to

$$\mathbf{W} = \sigma_f^2\mathbf{B}^T(\sigma_f^2\mathbf{B}\mathbf{B}^T + \mathbf{K}_n)^{-1} \tag{14.6-12}$$

Under the same condition, Eq. 14.6-11 simplifies to

$$\mathbf{W} = (\mathbf{B}^T\mathbf{K}_n^{-1}\mathbf{B} + \sigma_f^{-2}\mathbf{I})^{-1}\mathbf{B}^T\mathbf{K}_n^{-1} \tag{14.6-13}$$

For a white-noise process with energy σ_n^2,

$$\mathbf{W} = \mathbf{B}^T\left[\mathbf{B}\mathbf{B}^T + \frac{\sigma_n^2}{\sigma_f^2}\mathbf{I}\right]^{-1} \tag{14.6-14}$$

and

$$\mathbf{W} = \left[\mathbf{B}^T\mathbf{B} + \frac{\sigma_f^{-2}}{\sigma_n^{-2}}\mathbf{I}\right]^{-1}\mathbf{B}^T \tag{14.6-15}$$

(a) $b_R = b_C = 1.2$, Var $= 10.0$, $\rho = 0.75$, SNR $= 200.0$ (b)

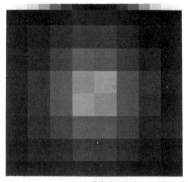

(c) $b_R = b_C = 50.0$, Var $= 10.0$, $\rho = 0.75$, SNR $= 200.0$ (d)

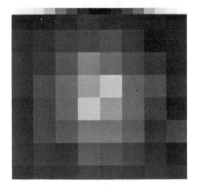

(e) $b_R = b_C = 50.0$, Var $= 100.0$, $\rho = 0.75$, SNR $= 60.0$ (f)

FIGURE 14.6-2. Examples of Wiener estimation for test image blurred with Gaussian shaped impulse response. Underdetermined model, $M = 8$, $N = 12$, $L = 5$. (a) Blurred, PMSE $= 4.91\%$; (b) restored, PMSE $= 3.17\%$. (c) Blurred, PMSE $= 7.99\%$; (d) restored, PMSE $= 4.20\%$. (e) Blurred, PMSE $= 7.93\%$; (f) restored, PMSE $= 4.74\%$.

As the ratio of image energy to noise energy $(\sigma_f/\sigma_n)^2$ approaches infinity, the Wiener estimator of Eq. 14.6-14 becomes equivalent to the underdetermined generalized inverse estimator, while Eq. 14.6-15 approaches the expression for the overdetermined generalized inverse estimator.

Figure 14.6-2 contains restoration examples for the underdetermined model of Figure 13.7-3 for a Gaussian-shaped blur function. Wiener restorations of large size images are given in Figure 14.6-3 using a fast computational algorithm developed by Pratt and Davarian (20). In the example illustrating horizontal image motion blur, the impulse response is of rectangular shape of length $L = 11$. The center 129 pixels have been restored and replaced within the context of the blurred image to show the

(a)   (b)

(c)   (d)

FIGURE 14.6-3. Wiener image restoration examples. (a) Horizontal motion blur observation, $L = 11$. (b) Restoration of (a). (c) Electron microscope observation. (d) Restoration of (c).

visual restoration improvement. The noise level and blur impulse response of the electron microscope original were estimated directly from the photographic transparency using techniques to be described in Chapter 15. The parameters were then utilized to restore the center 129×129 pixel region, which was then replaced in the context of the blurred original.

14.7. SMOOTHING METHODS

Smoothing and regularization techniques (31–33) have been used in an attempt to overcome the ill-conditioning problems associated with image restoration. Basically, these methods attempt to force smoothness on the solution of a least-squares error problem.

Two formulations of these methods are considered (19). The first formulation consists of finding the minimum of $\hat{\mathbf{f}}^T \mathbf{S} \hat{\mathbf{f}}$ subject to the equality constraint

$$(\mathbf{g} - \mathbf{B}\hat{\mathbf{f}})^T \mathbf{M}(\mathbf{g} - \mathbf{B}\hat{\mathbf{f}}) = e \qquad (14.7\text{-}1)$$

where $\mathbf{S}$ is a smoothing matrix, $\mathbf{M}$ is an error weighting matrix, and e denotes a residual scalar estimation error. The error weighting matrix is often chosen to be equal to the inverse of the observation noise covariance matrix, $\mathbf{M} = \mathbf{K}_n^{-1}$. A common choice for the smoothing matrix is

$$\mathbf{S} = \mathbf{S}_1 \otimes \mathbf{S}_1 \qquad (14.7\text{-}2)$$

where

$$
\mathbf{S}_1 =
\begin{bmatrix}
1 & -2 & 1 & 0 & 0 & 0 & 0 & & & & 0 \\
-2 & 5 & -4 & 1 & 0 & 0 & 0 & & & & \cdot \\
1 & -4 & 6 & -4 & 1 & 0 & 0 & & & & \cdot \\
0 & 1 & -4 & 6 & -4 & 1 & 0 & & & & \cdot \\
0 & 0 & 1 & -4 & 6 & -4 & 1 & & & & \cdot \\
& & & & & \ddots & & & & & \\
& & & & & 1 & -4 & 6 & -4 & 1 & 0 \\
& & & & & 0 & 1 & -4 & 6 & -4 & 1 \\
& & & & & 0 & 0 & 1 & -4 & 5 & -2 \\
0 & & & & & 0 & 0 & 0 & 1 & -2 & 1 \\
\end{bmatrix}
\qquad (14.7\text{-}3)
$$

is a one-dimensional linear operator that forms a moving smoothing window for the estimator. By imposing the smoothing restriction the stationary point of the Lagrangian expression

$$F(\hat{\mathbf{f}}, \lambda) = \hat{\mathbf{f}}^T \mathbf{S}\mathbf{f} + \lambda[(\mathbf{g} - \mathbf{B}\hat{\mathbf{f}})\mathbf{M}^T(\mathbf{g} - \mathbf{B}\hat{\mathbf{f}}) - e] \qquad (14.7\text{-}4)$$

is sought. Taking derivatives with respect to $\mathbf{f}$ and λ and setting them to zero, the estimate for a nonsingular overdetermined system becomes

$$\hat{\mathbf{f}} = \left(\mathbf{B}\mathbf{M}^T \mathbf{B} + \frac{1}{\lambda}\mathbf{S}\right)^{-1} \mathbf{B}^T \mathbf{M}\mathbf{g} \qquad (14.7\text{-}5a)$$

and for a nonsingular underdetermined observation

$$\hat{\mathbf{f}} = \mathbf{S}^{-1}\mathbf{B}^T\left(\mathbf{B}\mathbf{S}^{-1}\mathbf{B}^T + \frac{1}{\lambda}\mathbf{M}^{-1}\right)^{-1} \mathbf{g} \qquad (14.7\text{-}5b)$$

In Eq. 14.7-5 the Lagrangean factor λ is chosen so that Eq. 14.7-1 is satisfied, that is, the compromise between residual error and smoothness of the estimator is deemed satisfactory.

Now consider the second formulation, which involves solving an equality-constrained least-squares problem by mininimizing $(\mathbf{g} - \mathbf{B}\hat{\mathbf{f}})^T \mathbf{M}(\mathbf{g} - \mathbf{B}\hat{\mathbf{f}})$ such that

$$\hat{\mathbf{f}}^T \mathbf{S}\hat{\mathbf{f}} = d \qquad (14.7\text{-}6)$$

where the scalar d represents a fixed degree of smoothing. In this case the Lagrangean expression is

$$G(\hat{\mathbf{f}}, \gamma) = (\mathbf{g} - \mathbf{B}\hat{\mathbf{f}})\mathbf{M}^T(\mathbf{g} - \mathbf{B}\hat{\mathbf{f}}) + \gamma(\hat{\mathbf{f}}^T \mathbf{S}\hat{\mathbf{f}} - d) \qquad (14.7\text{-}7)$$

The optimal solution for an overdetermined nonsingular system is then found to be

$$\hat{\mathbf{f}} = (\mathbf{B}^T \mathbf{M}\mathbf{B} + \gamma\mathbf{S})^{-1}\mathbf{B}^T \mathbf{M}\mathbf{g} \qquad (14.7\text{-}8a)$$

For the underdetermined system the smoothing estimate becomes

$$\hat{\mathbf{f}} = \mathbf{S}^{-1}\mathbf{B}^T (\mathbf{B}\mathbf{S}^{-1}\mathbf{B}^T + \gamma\mathbf{M}^{-1})^{-1}\mathbf{g} \qquad (14.7\text{-}8b)$$

A comparison of Eqs. 14.7-5 and 14.7-8 reveals that the two inverse problems are solved by the same expression, the only difference being the Lagrange multipliers, which are inverses of one another. The smoothing estimates of Eq. 14.7-8 are closely related to the regression and Wiener estimates derived previously. If $\gamma = 0$, $\mathbf{S} = \mathbf{I}$, and $\mathbf{M} = \mathbf{K}_n^{-1}$ where $\mathbf{K}_n$ is the observation noise covariance matrix, then the smoothing and regression estimates become equivalent. Substitution of $\gamma = 1$, $\mathbf{S} = \mathbf{K}_f^{-1}$, and $\mathbf{M} = \mathbf{K}_n^{-1}$ where $\mathbf{K}_f$ is the image covariance matrix results in equivalence to the Wiener estimator. These equivalences account for the relative smoothness of the estimates obtained with regression and Wiener restoration as compared to pseudoinverse restoration. A problem that occurs with the smoothing and regularizing techniques is that even though the variance of a solution can be calculated, its bias can only be determined as a function of $\mathbf{f}$.

The continuous Fourier domain least-squares image restoration filter of Eq. 14.1-22, developed by Hunt (18), can be utilized as the basis of a fast computational algorithm for the smoothing restoration operation of Eq. 14.7-8 if the observation vector $\mathbf{g}$ is properly padded.

14.8. CONSTRAINED RESTORATION TECHNIQUES

Equality and inequality constraints have been suggested (19) as a means of improving restoration performance for ill-conditioned restoration models. Examples of constraints include the specification of individual pixel values, of ratios of the values of some pixels, or the sum of part or all of the pixels, or amplitude limits of pixel values.

For the overdetermined linear model a set of linear constraints can be defined as

$$\mathbf{A}\hat{\mathbf{f}} = \mathbf{t} \qquad (14.8\text{-}1)$$

where $\mathbf{A}$ is a $P \times N$ matrix of rank $P < N$ defining the constraints, $\hat{\mathbf{f}}$ is the constrained estimator, and $\mathbf{t}$ is a $P \times 1$ known vector. Minimization of the weighted error measure $(\mathbf{g} - \mathbf{Bf})\mathbf{K}_n^{-1}(\mathbf{g} - \mathbf{Bf})$ subject to the constraint leads to the esimate (28, p. 100)

$$\hat{\mathbf{f}} = \tilde{\mathbf{f}} + (\mathbf{B}^T\mathbf{K}_n^{-1}\mathbf{B})^{-1}\mathbf{A}^T[\mathbf{A}(\mathbf{B}^T\mathbf{K}_n^{-1}\mathbf{B})^{-1}\mathbf{A}^T]^{-1}(\mathbf{t} - \mathbf{A}\tilde{\mathbf{f}}) \qquad (14.8\text{-}2)$$

where $\tilde{\mathbf{f}}$ is the unconstrained solution. The covariance matrix of the optimal solution is

$$\mathbf{K}_{\hat{f}} = (\mathbf{B}^T\mathbf{K}_n^{-1}\mathbf{B})^{-1} - (\mathbf{B}^T\mathbf{K}_n^{-1}\mathbf{B})^{-1}\mathbf{A}^T[\mathbf{A}(\mathbf{B}^T\mathbf{K}_n^{-1}\mathbf{B})\mathbf{A}^T]^{-1}\mathbf{A}(\mathbf{B}^T\mathbf{K}_n^{-1}\mathbf{B})^{-1}$$

$$(14.8\text{-}3)$$

where $\mathbf{K}_{\tilde{f}} = (\mathbf{B}^T\mathbf{K}_n^{-1}\mathbf{B})$ is the (positive definite) covariance matrix of the unrestricted estimator. The second matrix in the expression of Eq. 14.8-3 can be shown to be non-negative definite with rank P. Therefore $\mathbf{K}_{\hat{f}}$ is equal to $\mathbf{K}_{\tilde{f}}$ minus a non-negative definite matrix. As a consequence each diagonal element of $\mathbf{K}_{\hat{f}}$ is less than or equal to the corresponding element of $\mathbf{K}_{\tilde{f}}$, and there is a reduction in the variance of each component of the constrained estimator vector as compared to the unconstrained one. However, this does not imply that the former is necessarily better than the latter. In fact, the constrained estimator may possess bias, as opposed to the unbiasedness of the unconstrained estimator. The bias of the constrained solution given by

$$\mathbf{b} = \mathbf{f} - E\{\hat{\mathbf{f}}\} = -(\mathbf{b}^T \mathbf{K}_n^{-1} \mathbf{B})^{-1} \mathbf{A}^T [\mathbf{A}(\mathbf{B}^T \mathbf{K}_n^{-1} \mathbf{B})^{-1} \mathbf{A}^T]^{-1} [\mathbf{t} - \mathbf{A}\mathbf{f}]$$
(14.8-4)

will be zero if and only if the specifications are satisfied by the true vector $\mathbf{f}$, that is, if and only if $\mathbf{A}\mathbf{f} = \mathbf{t}$. In this case the set of constraints could be regarded as additional noise-free observations. A reasonable equality constraint for image restoration would be that the sum of the restored pixel values might be set at some average value, perhaps the average value of the observation. Such a limitation, however, has not proved to be very helpful in restricting the effects of ill-conditioning because the constraint only affects one degree of freedom in a vector space of dimensionality N^2.

Quite often a priori information is available in the form of inequality constraints involving pixel values. The physics of the image formation process requires that pixel values be non-negative quantities. Furthermore, an upper bound on these values is often known because images are digitized with a finite number of bits assigned to each pixel. Amplitude constraints are also inherently introduced by the need to "fit" a restored image to the dynamic range of a display. One approach is linearly to rescale the restored image to the display range. This procedure is usually undesirable because only a few out-of-range pixels will cause the contrast of all other pixels to be reduced. Also, the average luminance of a restored image is usually affected by rescaling. Another common display method involves clipping of all pixel values exceeding the display limits. Although this procedure is subjectively preferable to rescaling, bias errors may be introduced.

If a priori pixel amplitude limits are established for image restoration, it is best to incorporate these limits directly in the restoration process rather than arbitrarily invoke the limits on the restored image. Several techniques of inequality constrained restoration have been proposed.

Consider the general case of constrained restoration in which the vector estimate $\hat{\mathbf{f}}$ is subject to the inequality constraint

$$\mathbf{l} \le \hat{\mathbf{f}} \le \mathbf{u}$$
(14.8-5)

where $\mathbf{u}$ and $\mathbf{l}$ are vectors containing upper and lower limits of the pixel estimate, respectively. For least-squares restoration the quadratic error must be minimized subject to the constraint of Eq. 14.8-5. Under this framework, restoration reduces to the solution of a quadratic programming problem (19). In the case of an absolute error measure the restoration task can be formulated as a linear programming problem (34, 35). The a priori knowledge involving the inequality constraints may substantially reduce pixel uncertainty in the restored image; however, as in the case of equality constraints, an unknown amount of bias may be introduced.

Figure 14.8-1 contains an example of image restoration for the over-determined Gaussian blur model of Chapter 13 by pseudoinverse restoration and with inequality constrained restoration (19) in which the scaled luminance of each pixel of the restored image has been limited to the range of 0 to 255. The improvement obtained by the constraint is substantial. Unfortunately, the quadratic programming solution employed in this example requires a considerable amount of computation. A brute force extension of the procedure does not appear feasible.

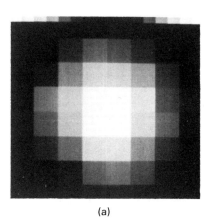

(a)

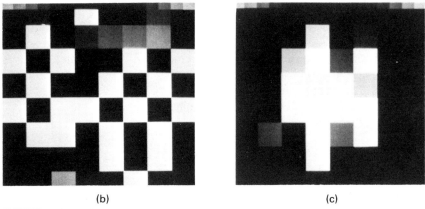

(b)　　　　　　　　　　　　　　　　　　(c)

FIGURE 14.8-1. Comparison of unconstrained and inequality constrained restoration for image blurred with Gaussian shaped impulse response, $b_R = b_C = 1.2$. Overdetermined model, $M = 12$, $N = 8$, $L = 5$; noisy observation, Var = 10.0. (a) Blurred observation. (b) Unconstrained restoration. (c) Inequality constrained restoration.

Several other methods have been proposed for constrained image restoration. One simple approach, based on the concept of homomorphic filtering, is to take the logarithm of each observation. Exponentiation of the corresponding estimates automatically yields a strictly positive result. Burg (5, 36, 37) and Frieden (5, 38, 39) have developed restoration methods providing a positivity constraint, which are based upon a maximum entropy principle originally employed to estimate a probability density from observation of its moments. Burg's technique, which yields a closed-form solution, has proved somewhat unstable in the presence of noise. Frieden's iterative method has been applied to one-dimensional signals and small images with good results. Jansson et al. (40) have developed an iterative constrained restoration method derived from earlier work of van Cittert (41). The method is defined by the iterative equations (5, 40)

$$\hat{\mathbf{g}}_k = \mathbf{B}\hat{\mathbf{f}}_k \qquad (14.8\text{-}6)$$

$$\hat{\mathbf{f}}_{k+1} = \hat{\mathbf{f}}_k + \mathbf{R}[\mathbf{g} - \hat{\mathbf{g}}_K] \qquad (14.8\text{-}7)$$

where the subscript defines the iteration stage number and $\hat{\mathbf{f}}_0 = \mathbf{g}$. Matrix $\mathbf{R}$ is of diagonal form defined as

$$R(n, n) = C\left[1 - \frac{2}{\mu(n) - l(n)}\left|\hat{f}_k(n) - \frac{l(n) + \mu(n)}{2}\right|\right] \qquad (14.8\text{-}8)$$

where C is a constant. As an element of the restored image approaches an upper or lower amplitude limit, the corresponding weighting factor $R(n, n)$ approaches zero, thereby stabilizing that term of the estimate. Good results have been obtained with one-dimensional signals. Huang et al (41, 42) have introduced a projection method of constrained image restoration in which the set of equations $\mathbf{g} = \mathbf{Bf}$ are iteratively solved by numerical means. At each stage of the solution the intermediate estimates are amplitude clipped to conform to amplitude limits.

Constrained image restoration is an area of ongoing research. Efficient computational techniques are being sought to minimize the estimation error subject to the side constraints.

14.9. STOCHASTIC ESTIMATION TECHNIQUES

Most of the image restoration methods previously described in this chapter have been based on the simple model of a blurred image plus noise. Furthermore, almost all of these methods have been derived for a least-square or mean-square error criterion. Attention is now directed to a more general class of image restoration techniques based on the theory of stochastic estimation.

From Eq. 13.7-2 the general vector-space relationship between the observation vector **g** and an ideal image vector **f** and a noise vector **n** can be expressed as

$$\mathbf{g} = \mathcal{O}_M\{\mathbf{f}, \mathbf{n}\} \tag{14.9-1}$$

where $\mathcal{O}_M(\cdot)$ represents a general transfer function modeling point and spatial image degradation. There are two general approaches, batch and recursive processing, to the generation of an estimate $\hat{\mathbf{f}}$ from Eq. 14.9-1. A batch processor utilizes all pixels of the observation **g** to develop the estimate, while a recursive processor is limited to those pixels of **g** lying in some corresponding neighborhood of the pixel to be estimated. If the elements of **g** are highly correlated, then clearly the batch processor will provide a more exact estimate because it utilizes more available data. Several stochastic estimation techniques (44–48) potentially applicable to the image restoration model of Eq. 14.9-1 are described below.

The most common stochastic estimate is that which minimizes some average functional error as defined by

$$\mathcal{E} = E\{\psi(\mathbf{f} - \hat{\mathbf{f}})|\mathbf{g}\} = \int \psi(\mathbf{f} - \hat{\mathbf{f}})p(\mathbf{f}|\mathbf{g}) \, d\mathbf{f} \tag{14.9-2}$$

where $\psi(\cdot)$ is an error or cost function and $p(\mathbf{f}|\mathbf{g})$ is the a posteriori probability density of the ideal image vector **f** given the observation vector **g**. If the error functional is the mean-square error as defined in Eq. 14.6-2, the optimal estimate is the so-called Bayes estimate

$$\hat{\mathbf{f}} = E\{\mathbf{f}|\mathbf{g}\} = \int \mathbf{f}p(\mathbf{f}|\mathbf{g}) \, d\mathbf{f} \tag{14.9-3}$$

which is the mean of the ideal image vector conditioned on the observation. The Bayes estimate is also optimal for many other error functionals, such as the absolute error, provided that the error functional is symmetric and that the a posteriori probability density is symmetric and unimodel (48). Unfortunately, determination of the Bayes estimate of Eq. 14.9-3 is usually very difficult when the observation model of Eq. 14.9-1 is nonlinear. Naraghi (49) has developed an image restoration algorithm that yields an approximate evaluation of Eq. 14.9-3.

Another common stochastic estimate is the maximum a posteriori (MAP) estimate, which is the mode value of the a posteriori probability density $p(\mathbf{f}|\mathbf{g})$. Explicit knowledge of the a posteriori density is not neces-sary to determine its mode. By Bayes' theorem the a posteriori density

$$p(\mathbf{f}|\mathbf{g}) = \frac{p(\mathbf{g}|\mathbf{f})p(\mathbf{f})}{p(\mathbf{g})} \tag{14.9-4}$$

can be expressed in terms of the marginal densities $p(\mathbf{f})$ and $p(\mathbf{g})$ and the conditional density $p(\mathbf{g}|\mathbf{f})$. Taking the logarithm of both sides of Eq. 14.9-4 and differentiating with respect to $\mathbf{f}$ yields a characteristic equation

$$\frac{\partial \ln\left[p(\mathbf{g}|\mathbf{f})\right]}{\partial \mathbf{f}} + \frac{\partial \ln\left[p(\mathbf{f})\right]}{\partial \mathbf{f}} = 0 \tag{14.9-5}$$

to be solved for the estimate $\hat{\mathbf{f}}$ for appropriate density models for $p(\mathbf{g}|\mathbf{f})$ and $p(\mathbf{f})$. Most solutions rely on a Gaussian assumption for $\mathbf{f}$ and $\mathbf{n}$. Hunt (3) has applied the MAP estimation technique to image restoration for the model

$$\mathbf{g} = \mathcal{O}_M\{\mathbf{Bf}\} + \mathbf{n} \tag{14.9-6}$$

where $\mathbf{B}$ denotes a blur matrix and $\mathcal{O}_M(\cdot)$ is a known point nonlinear operation on each element of the vector $\mathbf{Bf}$. Under a Gaussian assumption Hunt has reduced Eq. 14.9-5 to a recursive form that can be solved by iteration techniques.

The maximum likelihood estimate is that value $\hat{\mathbf{f}}$ which maximizes the a posteriori density $p(\mathbf{g} = \tilde{\mathbf{g}}|\mathbf{f})$ for an actual observation $\mathbf{g}$. Mathematically, the estimate is defined by

$$p(\tilde{\mathbf{g}}|\hat{\mathbf{f}}) = \max_{\mathbf{f}} p(\tilde{\mathbf{g}}|\mathbf{f}) \tag{14.9-7}$$

If the ideal image vector $\mathbf{f}$ is uniformly distributed, the maximum likelihood and MAP estimates are identical

Stochastic estimation techniques offer potential promise for image res-toration tasks in which the observation model is nonlinear. In such cases linear estimation methods are not likely to produce good results. However, stochastic restoration methods are presently limited by problems of statis-tical modeling, analytic manipulation, and implementation complexity.

REFERENCES

1. M. M. Sondhi, "Image Restoration: The Removal of Spatially Invariant Degradations," *Proc. IEEE*, **60**, 7, July 1972, 842–853.

2. H. C. Andrews, "Digital Image Restoration: A Survey," *IEEE Computer*, **7**, 5, May 1974, 36–45.

3. B. R. Hunt, "Digital Image Processing," *Proc. IEEE*, **63**, 4, April 1975, 693–708.

4. H. C. Andrews and B. R. Hunt, *Digital Image Restoration*, Prentice-Hall, Englewood Cliffs, N.J., 1977.

5. B. R. Frieden, "Image Enhancement and Restoration," in *Picture Processing and Digital Filtering*, T. S. Huang, Ed., Springer-Verlag, New York, 1975.

6. A. Marechal, P. Croce, and K. Dietzel, "Amelioration du Contrast des Details des Images Photographiques par Filtrage des Frequencies Spatiales," *Opta Acta*, **5**, 1958, 256–262.

7. J. Tsujiuchi, "Correction of Optical Images by Compensation of Aberrations and by Spatial Frequency Filtering," in *Progress in Optics*, Vol. 2, E. Wolf, Ed., Wiley, New York, 1963, 131–180.

8. J. L. Harris, Sr., "Image Evaluation and Restoration," *J. Opt. Soc. Am.*, **56**, 5, May 1966, 569–574.

9. B. L. McGlamery, "Restoration of Turbulence-Degraded Images," *J. Opt. Soc. Am.*, **57**, 3, March 1967, 293–297.

10. P. F. Mueller and G. O. Reynolds, "Image Restoration by Removal of Random Media Degradations," *J. Opt. soc. Am.*, **57**, 11, November 1967, 1338–1344.

11. C. W. Helstrom, "Image Restoration by the Method of Least Squares," *J. Opt. Soc. Am.*, **57**, 3, March 1967, 297–303.

12. J. L. Harris, Sr., "Potential and Limitations of Techniques for Processing Linear Motion-Degraded Imagery," in *Evaluation of Motion Degraded Images*, U. S. government Printing Office, Washington D.C., 1968, 131–138.

13. J. L. Horner, "Optical Spatial Filtering with the Least-Mean-Square-Error Filter," *J. Opt. Soc. Am.*, **51**, 5, May 1969, 553–558.

14. J. L. Horner, "Optical Restoration of Images Blurred by Atmospheric Turbulence Using Optimum Filter Theory," *Applied Op.*, **9**, 1, January 1970, 167–171.

15. B. L. Lewis and D. J. Sakrison, "Computer Enhancement of Scanning Electron Micrographs," *IEEE Trans. Circuits and Systems*, **CAS-22**, 3, March 1975, 267–278.

16. D. Slepian, "Restoration of Photographs Blurred by Image Motion," *Bell Syst. Tech. J.*, **XLVI**, 10, December 1967, 2353–2362.

17. E. R. Cole, "The Removal of Unknown Image Blurs by Homomorphic Filtering," Ph.D. Dissertation, Department of Electrical Engineering, University of Utah, Salt Lake City, June 1973.

18. B. R. Hunt, "The Application of Constrained Least Squares Estimation to Image Restoration by Digital Computer," *IEEE Trans. Computers*, **C-23**, 9, September 1973, 805–812.

19. N. D. A. Mascarenhas and W. K. Pratt, "Digital Image Restoration Under a Regression Model," *IEEE Trans. Circuits and Systems*, **CAS-22**, 3, March 1975, 252–266.

20. W. K. Pratt and F. Davarian, "Fast Computational Techniques for Pseudoinverse and Wiener Image Restoration," *IEEE Trans. Computers*, **C-26**, 6, June 1977, 571–580.

21. W. K. Pratt, "Pseudoinverse Image Restoration Computational Algorithms," in *Optical Information Processing Vol. II*, G. W. Stroke, Y. Nesterikhin, and E. S. Barrekette, Eds., Plenum Press, New York, 1977.

22. B. W. Rust and W. R. Burrus, *Mathematical Programming and the Numerical Solution of Linear Equations*, American Elsevier, New York, 1972.

23. A. Albert, *Regression and the Moore-Penrose Pseudoinverse*, Academic Press, New York, 1972.

24. H. C. Andrews and C. L. Patterson, "Outer Product Expansions and Their Uses in Digital Image Processing," *Am. Math. Monthly*, **1**, 82, January 1975, 1–13.

25. H. C. Andrews and C. L. Patterson, "Outer Product Expansions and Their Uses in Digital Image Processing," *IEEE Trans. Computers*, **C-25**, 2, February 1976, 140–148.

26. T. S. Huang and P. M. Narendra, "Image Restoration by Singular Value Decomposition," *Appl. Opt.*, **14**, 9, September 1975, 2213–2216.

27. H. C. Andrews and C. L. Patterson, "Singular Value Decompositions and Digital Image Processing," *IEEE Trans. Acoustics, Speech, and Signal Processing*, **ASSP-24**, 1, February 1976, 26–53.

28. T. O. Lewis and P. L. Odell, *Estimation in Linear Models*, Prentice Hall, Englewood Cliffs, N. J., 1971.

29. W. K. Pratt, "Generalized Wiener Filter Computation Techniques," *IEEE Trans. Computers*, **C-21**, 7, July 1972, 636–641.

30. A. Papoulis, *Probability Random Variables and Stochastic Processes*, McGraw-Hill, New York, 1965.

31. S. Twomey, "On the Numerical Solution of Fredholm Integral Equations of the First Kind by the Inversion of the Linear System Produced by Quadrature," *J. Assoc. Computing Machinery*, **10**, 1963, 97–101.

32. D. L. Phillips, "A Technique for the Numerical Solution of Certain Integral Equations of the First Kind," *J. Assoc. Computing Machinery*, **9**, 1964, 84–97.

33. A. N. Tikonov, "Regularization of Incorrectly Posed Problems," *Soviet Mathematics*, **4**, 6, 1963, 1624–1627.

34. E. B. Barrett and R. N. Devich, "Linear Programming Compensation for Space-Variant Image Degradation," *Processing SPIE/OSA Conference on Image Processing*, J. C. Urbach, Ed., Pacific Grove, California, February 1976, Vol. 74, 152–158.

35. D. P. MacAdam, "Digital Image Restoration by Constrained Deconvolution," *J. Opt. Soc. Am.*, **60**, 12, December 1970, 1617–1627.

36. J. P. Burg, "Maximum Entropy Spectral Analysis," 37th Annual Society of Exploration Geophysicists Meeting, Oklahoma City, 1967.

37. J. A. Edward and M. M. Fitelson, "Notes on Maximum Entropy Processing," *IEEE Trans. Information Theory*, **IT-19**, 2, March 1973, 232–234.

38. B. R. Frieden, "Restoring with Maximum Likelihood and Maximum Entropy," *J. Opt. Soc. Am.*, **62**, 4, April 1972, 511–518.

39. B. R. Frieden, "Maximum Entropy Restorations of Garrymede," in *Proceedings SPIE/OSA Conference on Image Processing*, J. C. Urbach, Ed., Pacific Grove, California, February 1976, Vol. 74, 160–165.

40. P. A. Jansson, R. H. Hunt, and E. K. Peyler, "Resolution Enhancement of Spectra," *J. Opt. Soc. Am.*, **60**, 5, May 1970, 596–599.

41. P. H. van Cittert, "Zun einflusz der Spaltbreite auf die Intensitatsverteilung in spektrallinien-Part II," *Z. Physik*, **69**, 1931, 298–308.

42. T. S. Huang, D. S. Baker, and S. P. Berger, "Iterative Image Restoration," *Appl. Opt.*, **14**, 5, May 1975, 1165–1168.

43. T. S. Huang, "Restoring Images with Shift-Varying Degradations," *Proceedings SPIE/OSA Conference on Image Processing*, J. C. Urbach, Ed., Pacific Grove, California, February 1976, Vol. 74, 149–151.

44. C. W. Helstrom, *Statistical Theory of Signal Detection*, Pergamon Press, New York, 1960.

45. D. Middleton, *An Introduction to Statistical Communication Theory*, McGraw-Hill, New York, 1960.

46. R. Deutsch, *Estimation Theory*, Prentice-Hall, Englewood Cliffs, N.J., 1965.

47. H. L. Van Trees, *Detection, Estimation, and Modulation Theory*, Vol. I, Wiley, New York, 1968.

48. N. E. Nahi, *Estimation Theory and Applications*, Wiley, New York, 1969.

49. M. Naraghi, "An Algorithmic Image Estimation Method Applicable to Nonlinear Observations," University of Southern California, Image Processing Institute, USCIPI Report 580, 1975.

15 SPECIALIZED SPATIAL IMAGE RESTORATION TECHNIQUES

In the previous chapter basic techniques of spatial image restoration were developed. This chapter presents application of these methods to several specialized spatial image restoration tasks.

15.1. ALIASING ERROR RESTORATION

If a continuous image field is spatially sampled at a spatial rate less than twice its highest spatial frequency, the resultant array of samples will contain aliasing error artifacts caused by spectral foldover of the periodic sampled image spectrum. Restoration can be performed to reduce the aliasing error effect (1, 2).

Figure 15.1-1 contains a block diagram of an image sampling–reconstruction system. In the system an original image $F_I(x, y)$ is sampled at a spatial rate ω_{xs} and ω_{ys} along the x and y coordinates, respectively. The sampling pulses are assumed to be an infinite array of Dirac delta functions, but the sampling rate is less than the Nyquist limit. If sampling were performed at the Nyquist rate, a zonal low-pass filter with a passband of $\pm\omega_{xs}/2$ and $\pm\omega_{ys}/2$ would provide an output reconstruction identical to the original image. Applying the zonal low-pass interpolation filter to the undersampled image yields an interpolated image

$$F_R(x, y) = F_I(x, y) + A(x, y) \tag{15.1-1}$$

where $A(x, y)$ represents the aliasing error artifact. Referring to Eq. 4.2-

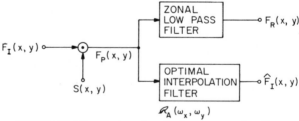

FIGURE 15.1-1. System for aliasing error restoration.

16, the aliasing error component can be expressed as

$$A(x, y) = \frac{1}{4\pi^2} \int_{-\omega_{xs}/2}^{\omega_{xs}/2} \int_{-\omega_{ys}/2}^{\omega_{ys}/2} \mathscr{F}_Q(\omega_x, \omega_y) \exp\{i[\omega_x x + \omega_y y]\} \, d\omega_x \, d\omega_y$$

(15.1-2)

where

$$\mathscr{F}_Q(\omega_x, \omega_y) = \sum_{\substack{j_1=-\infty \\ j_1, j_2 \neq 0}}^{\infty} \sum_{j_2=-\infty}^{\infty} \mathscr{F}_I(\omega_x - j_1\omega_{xs}, \omega_y - j_2\omega_{ys})$$

(15.1-3)

represents the spectrum of higher-order components of the sampled image spectrum.

Equation 15.1-1 follows the classical model of signal plus interference; hence the classical image restoration techniques of Chapter 14 can be applied to the problem. If the original image $F_I(x, y)$ is treated as a sample of a two-dimensional random process, then $A(x, y)$ will also be a stochastic field. Under these conditions Wiener estimation techniques can be utilized to determine the transfer function of an optimal interpolation filter to minimize the mean-square error between F_I and $\hat{F}_I$. In the continuous image domain the optimal interpolation filter transfer function in the zonal low-pass filter passband is found to be

$$\mathscr{R}_A(\omega_x, \omega_y) = \frac{\mathscr{W}_{F_I F_R}(\omega_x, \omega_y)}{\mathscr{W}_{F_R}(\omega_x, \omega_y)}$$

(15.1-4)

where the numerator of Eq. 15.1-4 is the cross-power spectral density of F_I and the interpolated image F_R, and the denominator of Eq. 15.1-4 is the power-spectral density of F_R. If it is assumed that the high and low spatial frequency components of an image are relatively independent, then the elements $F_I(x, y)$ and $A(x, y)$ can be considered independent. Under this approximation, the interpolation filter transfer function in the passband assumes the form

$$\mathscr{R}_A(\omega_x, \omega_y) = \frac{\mathscr{W}_{F_I}(\omega_x, \omega_y)}{\mathscr{W}_{F_I}(\omega_x, \omega_y) + \mathscr{W}_A(\omega_x, \omega_y)}$$

(15.1-5)

where $\mathscr{W}_A(\omega_x, \omega_y)$ is the power-spectral density of the aliasing error component $A(x, y)$.

15.2. INTERPOLATION ERROR CORRECTION

It is difficult precisely to design and control the writing aperture or spot of most image displays. Consequently, practical image display devices seldom provide optimal interpolation of digital image samples. In many cases, however, digital compensation can be performed before display to correct for subsequent interpolation errors. Photographic or electronic records of improperly interpolated images can also be restored in many situations.

In Section 13.5 models are developed for the display interpolation process. A continuous interpolated image field can be modeled as

$$F_R(x, y) = \sum_{k_1=-K}^{K} \sum_{k_2=-K}^{K} F_G(k_1, k_2) R(x - k_1 \Delta S, y - k_2 \Delta S)$$

(15.2-1)

where $F_G(k_1, k_2)$ is an array of image samples, ΔS is the sample period, and $R(x, y)$ is the display interpolation function assumed space invariant. The desired interpolated image is defined by

$$F_D(x, y) = \sum_{k_1=-K}^{K} \sum_{k_2=-K}^{K} F_G(k_1, k_2) R_D(x - k_1 \Delta S, y - k_2 \Delta S)$$

(15.2-2)

where $R_D(x, y)$ represents a desired interpolation function. If R_D is composed of two-dimensional sinc functions, F_D will be a perfect replica of the original image F_I except for the truncation error caused by the finite limits of the expansion, provided that F_G represents a set of Nyquist samples.

Comparison of the continuous image fields F_R and F_D can be accomplished by evaluating corresponding points on the fields extracted over a grid of spacing of ΔI. From Eqs. 13.5-4 and 13.5-5 let

$$\mathbf{f}_R = \mathbf{R}\mathbf{f}_G$$

(15.2-3)

$$\mathbf{f}_D = \mathbf{R}_D\mathbf{f}_G$$

(15.2-4)

denote the vector representations of these sampled arrays where $\mathbf{R}$ and $\mathbf{R}_D$ are matrices whose elements are samples of $R(x, y)$ and $R_D(x, y)$, respectively. As an example, for a one-dimensional interpolation function of five samples with width $\Delta S = \Delta I$, the interpolation matrix assumes the form

$$\mathbf{R} = \begin{bmatrix} r(3) & r(2) & r(1) & 0 & \cdots & 0 \\ r(4) & r(3) & r(2) & r(1) & & \vdots \\ r(5) & r(4) & r(3) & r(2) & & \vdots \\ 0 & r(5) & r(4) & r(3) & & \vdots \\ \vdots & & r(5) & r(4) & r(1) & 0 \\ \vdots & & & r(5) & r(2) & r(1) \\ \vdots & & & & r(3) & r(2) \\ 0 & \cdots & \cdots & 0 & r(4) & r(3) \end{bmatrix}$$

(15.2-5)

Each column of $\mathbf{R}$ consists of samples of $r(x)$ spaced by ΔI.

In the vector-space framework of Eqs. 15.2-3 and 15.2-4 correction for the improper set of interpolation functions $\mathbf{R}$ can be conceptually accomplished by a linear transformation of the image samples $\mathbf{f}_G$ by an operator $\mathbf{W}$ before interpolation. The operator $\mathbf{W}$ that minimizes the least-squares error between $\mathbf{f}_R$ and $\mathbf{f}_D$ is the generalized inverse operator $\mathbf{W} = \mathbf{R}^- \mathbf{R}_D$ where $\mathbf{R}^-$ is the generalized inverse of $\mathbf{R}$. An error-free transformation can only be attained if the row dimension is less than or equal to the column dimension of $\mathbf{R}$. If measurements on the interpolated image field $F_R(x, y)$ are limited to the Nyquist interval ΔS, $\mathbf{R}$ will be square, and $\mathbf{W} = \mathbf{R}^- \mathbf{R}_D$ will provide perfect interpolation at the image sample points if $\mathbf{R}^{-1}$ exists. Results are not predictable for the interval between samples.

Since $\mathbf{R}$ is enormously large, direct inversion or pseudoinversion is impractical. This problem can be avoided for square matrices by forcing $\mathbf{R}$ to be block circulant (3). In the one-dimensional example of Eq. 15.2-5 this can be easily accomplished by forming

$$\tilde{\mathbf{R}} = \mathbf{R} + \begin{bmatrix} 0 & \cdots & 0 & r(3) & r(4) \\ \vdots & & 0 & 0 & r(5) \\ \vdots & & 0 & 0 & 0 \\ \vdots & & \vdots & \vdots & \vdots \\ 0 & \cdots & 0 & 0 & 0 \end{bmatrix} \qquad (15.2\text{-}6)$$

and substituting $\tilde{\mathbf{R}}$ for $\mathbf{R}$. Matrix $\mathbf{R}_D$ can also be "circularized" in a similar fashion to form $\tilde{\mathbf{R}}_D$. Since $\tilde{\mathbf{R}}$ and $\mathbf{R}_D$ are circulant, operator $\tilde{\mathbf{W}} = \tilde{\mathbf{R}}^{-1} \tilde{\mathbf{R}}_D$ will also be circulant. Then, following the techniques outlined in Chapter 11, the restoration operation can be performed in the Fourier domain by scalar modification of the Fourier transform of the array $F_G(k_1, k_2)$ followed by an inverse Fourier transformation.

15.3. GEOMETRIC DISTORTION CORRECTION

Many imaging systems exhibit geometric nonlinearity. Figure 15.3-1 shows an example of pin cushion and barrel distortion often encountered in vidicon cameras and cathode ray tube displays. One approach to correction of such distortion is to deflect the scanning raster of the camera or display in a nonlinear manner so as to compensate for the anticipated distortion. A posteriori correction can be accomplished by fitting a polynomial curve to each distorted grid line in the horizontal and vertical direction, and then computing inverse correction functions for each cell (4). Spatial warping is also useful for the correction of perspective distortion. The image of an

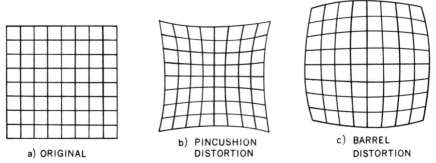

a) ORIGINAL   b) PINCUSHION DISTORTION   c) BARREL DISTORTION

FIGURE 15.3-1. Example of geometric distortion.

extended object viewed from an oblique angle can be warped so that the object appears as if it were viewed at a normal angle. Another important application is the rectification of a pair of images of the same scene obtained from different viewing angles.

The concept of spatial warping to compensate for spatial distortion caused by a physical imaging system is illustrated in Figure 15.3-2. An ideal image undergoes a spatial distortion described by a mapping of an ideal image coordinate point (j, k) to an observed image coordinate point

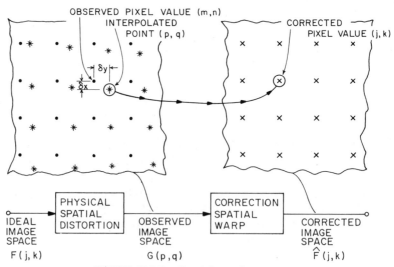

FIGURE 15.3-2. Spatial warping concept.

(p, q) according to the relation

$$p = \mathcal{O}_p\{j, k\} \tag{15.3-1a}$$

$$q = \mathcal{O}_q\{j, k\} \tag{15.3-1b}$$

where $\mathcal{O}_p\{\cdot\}$ and $\mathcal{O}_q\{\cdot\}$ are general monotonic mapping functions. The dots in Figure 15.3-2 represent observed pixels corresponding to integer values of (p, q). The corrected image points, denoted by Xs, are a result of a corrective warp or mapping of points from the observation space, indicated by asterisks, which generally do not coincide with observed pixel values. Corrective warping may be considered a two-stage process. In the first stage the coordinate of the point (p, q) that maps into a corrected pixel value is determined. Next, the image amplitude at point (p, q) is estimated by interpolation of the amplitudes of surrounding observed pixels, and this estimated amplitude is assigned to the corrected pixel value.

If the physical spatial distortion functions $\mathcal{O}_p\{\cdot\}$ and $\mathcal{O}_q\{\cdot\}$ are known, then the mapping pairs (p, q) and (j, k) of Eq. 15.3-1 can be directly determined for all integer values of j and k. Most generally, this information is not available, and recourse must be made to some mathematical model of the physical spatial distortion. Polynomial models are often employed. As an example of the procedure the second-order polynomial estimate of the physical spatial distortion is given by

$$\hat{p} = a_0 + a_1 j + a_2 k + a_3 j^2 + a_4 jk + a_5 k^2 \tag{15.3-2a}$$

$$\hat{q} = b_0 + b_1 j + b_2 k + b_3 j^2 + b_4 jk + b_5 k^2 \tag{15.3-2b}$$

where a_i and b_i are constants. The polynomial constants of Eq. 15.3-2 are normally chosen to minimize the mean-square error between the actual observation coordinate (p_m, q_m) and its polynomial estimate $(\hat{p}_m, \hat{q}_m)$ for a set $(1 \leq m \leq M)$ of known data points (j_m, k_m) called control points. It is convenient to arrange the observation space coordinates into the vectors

$$\mathbf{p}^T = [p_1, p_2, \ldots, p_M] \tag{15.3-3a}$$

$$\mathbf{q}^T = [q_1, q_2, \ldots, q_M] \tag{15.3-3b}$$

Similarly, let the polynomial constants be expressed in vector form as

$$\mathbf{a}^T = [a_0, a_1, \ldots, a_5] \tag{15.3-4a}$$

$$\mathbf{b}^T = [b_0, b_1, \ldots, b_5] \tag{15.3-4b}$$

Then the mean-square estimation error can be written in the compact form

$$\mathcal{E} = (\mathbf{p} - \mathbf{Aa})^T (\mathbf{p} - \mathbf{Aa}) + (\mathbf{q} - \mathbf{Ab})^T (\mathbf{q} - \mathbf{Ab}) \tag{15.3-5}$$

where

$$
A = \begin{bmatrix} 1 & j_1 & k_1 & j_1^2 & j_1 k_1 & k_1^2 \\ 1 & j_2 & k_2 & j_2^2 & j_2 k_2 & k_2^2 \\ \vdots & \vdots & \vdots & \vdots & \vdots & \vdots \\ 1 & j_M & k_M & j_M^2 & j_M k_M & k_M^2 \end{bmatrix} \qquad (15.3\text{-}6)
$$

From Chapter 8 it is known that the error will be minimum if

$$
\mathbf{a} = \mathbf{A}^{-}\mathbf{p} \qquad (15.3\text{-}7a)
$$

$$
\mathbf{b} = \mathbf{A}^{-}\mathbf{q} \qquad (15.3\text{-}7b)
$$

where $\mathbf{A}^{-}$ is the generalized inverse of $\mathbf{A}$. If the number of control points is chosen greater than the number of polynomial coefficients,

$$
\mathbf{A}^{-} = (\mathbf{A}^T \mathbf{A})^{-1} \mathbf{A}^T \qquad (15.3\text{-}8)
$$

Following this procedure the polynomial constants a_i, b_i can be easily computed, and Eq. 15.3-2 can be utilized to compute the observation space coordinate (the asterisks of Figure 15.3-2) of each point that maps into an integer corrected pixel value (the Xs of Figure 15.3-2).

Now the pixel amplitude at coordinate (j, k) in the corrected image space must be estimated in terms of the observation space coordinate (p, q) and the pixel amplitudes of the observed image. This task can be accomplished by interpolation. From Eq. 4.1-9 the interpolated continuous image in the observation space can be expressed as

$$
G(x, y) = \sum_m \sum_n G(m\Delta, n\Delta) R(x - m\Delta, y - n\Delta) \qquad (15.3\text{-}9)
$$

where $R(x, y)$ represents the interpolation function and Δ is the spatial sampling period. The corrected image estimate is then

$$
\hat{F}(j, k) = G(p\Delta, q\Delta) \qquad (15.3\text{-}10)
$$

where (p, q) is the noninteger index of the interpolated point. Optimal interpolation can be obtained, in theory, with sinc or Bessel interpolation functions. In practice, the more easily implemented interpolation functions, such as the square, triangle, and spline functions defined in Section 4.3, are usually employed for interpolation. Some warping systems even employ nearest-neighbor interpolation.

15.4. HOMOMORPHIC IMAGE RESTORATION

Homomorphic filtering (5), illustrated in Figure 15.4-1, is a useful technique for image restoration when an observed image is subject to multiplicative interference or degradation. Consider a continuous observed

FIGURE 15.4-1. Homomorphic image restoration.

image field

$$F_O(x, y) = F_I(x, y)E(x, y) \qquad (15.4\text{-}1)$$

composed of an ideal image multiplied by a two-dimensional function $E(x, y)$. The function $E(x, y)$ could represent a multiplicative noise field or perhaps a spatially nonuniform field of illumination. In either case the objective is to estimate $F_I(x, y)$ by processing of the observation. Taking the logarithm of Eq. 15.4-1 yields the additive result

$$\log [F_O(x, y)] = \log [F_I(x, y)] + \log [E(x, y)] \qquad (15.4\text{-}2)$$

Conventional linear filtering techniques can now be employed to estimate the log of $F_I(x, y)$. Exponentiation provides an estimate of the ideal image.

15.5. BLIND IMAGE RESTORATION

Most image restoration techniques are based on some a priori knowledge of the image degradation; the point luminance and spatial impulse responses of the system degradation are assumed known. In many applications such knowledge is simply not available. The degradation may be difficult to measure or time varying in an unpredictable manner. In such cases information about the degradation must be extracted from the observed image either explicitly or implicitly. This task is called blind image restoration (6–10). Discussion is limited here to blind image restoration methods for blurred images subject to additive noise.

There are two major approaches to blind image restoration: direct measurement and indirect estimation. With the former approach, the blur impulse response and noise level are first estimated from an image to be restored, and then these parameters are utilized in the restoration. Indirect estimation techniques employ temporal or spatial averaging to either obtain a restoration or to determine key elements of a restoration algorithm.

15.5.1. Direct Measurement Methods

Direct measurement blind restoration of a blurred noisy image usually requires measurement of the blur impulse response and noise power spectrum or covariance function of the observed image. The blur impulse response is usually measured by isolating the image of a suspected object within a picture. By definition, the blur impulse response is the image of a point-source object. Therefore, a point source in the observed scene yields a direct indication of the impulse response. The image of a suspected sharp edge can also be utilized to derive the blur impulse response. Averaging several parallel line scans normal to the edge will significantly reduce noise effects. The noise covariance function of an observed image can be estimated by measuring the image covariance over a region of relatively constant background luminance. References 6–8 provide further details on direct measurement methods.

15.5.2. Indirect Estimation Methods

Temporal redundancy of scenes in real-time television systems can be exploited to perform blind restoration indirectly. As an illustration consider the ith observed image frame

$$G_i(x, y) = F_I(x, y) + N_i(x, y) \qquad (15.5\text{-}1)$$

of a television system in which $F_I(x, y)$ is an ideal image and $N_i(x, y)$ is an additive noise field independent of the ideal image. If the ideal image remains constant over a sequence of M frames, then temporal summation of the observed images yields the relation

$$F_I(x, y) = \frac{1}{M} \sum_{i=1}^{M} G_i(x, y) - \frac{1}{M} \sum_{i=1}^{M} N_i(x, y) \qquad (15.5\text{-}2)$$

The value of the noise term on the right will tend toward its ensemble average $E\{N(x, y)\}$ for M large. In the common case of zero-mean, white Gaussian noise, the ensemble average is zero at all (x, y), and it is reasonable to form the estimate as

$$\hat{F}_I(x, y) = \frac{1}{M} \sum_{i=1}^{M} G_i(x, y) \qquad (15.5\text{-}3)$$

The concept of temporal averaging is also useful for image deblurring. Consider an imaging system in which sequential frames contain a relatively stationary object degraded by a different linear-shift-invariant impulse response $H_i(x, y)$ over each frame. This type of imaging would be encountered, for example, when photographing distant objects through a turbulent atmosphere, if the object does not move significantly between frames. By taking a short exposure at each frame the atmospheric turbulence is "frozen" in space at each frame interval. For this type of object the degraded image at the ith frame interval is given by

$$G_i(x, y) = F_I(x, y) \circledast H_i(x, y) \qquad (15.5\text{-}4)$$

for $i = 1, 2, \ldots, M$. The Fourier spectra of the degraded images are then

$$\mathcal{G}_i(\omega_x, \omega_y) = \mathcal{F}_I(\omega_x, \omega_y)\mathcal{H}_i(\omega_x, \omega_y) \qquad (15.5\text{-}5)$$

On taking the logarithm of the degraded image spectra,

$$\ln\left[\mathcal{G}_i(\omega_x, \omega_y)\right] = \ln\left[\mathcal{F}_I(\omega_x, \omega_y)\right] + \ln\left[\mathcal{H}_i(\omega_x, \omega_y)\right] \qquad (15.5\text{-}6)$$

the spectra of the ideal image and the degradation transfer function are found to separate additively. It is now possible to apply any of the common methods of statistical estimation of a signal in the presence of additive noise. If the degradation impulse responses are uncorrelated between frames, then it is worthwhile to form the sum

$$\sum_{i=1}^{M} \ln\left[\mathcal{G}_i(\omega_x, \omega_y)\right] = M \ln\left[\mathcal{F}_I(\omega_x, \omega_y)\right] + \sum_{i=1}^{M} \ln\left[\mathcal{H}_i(\omega_x, \omega_y)\right]$$

$$(15.5\text{-}7)$$

because for large M the latter summation approaches the constant value

$$\mathcal{H}_M(\omega_x, \omega_y) = \lim_{M \to \infty} \sum_{i=1}^{M} \left[\mathcal{H}_i(\omega_x, \omega_y)\right] \qquad (15.5\text{-}8)$$

The term $\mathcal{H}_H(\omega_x, \omega_y)$ may be viewed as the average logarithm transfer function of the atmospheric turbulence. An image estimate can be expressed as

$$\hat{\mathcal{F}}_I(\omega_x, \omega_y) = \exp\left\{-\frac{\mathcal{H}_H(\omega_x, \omega_y)}{M}\right\} \prod_{i=1}^{M} \left[\mathcal{G}_i(\omega_x, \omega_y)\right]^{1/M} \qquad (15.5\text{-}9)$$

An inverse Fourier transform then yields the spatial domain estimate. In any practical imaging system Eq. 15.5-4 must be modified by the addition of a noise component $N_i(x, y)$. This noise component unfortunately invalidates the separation step of Eq. 15.5-6, and therefore destroys the remainder of the derivation. One possible ad hoc solution to this problem would be to perform noise smoothing or filtering on each observed image field, and then utilize the resulting estimates as assumed noiseless observations in Eq. 15.5-9. Alternatively, the blind restoration technique of Stockham, Cannon, and Ingebretsen (9) developed for nonstationary speech signals may be adapted to the multiple-frame image restoration problem.

Stockham et al. (9–11) have developed a blind restoration technique for blurred and noisy single frame images modeled as

$$F_O(x, y) = F_I(x, y) \circledast H_D(x, y) + N(x, y) \qquad (15.5\text{-}10)$$

where $H_D(x, y)$ is the space-invariant blur impulse response. Restoration is performed by linear filtering with the power-spectrum restoration filter defined in Eq. 14.1-16 by the transfer function

$$\mathscr{H}_R(\omega_{x,y}) = \left[\frac{\mathscr{W}_{F_I}(\omega_x, \omega_y)}{|\mathscr{H}_D(\omega_x, \omega_y)|^2 \mathscr{W}_{F_I}(\omega_x, \omega_y) + \mathscr{W}_N(\omega_x, \omega_y)} \right]^{1/2}$$

$$(15.5\text{-}11)$$

where $\mathscr{W}_{F_I}(\omega_x, \omega_y)$ and $\mathscr{W}_N(\omega_x, \omega_y)$ are the ideal image and noise power spectra, respectively, and $\mathscr{H}_D(\omega_x, \omega_y)$ is the blur transfer function. In the Stockham blind restoration procedure the denominator of Eq. 15.5-11 is estimated from the observed image by sectioning the image into 64×64 pixel blocks, which are modeled as

$$\tilde{F}_{Oi}(x, y) = \tilde{F}_{Ii}(x, y) \circledast H_D(x, y) + \tilde{N}_i(x, y) \qquad (15.5\text{-}12)$$

Each block is then Fourier transformed after suitable windowing to produce

$$\tilde{\mathscr{F}}_{Oi}(\omega_x, \omega_y) = \tilde{\mathscr{F}}_{Ii}(\omega_x, \omega_y) \mathscr{H}_D(\omega_x, \omega_y) + \tilde{\mathscr{N}}_i(\omega_x, \omega_y) \qquad (15.5\text{-}13)$$

Next, the logarithm of the magnitude of each block is formed, and the resulting data are averaged, yielding

$$\mathscr{L} = \mathscr{R} \qquad (15.5\text{-}14)$$

where

$$\mathscr{L} \equiv \frac{1}{N_B} \sum_{i=1}^{N_B} \log \left| \tilde{\mathscr{F}}_{Oi}(\omega_x, \omega_y) \right| \qquad (15.5\text{-}15a)$$

$$\mathscr{R} = \frac{1}{N_B} \sum_{i=1}^{N_B} \log \left| \tilde{\mathscr{F}}_{Ii}(\omega_x, \omega_y) \mathscr{H}_D(\omega_x, \omega_y) + \mathscr{N}(\omega_x, \omega_y) \right|$$

$$(15.5\text{-}15b)$$

with N_B denoting the number of blocks. For N_B sufficiently large the spatial averages of both sides of Eq. 15.5-14 will converge to the corresponding ensemble averages. It has been shown that the mean and variance of Eq. 15.5-15b are (9)

$$\bar{\mathcal{R}} = \tfrac{1}{2} \log \left[\mathcal{W}_{F_I}(\omega_x, \omega_y) \left| \mathcal{H}_D(\omega_x, \omega_y) \right|^2 + \mathcal{N}(\omega_x, \omega_y) \right] + \frac{C}{2}$$

(15.5-16a)

$$\sigma_{\mathcal{R}}^2 = \frac{\pi^2}{24 N_B}$$

(15.5-16b)

where $C = 0.57221\ldots$ is Euler's constant. Hence, setting $\mathcal{L} = \bar{\mathcal{R}}$ provides an estimate for the denominator of the restoration filter transfer function of Eq. 15.5-11. The numerator of Eq. 15.5-11 is estimated in a similar procedure by generating noise-free, blur-free prototype images whose content is similar to the suspected content of the ideal image field. For example, if $F_I(x, y)$ is suspected to be a blurred and noisy image of typewritten text, then the prototype will be chosen to be a clear, noise-free typewritten document. It is most interesting to note that this blind restoration procedure does not require explicit estimation of the blur transfer function nor the noise power spectrum. Experimental results have been promising (9).

15.6. ANALYTIC CONTINUATION

The transfer function of an inverse filter for image restoration is given by

$$\mathcal{H}_R(\omega_x, \omega_y) = \frac{1}{\mathcal{H}_D(\omega_x, \omega_y)}$$

(15.6-1)

where $\mathcal{H}_D(\omega_x, \omega_y)$ is the transfer function of the source spatial degradation process. It was found in Chapter 14 that utilization of this filter often leads to problems because of noise amplification at high spatial frequencies for which the degradation transfer function is small. Furthermore, for any physical degradation process, $\mathcal{H}_D$ is zero outside some range $(\omega_x^2 + \omega_y^2) > A$ where A is a constant, because of the diffraction limit of the imaging system. Thus it would seem that the inverse filtering process, even in the absence of noise, is limited to the restoration of image components in the passband of the imaging system. Suppose, however, that the ideal image $F_I(x, y)$ is limited in spatial extent. Then its spectrum $\mathcal{F}_I(\omega_x, \omega_y)$ must be infinite. Since $\mathcal{F}_I(\omega_x, \omega_y)$ is an analytic function, if the ideal image spectrum can be determined in the passband, the spectrum, in principle, can be uniquely continued beyond the passband. An inverse Fourier transform then results in an image reconstruction with resolution beyond the diffraction limit. This is the basic concept of the "superresolution" technique of image resolution improvement (12–15).

One method of continuing an image spectrum beyond the diffraction limit is through the use of prolate spheroidal wave functions (16). In one-dimensional space these functions satisfy the following properties: For a given $T > 0$ and $\Omega > 0$ there exist a countably infinite set of real functions (eigenfunctions) $\Psi_i(t)$ and a corresponding set of real numbers (eigenvalues) λ_i such that:

1. The Fourier transform of $\Psi(t)$ is zero for $|\omega| > \Omega$.
2. The $\Psi_i(t)$ are orthonormal on the real line

$$\int_{\infty}^{\infty} \Psi_i(t)\Psi_j(t)\,dt = \delta(i-j) \tag{15.6-2}$$

3. The $\Psi(t)$ are orthonormal in the interval $-T/2 < t < T/2$

$$\int_{-T/2}^{T/2} \Psi_i(t)\Psi_j(t)\,dt = \lambda_i \delta(i-j) \tag{15.6-3}$$

4. For all t

$$\lambda_i \Psi_i(t) = \int_{-T/2}^{T/2} \frac{\sin \Omega(t-\alpha)}{\pi(t-\alpha)} \Psi_i(\alpha)\,d\alpha \tag{15.6-4}$$

The prolate spheroidal wave functions $\Psi_i(t)$ are functions of space T and the frequency limits Ω through the space-bandwidth product $c = T\Omega/2$. Figure 15.6-1a illustrates several prolate spheroidal wave functions. Suppose that an ideal image $F_I(x, y)$ is limited in extent such that

$$F_I(x, y) = 0 \qquad \text{if } |x| > L \quad \text{or} \quad |y| > L \tag{15.6-5}$$

where L is a constant. Then let $\mathscr{F}_I(\omega_x, \omega_y)$ be the two-dimensional Fourier

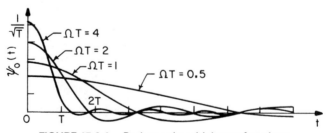

FIGURE 15.6-1.   Prolate spheroidal wavefunctions.

transform of $F_I(x, y)$ which is known over some passband

$$|\omega_x| \leq \frac{\omega_{xc}}{2} \qquad (15.6\text{-}6a)$$

$$|\omega_y| \leq \frac{\omega_{yc}}{2} \qquad (15.6\text{-}6b)$$

Now expanding $\mathscr{F}_I(\omega_x, \omega_y)$ in terms of the spatial frequency domain prolate spheroidal wave functions with spatial frequency variable, one obtains

$$\mathscr{F}_I(\omega_x, \omega_y) = \sum_{i=0}^{\infty} \sum_{j=0}^{\infty} a_{ij} \Psi_i(\omega_x) \Psi_j(\omega_y) \qquad (15.6\text{-}7)$$

for all ω_x, ω_y. Multiplying both sides of Eq. 15.6-7 by $\Psi_m(\omega_x)\Psi_n(\omega_y)$ and integrating over the passband gives

$$\int_{-\omega_{xc}/2}^{\omega_{xc}/2} \int_{-\omega_{yc}/2}^{\omega_{yc}/2} \Psi_m(\omega_x)\Psi_n(\omega_y)\mathscr{F}_I(\omega_x, \omega_y) \, d\omega_x \, d\omega_y$$

$$= \sum_{i=0}^{\infty} \sum_{j=0}^{\infty} a_{ij} \int_{-\omega_{xc}/2}^{\omega_{xc}/2} \int_{-\omega_{yc}/2}^{\omega_{yc}/2} \Psi_m(\omega_x)\Psi_n(\omega_y)\Psi_i(\omega_x)\Psi_j(\omega_y) \, d\omega_x \, d\omega_y \qquad (15.6\text{-}8)$$

By property (3) the term on the right-hand side of Eq. 15.6-8 becomes

$$\sum_{i=0}^{\infty} \sum_{j=0}^{\infty} a_{ij}\lambda_i\lambda_j\delta(i - m, j - m) \qquad (15.6\text{-}9)$$

Hence

$$a_{mn} = \frac{1}{\lambda_m\lambda_n} \int_{-\omega_{xc}/2}^{\omega_{xc}/2} \int_{-\omega_{yc}/2}^{\omega_{yc}/2} \Psi_m(\omega_x)\Psi_n(\omega_y)\mathscr{F}_I(\omega_x, \omega_y) \, d\omega_x \, d\omega_y \qquad (15.6\text{-}10)$$

Since $\mathscr{F}_I(\omega_x, \omega_y)$ is known over the passband, substitution of the prolate spheroical wave functions and their eigenvalues into Eq. 15.6-10 gives the coefficients a_{mn}. The a_{mn} in turn can be substituted into Eq. 15.6-7 to provide an expansion of $\mathscr{F}_I(\omega_x, \omega_y)$ for all ω_x, ω_y.

While the technique of analytic continuation is theoretically valid, there are three major limitations in its utilization:

1. It is difficult to compute the prolate spheroidal wave functions and their eigenvalues to the desired degree of accuracy for reasonably high space-bandwidth products;
2. The analytic continuation expansion of Eq. 15.6-7 can only be evaluated for finite limits, that is, a finite number of expansion terms, and therefore there is a truncation error;

3. The spectrum measured in the passband that is to be substituted into Eq. 15.6-10 in order to evaluate the expansion coefficients a_{mn} is in practice composed of two parts, the actual image spectrum and a noise spectrum. Thus the expansion coefficients can never be computed perfectly accurately.

The major hindrance to the implementation of an analytic continuation process has been the noise problem. Some analyses (15) indicate that the image signal-to-noise ratio must be greater than $1000:1$ to permit continuation to just a few spatial frequencies beyond the diffraction limit. At present only a few one-dimensional simulations have been performed (13, 14).

15.7. SPACE-VARIANT RESTORATION

If the source degradation of an imaging system is modeled as a linear-shift-varying operator, the degraded image becomes

$$F_O(x, y) = \int\int_{-\infty}^{\infty} F_I(\alpha, \beta) H_D(x, y; \alpha, \beta) \, d\alpha \, d\beta \qquad (15.7\text{-}1)$$

where $H_D(x, y; \alpha, \beta)$ represents the output image at position (x, y) as a result of a point source at position (α, β). The basic restoration problem is to estimate $F_I(x, y)$ from the integral equation given knowledge of $H_D(x, y; \alpha, \beta)$ and $F_O(x, y)$. A general solution to this problem can be obtained by an eigenfunction expansion of $H_D(x, y; \alpha, \beta)$. However, in most imaging situations the eigenfunctions of the kernel are not known or may not even exist.

Another approach to the problem is to break up the image into small blocks over which the source degradation is linear shift invariant and then proceed by the techniques discussed earlier. There is no general theory for determining the size blocks needed to achieve a given degree of accuracy in the overall estimation process.

Finally, there is a special class of linear-shift-variant imaging problems in which the source degradation impulse response can be considered as a cascade of a spatial coordinate distortion, followed by a linear-shift-invariant system, followed by another spatial coordinate distortion as indicated in Figure 15.7-1 (17). In such a system the ideal image undergoes a spatial coordinate distortion to assume the value

$$F_{O1}(x_1, y_1) = F_I[x(x_1, y_1), y(x_1, y_1)] \qquad (15.7\text{-}2)$$

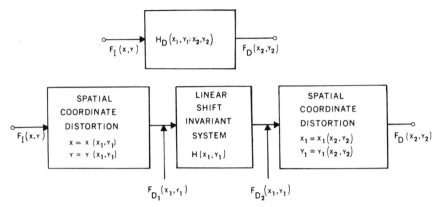

FIGURE 15.7-1. Spatial decomposition for linear-shift-variant imaging systems.

The output of the linear shift invariant system is then

$$F_{O2}(x_1, y_1) = F_{O1}(x_1, y_1) \circledast H_D(x_1, y_1) \tag{15.7-3}$$

and the final degraded image becomes

$$F_O(x_2, y_2) = F_{O2}[x_1(x_2, y_2), y_1(x_2, y_2)] \tag{15.7-4}$$

If the two spatial coordinate distortion operators have unique inverses, then the linear-shift-variant system can be reduced to a linear-shift-invariant system and the solution can be performed using the techniques described previously. This method has been used with success for the compensation of third-order coma aberration of a spherical lens (18, 19) and image motion compensation (17).

15.8. RECURSIVE IMAGE RESTORATION

In the past few years there has been great interest in the development of recursive filtering techniques for time domain signals (20–22). These techniques have been recently applied to image restoration (23–25). The image restoration problem solution based on recursive estimation has been formulated in two ways: as the processing of a purely two-dimensional signal and as the processing of a one-dimensional signal obtained by scanning.

15.8.1. Two-Dimensional Formulation

Consider an image field statistically characterized by an autocorrelation function of the form

$$R(\tau_1, \tau_2) = \sigma_S^2 \exp\{-\alpha_1|\tau_1| - \alpha_2|\tau_2|\} \qquad (15.8\text{-}1)$$

where τ_1 and τ_2 are increments in the horizontal and vertical directions. A discrete random field $F(j, k)$ with this autocorrelation can be generated by the recursive formula

$$F(j + 1, k + 1) = \rho_1 F(j + 1, k) + \rho_2 F(j, k + 1) - \rho_1\rho_2 F(j, k)$$
$$+ \sqrt{(1 - \rho_1^2)(1 - \rho_2^2)}\,u(j, k) \qquad (15.8\text{-}2)$$

where ρ_1 and ρ_2 are horizontal and vertical adjacent image point correlations and $u(j, k)$ is an uncorrelated random field with the same variance as elements of the image.

In the case in which an observed image field $F_O(j, k)$ is modeled as the sum

$$F_O(j, k) = F_I(j, k) + N(j, k) \qquad (15.8\text{-}3)$$

of an ideal image field $F_I(j, k)$ plus an additive noise field $N(j, k)$, the two-dimensional recursive estimate of the ideal image has been found to be (25)

$$\hat{F}_I(j + 1, k + 1) = K_1(j, k)\hat{F}_I(j + 1, k) + K_2(j, k)\hat{F}_I(j, k + 1)$$
$$+ K_3(j, k)\hat{F}_I(j, k) + K_4(j, k)F_O(j + 1, k + 1)$$

$$(15.8\text{-}4)$$

where the $K_i(j, k)$ are weighting terms. Equation 15.8-4 employs three previous image point estimates and the noisy image observation to form the new estimate at each image point. A minimum mean-square estimate is obtained when

$$K_1(j, k) = \rho_1 \qquad (15.8\text{-}5a)$$

$$K_2(j, k) = \rho_2 \qquad (15.8\text{-}5b)$$

$$K_3(j, k) = \rho_1\rho_2 + K_4(j, k) \qquad (15.8\text{-}5c)$$

and $K_4(j, k)$ is a complicated function of the covariance of the estimation error (25). The two-dimensional recursive estimate defined by Eq. 15.8-4 is limited to image restoration for images described by an exponential autocorrelation function. There is no known general method that leads to a dynamic model of a random field for an arbitrary autocorrelation function.

15.8.2. One-Dimensional Formulation

In the one-dimensional recursive estimation process the observation

$$f_O(t) = f_I(t) + n(t) \tag{15.8-6}$$

obtained from a time-scanned image is assumed to be composed of ideal image $f_I(t)$ and additive noise $n(t)$ components. If the image autocorrelation function is of exponential form, as in Eq. 15.8-1, the autocorrelation function of $f_I(t)$ can be determined (26). The resulting recursive estimate of the jth sample of $f_I(t)$ is then given by

$$\hat{f}_I(j) = k_1(j-1)\hat{f}_I(j) + k_2(j-1)f_O(j-1) \tag{15.8-7}$$

where $k_1(j)$ and $k_2(j)$ are weighting terms dependent on the correlation function of $f_I(t)$ (23, 24).

15.9. FILM-GRAIN NOISE RESTORATION

Film-grain noise is often a limiting factor in the restoration of film recorded images, especially for high-magnification pictures. Section 13.6 presented several models of the film recording process incorporating film-grain noise effects. The unfortunate common feature of these models is the nonlinear and nonstationary relationship between the ideal and observed image fields.

Walkup and Choens (27) have proposed Wiener filtering as a means of film-grain restoration for the imaging model

$$F_O(x, y) = F_I(x, y) + \alpha [F_I(x, y)]^{1/3} N(x, y) \tag{15.9-1}$$

where α is a constant. The continuous image domain filter transfer function for this model is found to be

$$\mathscr{H}_R(\omega_x, \omega_y) = \frac{\mathscr{W}_{F_I}(\omega_x, \omega_y)}{\mathscr{W}_{F_I}(\omega_x, \omega_y) + \alpha^2 E\{[F_I(x, y)]^{2/3}\}} \tag{15.9-2}$$

where $\mathscr{W}_{F_I}(\omega_x, \omega_y)$ is the ideal image power spectrum and $E(\cdot)$ denotes the expectation operator. In the derivation of the filter it is implicitly assumed that the first and second moments of the ideal image process are stationary. Naderi and Sawchuk (28) have developed a Wiener estimation procedure for discrete images based on the photographic film image recording model of Figure 13.6-2. This model incorporates chemical effects of the film such as the nonlinear density versus exposure relationship and the chemical diffusion adjacency effect as well as the film-grain noise relationship of Eq. 15.9-1. One of the major advantages of this Wiener estimator, in addition to the generality of the model, is that the estimator is inherently adaptive, and therefore it is able to accommodate to spatially varying first- and second-order moments of the ideal image field.

An ad hoc nonlinear restoration method, called noise cheating, has been developed by Zweig et al. (29, 30) to combat the effects of film-grain noise in low-contrast imagery. In this technique an image is scanned at high resolution and each pixel is finely quantized. The high-resolution pixels are then combined in nonoverlapping two-by-two pixel groups to produce a lower-resolution picture. The high-resolution image provides better edge rendition than the low-resolution picture, but its noise variance is higher. If the noise is white, the noise variance per pixel of the low-resolution image is one-fourth the variance of the high-resolution image as a result of the spatial averaging process. The low-resolution image is then requantized over a uniform scale chosen so that the quantization levels are spaced by four noise standard deviation units. This ensures 95% correct quantization

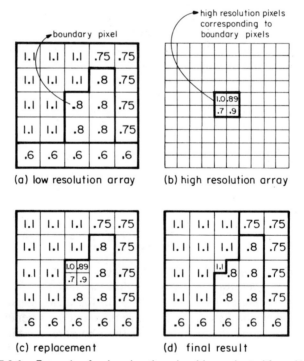

FIGURE 15.9-1. Example of noise-cheating algorithm, adapted from Naderi (31).

for Gaussian noise. Then the quantized low-resolution pixels are examined over 3×3 pixel neighborhoods. If the eight outer pixels are quantized to the same level, and the center pixel is different, the isolated center pixel is assumed to be in error as a result of noise, and is set to the value of its neighbors. If the center pixel is a border pixel, as shown in Figure 15.9-1, it is subdivided into four high-resolution points whose values are assigned according to the levels of the corresponding high-resolution pixels and the values of the neighboring low-resolution points. One simple algorithm is to set the value of a high-resolution point at the value of the four-connected neighbor (North and East or North and West, etc.) closest to the value of the corresponding high-resolution pixel. Simulation tests of the noise-cheating algorithm have shown that it is effective in the restoration of low-contrast images subject to relatively severe film-grain noise (28). Naderi (31) has extended the concept of the noise-cheating algorithm to permit the restoration of high-contrast images in which the film-grain noise is image dependent.

REFERENCES

1. J. J. Downing, "Data Sampling and Pulse Amplitude Modulation," in *Aerospace Telemetry*, H. L. Stiltz, Ed., Prentice-Hall, Englewood Cliffs, N.J., 1961.

2. R. Lesault, "Aliasing Problems in Two Dimensional Sampled Imagery," *Perception of Displayed Information*, L. Biberman, Ed., Plenum Press, New York, 1973, Chapter 7.

3. H. C. Andrews and C. L. Patterson, "Digital Interpolation of Discrete Images," *IEEE Trans. Computers*, **C-25**, 2, February 1976, 196–202.

4. D. A. O'Handley and W. B. Green, "Recent Developments in Digital Image Processing at the Image Processing Laboratory at the Jet Propulsion Laboratory," *Proc. IEEE*, **60**, 7, July 1972, 821–828.

5. A. V. Oppenheim, R. W. Schafer, and T. G. Stockham, Jr., "Nonlinear Filtering of Multiplied and Convolved Signals," *Proc. IEEE*, **56**, 8, August 1968, 1264–1291.

6. H. C. Andrews and B. R. Hunt, *Digital Image Restoration*, Prentice-Hall, Englewood Cliffs, N.J., 1976.

7. A. Papoulis, "Approximations of Point Spreads for Deconvolution," *J. Opt. Soc. Am.*, **62**, 1, January 1972, 77–80.

8. B. Tatian, "Asymptotic Expansions for Correcting Truncation Error in Transfer-Function Calculations," *J. Opt. Soc. Am.*, **61**, 9, September 1971, 1214–1224.

9. T. G. Stockham, Jr., T. M. Cannon, and P. B. Ingebretsen, "Blind Deconvolution Through Digital Signal Processing," *Proc. IEEE*, **63**, 4, April 1975, 678–692.

10. E. R. Cole, "The Removal of Unknown Image Blurs by Homomorphic Filtering," University of Utah, Computer Science Department, Report UTEC-CSc-74-029, June 1973.

11. T. M. Cannon, "Digital Image Deblurring by Nonlinear Homomorphic Filtering," University of Utah, Computer Science Department, Report UTEC-CSc-74-091, August 1974.

12. B. R. Frieden, "Band-unlimited Reconstruction of Optical Objects and Spectra," *J. Opt. Soc. Am.*, **57**, 8, August 1967, 1013–1019.

13. J. L. Harris, "Image Evaluation and Restoration," *J. Opt. Soc. Am.*, **56**, 5, May 1966, 569–574.

14. T. S. Huang, W. F. Schreiber, and O. J. Tretiak, "Image Processing," *Proc. IEEE*, **59**, 11, November 1971, 1586–1609.

15. D. C. Youla, "Restoration by the Method of Alternating Orthogonal Projections," Proceedings Symposium on Current Mathematical Problems in Image Science, Monterey, California, November 1976.

16. D. Slepian and H. O. Pollak, "Prolate Spheroidal Wave Functions, Fourier Analysis, and Uncertainty—I," *Bell Syst. Tech. J.*, **40**, January 1961, 43–63.

17. A. A. Sawchuk, "Space-Variant Image Motion Degradation and Restoration," *Proc. IEEE*, **60**, 7, July 1972, 854–861.

18. G. M. Robbins and T. S. Huang, "Inverse Filtering for Linear Shift-Variant Imaging Systems," *Proc. IEEE*, **60**, 7, July 1972, 862–872.

19. A. A. Sawchuk, "Space-Variant Image Restoration by Coordinate Transformations," *J. Opt. Soc. Am.*, **64**, 2, February 1974, 138–144.

20. R. E. Kalman, "A New Approach to Linear Filtering and Prediction Problems," *ASME Trans. (J. Basic Engineering)*, **820**, March 1960, 35–45.

21. R. E. Kalman and R. C. Bucy, "New Results in Linear Filtering and Prediction Theory," *ASME Trans. (J. Basic Engineering)*, **830**, March 1961, 95–108.

22. N. E. Nahi, *Estimation Theory and Applications*, Wiley, New York, 1969.

23. N. E. Nahi and T. Assefi, "Bayesian Recursive Image Estimation," Proceedings Two Dimensional Digital Signal Processing Conference, University of Missouri, October 1971.

24. N. E. Nahi, "Role of Recursive Estimation in Statistical Image Enhancement," *Proc. IEEE*, **60**, 7, July 1972, 872–877.

25. A. Habibi, "Two Dimensional Bayesian Estimate of Images," *Proc. IEEE*, **60**, 7, July 1972, 878–883.

26. L. E. Franks, "A Model for Random Video Process," *Bell Syst. Tech. J.*, **45**, April 1966, 609–630.

27. J. F. Walkup and R. C. Choens, "Image Processing in Signal Dependent Noise," *Opt. Eng.*, **13**, 3, May/June 1974, 258–266.

28. F. Naderi and A. A. Sawchuk, "Nonlinear Detection and Estimation of Images degraded by Film-Grain Noise," *Proceedings SPIE/OSA Conference on Image Processing*, J. C. Urbach, Ed., Pacific Grove, California, February 1976, Vol. 74, 17–24.

29. H. J. Zweig, E. B. Barrett, and P. C. Hu, "Noise Cheating Image Enhancement," *J. Opt. Soc. Am.*, **65**, 11, November 1975, 1347–1353.

30. H. J. Zweig et al., "Experiments in Digital Restoration of Defocused Grainy Photographs by Noise Cheating and Fourier Techniques," *Proceedings SPIE/OSA Conference on Image Processing*, J. C. Urbach. Ed., Pacific Grove, California, February 1976, Vol. 74, 10–16.

31. F. Naderi, "Estimation and Detection of Images Degraded by Film-Grain Noise," University of Southern California, Image Processing Institute, Report USCIPI-690, September 1976.

16 LUMINANCE, COLOR, AND SPECTRAL IMAGE RESTORATION

Physical image sensors often do not possess proper spectral or time responses. Another common defect is unwanted nonlinearities in the sensor and display systems. Postprocessing correction of sensor signals and preprocessing correction of display signals can reduce such degradations substantially. Furthermore, the restoration processing is usually relatively simple to implement.

16.1. SENSOR LUMINANCE POINT NONLINEARITY CORRECTION

In imaging systems in which the source degradation can be separated into cascaded spatial and point effects, it is often possible directly to compensate for the point degradation (1, 2). Consider a physical imaging system that produces an observed image field $F_O(x, y, t)$ according to the separable model

$$F_O(x, y, t) = \mathcal{O}_P\{C, \mathcal{O}_D\{x, y, t, \lambda ; C(x, y, t, \lambda)\}\} \qquad (16.1\text{-}1)$$

where $C(x, y, t, \lambda)$ is the spectral energy distribution of the input light field, $\mathcal{O}_P\{\cdot\}$ represents the point amplitude response of the sensor, and $\mathcal{O}_D\{\cdot\}$ denotes the spatial, time, and wavelength responses. Sensor luminance correction can then be accomplished by passing the observed image through a correction system with a point restoration operator $\mathcal{O}_R\{\cdot\}$ chosen such that

$$\mathcal{O}_R\{\mathcal{O}_P\{\cdot\}\} = 1 \qquad (16.1\text{-}2)$$

For continuous images in optical form, it may be difficult to implement a desired point restoration operator if the operator is nonlinear. Compensation for images in analog electrical form is easily accomplished with a nonlinear amplifier, while digital image compensation can be performed by arithmetic operators or by a table look-up procedure.

Figure 16.1-1 contains a block diagram describing the point luminance correction methodology. The sensor input is a point light distribution

447

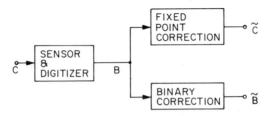

FIGURE 16.1-1. Point luminance correction for an image sensor.

function C that is converted to a binary number B for eventual entry into a computer or digital communications system. In some imaging applications processing will be performed directly on the binary representation, while in other applications, it will be preferable to convert to a real fixed point computer number linearly proportional to the sensor input luminance. In the former case the binary correction unit will produce a binary number $\tilde{B}$ that is designed to be linearly proportional to C, and in the latter case, the fixed point correction unit will produce a fixed point number $\tilde{C}$ that is designed to be equal to C.

A typical measured response B versus sensor input luminance level C is shown in Figure 16.1-2a, while Figure 16.1-2b shows the corresponding compensated response that is desired. The measured response can be obtained by scanning a gray scale test chart of known luminance values and observing the digitized binary value B at each step. Repeated measurements should be made in order to reduce the effects of noise and measurement errors. For calibration purposes it is convenient to regard the binary coded luminance as a fixed point binary number. As an example, if the luminance range is sliced to 4096 levels and coded with 12 bits, then the binary representation would be

$$B = b_8 \ b_7 \ b_6 \ b_5 \ b_4 \ b_3 \ b_2 \ b_1 \cdot b_{-1} \ b_{-2} \ b_{-3} \ b_{-4} \qquad (16.1\text{-}3)$$

The whole number part in this example ranges from 0 to 255 and the fractional part divides each integer step into 16 subdivisions. In this format the scanner can produce output levels over the decimal range of

$$255.9375 \leq B \leq 0.0 \qquad (16.1\text{-}4)$$

After the measured gray scale data points of Figure 16.1-2a have been obtained, a smooth analytic curve

$$C = g\{B\} \qquad (16.1\text{-}5)$$

is fitted to the data. The desired luminance response in real number and

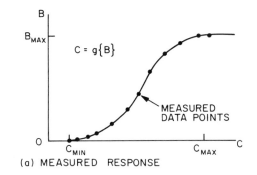

(a) MEASURED RESPONSE

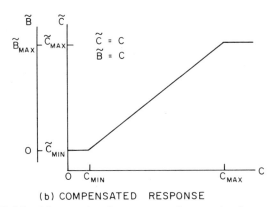

(b) COMPENSATED RESPONSE

FIGURE 16.1-2. Measured and compensated sensor luminance response.

binary number forms is

$$\tilde{C} = C \tag{16.1-6a}$$

and

$$\tilde{B} = B_{\text{MAX}} \frac{(C - C_{\text{MIN}})}{(C_{\text{MAX}} - C_{\text{MIN}})} \tag{16.1-6b}$$

Hence the required compensation relationships are

$$\tilde{C} = g\{B\} \tag{16.1-7a}$$

and

$$\tilde{B} = B_{\text{MAX}} \frac{(g\{B\} - C_{\text{MIN}})}{(C_{\text{MAX}} - C_{\text{MIN}})} \tag{16.1-7b}$$

The limits of the luminance function are commonly normalized to the range 0 to 1.

To improve the accuracy of the calibration procedure it is wise to first perform a rough calibration and then repeat the procedure as often as required to refine the correction curve. It should be observed that since B is a binary number, the corrected luminance value $\tilde{C}$ will be a quantized real number. Furthermore, the corrected binary coded luminance $\tilde{B}$ will be subject to binary roundoff of the right-hand side of Eq. 16.1-7*b*. As a consequence of the nonlinearity of the fitted curve $C = g\{B\}$ and the amplitude quantization inherent to the digitizer, it is possible that some of the corrected binary coded luminance values may be unoccupied. In other words the histogram of $\tilde{B}$ for an image may possess holes. To minimize this effect, the number of output levels can be limited to less than the number of input levels. For example, B may be coded to 12 bits and $\tilde{B}$ coded to only 8 bits. Another alternative is to add pseudorandom noise to $\tilde{B}$ to smooth out the occupancy levels.

Many image scanning devices such as vidicons and image dissector cameras exhibit a variable spatial nonlinear point luminance response. Conceptually, the point correction techniques previously described could be performed at each pixel value using the measured calibrated curve at that point. Such a process, however, would be mechanically prohibitive. An alternative approach that is often successful is to model the variable spatial response by some smooth normalized two-dimensional curve $G(j, k)$ over the sensor surface. Then the corrected spatial response can be obtained by the operation

$$\tilde{F}(j, k) = \frac{F(j, k)}{G(j, k)} \tag{16.1-8}$$

where $F(j, k)$ and $\tilde{F}(j, k)$ represent the raw and corrected sensor responses, respectively.

16.2. DISPLAY LUMINANCE POINT NONLINEARITY CORRECTION

Correction of an image display for point luminance nonlinearities is identical in principle to the correction of point luminance nonlinearities of an image sensor. The procedure illustrated in Figure 16.2-1 involves distortion of the binary coded image luminance variable B to form a corrected binary coded luminance function $\tilde{B}$ so that the displayed luminance $\tilde{C}$ will be linearly proportional to B. In this formulation the display may include a photographic record of a displayed light field. The desired overall response

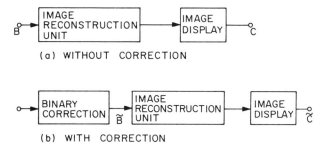

(a) WITHOUT CORRECTION

(b) WITH CORRECTION

FIGURE 16.2-1. Point luminance correction for an image display.

is

$$\tilde{C} = B\left[\frac{\tilde{C}_{MAX} - \tilde{C}_{MIN}}{B_{MAX}}\right] + \tilde{C}_{MIN} \qquad (16.2\text{-}1)$$

Normally, the maximum and minimum limits of the displayed luminance function $\tilde{C}$ are not absolute quantities but rather are transmissivities or reflectivities normalized over a unit range. The measured response of the display and image reconstruction system is modeled by the nonlinear function

$$C = f\{B\} \qquad (16.2\text{-}2)$$

Therefore the desired linear response can be obtained by setting

$$\tilde{B} = g\left\{B\left[\frac{\tilde{C}_{MAX} - \tilde{C}_{MIN}}{B_{MAX}}\right] + \tilde{C}_{MIN}\right\} \qquad (16.2\text{-}3)$$

where $g(\cdot)$ is the inverse function of $f(\cdot)$.

The experimental procedure for determining the correction function $g(\cdot)$ will be described for the common example of producing a photographic print from an image display. The first step involves the generation of a digital gray scale step chart over the full range of the binary number B. Usually about 16 equally spaced levels of B are sufficient. Next, the reflective luminance must be measured over each step of the developed print to produce a plot such as in Figure 16.2-2. The data points are then fitted by the smooth analytic curve $B = g(C)$, which forms the desired transformation of Eq. 16.2-2. It is important that enough bits be allocated to B so that the discrete mapping $g(\cdot)$ can be approximated to sufficient accuracy. Also, the number of bits allocated to B must be sufficient to prevent gray scale contouring as the result of the nonlinear spacing of display levels. An 8-bit representation of B and a 10-bit representation of $\tilde{B}$ should be adequate in most applications.

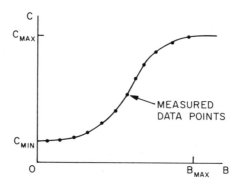

FIGURE 16.2-2. Measured image display response.

Image display devices such as cathode ray tube displays often exhibit spatial luminance variation. Typically, a displayed image is brighter at the center of the display screen than at its periphery. Correction techniques, as described by Eq. 16.1-8, can be utilized for compensation of spatial luminance variations. Figure 16.2-3a (3) contains a flying spot scanner photograph of a constant digital gray level image. In this photograph the center part of the image appears somewhat brighter than the periphery. The great disparity in luminance levels is readily apparent in Figure 16.2-3c in which a corner segment of Figure 16.2-3a has been cut out and pasted over the center of the display. Figures 16.2-3b and 16.2-3d contain the flat field scene after spatial luminance correction.

16.3. SPECTRAL RADIANCE ESTIMATION

Many tasks in color and multispectral image restoration involve the estimation of the spectral radiance function $C(\lambda)$ from a series of observations of the form

$$x_i = \int C(\lambda)s_i(\lambda)\,d\lambda + n_i \qquad (16.3\text{-}1)$$

where $s_i(\lambda)$ is the spectral sensitivity of a spectral measurement filter for $j = 1, 2, \ldots, P$ observations. The term n_i represents additive noise or uncertainty in the measurement. The discrete estimation techniques described in Chapter 14 can be applied to this problem solution (4). The first step is to discretize the continuous integral to form the vector equation

$$x_i = \mathbf{s}_i^T\mathbf{c} + n_i \qquad (16.3\text{-}2)$$

where $\mathbf{s}_i$ and $\mathbf{c}$ are $Q \times 1$ vectors of quadrature samples of $s_i(\lambda)$ and $C(\lambda)$,

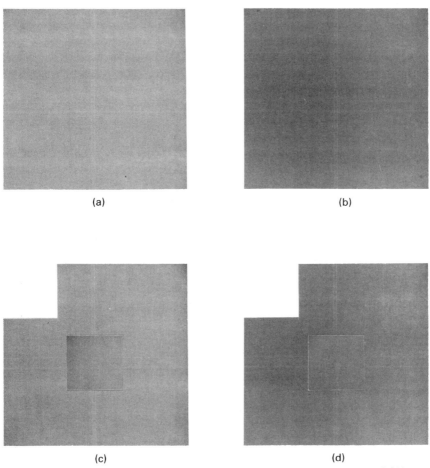

FIGURE 16.2-3. Examples of spatial luminance correction of image display. (a) Uncorrected flat field. (b) Corrected flat field. (c) Uncorrected flat field with superimposed corner. (d) Corrected flat field with superimposed corner.

respectively. Then the set of P observations may be arranged in the $P \times 1$ vector

$$\mathbf{x} = \mathbf{S}\mathbf{c} + \mathbf{n} \qquad (16.3\text{-}3)$$

where the vector $\mathbf{s}_i^T$ occupies the ith row of the matrix $\mathbf{S}$. The system of equations represented by Eq. 16.3-3 is normally highly underdetermined if sufficient quadrature mesh points are taken to reduce the quadrature error to reasonable bounds.

An estimate $\hat{\mathbf{c}}$ of the true spectral energy distribution $\mathbf{c}$ can be obtained by the generalized inverse estimate

$$\hat{\mathbf{c}} = \mathbf{S}^{-}\mathbf{x} = \mathbf{S}^{T}(\mathbf{S}\mathbf{S}^{T})^{-1}\mathbf{x} \qquad (16.3\text{-}4)$$

Although the generalized inverse provides a minimum mean-square error, minimum norm estimate of $\mathbf{c}$, ill-conditioning of $\mathbf{S}$ coupled with observational errors can lead to oscillatory estimates. Since $\mathbf{c}$ is generally quite smooth, it is reasonable to impose some smoothing constraints, as discussed in Section 14.7, to the solution. The resultant estimate then assumes the form

$$\hat{\mathbf{c}} = \mathbf{M}^{-1}\mathbf{S}^{T}(\mathbf{S}\mathbf{M}^{-1}\mathbf{S}^{T})^{-1}\mathbf{x} \qquad (16.3\text{-}5)$$

where $\mathbf{M}$ is a smoothing constant such as specified by Eq. 14.7-3. A third alternative is to apply Wiener estimation methods, as outlined in Section 14.6. The Wiener estimate is given by

$$\hat{\mathbf{c}} = \mathbf{K}_{c}\mathbf{S}^{T}[\mathbf{S}\mathbf{K}_{c}\mathbf{S}^{T} + \mathbf{K}_{n}]^{-1}\mathbf{x} \qquad (16.3\text{-}6)$$

where $\mathbf{K}_{c}$ is the covariance matrix of $\mathbf{c}$ and $\mathbf{K}_{n}$ is the covariance matrix of additive observational noise assumed independent of $\mathbf{c}$. Since $C(\lambda) \geq 0$ for all wavelengths, bounded restoration methods discussed in Section 14.8 should be rewarding.

In order to evaluate the estimation procedure, a computer simulation experiment has been performed in which simulated measurements are taken of a Gaussian-shaped spectral function through simulated absorption filters. Figure 16.3-1 contains plots of the spectral shapes of these filters. The simulated measurements are utilized as spectral observations for the

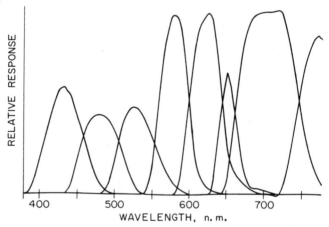

FIGURE   16.3-1. Spectral   shapes   of   absorption filters.

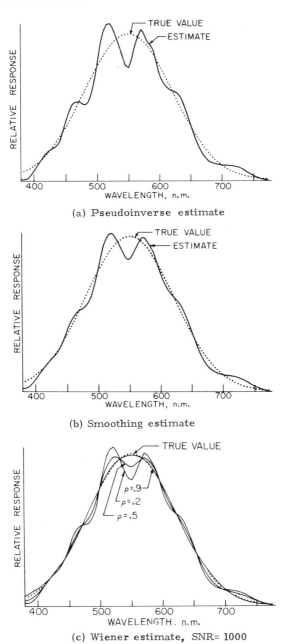

(a) Pseudoinverse estimate

(b) Smoothing estimate

(c) Wiener estimate, SNR= 1000

Figure 16.3-2. Comparison of actual and estimated spectral response for absorption filters obtained by computer simulation. (a) Pseudoinverse estimate. (b) Smoothing estimate. (c) Wiener estimate, SNR = 1000.

estimation of $C(\lambda)$. Figure 16.3-2 illustrates the performance of the pseudoinverse, smoothing, and Wiener estimation methods. The Wiener estimate assumes white noise and a Markov process for $C(\lambda)$. In these experiments the mean-square fit between the actual spectral function $C(\lambda)$ and its estimate $\hat{C}(\lambda)$ is best for the Wiener estimate with the Markov process correlation factor $\rho = 0.9$ and a signal-to-noise ratio of 1000.

Reference 4 contains an example of the spectral estimation procedure to the spectral calibration of a color image scanner.

16.4. SENSOR AND DISPLAY SPECTRAL RESPONSE CORRECTION

The spectral response of imaging sensors is generally determined by the sensitivity of available sensor materials; the spectral response is seldom ever an exact design parameter. It is possible, however, to perform correction for improper spectral response functions.

As an example let the actual luminance to a spectral energy distribution function $C(\lambda)$ be given by

$$X = \int C(\lambda)S(\lambda)\, d\lambda \qquad (16.4\text{-}1)$$

where $S(\lambda)$ is the sensor spectral response, and let the desired response be defined as

$$Y = \int C(\lambda)V(\lambda)\, d\lambda \qquad (16.4\text{-}2)$$

where $V(\lambda)$ is the desired luminance spectral sensitivity. The objective of the spectral response correction is to find some functional transformation $f\{X\}$ on X to provide an estimate $\hat{Y}$ of Y. That is,

$$\hat{Y} = f\{X\} \qquad (16.4\text{-}3)$$

If the spectral correction transformation is to be linear, then it is necessary that $S(\lambda)$ be some linear function of $V(\lambda)$. This condition is not usually achieveable. However, the simplicity of the linear transformation often dictates the search for a transformation for which an estimate

$$\hat{Y}(\lambda) = a_1 S(\lambda) + a_2 \qquad (16.4\text{-}4)$$

is formed to minimize some error function such as the mean-square error

$$\mathcal{E} = \int [Y(\lambda) - \hat{Y}(\lambda)]^2\, d\lambda \qquad (16.4\text{-}5)$$

The next section presents results of linear luminance sensor response correction. Nonlinear correction techniques may be useful for sensor luminance spectral compensation; however, no effective nonlinear methods have yet been developed.

The concept of spectral sensitivity correction for image sensors can be extended to image displays. Consider an image display whose spectral emission function is $E_A(\lambda)$ and an idealized display with a desired spectral emission function $E_I(\lambda)$. The energy distribution at a pixel point $F(j, k)$ on the display is equal to the product $F(j, k)E_A(\lambda)$. Linear compensation can be performed to produce the compensated image field

$$G(j, k) = a_1 F(j, k) + a_2 \qquad (16.4\text{-}6)$$

where a_1 and a_2 are constants so that the energy distributions $G(j, k)E_A(\lambda)$ and $F(j, k)E_I(\lambda)$ form a minimum mean-square error match over all wavelengths.

16.5. SENSOR TRISTIMULUS VALUE ESTIMATION

A color image scanner produces three signals X_R, X_G, X_B, which are nominally proportional to the red, green, and blue content of the scene, as modeled by

$$X_R = \int C(\lambda)S_R(\lambda)\,d\lambda \qquad (16.5\text{-}1a)$$

$$X_G = \int C(\lambda)S_G(\lambda)\,d\lambda \qquad (16.5\text{-}1b)$$

$$X_B = \int C(\lambda)S_B(\lambda)\,d\lambda \qquad (16.5\text{-}1c)$$

where $C(\lambda)$ is the input light spectral energy distribution, and $S_R(\lambda)$, $S_G(\lambda)$, $S_B(\lambda)$ are the spectral sensitivities of the red, green, and blue sensors, respectively. The light described by $C(\lambda)$ can be colorimetrically reproduced by a linear combination of a set of primaries with fixed spectral-energy distributions. The amounts of the primaries required to form the match are the tristimulus values

$$T_R = \int C(\lambda)T_{SR}(\lambda)\,d\lambda \qquad (16.5\text{-}2a)$$

$$T_G = \int C(\lambda)T_{SG}(\lambda)\,d\lambda \qquad (16.5\text{-}2b)$$

$$T_B = \int C(\lambda)T_{SB}(\lambda)\,d\lambda \qquad (16.5\text{-}2c)$$

where $T_{SR}(\lambda)$, $T_{SG}(\lambda)$, $T_{SB}(\lambda)$ are the spectral tristimulus curves of the primaries. The scanner signals X_R, X_G, X_B will be tristimulus values for some set of primaries if the sensor spectral sensitivity functions $S_R(\lambda)$, $S_G(\lambda)$, $S_B(\lambda)$ are linear combinations of the spectral tristimulus values

$T_{SR}(\lambda)$, $T_{SG}(\lambda)$, $T_{SB}(\lambda)$. However, this condition seldom holds. Consideration is now directed to the development of techniques of estimating tristimulus values in terms of measured color scanner signals (5). The simplest approach is to form estimates of spectral tristimulus values by the linear operations

$$\hat{T}_{SR}(\lambda) = m_{11}S_R(\lambda) + m_{12}S_G(\lambda) + m_{13}S_B(\lambda) \tag{16.5-3a}$$

$$\hat{T}_{SG}(\lambda) = m_{21}S_R(\lambda) + m_{22}S_G(\lambda) + m_{23}S_B(\lambda) \tag{16.5-3b}$$

$$\hat{T}_{SB}(\lambda) = m_{31}S_R(\lambda) + m_{32}S_G(\lambda) + m_{33}S_B(\lambda) \tag{16.5-3c}$$

where the m_{ij} are constants. Multiplying both sides of Eq. 16.5-3 by $C(\lambda)$ and integrating over the wavelength limits yields the matrix equation

$$\begin{bmatrix} \hat{T}_R \\ \hat{T}_G \\ \hat{T}_B \end{bmatrix} = \begin{bmatrix} m_{11} & m_{12} & m_{13} \\ m_{21} & m_{22} & m_{23} \\ m_{31} & m_{32} & m_{33} \end{bmatrix} \begin{bmatrix} X_R \\ X_G \\ X_B \end{bmatrix} \tag{16.5-4}$$

In abbreviated form

$$\hat{t} = Mx \tag{16.5-5}$$

One strategy for determining the estimated tristimulus values $\hat{t}$ for the sensor signals x is to select the elements of the transformation matrix M to minimize the mean-square errors of $T_{SR}(\lambda) - \hat{T}_{SR}(\lambda)$, $T_{SG}(\lambda) - \hat{T}_{SG}(\lambda)$, $T_{SB}(\lambda) - \hat{T}_{SB}(\lambda)$ for all wavelengths. This procedure has been performed for typical color film layer sensitivities for 10 test colors listed in Table 16.5-1 (6). The chromaticity coordinates of these colors are indicated as squares in Figure 16.5-1. Table 16.5-1 contains a listing of the corresponding luminances. The estimated luminances are seen to be quite close to the actual luminances for all of the test colors, but the chromaticity coordinates corresponding to the estimated tristimulus values show a marked deviation from the actual values.

Another approach to the estimation of tristimulus values is to select three key colors and then compute the coefficients m_{ij} that result in exact colorimetric reproduction of the key colors. Then, hopefully, any other arbitrary color will not depart substantially from its true colorimetric values. The colors that are generally reproduced with the greatest error in chromaticity are the highly saturated colors. For this reason the three key colors have been chosen to be the red #9, green #7, and blue #6 dyes of the test colors listed in Table 16.5-1. With these test colors $[C_i]$ of known

TABLE 16.5-1. Comparison of colorimetric fidelity for tristimulus estimation methods

Color	Actual Luminance	Spectral Match			Exact Key Color—A			Exact Key Color—B		
		Luminance	$\varepsilon_Y\%$	$\varepsilon_c\%$	Luminance	$\varepsilon_Y\%$	$\varepsilon_c\%$	Luminance	$\varepsilon_Y\%$	$\varepsilon_c\%$
1. Flesh	0.331	0.329	0.48	7.36	0.349	5.55	5.81	0.331	0.08	4.86
2. Grass	0.121	0.129	6.28	9.01	0.128	5.59	3.34	0.123	0.05	0.18
3. Sky blue	0.466	0.463	0.73	7.19	0.482	3.49	11.40	0.466	0.09	0.08
4. Red brick	0.141	0.139	1.33	8.32	0.150	6.08	3.83	0.141	0.00	0.03
5. Purple flower	0.181	0.182	0.55	18.80	0.207	14.20	13.50	0.198	9.17	16.80
6. Blue dye	0.087	0.081	6.99	29.80	0.087	0.30	0.15	0.086	1.11	21.08
7. Green dye	0.234	0.244	4.48	7.83	0.233	0.38	0.06	0.220	5.85	7.61
8. Yellow dye	0.440	0.453	2.85	5.03	0.453	2.96	5.94	0.426	3.22	5.56
9. Red dye	0.105	0.086	18.10	5.97	0.105	0.13	0.02	0.099	5.49	4.53
10. Gray	0.500	0.500	0.01	8.86	0.517	3.38	3.58	0.494	1.24	2.12

$$\mathscr{e}_Y^2 = \left[\frac{Y(C) - \hat{Y}(C)}{Y(C)}\right]^2$$

$$\mathscr{e}_C = \left[\frac{u(C) - \hat{u}(C)}{u(C)}\right]^2 + \left[\frac{v(C) + \hat{v}(C)}{v(C)}\right]^2$$

459

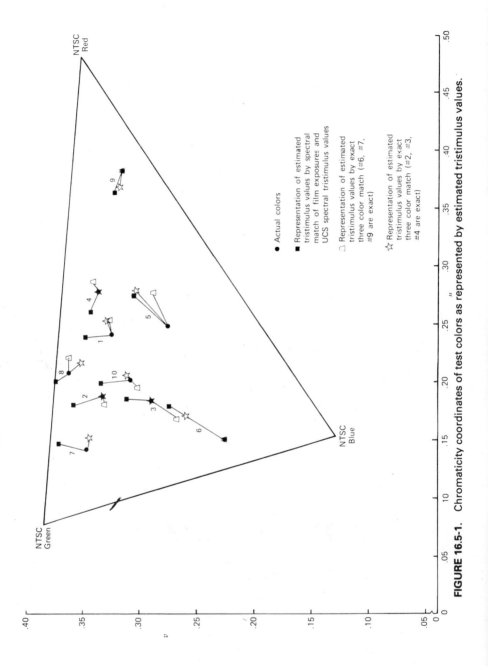

FIGURE 16.5-1. Chromaticity coordinates of test colors as represented by estimated tristimulus values.

NTSC Red

NTSC Blue

NTSC Green

• Actual colors

■ Representation of estimated tristimulus values by spectral match of film exposures and UCS spectral tristimulus values

◻ Representation of estimated tristimulus values by exact three color match (≠6, ≠7, ≠9 are exact)

☆ Representation of estimated tristimulus values by exact three color match (≠2, ≠3, ≠4 are exact)

.05   .10   .15   .20   .25   .30   .35   .40   .45   .50

.40   .35   .30   .25   .20   .15   .10   .05   0

v

tristimulus values $U(C_i)$, $V(C_i)$, $W(C_i)$ three matrix equations are formed,

$$\mathbf{t}(C_6) = \mathbf{Mx}(C_6) \qquad\qquad (16.5\text{-}6a)$$

$$\mathbf{t}(C_7) = \mathbf{Mx}(C_7) \qquad\qquad (16.5\text{-}6b)$$

$$\mathbf{t}(C_9) = \mathbf{Mx}(C_9) \qquad\qquad (16.5\text{-}6c)$$

The three equations may then be solved simultaneously for the coefficients m_{ij}. Figure 16.5-1 shows the chromaticities for all 10 test colors using the conversion matrix obtained from Eq. 16.5-6. The luminance of the colors are also listed in Table 16.5-1. The procedure has been repeated using the less saturated colors of red brick #4, grass #2, and sky blue #3 as key colors. Again, the results are presented in Figure 16.5-1 and Table 16.5-1. As expected, the chromaticities of the estimated key colors are exact. In both examples the departures in chromaticity for the nonkey colors is much less for this three color exact matching procedure than for the spectral tristimulus value curve fit method described previously. Also, there is an obvious compromise to be made in the selection of the key colors. If the key colors are the most saturated of the gamut of colors under consideration, the interior nonkey colors tend to shift toward higher saturation. On the other hand, if the key colors are of medium saturation, the extremely saturated colors of the gamut become desaturated.

A third approach to the linear estimation of tristimulus values involves the discrete estimation techniques of Chapter 14. As a first step the continuous integrals of Eqs. 16.5-1 and 16.5-2 are expressed in discrete form as

$$\mathbf{x} = \mathbf{Sc} \qquad\qquad (16.5\text{-}7)$$

and

$$\mathbf{t} = \mathbf{T}_S \mathbf{c} \qquad\qquad (16.5\text{-}8)$$

where $\mathbf{c}$ is a $Q \times 1$ vector of discrete points of the spectral energy distribution $C(\lambda)$ and $\mathbf{S}$ and $\mathbf{T}_S$ are $3 \times Q$ matrices whose rows are the sampled elements of sensor spectral sensitivity functions and the spectral tristimulus curves, respectively. One then seeks the linear transformation matrix $\mathbf{M}$ such that the estimate $\hat{\mathbf{t}} = \mathbf{Mx}$ minimizes the mean-square error between $\mathbf{t}$ and $\hat{\mathbf{t}}$. The required estimator may be expressed as

$$\hat{\mathbf{t}} = \mathbf{T}_S \hat{\mathbf{c}} \qquad\qquad (16.5\text{-}9)$$

where $\hat{\mathbf{c}}$ is the estimate of the spectral energy distribution that resulted in the sensor signal observation $\mathbf{x}$. Thus the problem of estimating the sensor tristimulus functions is equivalent to the fundamental problem of spectral energy distribution estimation discussed in Section 16.3.

16.6. COLOR FILM EXPOSURE ESTIMATION

Color film may be regarded as a measurement tool in which the red, green, and blue emulsion exposure levels are spectral measurements of some incident spectral light distribution. The exposure levels, however, are not directly observable; some estimation procedures must be invoked to infer the exposure levels (5).

From Eq. 13.3-15 the exposure levels are modeled as

$$X_R = d_R \int C(\lambda) L_R(\lambda)\, d\lambda \qquad (16.6\text{-}1a)$$

$$X_G = d_G \int C(\lambda) L_G(\lambda)\, d\lambda \qquad (16.6\text{-}1b)$$

$$X_B = d_B \int C(\lambda) L_B(\lambda)\, d\lambda \qquad (16.6\text{-}1c)$$

where $C(\lambda)$ is the spectral energy distribution of the light exposing the film, d_R, d_G, d_B are exposure constants, and $L_R(\lambda)$, $L_G(\lambda)$, $L_B(\lambda)$ are the spectral sensitivities of the emulsion layers. The exposed film is developed to produce a photographic print or transparency. In the following discussion only transparencies are considered; the results are easily extended to prints. According to the models of Eqs. 13.3-16 to 13.3-18 the transparency transmittance is given by

$$\tau_T(\lambda) = 10^{-\{c D_{NC}(\lambda) + m D_{NM}(\lambda) + y D_{NY}(\lambda)\}} \qquad (16.6\text{-}2)$$

where c, m, y are the amounts of the cyan, magenta, and yellow dyes in the transparency and $D_{NC}(\lambda)$, $D_{NM}(\lambda)$, $D_{NY}(\lambda)$ are the spectral characteristics of these dyes.

Suppose now that the developed transparency is placed in a color image scanner that generates three electrical signals,

$$V_R = k_R \int H_R(\lambda) \tau_T(\lambda)\, d\lambda \qquad (16.6\text{-}3a)$$

$$V_G = k_G \int H_G(\lambda) \tau_T(\lambda)\, d\lambda \qquad (16.6\text{-}3b)$$

$$V_B = k_B \int H_B(\lambda) \tau_T(\lambda)\, d\lambda \qquad (16.6\text{-}3c)$$

where k_R, k_G, k_B are amplifier gains of the film scanner and $H_R(\lambda)$, $H_G(\lambda)$, $H_B(\lambda)$ represent the effective color separation filter transmittance.

The estimation task may then be formulated as the determination of a set of exposure estimates $\hat{X}_R$, $\hat{X}_G$, $\hat{X}_B$ based on the observations V_R, V_G,

V_B and a priori knowledge of the film model subject to some error criterion. Even with the relatively simple mean-square error criterion, exposure estimation is a rather difficult problem because of the non-linearities involved and the integral nature of the exposure for the scanner voltages. As a simplification the relationship between the dye densities and film layer exposures can be considered linear as given by

$$c = K_{FC} + \gamma_C \log_{10}(X_R) \tag{16.6-4a}$$

$$m = K_{FM} + \gamma_M \log_{10}(X_G) \tag{16.6-4b}$$

$$y = K_{FY} + \gamma_Y \log_{10}(X_B) \tag{16.6-4c}$$

where K_{FC}, K_{FM}, K_{FY} are constants and γ_c, γ_M, γ_Y represent the slopes of the film H and D curves. Then the expressions for the scanner signals can be written as

$$V_R = k_R \int K(\lambda) H_R(\lambda)(X_R)^{\Psi_C(\lambda)}(X_G)^{\Psi_M(\lambda)}(X_B)^{\Psi_Y(\lambda)} \, d\lambda \tag{16.6-5a}$$

$$\dot{V}_G = k_G \int K(\lambda) H_G(\lambda)(X_R)^{\Psi_C(\lambda)}(X_G)^{\Psi_M(\lambda)}(X_B)^{\Psi_Y(\lambda)} \, d\lambda \tag{16.6-5b}$$

$$V_B = k_B \int K(\lambda) H_B(\lambda)(X_R)^{\Psi_C(\lambda)}(X_G)^{\Psi_M(\lambda)}(X_B)^{\Psi_Y(\lambda)} \, d\lambda \tag{16.6-5c}$$

where

$$K(\lambda) = 10^{\{-[K_{FC}D_{NC}(\lambda)+K_{FM}D_{NM}(\lambda)+K_{FY}D_{NY}(\lambda)]\}}$$

$$\Psi_C(\lambda) = \gamma_C D_{NC}(\lambda)$$

$$\Psi_M(\lambda) = \gamma_M D_{NM}(\lambda)$$

$$\Psi_Y(\lambda) = \gamma_Y D_{NY}(\lambda)$$

With the formulation of Eq. 16.5-5 the minimization of the estimation error can be accomplished by a variety of numerical techniques such as Newton-Raphson iteration, steepest descent, or dynamic programming. A reasonably good initial estimate can be obtained by considering the color separation filters to be spectrally narrow.*

Then the equation for the scanner signals becomes

$$V_R = A_R(\hat{X}_R)^{\Psi_C(\lambda_R)}(\hat{X}_G)^{\Psi_M(\lambda_R)}(\hat{X}_B)^{\Psi_Y(\lambda_R)} \tag{16.6-6a}$$

$$V_G = A_G(\hat{X}_R)^{\Psi_C(\lambda_G)}(\hat{X}_G)^{\Psi_M(\lambda_G)}(\hat{X}_B)^{\Psi_Y(\lambda_G)} \tag{16.6-6b}$$

$$V_B = A_B(\hat{X}_R)^{\Psi_C(\lambda_B)}(\hat{X}_G)^{\Psi_M(\lambda_B)}(\hat{X}_B)^{\Psi_Y(\lambda_B)} \tag{16.6-6c}$$

---

* This is the actual case for a laser scanner.

where

$$A_R = k_R K(\lambda_R) \int H_R(\lambda) \, d\lambda$$

$$A_G = k_G K(\lambda_G) \int H_G(\lambda) \, d\lambda$$

$$A_B = k_B K(\lambda_B) \int H_B(\lambda) \, d\lambda$$

In Eq. 16.6-6 the wavelengths λ_R, λ_G, λ_B are the centroid wavelengths of the filter functions $H_R(\lambda)$, $H_G(\lambda)$, $H_B(\lambda)$ and the hat symbol has been employed to indicate the approximation. Now taking the natural logarithm of both sides of Eq. 16.6-6 results in the matrix equation

$$\begin{bmatrix} \ln V_R \\ \ln V_G \\ \ln V_B \end{bmatrix} = \begin{bmatrix} \Psi_C(\lambda_R) & \Psi_M(\lambda_R) & \Psi_Y(\lambda_R) \\ \Psi_C(\lambda_G) & \Psi_M(\lambda_G) & \Psi_Y(\lambda_G) \\ \Psi_C(\lambda_B) & \Psi_M(\lambda_B) & \Psi_Y(\lambda_B) \end{bmatrix} \begin{bmatrix} \ln \hat{X}_R \\ \ln \hat{X}_G \\ \ln \hat{X}_B \end{bmatrix} + \begin{bmatrix} \ln A_R \\ \ln A_G \\ \ln A_B \end{bmatrix}$$

$$(16.6\text{-}7)$$

Equation 16.6-7 can then simply be inverted and exponentiated to obtain the estimated exposures. Table 16.6-1 lists the values of the exposures, scanner signals, and estimated exposures, as given by Eq. 16.6-7 and indicated as the narrow-band solution along with the mean-square error for each of 10 test colors. Data were obtained for a typical color film scanned by a color flying spot scanner utilizing Wratten color separation filters. It should be noted that even for the gross approximations that resulted in Eq. 16.6-6, the estimation error is reasonably small by photographic standards.

A Newton-Raphson iterative process can be employed to improve the narrow-band estimate. In this process the estimated exposures given by the narrow-band estimation are substituted into Eq. 16.6-6 to obtain the corresponding values $\tilde{V}_R$, $\tilde{V}_G$, $\tilde{V}_B$ of the scanner signals. The differences between the sets of scanner signals are then used to generate correction terms ΔX_R, ΔX_G, ΔX_B to the narrow-band exposure estimates as given by

$$\begin{bmatrix} \Delta X_R \\ \Delta X_G \\ \Delta X_B \end{bmatrix} = \begin{bmatrix} \dfrac{\partial V_R}{\partial X_R} & \dfrac{\partial V_R}{\partial X_G} & \dfrac{\partial V_R}{\partial X_B} \\ \dfrac{\partial V_G}{\partial X_R} & \dfrac{\partial V_G}{\partial X_G} & \dfrac{\partial V_G}{\partial V_B} \\ \dfrac{\partial V_B}{\partial X_R} & \dfrac{\partial V_B}{\partial X_G} & \dfrac{\partial V_B}{\partial X_B} \end{bmatrix}^{-1} \begin{bmatrix} V_R - \tilde{V}_R \\ V_G - \tilde{V}_G \\ V_B - \tilde{V}_B \end{bmatrix} \qquad (16.6\text{-}8)$$

TABLE 16.6-1. Exposure estimation for test colors

Test Color	Exposures			Scanner Signals			Narrow Band Estimation				Newton-Raphson Estimation			
							Estimated Exposures			Estimation Error	Estimated Exposures			Estimation Error
	X_R	X_G	X_B	V_R	V_G	V_B	$\hat{X}_R$	$\hat{X}_G$	$\hat{X}_B$	$\mathcal{E}_X$	$\hat{X}_R$	$\hat{X}_G$	$\hat{X}_B$	$\mathcal{E}_X$
1. Flesh	50.0	27.9	20.4	0.450	0.301	0.245	36.3	34.0	27.3	49.1%	50.5	28.0	20.4	0.61%
2. Grass	8.8	12.8	6.5	0.062	0.073	0.055	6.4	16.5	11.0	81.5%	8.9	12.8	6.5	0.60%
3. Sky blue	37.5	51.9	76.0	0.499	0.611	0.771	31.5	55.4	58.8	28.5%	37.5	51.9	75.7	0.36%
4. Red brick	25.3	10.8	6.1	0.166	0.080	0.053	18.8	15.1	10.5	86.7%	25.3	10.8	6.1	0.36%
5. Purple flower	40.3	15.1	24.5	0.300	0.159	0.227	28.9	22.0	28.1	55.2%	40.1	15.1	24.5	0.62%
6. Blue dye	6.1	10.4	22.3	0.043	0.072	0.153	4.2	16.5	23.9	67.2%	6.1	10.4	22.3	0.41%
7. Green dye	6.1	25.4	7.0	0.065	0.138	0.078	5.3	26.6	13.2	89.6%	6.1	25.3	7.0	0.39%
8. Yellow dye	43.8	40.3	6.4	0.469	0.371	0.110	35.3	41.5	14.7	131.0%	43.5	40.2	6.4	0.71%
9. Red dye	30.1	4.6	8.3	0.143	0.038	0.052	20.9	8.6	11.3	97.2%	30.1	4.6	8.3	0.19%
10. Gray	50.0	50.0	50.0	0.585	0.587	0.593	38.2	53.4	48.0	24.9%	49.8	50.0	50.0	0.38%

465

The process can be iterated until the desired degree of accuracy is achieved. The results of the Newton-Raphson estimation are indicated in Table 16.6-1. In this example the mean-square estimation error of the exposures has been reduced to less than 1% with no more than five iterations. Higher-order terms can also be utilized in the expansions of Eqs. 16.6-7 and 16.6-8 to speed up convergence (5).

16.7. COLOR IMAGE DISPLAY COMPENSATION

Section 16.5 described methods of processing color image scanner signals to obtain estimates of the tristimulus values of a color image spectral energy distribution at an image point. These estimated tristimulus values may then be utilized to drive a trichromatic color image display, such as a shadow mask cathode ray tube, to produce a displayed replica of the original scene. Attention will now be directed to the practical problem of film recording of the light display to obtain a colorimetrically acceptable photographic record.

Consider the film processing chain of Figure 16.7-1. The set of tristimulus values (T_1, T_2, T_3) enters a compensation unit that generates a set of corrected tristimulus values $(\tilde{T}_1, \tilde{T}_2, \tilde{T}_3)$ that drive a color image light display. This light distribution is then recorded on trichromatic film to produce a positive color transparency that is projected onto a screen. A colorimeter measures the tristimulus values $(\hat{T}_1, \hat{T}_2, \hat{T}_3)$ of the projected image. The compensation unit is designed to minimize the colorimetric error between the colors defined by (T_1, T_2, T_3) and $(\hat{T}_1, \hat{T}_2, \hat{T}_3)$.

The display spectral energy distribution

$$C(\lambda) = \sum_{i=1}^{3} \tilde{T}_i P_{Si}(\lambda) \qquad (16.7\text{-}1)$$

is composed of a weighted sum of the display primary spectral energy

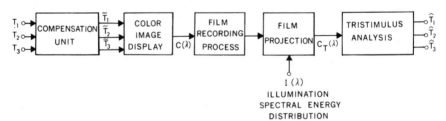

FIGURE 16.7-1. Color transparency recording and projection process for digital color image display.

distributions $P_{Si}(\lambda)$. The tristimulus values of the projected light spectral energy distributions are given by

$$\hat{T}_i = \int C_T(\lambda) T_{Si}(\lambda) \, d\lambda \qquad (16.7\text{-}2)$$

where $T_{Si}(\lambda)$ represent the spectral tristimulus values of the color coordinate system corresponding to the tristimulus values T_i.

There are two approaches (7) to color image display compensation: direct and indirect. In the direct approach a mathematical model, based on the color film model of Figure 13.3-8, is utilized to describe the step-by-step relations between $C(\lambda)$ and $C_T(\lambda)$. This model is then combined with Eqs. 16.7-1 and 16.7-2 to form a deterministic relationship between the sets of tristimulus values $\tilde{T}_i$ and $\hat{T}_i$. Ideally, this relationship should be unity, but it is not because of the inherent nonlinearities of the film exposure characteristic, interimage effects, and the overlapping dye spectral distributions. Nevertheless, if the input-output relationship can be quantitatively specified, its inverse can be determined. Wallis (7) has investigated this direct approach and obtained significant improvements in the colorimetric quality of photographically recorded colors. However, there are severe computational problems associated with the direct approach resulting from the relative complexity of the film model. The indirect approach to color image display compensation consists of the specification of some vector space operator $\mathbf{M}$ that will form a close fit between the tristimulus values T_i and $\hat{T}_i$. For example, the matrix operator $\mathbf{M}$ might include up to third-order terms and form the conversion.

$$\begin{bmatrix} \tilde{T}_1 \\ \tilde{T}_2 \\ \tilde{T}_3 \end{bmatrix} = \mathbf{M} \begin{bmatrix} T_1 \\ T_2 \\ T_3 \\ T_1^2 \\ T_2^2 \\ T_3^2 \\ T_1 T_2 \\ T_1 T_3 \\ T_2 T_3 \\ T_1^3 \\ T_2^3 \\ T_3^3 \end{bmatrix} + \begin{bmatrix} K_1 \\ K_2 \\ K_3 \end{bmatrix} \qquad (16.7\text{-}3)$$

where the K_i are constants. By extending the predictor vector to include terms of increasingly higher order, the estimation performance can be improved to almost any degree of accuracy. The third-order prediction of

Eq. 16.7-3 has proved to be sufficient for film recording from a shadow mask color image display (7). In order to specify the terms of the compensation matrix, the tristimulus values of a large number of colors are determined along with corresponding output tristimulus values $\hat{T}_i$ obtained without compensation. The weighting elements can then be determined by iteration to minimize some desired error functional getween T_i and $\hat{T}_i$.

REFERENCES

1. T. G. Stockham, Jr., "A-D and D-A Converters: Their Effect on Digital Audio Fidelity," in *Digital Signal Processing*, L. R. Rabiner and C. M. Rader, Eds., IEEE Press, New York, 1972, 484–496.

2. D. A. O'Handley and W. B. Green, "Recent Developments in Digital Image Processing at the Image Processing Laboratory at the Jet Propulsion Laboratory," *Proc. IEEE*, **60**, 7, July 1972, 821–828.

3. W. Frei (private communication).

4. W. K. Pratt and C. E. Mancill, "Spectral Estimation Techniques for the Spectral Calibration of a Color Image Scanner," *App. Opt.*, **14**, 11, November 1975, 73–75.

5. C. E. Mancill, "Digital Color Image Restoration," University of Southern California, Image Processing Institute, USCIPI Report 630, August 1975.

6. R. M. Evans, W. T. Hanson, Jr., and W. L. Brewer, *Principles of Color Photography*, Wiley, New York, 1953.

7. R. H. Wallis, "Film Recording of Digital Color Images," University of Southern California, Image Processing Institute, USCIPI Report 570, May 1975.

5 IMAGE ANALYSIS

Image analysis is concerned with the extraction of useful measurements, data, or information from an image field by automatic or semiautomatic devices and systems. In the literature this field has been called image data extraction, scene analysis, image description, automatic photo interpretation, image understanding, and a variety of other names.

Image analysis is distinguished from other types of image processing, such as coding, restoration, and enhancement, in that the ultimate product of an image analysis system is usually numerical output rather than a picture. Image analysis also diverges from classical pattern recognition in that analysis systems, by definition, are not limited to the classification of scene regions to a fixed number of categories, but rather are designed to provide a description of complex scenes whose variety may be enormously large and ill-defined in terms of a priori expectation. Furthermore, image analysis systems often rely on some knowledge base relating objects within a scene to one another and to the scene background. Artificial intelligence techniques may also be utilized in an image analysis system to provide control of the various stages of the system and efficient access to the knowledge base.

17 IMAGE FEATURE EXTRACTION

An image feature is a distinguishing primitive characteristic or attribute of an image field. Some features are natural in the sense that such features are defined by the visual appearance of an image, while other so-called artificial features result from specific manipulations or measurements of an image. Natural features include the brightness of a region of pixels, edge outlines of objects, and gray scale textural regions. Image amplitude histograms and spatial frequency spectra are examples of artificial features.

17.1. AMPLITUDE FEATURES

The most basic of all image features is the measure of image amplitude in terms of spectral value, luminance, tristimulus values, or other units. Amplitude measurements may be made at specific image points or over neighborhoods. For example, the average image luminance of a $(2W + 1)$ by $(2W + 1)$ pixel neighborhood is given by

$$\bar{Y}(j, k) = \frac{1}{(2W + 1)^2} \sum_{m=-W}^{W} \sum_{n=-W}^{W} Y(j + m, k + n) \qquad (17.1\text{-}1)$$

There are many degrees of freedom in establishing image amplitude features. Image variables such as luminance or tristimulus values may be utilized directly, or alternatively some linear, nonlinear, or perhaps noninvertible transformation can be performed to a new image amplitude space.

Image amplitude measurements are of major importance in the isolation of objects within pictures (symbolic description) and the labeling of such objects (interpretation). These topics are covered in subsequent chapters.

17.2. HISTOGRAM FEATURES

Chapter 5 introduced the concept of representing a discrete image array $F(j, k)$ as a sample of a two-dimensional stochastic process described by a joint probability distribution model. Techniques were also developed for estimating image probability distributions in terms of measured image amplitude features. These histograms can also be utilized to generate a class of image features.

The first-order probability distribution of image amplitude may be defined as

$$P(b) \equiv P_R\{F(j, k) = b\} \tag{17.2-1}$$

where $0 \le b \le L - 1$ denotes the quantized amplitude level. The first-order histogram estimate of $P(b)$ is simply

$$P(b) \approx \frac{N(b)}{M} \tag{17.2-2}$$

where M represents the total number of pixels in a measurement window centered about (j, k) and $N(b)$ is the number of pixels of amplitude b in the window. Often, under the assumption of stationarity, the window is the full image.

The shape of an image histogram provides many clues as to character of the image. For example, a narrowly distributed histogram indicates a low-contrast picture while a bimodel histogram suggests regions of differing brightness. The following measures have been formulated (1) as a concise means of describing the shape of first-order image histograms.

Mean

$$\bar{b} = \sum_{b=0}^{L-1} bP(b) \tag{17.2-3}$$

Variance

$$\sigma_b^2 = \sum_{b=0}^{L-1} (b - \bar{b})^2 P(b) \tag{17.2-4}$$

Skewness

$$b_S = \frac{1}{\sigma_b^3} \sum_{b=0}^{L-1} (b - \bar{b})^3 P(b) \tag{17.2-5}$$

Kurtosis

$$b_K = \frac{1}{\sigma_b^4} \sum_{b=0}^{L-1} (b - \bar{b})^4 P(b) - 3 \tag{17.2-6}$$

Energy

$$b_N = \sum_{b=0}^{L-1} [P(b)]^2 \tag{17.2-7}$$

Entropy

$$b_E = -\sum_{b=0}^{L-1} P(b) \log_2 [P(b)] \qquad (17.2\text{-}8)$$

The factor three inserted in the expression for the Kurtosis measure normalizes b_K to zero for a zero-mean Gaussian process in the limit for fine quantization.

Second-order histogram features are based on the definition of the joint probability distribution of pairs of pixels. Consider two pixels $F(j, k)$ and $F(m, n)$ that are located at coordinates (j, k) and (m, n), respectively, and that are separated by r radial units at an angle θ with respect to the horizontal axis. The joint distribution of image amplitude values is then expressed as

$$P(a, b) \equiv P_R \{F(j, k) = a, F(m, n) = b\} \qquad (17.2\text{-}9)$$

where a and b represent the quantized amplitude values. As a result of the discrete rectilinear representation of an image, the separation parameters (r, θ) may only assume certain discrete values. The histogram estimate of the second-order distribution is

$$P(a, b) = \frac{N(a, b)}{M} \qquad (17.2\text{-}10)$$

where M is the total number of pixels in the measurement window and $N(a, b)$ denotes the number of occurrences for which $F(j, k) = a$ and $F(m, n) = b$.

If the pixel pairs within an image are highly related, the entries in $P(a, b)$ will be clustered along the diagonal of the array. Various measures, listed below, have been suggested (1, 2) to specify the energy spread about the diagonal of $P(a, b)$.

Autocorrelation

$$B_A = \sum_{a=0}^{L-1} \sum_{b=0}^{L-1} ab P(a, b) \qquad (17.2\text{-}11)$$

Covariance

$$B_C = \sum_{a=0}^{L-1} \sum_{b=0}^{L-1} (a - \bar{a})(b - \bar{b}) P(a, b) \qquad (17.2\text{-}12)$$

Inertia

$$B_I = \sum_{a=0}^{L-1} \sum_{b=0}^{L-1} (a - b)^2 P(a, b) \qquad (17.2\text{-}13)$$

Absolute Value

$$B_V = \sum_{a=0}^{L-1} \sum_{b=0}^{L-1} |a - b| P(a, b) \qquad (17.2\text{-}14)$$

Inverse Difference

$$B_D = \sum_{a=0}^{L-1} \sum_{b=0}^{L-1} \frac{P(a, b)}{1 + (a - b)^2} \qquad (17.2\text{-}15)$$

Energy

$$B_N = \sum_{a=0}^{L-1} \sum_{b=0}^{L-1} [P(a, b)]^2 \qquad (17.2\text{-}16)$$

Entropy

$$B_E = - \sum_{a=0}^{L-1} \sum_{b=0}^{L-1} P(a, b) \log_2 [P(a, b)] \qquad (17.2\text{-}17)$$

The utilization of second histogram measures for texture analysis is considered in Section 17.8.

17.3. TRANSFORM COEFFICIENT FEATURES

The coefficients of a two-dimensional transform specify the amplitude of the brightness patterns (two-dimensional basis functions) of a transformation such that the weighted sum of the brightness patterns is identical to the image. By this characterization of a transformation the coefficients may be considered to indicate the correlation of a particular brightness pattern with an image field. If a basis pattern is of the same spatial form as a feature to be detected within the image, then image detection can be performed simply by monitoring the value of the appropriate transform coefficient. The problem, in practice, is that objects to be detected within an object are often of complex shape and brightness distribution, and hence do not correspond exactly to the more primitive brightness patterns of most image transforms.

Lendaris and Stanley (3, 4) have investigated the application of the continuous two-dimensional Fourier transform of an image, obtained by a coherent optical processor, as a means of image feature extraction. The optical system produces an electric field radiation pattern proportional to

$$\mathcal{F}(\omega_x, \omega_y) = \int_{-\infty}^{\infty} \int_{-\infty}^{\infty} F(x, y) \exp\{-i(\omega_x x + \omega_y y)\} \, dx \, dy \qquad (17.3\text{-}1)$$

where (ω_x, ω_y) are the image spatial frequencies. An optical sensor produces an output

$$\mathcal{M}(\omega_x, \omega_y) = |\mathcal{F}(\omega_x, \omega_y)|^2 \qquad (17.3\text{-}2)$$

proportional to the intensity of the radiation pattern. It should be observed that $\mathcal{F}(\omega_x, \omega_y)$ and $F(x, y)$ are unique transform pairs, but $\mathcal{M}(\omega_x, \omega_y)$ is not uniquely related to $F(x, y)$. For example, $\mathcal{M}(\omega_x, \omega_y)$ does not change if the origin of $F(x, y)$ is shifted. In some applications the translation invariance of $\mathcal{M}(\omega_x, \omega_y)$ may be a virtue. Angular integration of $\mathcal{M}(\omega_x, \omega_y)$ over the spatial frequency plane produces a spatial frequency feature that is invariant to translation and rotation. Representing $\mathcal{M}(\omega_x, \omega_y)$ in polar form, this feature is defined as

$$\mathcal{N}(\rho) = \int_0^{2\pi} \mathcal{M}(\rho, \theta)\, d\theta \qquad (17.3\text{-}3)$$

where $\theta = \arctan(\omega_y/\omega_x)$ and $\rho^2 = \omega_x^2 + \omega_y^2$. Invariance to changes in scale is an attribute of the feature

$$\mathcal{P}(\theta) = \int_0^{\infty} \mathcal{M}(\rho, \theta)\rho\, d\rho \qquad (17.3\text{-}4)$$

If the input image is spatially limited in extent, the Fourier transform field $\mathcal{F}(\omega_x, \omega_y)$ will be attenuated over its range. It can be easily shown that if $F(x, y)$ is multiplied by a window function $W(x, y)$, which is unity within some rectangular limits and zero elsewhere, the Fourier transform of the product is equal to the convolution of $\mathcal{F}(\omega_x, \omega_y)$ with the Fourier transform $\mathcal{W}(\omega_x, \omega_y)$ of the window function. The attenuation caused by windowing should be taken into consideration in assessing the relative values of Fourier coefficients at different spatial frequencies.

The Fourier domain intensity pattern $\mathcal{M}(\omega_x, \omega_y)$ is normally examined in specific regions to isolate image features. As an example, Figure 17.3-1 defines regions for the following Fourier features:

Horizontal Slit

$$S_1(m) = \int_{\omega_y(m)}^{\omega_y(m+1)} \mathcal{M}(\omega_x, \omega_y)\, d\omega_y \qquad (17.3\text{-}5)$$

Vertical Slit

$$S_2(m) = \int_{\omega_x(m)}^{\omega_x(m+1)} \mathcal{M}(\omega_x, \omega_y)\, d\omega_x \qquad (17.3\text{-}6)$$

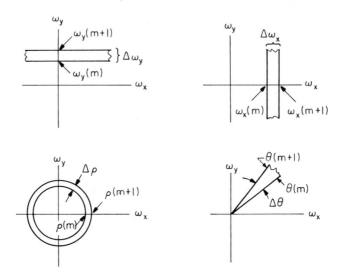

FIGURE 17.3-1.   Fourier transform feature masks.

Ring

$$S_3(m) = \int_{\rho(m)}^{\rho(m+1)} \mathcal{M}(\rho, \theta)\, dp \qquad\qquad (17.3\text{-}7)$$

Sector

$$S_4(m) = \int_{\theta(m)}^{\theta(m+1)} \mathcal{M}(\rho, \theta)\, d\theta \qquad\qquad (17.3\text{-}8)$$

For a discrete image array $F(j, k)$ the discrete Fourier transform

$$\mathcal{F}(u, v) = \frac{1}{N} \sum_{j=0}^{N-1} \sum_{k=0}^{N-1} F(j, k) \exp\left\{ \frac{-2\pi i}{N} (ux + vy) \right\} \qquad (17.3\text{-}9)$$

for $u, v = 0, \ldots, N - 1$ can be examined directly for feature extraction purposes. Horizontal slit, vertical slit, ring, and sector features can be defined analogous to Eqs. 17.3-5 to 17.3-8. This concept can also be extended to other unitary transforms such as the Hadamard and Haar transforms. Figure 17.3-2 presents Fourier transform log magnitude displays of several geometric shapes.

Transform coefficient feature extraction has proved practical in several applications in which the transform domain features are used as inputs to a pattern recognition classification system. Applications range from land usage classification (5) to disease diagnosis from radiographs (6-8).

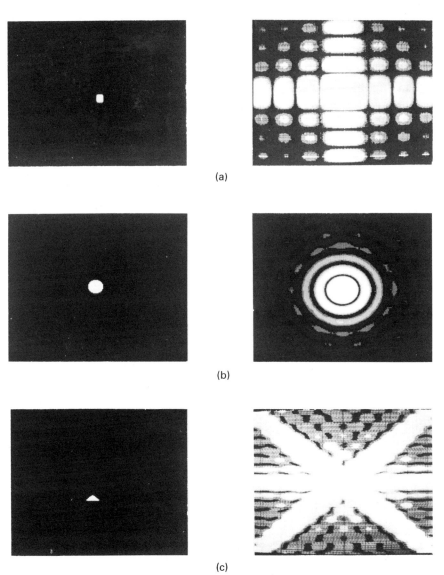

(a)

(b)

(c)

FIGURE 17.3-2. Examples of discrete Fourier spectra of objects. Log magnitude displays for $N = 256$. (a) Rectangle. (b) Ellipse. (c) Triangle.

17.4. LUMINANCE EDGE FEATURES

Changes or discontinuities in an image attribute such as luminance, tristimulus value, or texture are fundamentally important primative features of an image since they often provide an indication of the physical extent of objects within the image. Local discontinuities in image luminance or amplitude level are called luminance edges. Global discontinuities, called boundary segments, are considered in Chapter 18. In this section the definition of a luminance edge is limited to image amplitude discontinuities between reasonably smooth regions. Discontinuity detection between textured regions is considered in Section 18.7. Edge discontinuity detection in color images is covered in Section 17.6.

Figure 17.4-1 contains sketches of one- and two-dimensional edges each represented as a ramp increase in image amplitude level from a low to a high level. In the one-dimensional case the edge is characterized by its height, the slope angle, and x coordinate of the slope midpoint. An edge exists if both the slope angle and height are larger than specified critical values. For the two-dimensional example the orientation with respect to the x axis is also of importance. An ideal edge detector processing the image regions of Figure 17.4-1 should produce an edge indication localized to a single pixel located at the midpoint of the slope.

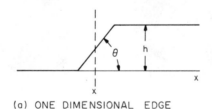

(a) ONE DIMENSIONAL EDGE

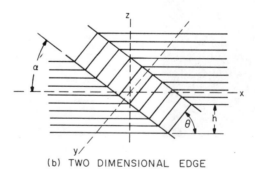

(b) TWO DIMENSIONAL EDGE

FIGURE 17.4-1.   One- and two-dimensional edges.

A common approach to monochrome edge detection is illustrated in Figure 17.4-2 in which an original monochrome image $F(j, k)$ undergoes a gray scale edge enhancement by linear or nonlinear processing to produce an image field $G(j, k)$ with accentuated spatial brightness changes. Next, a threshold operation is performed to determine the pixel location of significant edges. A negative going edge exists if

$$G(j, k) < T_L(j, k) \qquad\qquad (17.4\text{-}1a)$$

and a positive going edge exists if

$$G(j, k) \geq T_U(j, k) \qquad\qquad (17.4\text{-}1b)$$

where $T_L(j, k)$ and $T_U(j, k)$ are lower and upper threshold values, respectively. These threshold values may be made spatially varying to compensate for gross spatial luminance changes. Threshold selection is one of the key issues in edge detection. A threshold level set too high will not permit detection of low-amplitude structural image elements. Conversely, a threshold level set too low will cause noise to be falsely detected as an image edge. An edge location map $E(j, k)$ is often generated to indicate the positions of edges within an image. For example, all positive edge locations could be indicated by white pixel values against a black background. Alternatively, positive going edges could be noted by white pixels, negative going edges by black pixels, and nonedge regions by midgray pixels.

A second major approach to luminance edge detection involves fitting of a local region of pixel values to some ideal representation of a one- or two-dimensional edge, as defined in Figure 17.4-1. If the fit is sufficiently close, an edge is said to exist, and its assigned parameters are those of the ideal edge.

17.4.1. Linear Edge Enhancement Methods

A variety of edge enhancement techniques can be utilized to accentuate edges before threshold detection. One of the simplest techniques is discrete differencing analogous to continuous spatial differentiation. Horizontal edge sharpening can be obtained by the running difference operation,

FIGURE 17.4-2. Threshold edge detection system.

which produces an output image according to the relation

$$G(j, k) = F(j, k) - F(j, k + 1) \qquad (17.4\text{-}2a)$$

Similarly, vertical sharpening results from the operation

$$G(j, k) = F(j, k) - F(j + 1, k) \qquad (17.4\text{-}2b)$$

Diagonal sharpening can be obtained by subtraction of diagonal pairs of pixels. Figure 17.4-3 provides examples of horizontal and vertical differencing edge detection. The edge plots have been obtained by thresholding the magnitude of the difference planes at a threshold level corresponding to the 85% level of the gradient magnitude histogram.

Edge enhancement

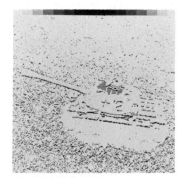

Horizontal   Vertical

Edge map

FIGURE 17.4-3. Examples of horizontal and vertical differencing edge detection.

Horizontal edge accentuation can also be accomplished by forming the differences between the slopes of the image amplitude along a line according to the relation

$$G(j, k) = [F(j, k) - F(j, k - 1)] - [F(j, k + 1) - F(j, k)] \qquad (17.4\text{-}3a)$$

or equivalently

$$G(j, k) = 2F(j, k) - F(j, k - 1) - F(j, k + 1) \qquad (17.4\text{-}3b)$$

Similar expressions exist for vertical and diagonal slope differences.

Two-dimensional discrete differentiation can be performed by convolving the original image array with the compass gradient masks listed below (9, p. 111):

North

$$\mathbf{H} = \begin{matrix} 1 & 1 & 1 \\ 1 & -2 & 1 \\ -1 & -1 & -1 \end{matrix} \qquad (17.4\text{-}4a)$$

Northeast

$$\mathbf{H} = \begin{matrix} 1 & 1 & 1 \\ -1 & -2 & 1 \\ -1 & -1 & 1 \end{matrix} \qquad (17.4\text{-}4b)$$

East

$$\mathbf{H} = \begin{matrix} -1 & 1 & 1 \\ -1 & -2 & 1 \\ -1 & 1 & 1 \end{matrix} \qquad (17.4\text{-}4c)$$

Southeast

$$\mathbf{H} = \begin{matrix} -1 & -1 & 1 \\ -1 & -2 & 1 \\ 1 & 1 & 1 \end{matrix} \qquad (17.4\text{-}4d)$$

South

$$\mathbf{H} = \begin{matrix} -1 & -1 & -1 \\ 1 & -2 & 1 \\ 1 & 1 & 1 \end{matrix} \qquad (17.4\text{-}4e)$$

Southwest

$$\mathbf{H} = \begin{matrix} 1 & -1 & -1 \\ 1 & -2 & -1 \\ 1 & 1 & 1 \end{matrix} \qquad (17.4\text{-}4f)$$

West

$$\mathbf{H} = \begin{array}{rrr} 1 & 1 & -1 \\ 1 & -2 & -1 \\ 1 & 1 & -1 \end{array} \qquad\qquad (17.4\text{-}4g)$$

Northwest

$$\mathbf{H} = \begin{array}{rrr} 1 & 1 & 1 \\ 1 & -2 & -1 \\ 1 & -1 & -1 \end{array} \qquad\qquad (17.4\text{-}4h)$$

The compass names indicate the slope direction of maximum response; for example, the East gradient mask produces a maximum output for horizontal luminance changes from left to right. It should be noted that the gradient masks have zero weighting (the sum of the array elements is zero) so that there is no output response over constant luminance regions of the image. Figure 17.4-4 contains split images of the gradient edge enhancement planes and the corresponding magnitude edge maps.

Edge sharpening, without regard to edge direction, can be obtained by convolution of an image with a Laplacian mask. Several types of Laplacian masks are listed below:

Mask 1

$$\mathbf{H} = \begin{array}{rrr} 0 & -1 & 0 \\ -1 & 4 & -1 \\ 0 & -1 & 0 \end{array} \qquad\qquad (17.4\text{-}5a)$$

Mask 2

$$\mathbf{H} = \begin{array}{rrr} -1 & -1 & -1 \\ -1 & 8 & -1 \\ -1 & -1 & -1 \end{array} \qquad\qquad (17.4\text{-}5b)$$

Mask 3

$$\mathbf{H} = \begin{array}{rrr} 1 & -2 & 1 \\ -2 & 4 & -2 \\ 1 & -2 & 1 \end{array} \qquad\qquad (17.4\text{-}5c)$$

Figure 17.4-5 illustrates the performance of the Laplacian edge detector.

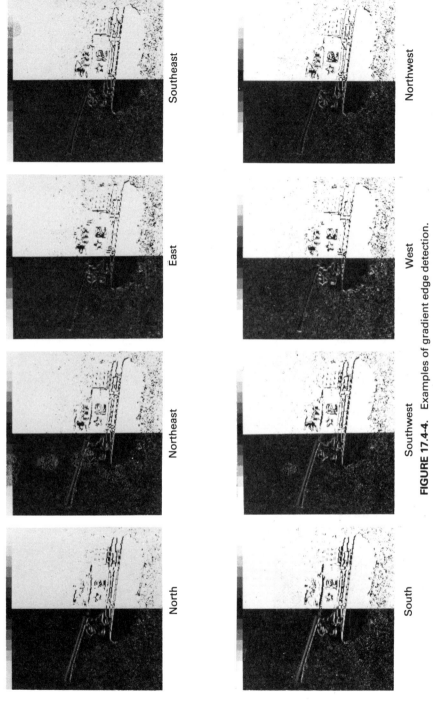

Southeast

Northwest

East

West

Northeast

Southwest

North

South

FIGURE 17.4-4. Examples of gradient edge detection.

483

Mask No. 1

Mask No. 2

Enhancement   Mask No. 3   Edge maps

FIGURE 17.4-5. Examples of Laplacian edge detection.

Edge sharpening can be made proportional to the statistical correlation of pixel values by the statistical mask (9, p. 125)

$$\mathbf{H} = \begin{bmatrix} \rho_C\rho_R & -\rho_C(1+\rho_R^2) & \rho_C\rho_R \\ -\rho_R(1+\rho_C^2) & (1+\rho_C^2)(1+\rho_R^2) & -\rho_R(1+\rho_C^2) \\ \rho_C\rho_R & -\rho_C(1+\rho_R^2) & \rho_C\rho_R \end{bmatrix} \quad (17.4\text{-}6)$$

in which ρ_R and ρ_C represent the assumed Markovian correlation factor between adjacent row and column pixels. If $\rho_R = \rho_C = 0$, there is no adjacent element correlation, and the statistical mask has no effect; in the extreme, if $\rho_R = \rho_C = 1$, the statistical mask reduces to the Laplacian mask of Eq. 17.4-5c. Figure 17.4-6 provides examples of edge detection with a statistical mask.

Argyle (10) and Macleod (11, 12) have proposed Gaussian-shaped weighting functions as a means of edge enhancement. The Argyle function

Edge enhancement

 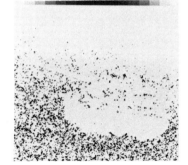

$\rho_R = \rho_C = 0.5$ Edge maps $\rho_R = \rho_C = 0.8.$

FIGURE 17.4-6. Examples of statistical mask edge detection.

is a split Gaussian function defined in one dimension as

$$h(x) = \exp\left\{-\frac{1}{2}\left(\frac{x}{p}\right)^2\right\} \qquad x \geq 0$$

$$h(x) = -\exp\left\{-\frac{1}{2}\left(\frac{x}{p}\right)^2\right\} \qquad x < 0$$

(17.4-7)

where p is a spread constant. The Macleod function given by

$$H(x, y) = \exp\left\{-\frac{1}{2}\left(\frac{y}{t}\right)^2\right\}\left[\exp\left\{-\frac{1}{2}\left(\frac{x-p}{p}\right)^2\right\} - \exp\left\{-\frac{1}{2}\left(\frac{x+p}{p}\right)^2\right\}\right]$$

(17.4-8)

where p and t are spread constants, suppresses the effect of pixel values in the edge transition region and edges in rows above and below the edge to be detected. Examples of edge detection with these masks are presented in Figure 17.4-7.

Edge enhancement

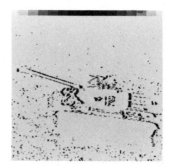

Argyle 1×7 masks $p = 2$ Edge maps   Macleod 5×9 mask $p = 2$, $t = 2$

FIGURE 17.4-7.   Examples of Argyle and Macleod mask edge detection.

A common limitation of the linear edge sharpening methods previously discussed is the amplification of high spatial frequency noise and artifacts as a result of the inherent differencing operations involved. Noise smoothing can be incorporated into the linear edge sharpening methods by performing the linear masking on regions of pixels rather than on individual pixels (13). This can be accomplished by forming a linear mask

$$H(j, k) = H_S(j, k) \circledast H_E(j, k) \qquad (17.4\text{-}9)$$

by convolving one of the edge enhancement masks $H_E(j, k)$ previously defined with a low-pass filter averaging mask $H_S(j, k)$ as defined in Eq. 12.3-2. Such spatial averaging, of course, leads to a smoothing of edges as well as noise.

17.4.2. Nonlinear Edge Enhancement Methods

Nonlinear edge detection systems utilize nonlinear combinations of pixels as a means of edge enhancement before thresholding. Most techniques are limited to processing over 2×2 or 3×3 windows.

Roberts (14) has introduced the simple nonlinear cross operation

$$G_R(j, k) = ([F(j, k) - F(j+1, k+1)]^2 + [F(j, k+1) - F(j+1, k]^2)^{1/2}$$
$$(17.4\text{-}10)$$

as a two-dimensional differencing method for edge sharpening and edge isolation. Another spatial differencing operation, which is of computationally simpler form, is given by

$$G_A(j, k) = |F(j, k) - F(j+1, k+1)| + |F(j, k+1) - F(j+1, k)|$$
$$(17.4\text{-}11)$$

It can be easily shown that

$$G_R(j, k) \le G_A(j, k) \le \sqrt{2} G_R(j, k) \qquad (17.4\text{-}12)$$

Crude directional information can be extracted by noting which of the four pixels is largest at a detected edge point. Figure 17.4-8 illustrates the operation of the Roberts square-root and magnitude cross-difference operators.

Sobel (15, p. 271) has suggested a 3×3 nonlinear edge enhancement operator described by the pixel numbering convention of Figure 17.4-9. The edge enhancement plane is defined as

$$G(j, k) = \sqrt{X^2 + Y^2} \qquad (17.4\text{-}13a)$$

Edge enhancement

Edge maps

Square root   Magnitude

FIGURE 17.4-8. Examples of Roberts square root and magnitude cross difference edge detection.

A_0	A_1	A_2
A_7	$F(j,k)$	A_3
A_6	A_5	A_4

FIGURE 17.4-9. Numbering for 3×3 edge detection operators.

where

$$X = (A_2 + 2A_3 + A_4) - (A_0 + 2A_7 + A_6) \qquad (17.4\text{-}13b)$$

$$Y = (A_0 + 2A_1 + A_2) - (A_6 + 2A_5 + A_4) \qquad (17.4\text{-}13c)$$

Results of sobel edge detection are shown in Figure 17.4-10.

Another 3×3 nonlinear edge enhancement algorithm has been introduced by Kirsch (16). Referring to the notation of Figure 17.4-9, the enhancement is given as

$$G(j, k) = \max \left\{ 1, \max_{i=0}^{7} [|5S_i - 3T_i|] \right\} \qquad (17.4\text{-}14a)$$

where

$$S_i = A_i + A_{i+1} + A_{i+2} \qquad (17.4\text{-}14b)$$

$$T_i = A_{i+3} + A_{i+4} + A_{i+5} + A_{i+6} + A_{i+7} \qquad (17.4\text{-}14c)$$

The subscripts of A are evaluated modulo 8. Basically, the Kirsch operator provides the maximal compass gradient magnitude about an image point ignoring the pixel value $F(j, k)$. Examples of edge detection with the Kirsch operator are presented in Figure 17.4-11.

Wallis (17) has proposed a nonlinear edge detection scheme based on homomorphic image processing. According to this scheme an edge exists if the magnitude of the logarithm of the image luminance at a pixel exceeds the magnitude of the average logarithmic luminance of its four nearest neighbors by a fixed threshold value. With reference to Figure 17.4-9, the edge enhancement plane is defined as

$$G(j, k) = \log [F(j, k)] - \tfrac{1}{4} \log (A_1) - \tfrac{1}{4} \log (A_3) - \tfrac{1}{4} \log (A_5) - \tfrac{1}{4} \log (A_7) \qquad (17.4\text{-}15a)$$

Enhancement   Edge map

FIGURE 17.4-10.   Examples of Sobel edge detection.

Enhancement   Edge map

FIGURE 17.4-11.   Examples of Kirsch edge detection.

or equivalently

$$G(j, k) = \tfrac{1}{4} \log \left[\frac{(F(j, k))^4}{A_1 A_3 A_5 A_7} \right] \qquad (17.4\text{-}15b)$$

Comparison of $G(j, k)$ against upper and lower threshold values is exactly equivalent to comparison of the fraction in the brackets of Eq. 17.4-15b against a modified threshold. Therefore, logarithms need not be explicitly computed. The principal advantage of the logarithmic edge detector besides its computational simplicity is that the technique is insensitive to multiplicative changes in luminance level. Figure 17.4-12 contains examples of logarithmic edge detection.

The logarithmic edge enhancement scheme defined by Eq. 17.4-15 can be considered as a linear enhancement with the Laplacian mask operation of Eq. 17.4-5a performed on the logarithms of the pixel values. In this

Enhancement   Edge map

FIGURE 17.4-12.   Examples of logarithmic Laplacian edge detection.

context other edge enhancement methods can be easily formulated as a concatenation of point nonlinear operations followed by linear edge enhancement and thresholding.

Rosenfeld (18) has developed a nonlinear product averaging mask for edge sharpening and edge isolation. With this operator the running one-dimensional average

$$D_M(j, k) = \frac{1}{M}[F(j+M-1, k) + F(j+M-2, k) + \cdots + F(j, k)$$

$$-F(j-1, k) - F(j-2, k) - \cdots - F(j-M, k) \qquad (17.4\text{-}16)$$

is formed at each pixel point where $M = 2^m$ and m is an integer. This operation is performed for $M = 1, 2, 4, 8, 16, \ldots$, etc. up to some desired upper limit. Then the product

$$P_M(j, k) = D_1(j, k)D_2(j, k) \cdots D_M(j, k) \qquad (17.4\text{-}17)$$

is formed at each pixel. Conceptually, the higher-order averaging masks provide a broad indication of edges and some degree of noise suppression, while the lower-order averaging masks yield localized derivatives, which are much more noise sensitive. Together, it is hypothesized, the product of the variable-length averaging masks should give a positive indication in the vicinity of true edges. Rosenfeld's justification of the operation is as follows: "... the result $P_M(j, k)$ tends to yield sharply localized detections of major edges while suppressing noise. Intuitively, this is because the product is large only when all factors are large, and as soon as one moves away from a position 'just at' an edge point, the factors with low m's become small; while if one is not at or near a major edge, the factors with high m's are small."

Rosenfeld (19) has also proposed a nonlinear thresholding procedure for isolating large sharp edges in the neighborhood of smaller edges. This procedure, which will be called dominant neighbor suppression, is performed by scanning the edge enhanced plane $G(j, k)$ with a small pixel window. The value of $G(j, k)$ in the center of the window is suppressed (set to zero) unless its magnitude is the greatest of all samples within the window. Conventional amplitude thresholding then follows. A variation of the process is to permit suppression of $G(j, k)$ only if a neighbor in the window dominates by a significant amount. The dominant neighbor suppression thresholding algorithm has proved quite effective for edge detection when coupled with an edge enhancement method that provides some noise smoothing. Figure 17.4-13 presents an example of dominant neighbor suppression thresholding.

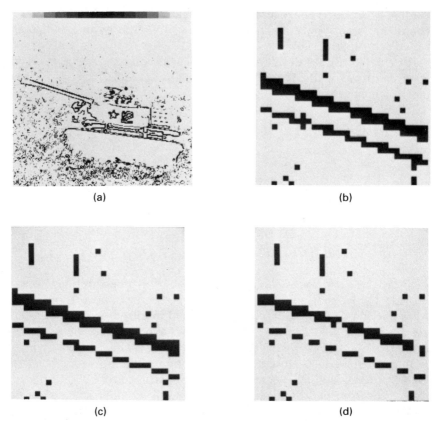

(a)   (b)

(c)   (d)

FIGURE 17.4-13. Comparison of standard and dominant neighbor suppression thresholding for Sobel edge detection. (a) Standard. (b) Blowup of barrel region of (a). (c) Blowup with dominance factor = 1.5. (d) Blowup with dominance factor = 1.2.

17.4.3. Edge Fitting Methods

Ideal edges may be viewed as one- or two-dimensional ramp signals of the form sketched in Figure 17.4-1. Actual image data can then be matched against, or fitted to, the ideal edge models. If the fit is sufficiently accurate at a given image location, an edge is assumed to exist with the same parameters as the ideal edge model.

In the one-dimensional edge fitting case described in Figure 17.4-14 the image signal $f(x)$ is fitted to a step function

$$s(x) = \begin{cases} b & x < x_0 \\ b + h & x \geq x_0 \end{cases} \tag{17.4-18}$$

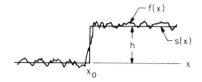

(a) ONE DIMENSIONAL

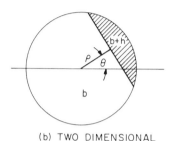

(b) TWO DIMENSIONAL

FIGURE 17.4-14. One- and two-dimensional edge fitting.

An edge is assumed present if the mean-square error

$$\mathscr{E} = \int_{x_0-L}^{x_0+L} [f(x) - s(x)]^2 \, dx \qquad (17.4\text{-}19)$$

is below some threshold value. In the two-dimensional formulation the ideal step edge is defined as

$$S(x, y) = \begin{cases} b & x \cos \theta + y \sin \theta < \rho \\ b+h & x \cos \theta + y \sin \theta \geq \rho \end{cases} \qquad (17.4\text{-}20)$$

where θ and ρ represent the polar distance from the center of a circular test region to the normal point of the edge. The edge fitting error is

$$\mathscr{E} = \iint_{\substack{\text{over} \\ \text{circle}}} [F(x, y) - S(x, y)]^2 \, dx \, dy \qquad (17.4\text{-}21)$$

Hueckel (20) has developed a procedure for two-dimensional edge fitting in which the image points within the circle of Figure 17.4-14 are expanded in a set of two-dimensional basis functions by a Fourier series in polar coordinates. Let $H_i(x, y)$ represent the basis functions. Then the weighting coefficients for the expansions of the image and the ideal step edge become

$$a_i = \iint H_i(x, y)F(x, y)\, dx\, dy \qquad (17.4\text{-}22a)$$

$$b_i = \iint H_i(x, y)S(x, y)\, dx\, dy \qquad (17.4\text{-}22b)$$

It should be noted that $S(x, y)$ is defined parametrically in terms of the set (b, h, ρ, θ). In Hueckel's algorithm the expansion is truncated to eight terms for computational economy and to provide some inherent noise smoothing. Minimization of the mean-square difference of Eq. 17.4-21 is equivalent to minimization of $(a_i - b_i)^2$ for all coefficients. Hueckel has performed this minimization, invoking some simplifying approximations, and has formulated a set of nonlinear equations expressing the edge parameter set $(\hat{b}, \hat{h}, \hat{\rho}, \hat{\theta})$ in terms of the expansions coefficients a_i. A test is performed to compare the actual image data $F(x, y)$ with the edge fit. If the resulting fit is poor, no edge is judged present, and if the fit is sufficiently close, a further test is made to determine if the edge contrast factor h is greater than a threshold factor.

The complexity of the Hueckel algorithm renders it difficult to analyze theoretically. However, experimental evidence indicates that the Hueckel operator performs quite well as an edge detector even for noisy and highly textured image fields (21). Figure 17.4-15 illustrates edge detection with the Hueckel algorithm.

Edge map

FIGURE 17.4-15. Examples of Hueckel edge fitting edge detection (21).

17.4.4. Statistical Edge Detection Methods

The general technique of edge enhancement followed by thresholding, in the variety of forms previously discussed, is heuristic in nature. Each method must be "tuned" by trial-and-error procedures with a set of test pictures. Usually, the resulting performance can only be measured, not predicted. The edge fitting approach, although mathematically formulated, suffers from many of the same defects. Additionally, both methods fail to cope effectively with noise. Attention is now directed to a class of edge detection techniques based on statistical detection theory.*

The performance of edge enhancement and edge fitting methods of edge detection in the presence of noise can be improved by statistically based processing techniques. Consider the common case in which the observed image $Y(j, k) = F(j, k) + N(j, k)$ is composed of the true image $F(j, k)$ plus a noise component $N(j, k)$. In the absence of noise, linear edge enhancement methods produce an enhanced image array $G(j, k) = H(j, k) \circledast F(j, k)$ where $H(j, k)$ is the impulse response of the enhancement system. With noise present the enhanced image $G_Y(j, k) = Y(j, k) \circledast H(j, k)$ contains an error component $H(j, k) \circledast N(j, k)$, which tends to be large at high spatial frequencies. This noise component can be minimized to a considerable extent by forming the estimate $\hat{G}(j, k)$ from the observation $Y(j, k)$ by conventional Wiener estimation techniques as described in Part 4. However, since Wiener estimation is a linear process, it is equivalent to form the estimate $\hat{G}(j, k) = H(j, k) \circledast \hat{F}(j, k)$ by estimation of the ideal image $F(j, k)$ from the noisy image $Y(j, k)$ before edge enhancement. It should be cautioned that this procedure is only optimal for purely linear processes. If edge thresholding is to be performed on the magnitude of $G_Y(j, k)$, mean-square estimation of $F(j, k)$ before enhancement is not necessarily optimal. However, this procedure is likely to produce better results than no preprocessing.

If an ideal edge signal can be characterized by some deterministic model, such as that of Figure 17.4-1, matched filtering techniques can be applied to edge detection. This subject is explored in Chapter 19.

17.5. LUMINANCE EDGE DETECTION PERFORMANCE

Relatively few studies of edge detector performance have been reported in the literature (24, 25). A performance evaluation is difficult because of the large number of proposed methods, difficulties in determining the best

---

* The statistical detection theory approach has been utilized in the detection of television image "detail" (22, 23).

parameters associated with each technique, and the lack of definitive performance criteria.

In developing performance criteria for an edge detector it is wise to distinguish between mandatory and auxiliary information to be obtained from the detector. Obviously, it is absolutely essential to determine the pixel location of an edge. Other information of interest includes the height and slope angle of the edge as well as its spatial orientation. Another useful item is a confidence factor associated with the edge decision, for example, the closeness of fit between actual image data and the idealized edge model. Unfortunately, few edge detectors provide this full gamut of information.

There are three major types of error associated with determination of an edge location: (1), missing valid edge points; (2), failure to localize edge points; (3), classification of noise pulses as edge points. Figure 17.5-1 illustrates a typical edge segment in a discrete image, an ideal edge representation, and edge representations subject to various types of error.

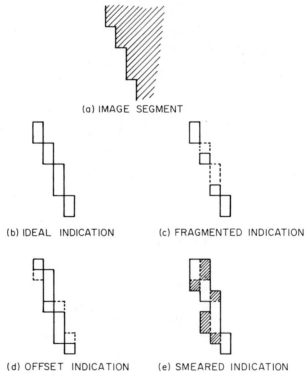

(a) IMAGE SEGMENT

(b) IDEAL INDICATION   (c) FRAGMENTED INDICATION

(d) OFFSET INDICATION   (e) SMEARED INDICATION

FIGURE 17.5-1. Indications of edge location.

A common strategy in signal detection problems is to establish some bound on the probability of false detection resulting from noise and then attempt to maximize the probability of true signal detection. Extending this concept to edge detection simply involves the setting of the edge detection threshold at a level such that the probability of false detection resulting from noise alone does not exceed some desired value. The probability of true edge detection can be readily evaluated by a coincidence comparison of the edge maps of an ideal and an actual edge detector. The penalty for nonlocalized edges is somewhat more difficult to assess. Edge detectors that provide a smeared edge location should clearly be penalized; however, credit should be given to edge detectors whose edge locations are localized but biased by a small amount. Edge location accuracy may be assessed by the figure of merit rating factor defined by

$$R = \frac{1}{I_N} \sum_{i=1}^{I_A} \frac{1}{1+\alpha d^2} \tag{17.5-1}$$

where $I_N = \max (I_I, I_A)$ and I_I and I_A represent the number of ideal and actual edge map points, α is a scaling constant, and d is the separation distance of an actual edge point normal to a line of ideal edge points. The rating factor is normalized so that $R = 1$ for a perfectly detected edge. The scaling factor α may be adjusted to penalize edges that are localized but offset from the true position. Normalization by the maximum of the actual and ideal number of edge points ensures a penalty for smeared or fragmented edges. As an example of performance, if $\alpha = \frac{1}{9}$, the rating of a vertical detected edge offset by one pixel becomes $R = 0.90$, and a two-pixel offset gives a rating of $R = 0.69$. With $\alpha = \frac{1}{9}$ a smeared edge of three pixels width centered about the true vertical edge yields a rating of $R = 0.93$ and a five-pixel-wide smeared edge gives $R = 0.84$. A higher rating for a smeared edge than for an offset edge is reasonable because it is possible to thin the smeared edge by postprocessing.

Some edge detectors provide an indication of edge height, slope angle, and orientation. For these detectors it is useful to determine the mean-square deviation in these quantities from their true values averaged over all true edge points that are coincident with detected edge points.

The performance evaluation methodology described above has been applied to the assessment of some of the most promising edge detection techniques introduced in Section 17.4 using a test image consisting of a 64×64-pixel array over a 0–255 amplitude range with a vertically oriented edge of variable contrast and slope placed at its center. Independent Gaussian noise of standard deviation σ_n has been added to the edge image, and the resultant picture has been clipped to the maximum display limits

(0–255). The signal-to-noise ratio is defined as

$$\text{SNR} = \frac{h^2}{\sigma_n^2} \qquad\qquad (17.5\text{-}2)$$

where h is the edge height. Since the purpose of the testing is to compare the performance of various edge detection methods, for fairness, it is

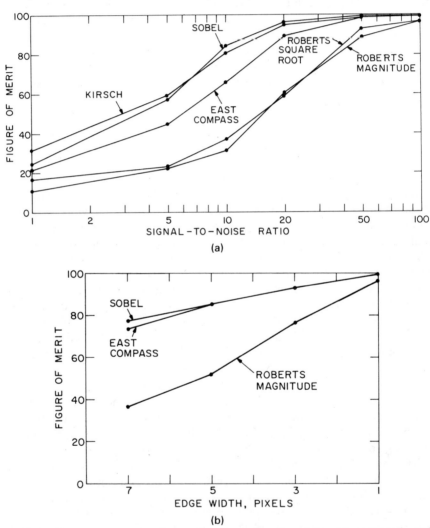

FIGURE 17.5-2. Edge location figure of merit as a function of signal-to-noise ratio and edge width. (a) Figure of merit versus SNR, $h = 25$, $w = 1$. (b) Figure of merit versus edge width, $h = 25$, SNR $= 100$.

important that each edge detector be tuned to its best capabilities. Consequently, each edge detector has been permitted to train both on random noise fields without edges and the actual test images before evaluation. For each edge detector the threshold parameter has been set to achieve the maximum figure of merit subject to the maximum allowable false detection rate.

Figure 17.5-2a contains a plot of the figure of merit as a function of signal-to-noise ratio for several edge detectors with $\alpha = \frac{1}{9}$. The figure of merit is also plotted in Figure 17.5-2b as a function of edge width. The figure of merit in Figure 17.5-2 generally follows expected trends: low for low-constrast, wide, noisy edges; and high in the opposite case. Some of the edge detection methods are universally superior to others for all test images. As a check on the subjective validity of the edge location figure of merit, Figures 17.5-3 and 17.5-4 present the edge location maps obtained for several test images for high- and low-ranking edge detectors. These figures tend to corroborate the utility of the figure of merit. A high figure of merit generally corresponds to a well-located edge upon visual analysis and vice versa.

17.6. COLOR EDGE FEATURES

Color images may be described quantitatively at each pixel by a set of three tristimulus values T_1, T_2, T_3, which are proportional to the amount of red, green, and blue primary lights required to match the pixel color. The luminance of the color is a weighted sum $Y = \alpha_1 T_1 + \alpha_2 T_2 + \alpha_3 T_3$ of the tristimulus values where the α_i are constants.

Several definitions of color edges are possible (26, 27). An edge in a color image could be defined to exist only if the luminance field contains an edge. However, this definition eliminates discontinuities in hue and saturation in regions of constant luminance. Another approach would be to examine each of the tristimulus arrays separately and only judge a color edge to be present if an edge exists simultaneously in all arrays. A third definition would be to define an edge to exist if the vector difference between the tritimulus value vectors of two colors exceeds some threshold level. With the latter two definitions of color edges, results are quite dependent on the tristimulus color coordinate systems chosen for representation. It is well known that equal changes in the red, green, and blue tristimulus values of a color are not equally perceptible. In Chapter 3 the L-a-b and $U^* - V^* - W^*$ color coordinate systems, which are nonlinear transformations, of tristimulus values, have been introduced. These color coordinate systems possess a metric color difference sensitivity to a

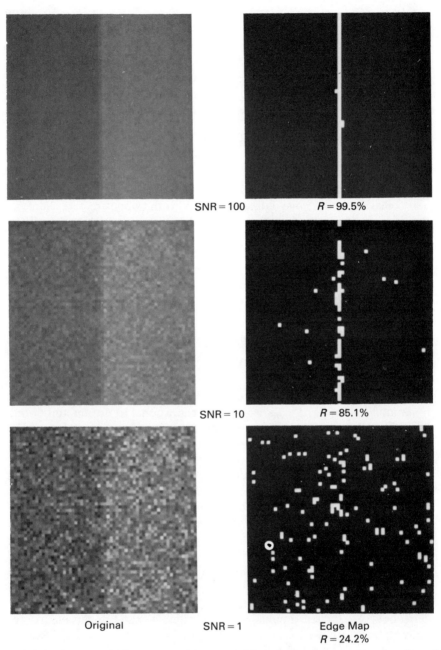

SNR = 100   R = 99.5%

SNR = 10   R = 85.1%

Original   SNR = 1   Edge Map
R = 24.2%

FIGURE 17.5-3. Edge location performance of Sobel edge detector as a function of signal-to-noise ratio, $h = 25$, $w = 1$, $\alpha = \frac{1}{9}$.

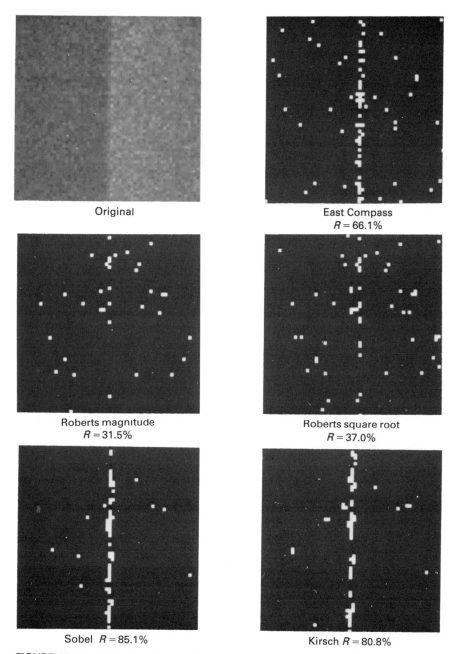

Original

East Compass
$R = 66.1\%$

Roberts magnitude
$R = 31.5\%$

Roberts square root
$R = 37.0\%$

Sobel $R = 85.1\%$

Kirsch $R = 80.8\%$

FIGURE 17.5-4. Edge location performance of several edge detectors for SNR $= 10$, $h = 25$, $w = 1$, $\alpha = \frac{1}{9}$.

good approximation, and hence are reasonable choices for color image edge analysis.

17.7. SPOT AND LINE FEATURES

An image spot is a relatively small region whose amplitude differs significantly from its neighborhood. A line segment is defined by its amplitude cross section, which must be U-shaped in a positive or negative sense over some extended region.

Rosenfeld et al. (28–30) have suggested an algorithm for spot detection in which an image is first smoothed with a $W \times W$ low-pass filter mask. Then the value of each point in the averaged image is compared to the average value of its four neighbors (right, left, up, down) spaced W pixels away. A spot is detected if the difference is sufficiently large. A similar approach (31) involves formation of the difference of the average pixel amplitude in a $W \times W$ window and the average amplitude in a surrounding ring region of width W. Both of these methods are special cases of linear spot enhancement followed by thresholding in which the enhancement mask is a composite mask of the form

$$H(j, k) = H_S(j, k) \circledast H_L(j, k) \tag{17.7-1}$$

where $H_S(j, k)$ is a low-pass filter smoothing mask as defined in Eq. 12.3-2 and $H_L j, k$ is one of the Laplacian masks of Eq. 17.4-5.

Lines and streaks, as defined here, are local segments of perhaps larger structures. A line is said to exist at a point if the image amplitude normal to the line moves from a lower to higher to lower level (or vice versa) at the given point and its two nearest neighbors along the direction of the curve (29). One approach to line detection is to spatially combine (link) the outputs of an edge detector within a local neighborhood. This subject is explored further in Chapter 18. Lines of unit width can be detected by convolving an image with a set of line masks

$$\mathbf{H}_1 = \begin{bmatrix} -1 & 2 & -1 \\ -1 & 2 & -1 \\ -1 & 2 & -1 \end{bmatrix} \tag{17.7-2a}$$

$$\mathbf{H}_2 = \begin{bmatrix} -1 & -1 & -1 \\ 2 & 2 & 2 \\ -1 & -1 & -1 \end{bmatrix} \tag{17.7-2b}$$

$$\mathbf{H}_3 = \begin{bmatrix} -1 & -1 & 2 \\ -1 & 2 & -1 \\ 2 & -1 & -1 \end{bmatrix} \qquad (17.7\text{-}2c)$$

$$\mathbf{H}_4 = \begin{bmatrix} 2 & -1 & -1 \\ -1 & 2 & -1 \\ -1 & -1 & 2 \end{bmatrix} \qquad (17.7\text{-}2d)$$

which enhance vertical, horizontal, and diagonal line segments. Thresholding of the enhanced arrays yields the line segment location. Hueckel (32) has generalized the concept of edge fitting to include the detection of line segments within a circular neighborhood. Pixel values within a circular window are fitted to an idealized line segment consisting of a parallel line strip whose amplitude is different from its neighboring regions. If the fit is close, the line segment is assigned the parameters of ideal line.

17.8. TEXTURE FEATURES

Many portions of natural scenes are devoid of significant detail over large areas. In these areas the scene can often be characterized ·as exhibiting a repetitive structure analogous to the texture of cloth or the pattern of a tile floor. In many imaging applications one may wish to measure the boundaries of the texture area and the "coarseness" of the texture within each region. The former task is covered in Section 18.7. This section considers the quantitative assessment of texture.

Several authors have attempted qualitatively to define texture. Pickett (33) states that "texture is used to describe two dimensional arrays of variations . . . The elements and rules of spacing or arrangement may be arbitrarily manipulated, provided a characteristic repetitiveness remains." Hawkins (34) has provided a more detailed description of texture: "The notion of texture appears to depend upon three ingredients: (1) some local 'order' is repeated over a region which is large in comparison to the order's size, (2) the order consists in the nonrandom arrangement of elementary parts, and (3) the parts are roughly uniform entities having approximately the same dimensions everywhere within the textured region." Although these descriptions of texture seem perceptually reasonable, they do not immediately lead to simple quantitative textural measures in the sense that the description of edge discontinuity leads to the quantitative definition of an edge in terms of its location, slope angle, and height.

Texture may be classified as being artificial or natural. Artificial textures consist of arrangements of symbols placed against a neutral background. These symbols may be line segments, dots, stars, or alphanumeric characters. Several examples of artificial texture are presented in Figure 17.8-1.

FIGURE 17.8-1.   Examples of artificial texture (33).

Natural textures, as the name implies, are images of natural scenes containing semirepetitive arrangements of pixels. Examples include photographs of brick walls, terrazo tile, sand, grass, etc. Brodatz (35) has published an album of naturally occurring textures. Figure 17.8-2 illustrates several examples of natural textures. The following analysis is restricted to natural textures.

Texture is often qualitatively described by its coarseness in the sense that a patch of wool cloth is coarser than a patch of silk cloth under the same viewing conditions. The coarseness index is related to the spatial repetition period of the local structure. A large period implies a coarse texture and a small period, a fine texture. This perceptual coarseness index is clearly not sufficient as a quantitative texture measure, but can at least be used as a guide for the slope of textural measures, that is, small numerical measures of texture should imply fine texture, and large numerical measures should

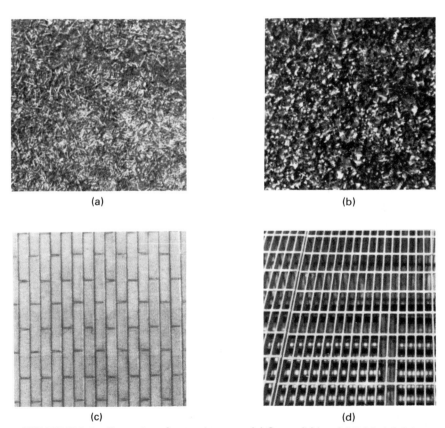

(a)   (b)

(c)   (d)

FIGURE 17.8-2.   Examples of natural texture. (a) Grass. (b) Ivy. (c) Brick. (d) Grill.

indicate coarse texture. It should be recognized that texture is a neighborhood property of an image point. Therefore, texture measures are inherently dependent on the size of the observation neighborhood employed in their formulation. Since texture is a spatial property, measurements should be restricted to regions of relative uniformity. Hence it is necessary to establish the limits of a uniform textural region by observation or by one of the automatic image segmentation methods described in Chapter 18 before attempting texture measurements.

Several studies (4, 34, 35) have considered textural analysis in terms of the Fourier spectrum of a region, as discussed in Section 17.3. Since the degree of texture coarseness is proportional to spatial period, a region of coarse texture should have its Fourier spectral energy concentrated at low spatial frequencies. Conversely, regions of fine texture should exhibit a concentration of spectral energy at high spatial frequencies. Although this correspondence exists to some degree, difficulties often arise because of spatial changes in the period and phase of pattern repetitions. Experiments (32, 34) have shown that there is considerable spectral overlap of regions of distinctly different natural texture such as urban, rural, and woodland regions extracted from aerial photographs. On the other hand Fourier spectral analysis has proved successful (7, 8) in the detection and classification of coal miners' black lung disease, which visually appears as diffuse textural deviations from the norm.

The spatial autocorrelation function has been suggested as the basis of a texture measure (36). Consider the autocorrelation function

$$A(\varepsilon, \eta; j, k) = \frac{\displaystyle\sum_{m=j-W}^{j+W} \sum_{n=k-W}^{k+W} F(m, n)F(m-\varepsilon, m-\eta)}{\displaystyle\sum_{m=j-W}^{j+W} \sum_{n=k-W}^{k+W} [F(m, n)]^2} \qquad (17.8\text{-}1)$$

computed over a $(2W+1) \times (2W+1)$ window at each image point (j, k) for a set of offset values, $\varepsilon, \eta = 0, \pm1, \pm2, \ldots, \pm T$. Presumably a region of coarse texture will exhibit a higher correlation for a fixed shift (ε, η) than a region of fine texture. Thus texture coarseness should be proportional to the spread of the autocorrelation function. One possible measure of the autocorrelation spread is given by the second moment measure,

$$T(j, k) = \sum_{\varepsilon=-T}^{T} \sum_{\eta=-T}^{T} \varepsilon^2 \eta^2 A(\varepsilon, \eta; j, k) \qquad (17.8\text{-}2)$$

Rosenfeld and Troy (36) have suggested some measure of the number of edges in a neighborhood about a point as a textural measure. As a first step an edge location array $E(j, k)$ is produced by some edge detection system such that $E(j, k) = 1$ for an edge and $E(j, k) = 0$ otherwise. Usually the detection threshold is set lower than the normal setting for isolation of boundary points. Then the texture measure is formed as

$$T(j, k) = \frac{1}{(2W+1)^2} \sum_{m=j-W}^{j+W} \sum_{n=k-W}^{k+W} E(m, n) \qquad (17.8\text{-}3)$$

over a $(2W+1) \times (2W+1)$ window for each image point under consideration.

Haralick, Shanmugan, and Dinstein (2) have proposed a number of textural measures based on the joint amplitude histogram of pairs of geometrically related image points. If an image region contains fine texture, the two-dimensional histogram of pairs of pixels will tend to be uniform, and for coarse texture the histogram values will be skewed toward the diagonal of the histogram. Consider the pair of pixels $F(j, k)$ and $F(m, n)$ that are separated by r radial units at an angle θ with respect to the horizontal axis. Let $P(a, b; j, k, r, \theta)$ represent the two-dimensional histogram measurement of the image field over some $(2W+1) \times (2W+1)$ window where each pixel amplitude is quantized over a range $0 \le a, b \le L-1$. The two-dimensional histogram can be considered as an estimate of the joint probability distribution

$$P(a, b; j, k, r, \theta) \approx P_R\{F(j, k) = a, F(m, n) = b\} \qquad (17.8\text{-}4)$$

For each member of the parameter set (j, k, r, θ) the two-dimensional histogram may be regarded as an $L \times L$ array of numbers relating the measured statistical dependency of pairs of pixels. Such arrays have been called gray level dependency matrices or joint occurrence matrices. Since an $L \times L$ histogram array must be accumulated for each image point (j, k) and separation set (r, θ) under consideration, it is usually computationally necessary to restrict the angular and radial separation to few values. Figure 17.8-3 illustrates geometrical relationships of histogram measurements made for four radial separation points and angles of $\theta = 0, \pi/4, \pi/2$, and $3\pi/4$ radians under the assumption of angular symmetry. In order to obtain statistical confidence in estimation of the joint probability distribution, the histogram must contain a reasonably large average occupancy level. This can be achieved either by restricting the number of amplitude quantization levels or by utilizing a relatively large measurement window. The former approach results in a loss of accuracy in the measurement of low-amplitude texture, while the latter approach causes errors if the texture changes over the window region. A typical compromise is to use 16 gray levels and a window of about 30–50 pixels on each side.

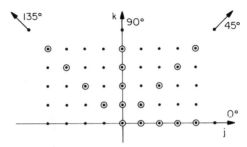

FIGURE 17.8-3.   Geometry for measurement of gray level dependency matrix.

Perspective views of joint amplitude histograms are presented in Figure 17.8-4 as a function of (r, θ) for coarse and fine texture regions. For a given separation set (r, θ) the histograms obtained for fine texture tend to be more uniformly dispersed than the histogram for coarse texture. Texture coarseness can be measured in terms of the relative spread of histogram occupancy cells about the main diagonal. Haralick et al. (2) have proposed a number of histogram spread indicators for texture measure. Several of these have been presented in Section 17.2. As an example, the inertia function of Eq. 17.2-13 results in a texture measure of the form

$$T(j, k, r, \theta) = \sum_{a=0}^{L-1} \sum_{b=0}^{L-1} (a-b)^2 P(a, b; j, k, r, \theta) \qquad (17.8\text{-}5)$$

If the textural region of interest is suspected to be angular invariant, then it is reasonable to average over the measurement angles of a particular texture measure to produce the mean textural measure (7)

$$M_T(j, k, r) = \frac{1}{N_\theta} \sum_\theta T(j, k, r, \theta) \qquad (17.8\text{-}6)$$

where the summation is over the angular measurements and N_θ represents the number of such measurements. Similarly, an angular independent texture variance may be defined as

$$V_T(j, k, r) = \frac{1}{N_\theta} \sum_\theta [T(j, k, r, \theta) - M_T(j, k, r)]^2 \qquad (17.8\text{-}7)$$

Another useful measurement is the angular independent spread defined by

$$S(j, k, r) = \max_\theta \{T(j, k, r, \theta)\} - \min_\theta \{T(j, k, r, \theta)\} \qquad (17.8\text{-}8)$$

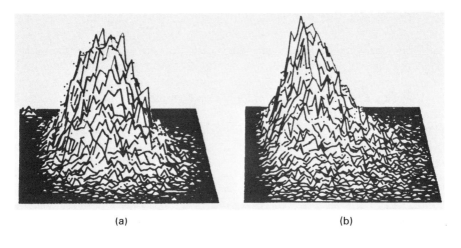

(a)   (b)

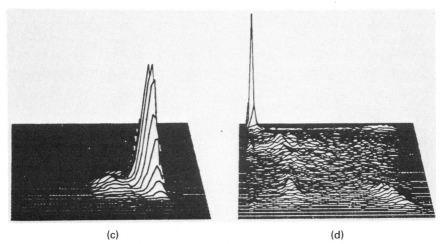

(c)   (d)

FIGURE 17.8-4. Perspective views of gray level dependency matrices for $r = 4$, $\theta = 0°$. (a) Grass. (b) Ivy. (c) Brick. (d) Grill.

Galloway (37) has proposed a variation of the image amplitude joint histogram texture measurement technique in which histograms of run lengths are utilized in place of amplitude histograms. A run length is defined in the conventional manner as the number of consecutive pixels of the same gray level lying in a particular coordinate direction. Coarse texture tends to create long runs while fine texture results in short runs. Several texture measures have been formulated in terms of the spread of run length counts.

Most research effort in texture analysis has been directed toward the utilization of texture descriptors as features for pattern recognition classification, rather than the development of texture measures. For example, Haralick and Shanmugan (38) have utilized joint luminance histogram texture descriptors to perform classification of aerial multispectral imagery, and Weska, Dyer, and Rosenfeld (39) have studied the terrain classification performance of several textural descriptors. Kruger, Thompson, and Turner (7) have applied textural descriptors to the detection and classification of coal miner's black lung disease from chest radiographs. In addition, Zobrist and Thompson (40) have used textural descriptors to develop a perceptual distance function that estimates the perceived dissimilarity between textural regions.

17.9. TEXTURE SYNTHESIS

There are many applications in image processing in which texture synthesis is useful. For example, if a region of a picture is missing or highly corrupted by error, artificial texture can be generated to replace the data. Also, for image coding applications, textural regions devoid of significant detail can be detected and measured; artificial texture can then be substituted for the original region. Presumably, coding of the artificial texture will be more efficient than direct image coding.

A fundamental approach to texture synthesis is to create some basic primitive pattern and spatially repeat the pattern according to some placement rules (41). The basic pattern could be a small section extracted from a natural texture region, or perhaps constructed from smaller primitive elements such as dot or line segments. Placement of the primitive pattern can be deterministic or probabilistic or it can follow some mixed strategy. Consideration must also be given to edge effects occurring when primitive patterns are placed spatially adjacent. Some smoothing of the interface is usually essential.

Another technique of texture synthesis is based upon the generation of correlated two-dimensional random field. Julesz (42) has found that viewers are unable to discriminate between textural fields that possess the same second-order statistics. Thus if an adequate texture measure is available, then it should be possible to generate a two-dimensional second-order process matched to a segment of natural texture provided that the artificial and natural texture regions possess similar texture measure values. Figure 17.9-1 contains photographs of "grass" and "gravel" natural textures and a set of two-dimensional random fields shaped to match the second-order statistics of the natural textures.

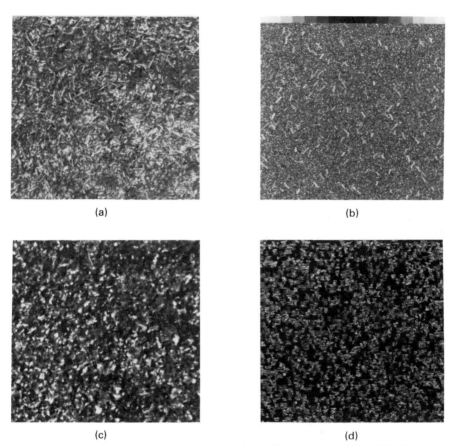

(a)   (b)

(c)   (d)

FIGURE 17.9-1.   Examples of texture synthesis. (a) Natural grass. (b) Artificial grass. (c) Natural ivy. (d) Artificial ivy.

REFERENCES

1. R. O. Duda, "Image Data Extraction," unpublished notes, July 1975.

2. R. M. Haralick, K. Shanmugan, and I. Dinstein, "Texture Features for Image Classification," *IEEE Trans. Systems, Man, and Cybernetics*, **SMC-3**, November 1973, 610–621.

3. G. G. Lendaris and G. L. Stanley, "An Opticalogical Self-Organizing Recognition System," in *Optical and Electro-Optical Information Processing*, J. T. Tippett et al., Eds., Massachusetts Institute of Technology Press, Cambridge, Mass., 1965.

4. G. G. Lendaris and G. L. Stanley, "Diffraction Pattern Sampling for Automatic Pattern Recognition," *Proc. IEEE*, **58**, 2, February 1970, 198–216.

5. R. M. Haralick and R. Bosley, "Spectral and Textural Processing of ERTS Imagery," Proceedings 3rd ERTS-1 Symposium, Vol. I, December 1973, 1929–1969.

6. E. L. Hall et al., "A Survey of Preprocessing and Feature Extraction Techniques for Radiographic Images," *IEEE Trans. Computers*, **C-20**, 9, September 1971, 1032–1044.

7. R. P. Kruger, W. B. Thompson, and A. F. Turner, "Computer Diagnosis of Pneumoconiosis," *IEEE Trans. Systems, Man, and Cybernetics*, **SMC-4**, 1, January 1974, 40–49.

8. R. N. Sutton and E. L. Hall, "Texture Measures for Automatic Classification of Pulmonary Disease," *IEEE Trans. Computers*, **C-21**, July 1972, 667 676.

9. J. M. S. Prewitt, "Object Enhancement and Extraction," in *Picture Processing and Psychopictorics*, B. S. Lipkin and A. Rosenfeld, Eds., Academic Press, New York, 1970.

10. E. Argyle, "Techniques for Edge Detection," *Proc. IEEE*, **59**, 2, February 1971, 285–287.

11. I. D. G. Macleod, "On Finding Structure in Pictures," in *Picture Language Machines*, S. Kaneff, Ed., Academic Press, New York, 1970, 231.

12. I. D. G. Macleod, "Comments on 'Techniques for Edge Detection,' " *Proc. IEEE*, **60**, 3, March 1972, 344.

13. A. Rosenfeld, M. Thurston, and Y. Lee, "Edge and Curve Detection: Further Experiments," *IEEE Trans. Computers*, **C-21**, 7, July 1972, 677–715.

14. L. G. Roberts, "Machine Perception of Three-Dimensional Solids," in *Optical and Electro-Optical Information Processing*, J. T. Tippett et al., Eds., Massachusetts Institute of Technology Press, Cambridge, Mass., 1965, 159–197.

15. R. O. Duda and P. E. Hart, *Pattern Classification and Scene Analysis*, Wiley, New York, 1973.

16. R. Kirsch, "Computer Determination of the Constituent Structure of Biological Images," *Computers and Biomedical Research*, **4**, 3, 1971, 315–328.

17. R. Wallis, private communication.

18. A. Rosenfeld, "A Nonlinear Edge Detection Technique," *Proc. IEEE Letters*, **58**, 5, May 1970, 814–816.

19. A. Rosenfeld and M. Thurston, "Edge and Curve Detection for Visual Scene Analysis," *IEEE Trans. Computers*, **C-20**, 5, May 1971, 562–569.

20. M. Hueckel, "An Operator which Locates Edges in Digital Pictures," *JACM*, **18**, 1, January 1971, 113–125.

21. R. Nevatia, "Object Boundary Determination in a Textured Environment," Proceedings ACM'75 Conference, Minneapolis, Minn., October 1975, 32–36.

22. G. G. Gouriet, "A Method for Measuring Television Picture Detail," *Electronic Engineering*, **24**, July 1952, 308–311.

23. M. H. Kubba, "Automatic Picture Detail Detection in the Presence of Random Noise," *Proc. IEEE*, **51**, 11, November 1963, 1518–1523.

24. A. Herskovits and T. O. Binford, "On Boundary Detection," MIT Project MAC, Artificial Intelligence Memo 183, July 1970.

25. J. R. Fram and E. S. Deutsch, "On the Evaluation of Edge Detection Schemes and Their Comparison with Human Performance," *IEEE Trans. Computers*, **C-24**, 6, June 1975, 616–628.

26. G. S. Robinson, "Color Edge Detection," Proceeding SPIE Symposium on Advances in Image Transmission Techniques, Vol. 87, San Diego, California, August 1976.

27. R. Nevatia, "Hueckel Color Edge Detector," University of Southern California, Image Processing Institute, Report USCIPI 660, March 1976, 70–81.

28. C. M. Cook and A. Rosenfeld, "Size Detectors," *Proc. IEEE Letters*, **58**, 12, December 1970, 1956–1957.

29. S. W. Zucker, A. Rosenfeld, and L. S. Davis, "Picture Segmentation by Texture Discrimination," *IEEE Trans. Computers*, **C-24**, 12, December 1975, 1228–1233.

30. M. Heuckel, "A Local Visual Operator Which Recognizes Edges and Lines," *JACM*, **20**, 4, October 1973, 634–647.

31. R. M. Pickett, "Visual Analysis of Texture in the Detection and Recognition of Objects," in *Picture Processing and Psychopictorics*, B. C. Lipkin and A. Rosenfeld, Eds., Academic Press, New York, 1970, 289–308.

32. J. K. Hawkins, "Textural Properties for Pattern Recognition," in *Picture Processing and Psychopictorics*, B. S. Lipkin and A. Rosenfeld, Eds., Academic Press, New York, 1970, 347–370.

33. P. Brodatz, *Texture: A Photograph Album for Artists and Designers*, Dover, New York, 1956.

34. H. R. Johnston et al., "Rapid Cartographic Processing System Study," AD 454086, October 1964.

35. A. Rosenfeld, "Automatic Recognition of Basic Terrain Types from Aerial Photographs," *Photogrammic Engineering*, **28**, 1, March 1962, 115–132.

36. A. Rosenfeld and E. B. Troy, "Visual Texture Analysis," Proceedings UMR-Mervin J. Kelly Communications Conference, University of Missouri-Rolla, Missouri, October 1970, Section 10-1.

37. M. M. Galloway, "Texture Analysis Using Gray Level Run Lengths," *Computer Graphics and Image Processing*, **4**, 2, June 1975, 172–179.

38. R. M. Haralick and K. Shanmugam, "Computer Classification of Reservoir Sandstones," *IEEE Trans. Geosci. Electronics*, **GE-11**, October 1973, 171–177.

39. J. S. Weska, C. R. Dyer, and A. Rosenfeld, "A Comparative Study of Texture Measures for Terrain Classification," *IEEE Trans. Systems, Man, and Cybernetics*, **SMC-6**, 4, April 1976, 269–285.

40. A. L. Zobrist and W. B. Thompson, "Building a Distance Function for Gestalt Grouping," *IEEE Trans. Computers*, **C-4**, 7, July 1975, 718–728.

41. A. Rosenfeld and B. S. Lipkin, "Texture Synthesis," in *Picture Processing and Psychopictorics*, A. Rosenfeld and B. S. Lipkin, Eds., Academic Press, New York, 1970, 309–345.

42. B. Julesz et al., "Inability of Humans to Discriminate Between Visual Textures that Agree in Second-Order Statistics-Revisted," *Perception*, **2**, 1973, 391–405.

18 SYMBOLIC IMAGE DESCRIPTION

Symbolic image description is the task of conversion or mapping between a set of primitive image features, such as amplitude values, edge points, or texture measures, to a much smaller set of descriptors that can serve as data for subsequent semantic interpretation. Typical image symbols include chains of edge points formed into an object boundary, connected regions of constant image amplitude, color, or texture, and elementary shapes such as rectangles, circles, and triangles.

In speech processing there is a universally accepted set of speech symbols called phonemes, which are the basic sounds of spoken words. For example, the sound of "p" in the word "pin" is a phoneme. From these phonemes it is theoretically possible to form a printed language representation of an utterance. There exist a variety of speech features including volume, pitch, and spectral energy. The conversion process from these or other speech features to phonemes forms the symbolic description of speech.

Unfortunately, there are no "visual phonemes" analogous to speech phonemes. That is, there is no accepted set of visual symbols that are necessary and sufficient to describe an image. This lack of a set of unique image symbols creates several difficulties in image analysis. First, there is the selection problem of determining which symbols should be formed from image features for a particular analysis task. Next, there is the problem of specifying the required accuracy of symbol formation.

At present the field of symbolic image description is at a very elementary state of development. A better comprehension of symbolic description appears to be the key to the eventual development of generalized image analysis systems. This chapter presents a survey of techniques of symbolic image formation.

18.1. CONNECTIVITY

A fundamental step in the formation of a symbolic description of a picture from an array of pixels or a collection of primitive features is to specify the geometrical relationship or connectivity of pixels that are

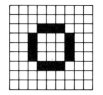

(a) RING FIGURE   (b) AMBIGUOUS FIGURE

FIGURE 18.1-1.   Illustrations of connectivity.

deemed to be of the same class (1, 2). In the binary picture of Figure 18.1-1*a* the ring of black pixels, by all reasonable definitions of connectivity, divides the picture into three pixel regions: the white pixels exterior to the ring, the white pixels interior to the ring, and the black pixels of the ring itself. The pixels within each region are said to be connected to one another. This concept of connectivity is easily understood for Figure 18.1-1*a*, but ambiguity arises when considering Figure 18.1-1*b*. Do the black pixels still define a ring, or do they instead represent four straight line segments? The answer to this question is not absolute, but rather subject to the desired definition of connectivity.

Returning to the more general case of gray level images, consider Figure 18.1-2*a*, in which a pixel (pixel *A*) is surrounded by eight neighbors (pixel

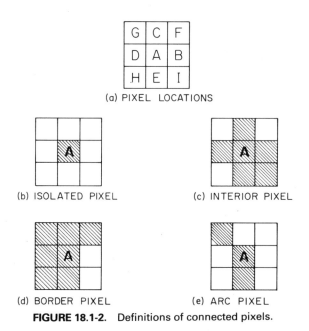

(a) PIXEL LOCATIONS

(b) ISOLATED PIXEL   (c) INTERIOR PIXEL

(d) BORDER PIXEL   (e) ARC PIXEL

FIGURE 18.1-2.   Definitions of connected pixels.

B to pixel *I*). Pixel *A* is assumed to belong to property set *S*; that is, some primitive description has been established for pixel *A* based on its brightness, color, texture, and so on. By the definition of four-connectivity, pixel *A* and pixel *B* are connected if both belong to property set *S*. Similarly, four-connectivity can potentially be established between pixel *A* and pixels, *B*, *C*, and *D*, which all share an extended boundary, provided that both members of the pair belong to the same property set. Eight-connectivity permits pixel *A* and one of its diagonal neighbors, with a common point boundary, for example, pixel *F*, to be connected if they both belong to identical property sets.

Under the definition of four-connectivity, Figure 18.1-1*b* contains four disconnected black line segments, but with the eight-connectivity definition, Figure 18.1-1*b* contains a ring of connected black pixels. Note, however, that under eight-connectivity, the white interior elements of the ring of Figure 18.1-1*b* are connected to the white exterior elements. Thus a paradox exists. If the black pixels are to be eight-connected together in a ring, one would expect a division between the interior and exterior white pixels of the ring. To eliminate this dilemma eight-connectivity can be defined for pixels of property set *S*, and four-connectivity can be established for pixels of property $\bar{S}$ ($\bar{S}$ is the complement of the set *S*) or vice versa.

Referring to Figure 18.1-2, let a shaded pixel be a member of property set *S* and an unshaded pixel a member of $\bar{S}$. Then pixel *A* in Figure 18.1-2*b* is called an isolated pixel if it is not eight-connected to any of its neighbors. In Figure 18.1-2*c* pixel *A* is an interior pixel that is four-connected to each of its neighbors *B*, *C*, *D*, *E*. A border pixel, as shown in Figure 18.1-2*d*, is not four-connected to at least one of its nearest neighbors. By this definition pixel *C* is not classified as a porder point. Figure 18.1-2*e* illustrates the definition of an arc point; pixel *A* is four-connected only to its upper and lower (or right and left) neighbors. An arc end pixel is four-connected to only one neighbor. Finally, a minimally connected arc is defined to be a set of arc points for which each interior arc point (nonarc end) is eight-connected to only two neighbors.

The preceding definitions concerning connectivity have been based on a digital image model obtained by sampling of a continuous image field over a rectangular array of points. Golay (3) has proposed a hexagonal grid structure as illustrated in Figure 18.1-3. With such a structure many of the relational problems associated with a rectangular grid are eliminated. In a hexagonal grid system neighboring pixels are said to be six-connected if they are in the same set and share a common edge boundary. Algorithms have been developed for the linking of boundary points for many feature extraction tasks (4). However, two major drawbacks have hindered wide

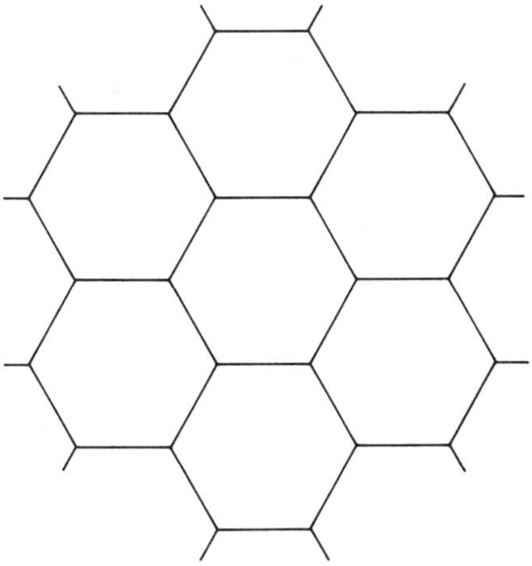

FIGURE 18.1-3. Hexagonal pixel grid.

acceptance of the hexagonal grid system. First, most image scanners are inherently oriented to rectangular scans; conversion to a hexagonal scan is often difficult. The second problems is that the hexagonal grid is not well suited to many spatial processing algorithms such as convolution and Fourier domain filtering.

18.2. SHRINKING, THINNING, AND SKELETONIZING

Shrinking and thinning are irreversible operations that seek to reduce a connected region of pixels of a given property set to a smaller size. Shrinking reduces the region to a single pixel, while thinning reduces a region to minimal cross-sectional width. Skeletonizing is a related operation that transforms a region to a stick figure representation.

Figure 18.2-1 illustrates a simple shrinking algorithm operating on a rectangular object and an irregularly shaped region. In this algorithm border points that are not arc points, indicated by Xs, are removed from a region if removal of a pixel does not result in a disconnected region under the definition of eight-connectivity. Arc points are removed only if they are arc end points and removal does not cause the region to vanish. The algorithm stops when a single pixel remains.

The operation of a simple thinning algorithm is described in Figure 18.2-2a for thinning of a rectangularly shaped object. In the first step of the first stage of the algorithm, border pixels on the left side of the object, denoted by Ls, are removed if they are not arc points and removal does not destroy eight-connectivity. In the second step border pixels on the right

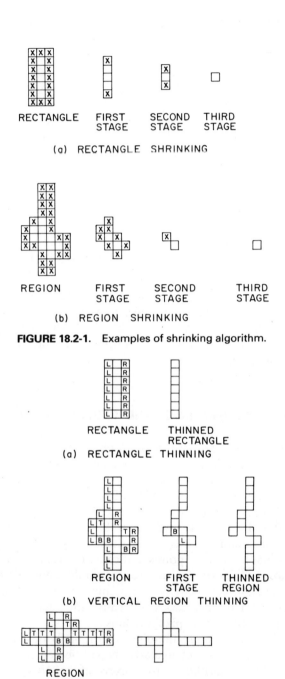

RECTANGLE   FIRST   SECOND   THIRD
            STAGE   STAGE   STAGE

(a) RECTANGLE SHRINKING

REGION   FIRST   SECOND   THIRD
            STAGE   STAGE   STAGE

(b) REGION SHRINKING

FIGURE 18.2-1. Examples of shrinking algorithm.

RECTANGLE   THINNED
             RECTANGLE

(a) RECTANGLE THINNING

REGION   FIRST   THINNED
             STAGE   REGION

(b) VERTICAL REGION THINNING

REGION

(c) HORIZONTAL REGION THINNING

FIGURE 18.2-2. Examples of thinning algorithm.

side of the object, indicated by Rs, are removed under the same conditions as for left border points. The removal process then proceeds to top (T) and bottom (B) border points, which are removed if they are not arc points and removal does not destroy eight-connectivity. After the four steps of the first stage, the algorithm repeats until no more pixels can be removed without affecting continuity. Figure 18.2-2*b* and 18.2-2*c* illustrate the operation of this algorithm applied to an irregularly shaped region oriented vertically and horizontally. The results are different because of the sequential ordering of steps.

Rosenfeld (1, 2, p. 82) and Preston (5) have developed and analyzed several sequential shrinking and thinning algorithms. Algorithms have also been developed for several parallel processing machines (6–9).

A skeleton or stick figure representation of an object is often sufficient to express the structural relationship of complex objects in a scene. Clearly, the stick figure of most objects can usually be represented much more efficiently than the object itself. One approach to object skeletonizing is to thin an object until a minimally connected chain of pixels is achieved. The difficulty with this approach is that the skeleton is not uniquely defined; the form of the resultant stick figure is usually highly dependent on the thinning algorithm.

Blum (10) has introduced a clever skeletonizing technique called the medial axis transformation that produces a unique skeleton for a given object. An intuitive definition of the medial axis transformation is based upon the "prairie fire" analogy (11–13). Consider the circle and rectangle regions of Figure 18.2-3, which are composed of dry grass on a bare dirt

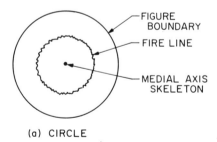

(a) CIRCLE

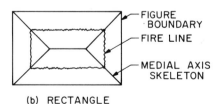

(b) RECTANGLE

FIGURE 18.2-3.   Examples of medial axis transforms.

background. If the fire were simultaneously started on the perimeter of the grass, the fire would proceed to burn toward the center of the figures until all of the grass was consumed. In the case of the circle the fire would burn to the center point of the circle, which is the quench point of the fire. For the rectangle the fire would proceed from each side. As the fire moved from the left and top the fire lines would meet and quench the fire. The locus of quench points forms the quench line of the figure. The quench points or quench lines of a figure are called its medial axis skeleton. More generally, the medial axis skeleton consists of the set of points that are equally distant from two closest points of a figure boundary. The minimal distance function is called the quench distance of the figure. From the medial axis skeleton of a figure and its quench distance it is possible to reconstruct the figure boundary. The figure boundary is determined by the union of a set of circular discs formed by circumscribing a circle whose radius is the quench distance at each point of the medial axis skeleton.

Practical problems occur in applying the medial axis transform to discrete objects defined over a rectangular grid. Definitions of distance must be properly defined to ensure uniqueness of the transformation. If an object has a complex shaped boundary, its skeleton will tend also to be complicated. Montanari (14, 15) has investigated the effect of simplifying an object skeleton in order to achieve a more compact representation of a figure. For many objects deletion or smoothing of parts of the skeleton produce an approximate object boundary that does not differ markedly from the original object boundary.

18.3. LINE DESCRIPTION

Straight and curved line segments form the basic structure of many pictures. In such images a mathematical relationship of detected points on an object boundary provides a symbolic description of the image. Two approaches to the establishment of mathematical relationships are described: curve fitting and line-to-point transformation.

18.3.1. Curve Fitting

Consider a set of points (x_i, y_i) for $i = 0, 1, 2, \ldots, M$ that originate from a boundary or boundary segment of a two-dimensional object as illustrated by the example of Figure 18.3-1. The points are assumed ordered in the sense that the pair of points (x_i, y_i) and (x_{i+1}, y_{i+1}) are nearest neighbors along the boundary path. If $x_{i+1} \geq x_i$ then the points are said to be causally

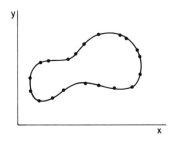 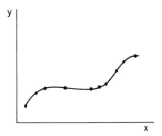

FIGURE 18.3-1. Object boundary points. (a) Object points. (b) Causally generated points.

related. A common example is points of a voltage-versus-time waveform.

Curve fitting to a set of points involves the determination of some functional relationship $\hat{y} = g(x)$ for which an error measure between the set of data points (x_i, y_i) and the set of functional points $[x_i, g(x_i)]$ is minimized. If the object points are causally related, the error is usually measured along the y coordinate. Typical error measures include the magnitude error

$$\mathscr{E} = \sum_{i=1}^{M} |y_i - g(x_i)| \tag{18.3-1a}$$

the least-square error

$$\mathscr{E} = \sum_{i=1}^{M} [y_i - g(x_i)]^2 \tag{18.3-1b}$$

and the peak error

$$\mathscr{E} = \max_{i} |y_i - g(x_i)| \tag{18.3-1c}$$

For general object points the error measures of Eq. 18.3-1 are often not meaningful. In such cases the dynamic error associated with each data point can be measured from (x_i, y_i) to a point normal to the fitting curve $y = g(x)$, and a magnitude, least-square, or maximum error relationship can be developed in a form analogous to Eq. 18.3-1. Minimization of the resulting error equation for general curve fitting functional relations is usually quite difficult.

The most common means of curve fitting for causal data points is a piecewise polynomial curve fit. For such a fit the approximating line assumes the form

$$\hat{y} = a_0 + a_1 x + a_2 x^2 + \cdots + a_N x^N \tag{18.3-2}$$

where the a_n are the polynomial weighting coefficients. Substitution of the observed data points into Eq. 18.3-2 yields the vector-space relationship

$$
\begin{bmatrix}
1 & x_0 & x_0^2 & \cdots & x_0^N \\
1 & x_1 & x_1^2 & \cdots & x_1^N \\
1 & x_2 & x_2^2 & \cdots & x_2^N \\
 & \vdots & & & \\
1 & x_M & x_M^2 & \cdots & x_M^N
\end{bmatrix}
\begin{bmatrix}
a_0 \\
a_1 \\
a_2 \\
\vdots \\
a_N
\end{bmatrix}
=
\begin{bmatrix}
\hat{y}_0 \\
\hat{y}_1 \\
\hat{y}_2 \\
\vdots \\
\hat{y}_M
\end{bmatrix}
\qquad (18.3\text{-}3a)
$$

which may be expressed in the compact relation

$$\mathbf{Xa} = \hat{\mathbf{y}} \qquad (18.3\text{-}3b)$$

For a least-squares error criterion

$$\mathscr{E} = (\mathbf{y} - \hat{\mathbf{y}})^T (\mathbf{y} - \hat{\mathbf{y}}) \qquad (18.3\text{-}4)$$

the optimal set of polynomial weighting coefficients is given by the generalized inverse solution

$$\mathbf{a} = \mathbf{X}^- \mathbf{y} \qquad (18.3\text{-}5)$$

In the overdetermined case $(M > N)$, for which the number of data points exceeds the number of polynomial coefficients, the generalized inverse can be expressed explicitly as

$$\mathbf{X}^- = (\mathbf{X}^T \mathbf{X})^{-1} \mathbf{X}^T \qquad (18.3\text{-}6)$$

provided that the data points x_i are distinct. For the common case of a linear curve fit, only the coefficients a_0 and a_1 are required. At the other extreme, if $\hat{y} = g(x)$ is specified to be an nth-order polynomial then $\mathbf{X}^- = \mathbf{X}^{-1}$ and equality of Eq. 18.3-3 holds at each data point. That is, the approximating polynomial passes through each data point. In this case the interpolating polynomial is mathematically unique, but it can be expressed and computed in a variety of forms, for example, Lagrange, Newton, Aitkens interpolation formulas (16).

   In their book, Duda and Hart (11) credit Forsen as being the developer of a simple piecewise linear curve fitting procedure called the iterated endpoint fit. In the first stage of the algorithm, illustrated in Figure 18.3-2, data endpoints A and B are connected by a straight line. The point of greatest departure from the straight line (point C) is examined. If the separation of this point is too large, the point becomes an anchor point for two straight line segments (A to C and C to B). The procedure then continues for each straight line segment until the data points are well fitted by line segments. The principal advantage of the algorithm is its simplicity;

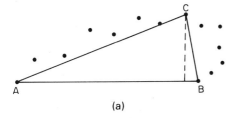

(a)

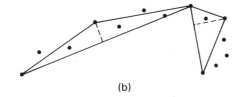

(b)

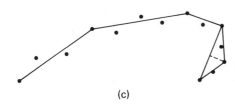

(c)

FIGURE 18.3-2. Iterative end point curve fitting. (a) First stage. (b) Second stage. (c) Third stage.

its disadvantage is error caused by incorrect data points. Ramer (17) has used a technique similar to the iterated endpoint fit procedure to determine a polygonal approximation to an arbitrary shaped closed curve. Pavlidas and Horowitz (18) have also developed related algorithms for polygonal curve fitting.

18.3.2. Line-to-Point Transformation

Another approach to line description, developed by Hough (19), involves the transformation of a line in Cartesian coordinate space to a point in polar coordinate space. A straight line may be parametrically described in Figure 18.3-3a as

$$\rho = x \cos \theta + y \sin \theta \qquad (18.3\text{-}7)$$

where ρ is the normal distance of the line from the origin and θ is the angle of the origin with respect to the x axis. The Hough transform of the line is

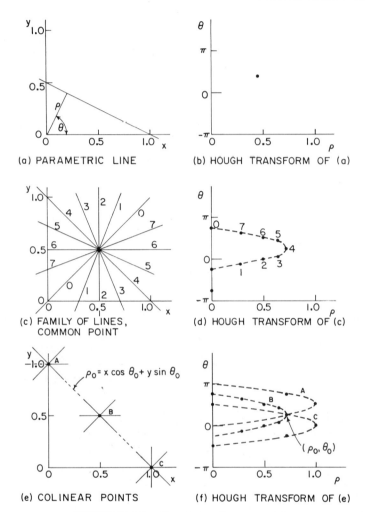

FIGURE 18.3-3.   Hough transform examples.

simply a point at coordinate (ρ, θ) in the polar domain as shown in Figure 18.3-3*b*. A family of lines passing through a common point, as shown in Figure 18.3-3*c*, maps into the connected set of ρ-θ points of Figure 18.3-3*d*. Now consider the three colinear points of Figure 18.3-3*e*. The Hough transformation of the family of curves passing through the three points results in the set of three parametric curves in the ρ-θ space of Figure 18.3-3*f*. These three curves cross at a single point (ρ_0, θ_0) corresponding to the dotted line passing through the colinear points.

Duda and Hart (20) have adapted the Hough transformation technique for line and curve detection in digital images. Each discrete data point in the x-y domain is transformed to a curve in the ρ-θ domain, which is quantized into cells. If an element of a curve falls in a cell, that particular cell is incremented by one count. After all data points are transformed, the ρ-θ cells are examined. Large cell counts correspond to colinear data points that may be fitted by a straight line with the appropriate (ρ, θ) parameters. Small counts in a cell generally indicate isolated points that can be deleted. O'Gorman and Clowes (21) have suggested a modification of the Hough transformation for linking edge points in an image. In their procedure the angle θ for entry in ρ-θ space is obtained from the gradient direction of an edge. The corresponding ρ value is then computed from Eq. 18.3-7 for the edge coordinate (x, y). However, instead of incrementing the (ρ, θ) cell by unity, the cell is incremented by the edge gradient magnitude in order to give greater importance to strong edges than weak edges.

18.4. SHAPE DESCRIPTION

Lines and curves may be considered as primitive elements of more global structures such as rectangles, triangles, circles, and free-form blobs. These global structures may then be described and analyzed by their shape attributes: metric, topological, and analytic. The discussion of shape in this section is limited to shape analysis by machine. References (22–24) describe research on shape from the standpoint of human perception in picture recognition.

18.4.1. Metric Attributes

Metric attributes of an image field are based on a distance measure between points in the field (11, 25). Distance is a real-valued function $d[(x_i, y_i), (x_j, y_j)]$ of two image points (x_i, y_i) and (x_j, y_j) satisfying the properties

$$d[(x_i, y_i), (x_j, y_j)] \geq 0 \qquad (18.4\text{-}1a)$$

$$d[(x_i, y_i), (x_j, y_j)] = d[(x_j, y_j), (x_i, y_i)] \qquad (18.4\text{-}1b)$$

$$d[(x_i, y_i), (x_j, y_j)] + d[(x_j, y_j), (x_k, y_k)] \geq d[(x_i, y_i), (x_k, y_k)] \qquad (18.4\text{-}1c)$$

There are a number of distance functions that satisfy the defining properties. The most common measures encountered in image analysis are the Euclidean distance

$$d_E = [(x_i - x_j)^2 + (y_i - y_j)^2]^{1/2} \qquad (18.4\text{-}2a)$$

the magnitude distance

$$d_M = |x_i - x_j| + |y_i + y_j| \qquad (18.4\text{-}2b)$$

and the maximum value distance

$$d_X = \max\{|x_i - x_j|, |y_i - y_j|\} \qquad (18.4\text{-}2c)$$

In discrete images the coordinate differences $(x_i - x_j)$ and $(y_i - y_j)$ are integers, but the Euclidean distance is usually not an integer. This factor inevitably leads to roundoff or truncation error in digital processing.

With the establishment of a distance measure, various metric attributes of an image may be developed. Among the most basic are the perimeter length P and the area A of an object. Another useful attribute is the thinness ratio, defined as

$$T = 4\pi\left(\frac{A}{P^2}\right) \qquad (18.4\text{-}3)$$

18.4.2 Topological Attributes

Topological shape attributes are properties of a shape that are invariant under "rubber-sheet" transformation (11, 26–28). Such a transformation or mapping can be visualized as the stretching of a rubber sheet containing an object of a given shape to produce some spatially distorted figure. Mappings that require cutting of the rubber sheet or connection of one part to another are not permissible. Metric distance is clearly not a topological attribute since distance can be altered by rubber sheet stretching. Also, the concepts of perpendicularity and parallelism between lines are not topological properties. Connectivity is a topological attribute. Figure 18.4-1a contains a binary valued figure with two connected components, and Figure 18.4-1b is a stretched version of the same figure. Clearly, there are no stretching operations that can either increase or decrease the connectivity of the figure. Connected components of a figure may contain holes, as illustrated in Figure 18.4-1c. The number of holes is obviously unchanged by a topological mapping. There is a fundamental relationship between the number of connected components C and the number of holes

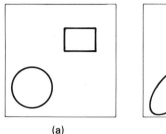 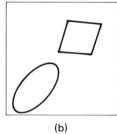 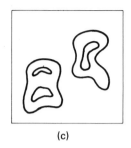

(a)   (b)   (c)

FIGURE 18.4-1. Examples of topological attributes. (a) Objects $C = 2$. (b) Objects after rubber sheet stretching. (c) Objects with holes $C = 2$, $H = 3$, $E = -1$.

H in a figure called the Euler number

$$E = C - H \qquad (18.4\text{-}4)$$

The Euler number is also a topological property since C and H are topological attributes.

    Irregularly shaped objects can be described by their topological constituents. Consider the tubular shaped object letter R of Figure 18.4-2a, and imagine a rubber band stretched about the object. The region enclosed by the rubber band is called the convex hull of the object. The set of points within the convex hull that are not in the object form the convex deficiency of the object. There are two types of convex deficiencies: regions totally enclosed by the object, called lakes; and regions lying between the convex hull perimeter and the object, called bays. In some applications it is simpler to describe an object indirectly in terms of its convex hull and convex

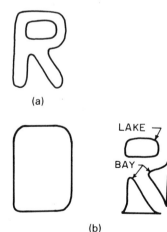

(a)

(b)

FIGURE 18.4-2. Definitions of convex shape descriptors. (a) Figure. (b) Convex hull. Bays and lakes.

deficiency. For objects represented over rectilinear grids, the definition of the convex hull must be modified slightly to remain meaningful. Objects such as discretized circles and triangles clearly should be judged as being convex even though their boundaries are jagged. This apparent difficulty can be handled by considering a rubber band to be stretched about the discretized object. A pixel lying totally within the rubber band, but not in the object, is a member of the convex deficiency. Sklansky et al. (29, 30) have developed practical algorithms for computing the convex attributes of discretized objects.

The topological attributes previously defined are useful as symbols for object recognition within images. Also, topological attributes can be employed to compute efficiently geometrical properties such as perimeter and area. The foundation of these applications is a collection of enumeration techniques for binary valued patterns (28). Consider an object defined over a rectangular grid containing pixels of value one against a background of zero valued pixels. The area of this object is obviously just the count of the ones in the image array. Symbolically,

$$A = n \boxed{1} \tag{18.4-5}$$

where $n \; (\cdot)$ represents the count of the number of patterns within the parentheses. If the object is completely enclosed by a border of white pixels, then its perimeter is equal to

$$P = 2 \cdot n \boxed{\begin{array}{c|c} 0 & 1 \end{array}} + 2 \cdot n \boxed{\begin{array}{c} 0 \\ \hline 1 \end{array}} \tag{18.4-6}$$

As an example for a 2×2-pixel square, $A = 4$ and $P = 8$. An object formed of three diagonally connected pixels possesses $A = 3$ and $P = 12$. Now consider the following set of 2×2-pixel patterns called bit quads:

$$Q_0 = \left\{ \begin{array}{c|c} 0 & 0 \\ \hline 0 & 0 \end{array} \right\} \tag{18.4-7a}$$

$$Q_1 = \left\{ \begin{array}{c|c} 1 & 0 \\ \hline 0 & 0 \end{array}, \begin{array}{c|c} 0 & 1 \\ \hline 0 & 0 \end{array}, \begin{array}{c|c} 0 & 0 \\ \hline 0 & 1 \end{array}, \begin{array}{c|c} 0 & 0 \\ \hline 1 & 0 \end{array} \right\} \tag{18.4-7b}$$

$$Q_2 = \left\{ \begin{array}{|c|c|}\hline 1 & 1 \\\hline 0 & 0 \\\hline\end{array}, \begin{array}{|c|c|}\hline 0 & 1 \\\hline 0 & 1 \\\hline\end{array}, \begin{array}{|c|c|}\hline 0 & 0 \\\hline 1 & 1 \\\hline\end{array}, \begin{array}{|c|c|}\hline 1 & 0 \\\hline 1 & 0 \\\hline\end{array} \right\} \qquad (18.4\text{-}7c)$$

$$Q_3 = \left\{ \begin{array}{|c|c|}\hline 1 & 1 \\\hline 0 & 1 \\\hline\end{array}, \begin{array}{|c|c|}\hline 0 & 1 \\\hline 1 & 1 \\\hline\end{array}, \begin{array}{|c|c|}\hline 1 & 0 \\\hline 1 & 1 \\\hline\end{array}, \begin{array}{|c|c|}\hline 1^{,} & 1 \\\hline 1 & 0 \\\hline\end{array} \right\} \qquad (18.4\text{-}7d)$$

$$Q_4 = \left\{ \begin{array}{|c|c|}\hline 1 & 1 \\\hline 1 & 1 \\\hline\end{array} \right\} \qquad (18.4\text{-}7e)$$

$$Q_D = \left\{ \begin{array}{|c|c|}\hline 1 & 0 \\\hline 0 & 1 \\\hline\end{array}, \begin{array}{|c|c|}\hline 0 & 1 \\\hline 1 & 0 \\\hline\end{array} \right\} \qquad (18.4\text{-}7f)$$

The area and perimeter of an image can be expressed in terms of the number of bit quad counts in the image as

$$A = \tfrac{1}{4}[n(Q_1) + 2 \cdot n(Q_2) + 3 \cdot n(Q_3) + 4 \cdot n(Q_4) + 2 \cdot n(Q_D)] \qquad (18.4\text{-}8a)$$

$$P = n(Q_1) + n(Q_2) + n(Q_3) + 2 \cdot n(Q_D) \qquad (18.4\text{-}8b)$$

These area and perimeter formulas may be in considerable error if they are utilized to represent the area of a continuous object that has been discretized. More accurate formulas for such applications have been derived by Duda (31):

$$A = \tfrac{1}{4} \cdot n(Q_1) + \tfrac{1}{2} \cdot n(Q_2) + \tfrac{7}{8} \cdot n(Q_3) + n(Q_4) + \tfrac{3}{4} \cdot n(Q_D) \qquad (18.4\text{-}9a)$$

$$P = n(Q_2) + \frac{1}{\sqrt{2}}[n(Q_1) + n(Q_3) + 2 \cdot n(Q_D)] \qquad (18.4\text{-}9b)$$

Bit quad counting provides a very simple means of determining the Euler number of an image. Gray (28) has determined that under the definition of four-connectivity the Euler number can be computed as

$$E = \tfrac{1}{4}[n(Q_1) - n(Q_3) + 2 \cdot n(Q_D)] \qquad (18.4\text{-}10a)$$

and for eight-connectivity

$$E = \tfrac{1}{4}[n(Q_1) - n(Q_3) - 2 \cdot n(Q_D)] \qquad (18.4\text{-}10b)$$

If an image contains many components but few holes, then the Euler number can be taken as an approximation of the number of components. Then the average area and perimeter of connected components may be expressed as (28)

$$\bar{A} \approx \frac{A}{E} \qquad (18.4\text{-}11a)$$

$$\bar{P} = \frac{P}{E} \qquad (18.4\text{-}11b)$$

For images containing thin objects such as typewritten or script characters, the average object length and width can be approximated by (28)

$$\bar{L} = \frac{\bar{P}}{2} \qquad (18.4\text{-}12a)$$

$$\bar{W} = \frac{2\bar{A}}{\bar{P}} \qquad (18.4\text{-}12b)$$

These simple measures are useful for distinguishing gross characteristics of an image: does it contain a multitude of small point-like objects, or fewer blob-like objects of larger size; are the objects fat or thin; and so on.

18.4.3.   Analytic Attributes

Analytic attributes of shape are mathematical descriptions that constitute an alternative representation. To be useful, of course, these descriptions must be simpler than the initial representation of a shape in terms of the location and amplitude of discrete samples over its domain.

The perimeter of an arbitrary closed curve can be represented by its instantaneous curvature at each perimeter point. Consider the continuous closed curve drawn on the complex plane of Figure 18.4-3 in which a point

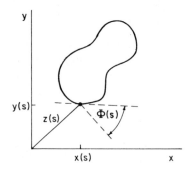

FIGURE   18.4-3.   Geometry   for   curvature definition.

on the perimeter is measured by its polar position $z(s)$ as a function of arc length s. The complex function $z(s)$ may be expressed in terms of its real part $x(s)$ and imaginary part $y(s)$ as

$$z(s) = x(s) + iy(s) \tag{18.4-13}$$

The tangent angle defined in Figure 18.4-3 is given by

$$\Phi(s) = \tan^{-1} \left[\frac{dy(s)/ds}{dx(s)/ds} \right] \tag{18.4-14}$$

and the curvature is the real function

$$k(s) = \frac{d\Phi(s)}{ds} \tag{18.4-15}$$

The coordinate points $x(s)$, $y(s)$ can be obtained from the curvature function by the reconstruction formulae

$$x(s) = x(0) + \int_0^s k(\alpha) \cos\left[\Phi(\alpha)\right] d\alpha \tag{18.4-16a}$$

$$y(s) = y(0) + \int_0^s k(\alpha) \sin\left[\Phi(\alpha)\right] d\alpha \tag{18.4-16b}$$

where $x(0)$ and $y(0)$ are the starting point coordinates.

Since the curvature function is periodic over the perimeter length P, it can be expanded in a Fourier series as

$$k(s) = \sum_{n=-\infty}^{\infty} c_n \exp\left\{\frac{2\pi i}{P} ns\right\} \tag{18.4-17a}$$

where the coefficients c_n are obtained from

$$c_n = \frac{1}{P} \int_0^P k(s) \exp\left\{-\frac{2\pi i}{P} n\right\} ds \tag{18.4-17b}$$

This result is the basis of an analysis technique developed by Cosgriff (32), Brill (33), and co-workers in which the Fourier expansion of a shape is truncated to a few terms to produce a set of Fourier descriptors. These Fourier descriptors are then utilized as a symbolic representation of shape for subsequent recognition and analysis.

If a shape has sharp discontinuities, for example, a rectangle, the curvature function is undefined at these points. This analytic difficulty can be overcome by the utilization of a cumulative shape function

$$\theta(s) = \int_0^s k(\alpha) \, d\alpha - \frac{2\pi s}{P} \tag{18.4-18}$$

proposed by Zahn (34). This function is also periodic over P and can therefore be expanded in a Fourier series for shape description.

Bennett and MacDonald (35) have analyzed the discretization error associated with the curvature function defined on discrete image arrays for a variety of connectivity algorithms. The discrete definition of curvature is given by

$$z(s_j) = x(s_j) + iy(s_j) \tag{18.4-19a}$$

$$\Phi(s_j) = \tan^{-1} \left[\frac{y(s_j) - y(s_{j-1})}{x(s_j) - x(s_{j-1})} \right] \tag{18.4-19b}$$

$$k(s_j) = \Phi(s_j) - \Phi(s_{j-1}) \tag{18.4-19c}$$

where s_j represents the jth step of arc position. Figure 18.4-4 contains results of the Fourier expansion of the discrete curvature function for a simple rule of four-connectivity.

Another approach to analytic shape description is by moment approximation. From probability theory the (m, n)th joint moment of the joint probability density $p(x, y)$ is defined as

$$M_{m,n} = \int_{-\infty}^{\infty} \int_{-\infty}^{\infty} x^m y^n p(x, y) \, dx \, dy \tag{18.4-20}$$

This moment can also be determined indirectly from the joint characteristic function

$$\Phi(\omega_x, \omega_y) = \int_{-\infty}^{\infty} \int_{-\infty}^{\infty} \exp\{i(\omega_x x + \omega_y y)\} p(x, y) \, dx \, dy \tag{18.4-21}$$

by the moment generating theorem

$$M_{m,n} = i^{-(m+n)} \frac{\partial^m \partial^n \Phi(\omega_x, \omega_y)}{\partial \omega_x^m \partial \omega_y^n} \bigg|_{\substack{\omega_x=0 \\ \omega_y=0}} \tag{18.4-22}$$

Joint central moments can be obtained by replacing x by $x - \eta_x$ and y by $y - \eta_y$ in Eq. 18.4-20 where η_x and η_y are the marginal density means of x and y, respectively.

These classical relationships of probability theory have been applied to shape description by Hu (38) and Alt (39). The concept is quite simple. The

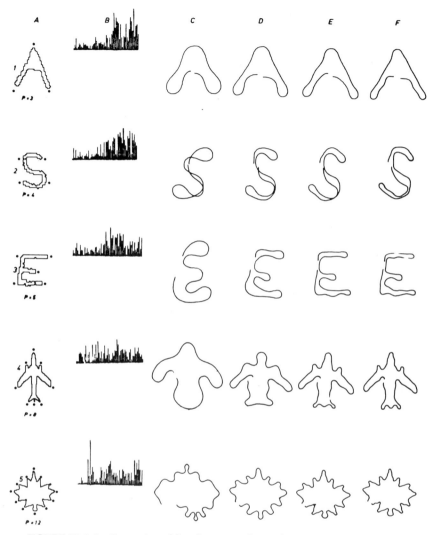

FIGURE 18.4-4. Examples of Fourier expansions of curvature function (35).

joint probability in Eqs. 18.4-20 and 18.4-21 is replaced by the image function $F(x, y)$. Object shape is represented by a few of the low-order moments. It should be observed that Eq. 18.4-21 is closely related to the standard continuous two-dimensional Fourier transform, and therefore a close connection should be expected between the moments and the low-order Fourier spectral components of the image function.

18.5.   AMPLITUDE SEGMENTATION

Segmentation of an image entails the division or separation of the image into regions of similar attribute. The most basic attribute for segmentation is image amplitude—luminance for a monochrome image and color coordinate for a color image. Section 18.6 considers segmentation based on edges, Section 18.7 discusses segmentation using texture as a discriminator, and shape segmentation is covered in Section 18.8. The definition of segmentation employed here is quite restrictive; no contextual information is permitted in the segmentation. Furthermore, segmentation does not involve labeling of each segment. The segmentor only subdivides an image; it does not attempt to recognize the individual segments or their relationships to one another. These important steps in an overall image understanding system are covered in Chapter 20.

18.5.1.   Luminance Thresholding

Many images can be characterized as containing some object of interest of reasonably uniform brightness placed against a background of differing brightness. Typical examples include handwritten and typewritten text, microscope medical samples, and airplanes on a runway. For such images, brightness is a distinguishing feature that can be utilized to locate the object. If an object of interest is white against a black background, or vice versa, it is a trivial task to set a midgray threshold to define the object points. Practical problems occur, however, when the observed image is subject to noise and both the object and background assume some broad range of gray scales. Another frequent difficulty is that the background may be nonuniform.

Figure 18.5-1a contains a photograph of digitized typewritten text consisting of dark letters against a lighter background. A gray scale histogram of the text is presented in Figure 18.5-1b. The expected bimodality of the histogram is masked by the relatively large percentage of background pixels. Figures 18.5-1d to 18.5-1f are threshold displays in which all points brighter than the threshold are mapped to a display luminance of 255, and the remaining points below the threshold are mapped to a zero level of display luminance. These photographs illustrate a common problem associated with image thresholding. If the threshold is set too low, portions of the letters are deleted (the stem of the letter "p" is fragmented). Conversely, if the threshold is set too high, object artifacts result (the loop of the letter "e" is filled in). The best compromise is usually determined by experimentation. An example of luminance thresholding of a gray level

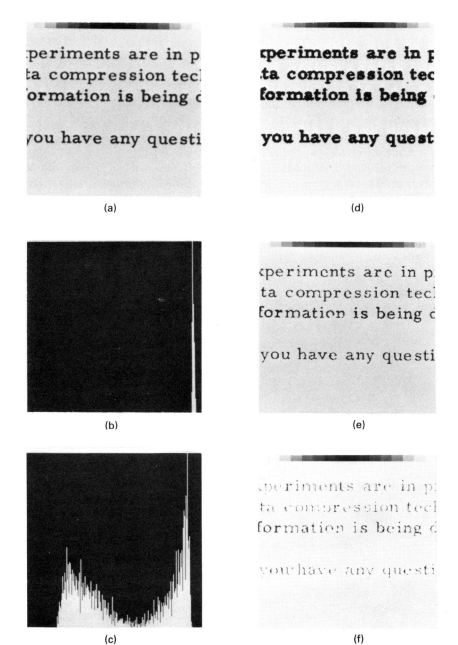

(a) (d)

(b) (e)

(c) (f)

FIGURE 18.5-1. Examples of luminance threshold segmentation of typewritten text. (a) Gray level image. (b) Image histogram. (c) Image histogram Laplacian mask. (d) High threshold, $T = 170$. (e) Medium threshold, $T = 127$. (f) Low threshold, $T = 25$.

image containing a single prominent object against a neutral background is provided in Figure 18.5-2.

Several analytic approaches to luminance thresholding have been suggested. One method is to set the gray level threshold at a level such that the cumulative gray level count matches an a priori assumption of the gray level probability distribution (38). For example, it may be known that black characters cover 25% of the area of a typewritten page. Thus the threshold level on the image might be set such that the quartile of pixels with the lowest brightness are judged to be black. Another approach to luminance thresholding is to select the threshold as the minimum point of the histogram between the bimodal peaks (39). Determination of the minimum is

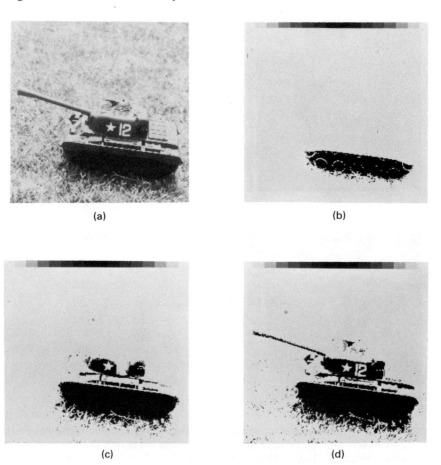

(a)   (b)

(c)   (d)

FIGURE 18.5-2.   Example of luminance threshold segmentation of TANK picture. (a) Original. (b) $T = 20$. (c) $T = 80$. (d) $T = 112$.

often difficult because of the jaggedness of the histogram. As a consequence, it is common practice to "fit" the histogram values between the peaks with some analytic function and obtain its minimum by differentiation. For example, let y and x represent the histogram ordinate and abscissa, respectively. Then the quadratic curve

$$y = ax^2 + bx + c \qquad (18.5\text{-}1)$$

where a, b, and c are constants provides a simple histogram approximation in the vicinity of the histogram valley. The minimum histogram value occurs for $x = -b/2a$.

Weszka, Nagel, and Rosenfeld (40) have suggested the use of a Laplacian operator to aid in luminance threshold detection. In a continuous image field the Laplacian operator

$$\nabla^2 F(x, y) = \frac{\partial^2 F(x, y)}{\partial x\,\partial y} \qquad (18.5\text{-}2)$$

forms the second partial derivative of the image field along the image coordinate directions. Consider an image region in the vicinity of an object in which the luminance increases from a low plateau level to a higher plateau level in a smooth ramp-like fashion. In the flat regions the Laplacian is zero and along the ramp it is nearly zero. Large positive values of the Laplacian will occur in the transition region from the low plateau to the ramp; large negative values will be produced in the transition from the ramp to high plateau. A gray level histogram formed of only those points of the original image that lie at coordinates corresponding to very high or low values of the Laplacian tends to be bimodal with a distinctive valley between the peaks since the histogram only contains gray levels occurring at the beginning and end of gray level slopes. Other edge isolation procedures covered in Chapter 17 can be used to aid in determination of the luminance threshold.

If the background of an image is nonuniform, it is necessary to adapt the luminance threshold to the mean luminance level (41, 42). This can be accomplished by subdividing the image into small blocks and determining the threshold for each block by the methods discussed previously. Threshold levels for each pixel may then be determined by interpolation between the block centers.

Image regions can sometimes be isolated by forming the average amplitude cross sections of an image (43, 44). The horizontal and vertical gray scale cross sections are defined as

$$H(k) = \frac{1}{N} \sum_{j=0}^{N-1} F(j, k) \qquad (18.5\text{-}3)$$

and

$$V(j) = \frac{1}{N} \sum_{k=0}^{N-1} F(j, k) \qquad (18.5\text{-}4)$$

Figure 18.5-3 illustrates an application of gray scale cross-section segmentation in determining the extent of an object in a reasonably uniform background field.

Effective segmentation can be achieved in some classes of images by a recursive luminance thresholding method suggested by Tomita, Yachida, and Tsuji (45). In the first stage of the process the image is thresholded to separate brighter regions from darker regions by locating a minimum between luminance modes of the histogram. Then histograms are formed of each of the segmented parts. If these histograms are not unimodal, the parts may again be thresholded. The process continues until the histogram

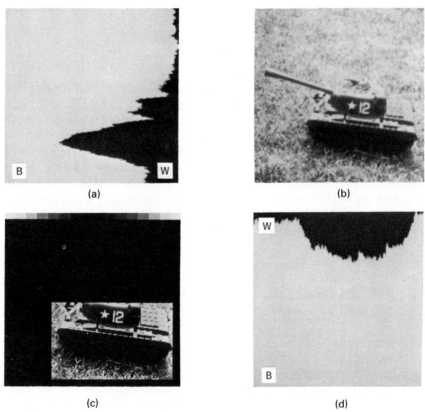

FIGURE 18.5-3.   Example of gray scale cross-section segmentation of TANK picture.
(a) Row histogram. (b) Original. (c) Segmentation. (d) Column Histogram.

of a part becomes unimodal or some desired level of segmentation is reached.

18.5.2. Multidimensional Thresholding

The luminance thresholding concept can be extended to the segmentation of color and multispectral images. Ohlander (46) has developed a segmentation scheme for natural color images based on multidimensional thresholding of color images represented by their red, green, blue (*R*, *G*,

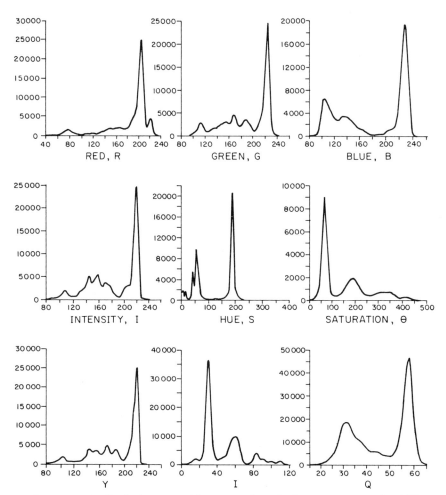

FIGURE 18.5-4. Typical property histograms for color image segmentation (46).

B) tristimulus values, their television transmission tristimulus values (*Y*, *I*, *Q*), and by a set of nonstandard color coordinates, loosely called intensity, hue, and saturation.* Figure 18.5-4 contains an example of the "property" histograms of these nine color coordinate signals for a room scene containing lounge furniture. The histograms of Figure 18.5-4 have been measured over those parts of the original scene that are relatively devoid of texture: the "nonbusy" parts of the scene. This important step of the segmentation method, covered in Section 18.8, is necessary to avoid false segmentation of homogeneous textured regions into many isolated parts. If the property histograms are not all unimodal, an ad hoc procedure is invoked to determine the best property and the best level for thresholding of that property. The first candidate is image intensity† in order to segment black or white regions. Other candidates are selected on a priority basis dependent on contrast level and location of the histogram modes. After a threshold level has been determined, the image is subdivided into its segmented parts. The procedure is then repeated on each part until the resulting property histograms become unimodal or the segmentation reaches a reasonable stage of separation under manual surveillance. Ohlander's segmentation technique using multidimensional thresholding aided by texture discrimination has proved quite effective in simulation tests. However, a large part of the simulation control structure has been performed by a human operator; human judgment predicated on trial threshold setting results is required for guidance.

In Ohlander's segmentation method the nine property values are obviously interdependent. The *Y*, *I*, *Q* signals are a linear combination of the *R*, *G*, *B* signals, and the intensity, hue, and saturation signals are nonlinear combinations of *R*, *G*, *B*. This observation raises several questions. What

---

* These unpublished color coordinates developed by J. M. Tenenbaum of Stanford Research Institute, which have been widely used by the scene analysis community, are defined below:

Intensity

$$I = R + G + B$$

Saturation

$$S = 1 - 3 \min (r, g, b)$$

where $r = R/I$, $g = G/I$, $b = B/I$.

Hue

$$\Phi = \cos^{-1}\left[\frac{2r - g - b}{\sqrt{6}[(r - \tfrac{1}{3})^2 + (g - \tfrac{1}{3})^2 + (b - \tfrac{1}{3})^2]^{1/2}} \right]$$

where $\theta = \Phi \ \text{modulo}(180°)$.

† The luminance signal *Y* would seem more appropriate because luminance is a psychophysical attribute, while intensity defined in this application as the sum $R + G + B$ is not.

types of linear or nonlinear transformations are best for segmentation? How many property values should be used? What is the best form of property thresholding or division? Perhaps answers to these questions may be forthcoming from a study of clustering techniques in pattern recognition (11, 47–49). Property value histograms are really the marginal histograms of a joint histogram of the property values. Clustering methods can be utilized to specify multidimensional decision boundaries for segmentation. This approach permits utilization of all the property values for segmentation, and inherently recognizes their respective cross correlation. Fisher's linear discriminant method (11, p. 114) can also be utilized to project simultaneously all of the property values to a line for one-dimensional thresholding.

18.5-3. Region Growing

Region growing is one of the conceptually simplest approaches to amplitude segmentation; neighboring pixels of similar amplitude are grouped together to form a segmented region. However, in practice, constraints, some of which are reasonably complex, must be placed on the growth pattern to achieve acceptable results.

Brice and Fennema (50) have developed and tested a region growing method based on a set of simple growth rules. In the first stage of the process, pairs of quantized pixels are combined together into groups called atomic regions if they are of the same amplitude and are four-connected. A pair of heuristic rules are next invoked to dissolve weak boundaries between atomic regions. Referring to Figure 18.5-5, let R_1 and R_2 be two adjacent regions with perimeters P_1 and P_2, respectively, which have been previously merged. After the initial stages of region growing, a region may

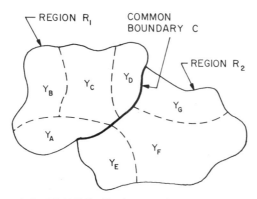

FIGURE 18.5-5. Region growing geometry.

contain previously merged subregions of different amplitude values. Also, let C denote the length of the common boundary and let D represent the length of that portion of C for which the amplitude difference ΔY across the boundary is smaller than a significance factor ε_1. The regions R_1 and R_2 are then merged if

$$\frac{D}{\min\{P_1, P_2\}} > \varepsilon_2 \qquad (18.5\text{-}5)$$

where ε_2 is a constant typically set at $\varepsilon_2 = \frac{1}{2}$. This heuristic prevents merger of adjacent regions of the same approximate size, but permits smaller regions to be absorbed into larger regions. The second rule merges weak common boundaries remaining after application of the first rule. Adjacent regions are merged if

$$\frac{D}{C} > \varepsilon_3 \qquad (18.5\text{-}6)$$

where ε_3 is a constant set at about $\varepsilon_3 = \frac{3}{4}$. Application of only the second rule tends to overmerge regions.

The Brice and Fennema region growing method provides reasonably accurate segmentation of simple scenes with few objects and little texture (50, 51), but does not perform well on more complex scenes. Yakimovsky and Feldman (52) have attempted to improve the region growing concept by establishing merging constraints based on estimated Bayesian probability densities of feature measurements of each region. Tenenbaum and Weyl (53) have utilized semantic knowledge for merging guidance. Both extensions provide improved results, but they are quite complex.

18.6. EDGE SEGMENTATION

A common operation in image analysis involves the outlining of objects within an image and recording of the outline location in terms of its Cartesian coordinates or an equivalent code. Often the outline is forced to follow a closed contour or some structured arc segment. There are three general approaches to the formulation of object boundaries: curve fitting, contour following, and edge point linking.

Curve Fitting

The curve fitting methods described in Section 18.3 can be used for edge segmentation by fitting an analytic curve to a set of edge map points produced by an edge detector. If a priori information is available as to the expected shape of an object in a picture, for example, a rectangle or a circle, the fit may be made directly to that shape. Otherwise, a polynomial approximation may be attempted by the iterated straight line fit methods of Section 18.3. The curve fitting approach is reasonably good for simply structured objects. Difficulties occur when an image contains many overlapping objects, and edge points form branch structures.

Contour Following

The contour following approach to boundary formulation is commonly called bug following. In the binary image examples of Figure 18.6-1a, a conceptual bug begins marching from the white margin to the black pixel region. When the bug crosses into a black pixel, it makes a left turn and proceeds to the next pixel. If that pixel is black, the bug again turns left, and if the pixel is white, the bug turns right. The procedure continues until the bug returns to the starting point. The Cartesian coordinate of each black-to-white or white-to-black crossing is recorded as the boundary location. In Figure 18.6-1 the spur pixel on the lower right-hand corner of the object, which is eight-connected to its nearest neighbor, is not included in the boundary. Note, however, that the spur pixel in Figure 18.6-1b is included in the boundary of the object when the starting point is moved. Thus the boundary definition is dependent on the starting point. Another difficulty is holes within an object, which can cause the bug to get lost. Problems of this nature can be overcome by providing the bug with some memory and intelligence that permit the bug to remember its past steps and backtrack if its present course is erroneous. Bug following is most often applied to luminance thresholded images, but the concept can be easily extended to gray scale imagery. One approach is to specify a boundary point if the luminance difference between neighboring pixels is sufficiently large. In effect, the bug follower forms edges as it moves.

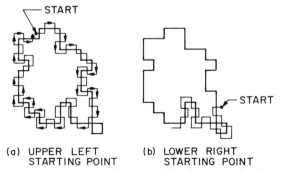

(a) UPPER LEFT   (b) LOWER RIGHT
    STARTING POINT   STARTING POINT

FIGURE 18.6-1. Examples of contour following to outline boundaries.

Edge Point Linking

An object or region within an image that one wishes to segment generally is separated from neighboring parts of the image by an edge gradient over its boundary. Consequently, edge point linkage can be utilized for segmentation.

The edge segmentation technique developed by Roberts is typical of the philosophy of most edge linkage methods. In Roberts' method analog edge gradients are examined in 4×4-pixel blocks. The pixel whose magnitude gradient is largest is declared a tentative edge point if its magnitude is greater than a threshold value. Then North, East, South, and West oriented lines of length five are fitted to the gradient data about the tentative edge point. If the ratio of the best to worst fit, measured in terms of the fit correlation, is greater than a second threshold, the tentative edge point is declared valid, and it is assigned the direction of the best fit. Next, straight lines are fitted between pairs of edge points if they are in adjacent 4×4 blocks, and if the line direction is within $\pm 23°$ of the edge direction of either edge point. Those points failing to meet the linking criteria are discarded. A typical boundary at this stage, shown in Figure 18.6-2a, will

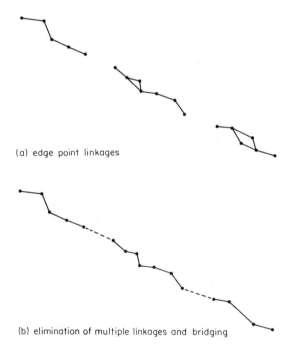

(a) edge point linkages

(b) elimination of multiple linkages and bridging

FIGURE 18.6-2. Examples of Roberts edge point linkage.

contain gaps and multiply-connected edge points. Small triangles are eliminated by deleting the longest side, and small rectangles are replaced by their longest diagonal, as indicated in Figure 18.6-2*b*. Short spur lines are also deleted. At this stage short gaps are bridged by straight line connection. This form of edge linkage can be used with a wide variety of edge detectors. Nevatia (55) has used a similar method for edge linkage of edges produced by a Hueckel edge detector.

Robinson (56) has suggested a simple, but effective, edge linkage algorithm in which edge points from an edge detector providing eight compass directions are examined in 3×3 blocks as indicated in Figure 18.6-3. The edge point in the center of the block is declared a valid edge point if it possesses directional neighbors in the proper orientation. Figure 18.6-4 illustrates the ability of the technique to remove apparently extraneous background edges. Extension to larger size windows should be beneficial, but the number of potential valid edge connections will grow rapidly with window size.

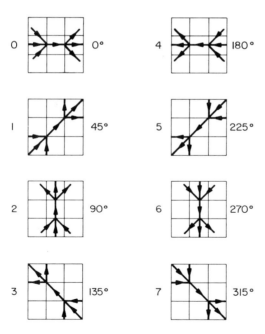

FIGURE 18.6-3. Edge linkage rules (56).

(a)   (b)

FIGURE 18.6-4. Example of edge detection using edge linking algorithm (56). (a) Without linking. (b) With linking.

18.7. TEXTURE SEGMENTATION

It has long been recognized that texture should be a valuable feature for image segmentation. Putting this concept to practice, however, has been hindered by the lack of reliable and efficient means of detecting and measuring texture.

One approach to texture segmentation, fostered by Rosenfeld et al. (57–59), is to compute some texture coarseness measure at all image points and then detect changes in the coarseness measure. In effect, the original image is preprocessed to convert texture to an amplitude scale for subsequent amplitude edge detection. A major problem with this approach is that texture is measured over a window area, and therefore texture measurements in the vicinity of the boundary between texture regions represent some average texture computation. As a result it becomes difficult accurately to locate a texture boundary.

Another approach to texture segmentation is to detect the transition between regions of differing texture. The basic concept of texture edge detection is identical to that of luminance edge detection; the dissimilarity between textured regions is enhanced over all points of the image, and then the enhanced plane is thresholded to locate texture discontinuities. Thompson (60) has suggested a means of texture enhancement analogous to the Roberts gradient presented in Section 17.4. Texture measures are computed in each of four adjacent $W \times W$-pixel regions scanned over the image, and the sum of the cross-difference magnitudes is formed and thresholded to locate significant texture changes. This method can be generalized to include computation in adjacent windows arranged in 3×3 groups. Then the resulting texture measures of each window can be combined in some linear or nonlinear manner analogous to the 3×3 luminance edge enhancement methods described in Section 17.4.

Zucker, Rosenfeld, and Davis (61) have proposed a histogram thresholding method of texture segmentation based on a texture analysis technique developed by Tsuji and Tomita (62). In this method a texture measure is computed at each image point by forming the spot gradient followed by the dominant neighbor suppression algorithm described in Section 17.4. Then a histogram is formed over the resultant modified gradient data. If the histogram is multimodal, thresholding of the gradient at the minimum between histogram modes should provide a segmentation of textural regions. The process may be repeated on the separate parts until segmentation is complete.

18.8. SHAPE SEGMENTATION

In image recognition tasks it is often useful to decompose a complex shaped object into a connected set of parts with simple, easily representable shapes. For example, the block letter T can be decomposed into connected rectangles. Shape segmentation can be accomplished in two stages. First, an object of arbitrary shape can be fitted by a set of connected straight or curved line segments. Then the approximated shape can be segmented at points of inflection. Figure 18.8-1 illustrates the segmentation of polygonally shaped objects. The basic segmentation rule is quite simple: nearest points of concavity are connected to form peninsular segments, which are then removed from the main body; the process continues until all parts are convex. Feng and Pavlidis (63) have developed algorithms for efficient polygonal shape segmentation.

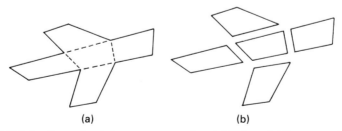

(a)   (b)

FIGURE 18.8-1.   Example of shape segmentation. (a) Object. (b) Segmented object.

REFERENCES

1. A. Rosenfeld, "Connectivity in Digital Pictures," *JACM*, **17**, 1, January 1970, 146–160.

2. A. Rosenfeld, *Picture Processing by Computer*, Academic Press, New York, 1969.

3. M. J. E. Golay, "Hexagonal Pattern Transformation," *IEEE Trans. Computers*, **C-18**, 8, August 1969, 733–740.

4. K. Preston, Jr., "Feature Extraction by Golay Hexagonal Pattern Transforms," *IEEE Trans. Computers*, **C-20**, 9, 1971, 1007–1014.

5. K. Preston, Jr., "The CELLSCAN System, a Leucocyte Pattern Analyzer," Western Joint Computer Conference, May 1961, 173–183.

6. S. H. Unger, "A Computer Oriented Towards Spatial Problems," Proc. IRE, **46**, 10, October 1958, 1744–1750.

7. S. Levialdi, "CLOPAN: A Closed Pattern Analyzer," *Proc. IRE*, **115**, 6, June 1968, 879–880.

8. B. Kruse, "A Parallel Picture Processing Machine," *IEEE Trans. Computers*, **C-22**, 12, December 1973, 1075–1087.

9. M. J. B. Duff et al., "A Cellular Logic Array for Image Processing," *Pattern Recognition*, **5**, 1973, 229–247.

10. H. Blum, "A Transformation for Extracting New Descriptors of Shape," in *Symposium Models for Perception of Speech and Visual Form*, Weiant Whaten-Dunn, Ed., MIT Press, Cambridge, Mass., 1967.

11. R. O. Duda and P. E. Hart, *Pattern Classification and Scene Analysis*, Wiley–Interscience, New York, 1973.

12. L. Calabi and W. E. Hartnett, "Shape Recognition, Prairie Fires, Convex Deficiencies and Skeletons," *Am. Math. Monthly*, **75**, 4, April 1968, 335–342.

13. J. C. Mott-Smith, "Medial Axis Transforms," in *Picture Processing and Psychopictorics*, B. S. Lipkin and A. Rosenfeld, Eds., Academic Press, New York, 1970.

14. U. Montanari, "A Method for Obtaining Skeletons Using a Quasi-Euclidean Distance," *JACM*, **15**, October 1968, 600–624.

15. U. Montanari, "Continuous Skeletons from Digitized Pictures," *JACM*, **16**, 4, October 1969, 534–549.

16. T. R. McCalla, *Introduction to Numerical Methods and FORTRAN Programming*, Wiley, New York, 1967.

17. U. Ramer, "An Iterative Procedure for the Polygonal Approximation of Plane Curves," *Computer Graphics and Image Processing*, **1**, 3, November 1972, 244–256.

18. T. Pavlidis and S. L. Horowitz, "Segmentation of Plane Curves," *IEEE Trans. Computers*, **C-23**, 8, August 1974, 860–870.

19. P. V. C. Hough, "Method and Means for Recognizing Complex Patterns," U.S. Patent 3069654, December 18, 1962.

20. R. O. Duda and P. E. Hart, "Use of the Hough Transformation to Detect Lines and Curves in Pictures," *Commun. ACM*, **15**, 1, January 1972, 11–15.

21. F. O'Gorman and M. B. Clowes, "Finding Picture Edges Through Collinearity of Feature Points," *IEEE Trans. Computers*, **C-25**, 4, April 1976, 449–456.

22. P. A. Kolers, "The Role of Shape and Geometry in Picture Recognition," in *Picture Processing and Psychopictorics*, B. S. Lipkin and A. Rosenfeld, Eds., Academic Press, New York, 1970.

23. F. Attneave, "Physical Determinants of the Judged Complexity of Shape," *J. Experimental Psychology*, **53**, 1957, 221–227.

24. F. Attneave and M. Arnoult, "The Quantitative Study of Shape and Pattern Perception," *Psychology Bull.*, **53**, 1956, 452–471.

25. A. Rosenfeld and J. L. Pflatz, "Distance Functions on Digital Pictures," *Pattern Recognition*, **1**, July 1968, 33–62.

26. E. C. Greanis et al., "The Recognition of Handwritten Numerals by Contour Analysis," *IBM J. Res. Devel.*, **7**, 1, January 1863, 14–21.

27. M. A. Fischler, "Machine Perception and Description of Pictorial Data," Proceedings International Joint Conference on Artificial Intelligence, D. E. Walker and L. M. Norton, Eds., May 1969, 629–639.

28. S. B. Gray, "Local Properties of Binary Images in Two Dimensions," *IEEE Trans. Computers*, **C-20**, 5, May 1971, 551–561.

29. J. Sklansky, "Recognizing Convex Blobs," Proceedings International Joint Conference on Artificial Intelligence, D. E. Walker and L. M. Norton, Eds., May 1969, 107–116.

30. J. Sklansky, L. P. Cordella, and S. Levialdi, "Parallel Detection of Concavities in Cellular Blobs," *IEEE Trans. Computers*, **C-25**, 2, February 1976, 187–196.

31. R. O. Duda, "Image Segmentation and Description," unpublished notes, 1975.

32. R. L. Cosgriff, "Identification of Shape," Ohio State University Research Foundation, Columbus, Ohio, Report 820-11, ASTIA AD 254 792, December 1960.

33. E. L. Brill, "Character Recognition Via Fourier Descriptors," WESCON Convention Record, Paper 25/3, Los Angeles, 1968.

34. C. T. Zahn and R. Z. Roskies, "Fourier Descriptors for Plane Closed Curves," *IEEE Trans. Computers*, **C-21**, 3, March 1972, 269–281.

35. J. R. Bennett and J. S. MacDonald, "On the Measurement of Curvature in a Quantized Environment," *IEEE Trans. Computers*, **C-25**, 8, August 1975, 803–820.

36. M. K. Hu, "Visual Pattern Recognition by Moment Invariants," *IRE Trans. Inf. Theory*, **IT-8**, 2, February 1962, 179–187.

37. F. L. Alt, "Digital Pattern Recognition by Moments," *JACM*, **9**, 2, April 1962, 240–258.

38. W. Doyle, "Operations Useful for Similarity-Invariant Pattern Recognition, *JACM*, **9**, 2, April 1962, 259–267.

39. J. M. S. Prewitt and M. L. Mendelsohn, "The Analysis of Cell Images," *Ann. N. Y. Acad. Sci.*, **128**, 1966, 1035–1053.

40. J. S. Weszka, R. N. Nagel, and A. Rosenfeld, "A Threshold Selection Technique," *IEEE Trans. Computers*, **C-23**, 12, December 1974, 1322–1326.

41. M. R. Bartz, "The IBM 1975 Optical Page Reader, Part II: Video Thresholding System," *IBM J. Res. Devel.*, **12**, September 1968, 354–363.

42. C. K. Chow and T. Kaneko, "Boundary Detection of Radiographic Images by a Threshold Method," in *Frontiers of Pattern Recognition*, S. Watanabe, Ed., Academic Press, New York, 1972.

43. H. C. Becker et al., "Digital Computer Determination of a Medical Diagnostic Index Directly from Chest X-ray Images," *IEEE Trans. Biomed. Eng.*, **BME-11**, 3, July 1964, 67–72.

44. R. P. Kruger et al., "Radiographic Diagnosis via Feature Extraction and Classification of Cardiac Size and Shape Descriptors," *IEEE Trans. Biomed. Eng.*, **BME-19**, 3, May 1972, 174–186.

45. F. Tomita, M. Yachida, and S. Tsuji, "Detection of Homogeneous Regions by Structural Analysis," Proceedings International Joint Conference on Artificial Intelligence, Stanford, California, August 1973, 564–571.

46. R. B. Ohlander, "Analysis of Natural Scenes," Carnegie-Mellon University, Department of Computer Science, Ph.D. thesis, April 1975.

47. H. C. Andrews, *Introduction to Mathematical Techniques in Pattern Recognition*, Wiley–Interscience, New York, 1972.

48. W. S. Meisel, *Computer-Oriented Approaches to Pattern Recognition*, Academic Press, New York, 1972.

49. R. M. Haralick and G. L. Kelly, "Pattern Recognition with Measurement Space and Spatial Clustering for Multiple Images," *Proc. IEEE*, **57**, 4, April 1969, 654–665.

50. C. R. Brice and C. L. Fenema, "Scene Analysis Using Regions," *Artificial Intelligence*, **1**, 1970, 205–226.

51. H. G. Barrow and R. J. Popplestone, "Relational Descriptions in Picture Processing," in *Machine Intelligence*, Vol. 6, B. Meltzer and D. Michie, Eds., University Press, Edinburgh, 1971, 377–396.

52. Y. Yakimovsky, "Scene Analysis Using a Semantic Base for Region Growing," Report AIM-209, Stanford University, 1973.

53. J. M. Tenenbaum and S. Weyl, "A Region Analysis Subsystem for Interactive Scene Analysis," Proceedings Fourth International Joint Conference on Artificial Intelligence, September 1975.

54. L. G. Roberts, "Machine Perception of Three Dimensional Solids," in *Optical and Electro-Optical Information Processing*, J. T. Tippett et al., Eds, MIT Press, Cambridge, Mass., 1965.

55. R. Nevatia, "Locating Object Boundaries in Textured Environments," *IEEE Trans. Computers*, **C-25**, 11, November 1976, 1170–1175.

56. G. S. Robinson, "Detection and Coding of Edges Using Directional Masks," Proceedings SPIE Conference on Advances in Image Transmission Techniques, San Diego, August 1976.

57. A. Rosenfeld and M. Thurston, "Edge and Curve Detection for Visual Scene Analysis," *IEEE Trans. Computers*, **C-20**, 5, May 1971, 562–569.

58. A. Rosenfeld, M. Thurston, and Y. H. Lee, "Edge and Curve Detection: Further Experiments," *IEEE Trans. Computers*, **C-21**, 7, July 1972, 677–715.

59. K. C. Hayes, Jr., A. N. Shah, and A. Rosenfeld, "Texture Coarseness: Further Experiments," *IEEE Trans. Systems, Man, and Cybernetics (Correspondence)*, **SMC-4**, 5, September 1974, 467–472.

60. W. B. Thompson, "Textural Boundary Analysis," University of Southern California, Image Processing Institute, Report USCIPI 620, September 1975, 124–134.

61. S. W. Zucker, A. Rosenfeld, and L. S. Davis, "Picture Segmentation by Texture Discrimination," *IEEE Trans. Computers*, **C-24**, 12, December 1975, 1228–1233.

62. S. Tsuji and F. Tomita, "A Structural Analyzer for a Class of Textures," *Computer Graphics and Image Processing*, **2**, 3/4, December 1973, 216–231.

63. H.-Y. F. Feng and T. Pavlidis, "Decomposition of Polygons into Simpler Components: Feature Generation for Syntactic Pattern Recognition," *IEEE Trans. Computers*, **C-24**, 6, June 1975, 636–650.

19 IMAGE DETECTION AND REGISTRATION

This chapter covers two related image analysis tasks: detection and registration. Image detection is concerned with the determination of the presence or absence of objects suspected of being in a picture. Image registration involves the spatial alignment of pairs of views of a scene.

19.1. TEMPLATE MATCHING

One of the most fundamental means of object detection within an image field is by template matching, in which a replica of an object of interest is compared to all unknown objects in the image field (1–4). If the template match between an unknown object and the template is sufficiently close, the unknown object is labeled as the template object.

As a simple example of the template matching process, consider the set of binary black line figures against a white background as shown in Figure 19.1-1a. In this example the objective is to detect the presence and location of equilateral triangles in the image field. Figure 19.1-1b contains a simple template for localization of equilateral triangles that possesses

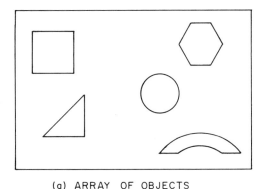

(a) ARRAY OF OBJECTS

(b) TRIANGLE TEMPLATE

FIGURE 19.1-1. Template matching.

unit value in the triangular region and zero elsewhere. The width of the legs of the triangle is chosen as a compromise between localization accuracy and size invariance of the template. In operation the template is sequentially scanned over the image field and the common region between the template and image field is compared for similarity.

A template match is rarely ever exact because of image noise, spatial and amplitude quantization effects, and a priori uncertainty as to the exact shape and structure of an object to be detected. Consequently, a common procedure is to produce a difference measure $D(m, n)$ between the template and the image field at all points of the image field, and then to designate a detected object wherever the difference is smaller than some established threshold level $L_D(m, n)$. Normally, the threshold level is constant over the image field. The usual difference measure is the mean-square difference or error as defined by

$$D(m, n) = \sum_j \sum_k [F(j, k) - T(j - m, k - n)]^2 \qquad (19.1\text{-}1)$$

where $F(j, k)$ denotes the image field to be searched and $T(j, k)$ is the template. The search, of course, is restricted to the overlap region between the translated template and the image field. A template match is then said to exist at coordinate (m, n) if

$$D(m, n) < L_D(m, n) \qquad (19.1\text{-}2)$$

Now let Eq. 19.1-1 be expanded to yield

$$D(m, n) = D_1(m, n) - 2D_2(m, n) + D_3(m, n) \qquad (19.1\text{-}3)$$

where

$$D_1(m, n) = \sum_j \sum_k [F(j, k)]^2 \qquad (19.1\text{-}4a)$$

$$D_2(m, n) = \sum_j \sum_k F(j, k)T(j - m, k - n) \qquad (19.1\text{-}4b)$$

$$D_3(m, n) = \sum_j \sum_k [T(j - m, k - n)]^2 \qquad (19.1\text{-}4c)$$

The term $D_3(m, n)$ represents a summation of the template energy and is constant valued independent of the coordinate (m, n). The image energy over the window area represented by the first term $D_1(m, n)$ generally varies rather slowly over the image field. The second term should be recognized as the cross correlation $R_{FT}(m, n)$ between the image field and the template. At the coordinate location of a template match, the cross correlation should become large to yield a small difference. However, the magnitude of the cross correlation is not always an adequate measure of template difference since the image energy term $D_1(m, n)$ is position variant. For example, the cross correlation can become large, even under a condition of template mismatch, if the image amplitude over the template region is high about a particular coordinate (m, n) This difficulty can be avoided by comparison of the normalized cross correlation

$$\tilde{R}_{FT}(m, n) = \frac{D_2(m, n)}{D_1(m, n)} = \frac{\sum_j \sum_k F(j, k)T(j - m, k - n)}{\sum_j \sum_k [F(j, k)]^2} \qquad (19.1\text{-}5)$$

to a threshold level $L_R(m, n)$. A template match is said to exist if

$$\tilde{R}_{FT}(m, n) > L_R(m, n) \qquad (19.1\text{-}6)$$

The normalized cross correlation has a maximum value of unity that occurs if and only if the image function under the template exactly matches the template.

One of the major limitations of template matching is that an enormous number of templates must often be test matched against an image field to account for changes in rotation and magnification of template objects. For this reason template matching is usually limited to smaller local features, which are more invariant to size and shape variations of an object. Such features, for example, include edges joined in a Y or T arrangement.

19.2. MATCHED FILTERING OF DETERMINISTIC CONTINUOUS FIELDS

The matched filter, implemented by electrical circuits, is widely used in one-dimensional signal detection applications such as radar and digital communication (5–7). It is also possible to detect objects within images by a two-dimensional version of the matched filter (8–12).

In the context of image processing, the matched filter is a spatial filter that provides an output measure of the spatial correlation between an input image and a reference image. This correlation measure may then be utilized, for example, to determine the presence or absence of a given input image, or to assist in the spatial registration of two images.

As an introduction to the concept of the matched filter, consider the problem of detecting the presence or absence of a known continuous signal or reference image $F(x, y)$ in an unknown or input image field $F_U(x, y)$ corrupted by an additive stationary noise field $N(x, y)$ independent of $F(x, y)$. Thus $F_U(x, y)$ is composed of the signal image plus noise

$$F_U(x, y) = F(x, y) + N(x, y) \qquad (19.2\text{-}1a)$$

or noise alone

$$F_U(x, y) = N(x, y) \qquad (19.2\text{-}1b)$$

The unknown image is spatially filtered by the matched filter, with impulse response $H(x, y)$ and transfer function $\mathcal{H}(\omega_x, \omega_y)$, to produce an output field

$$F_O(x, y) = F_U(x, y) \circledast H(x, y) \qquad (19.2\text{-}2)$$

The matched filter is designed so that the ratio of the signal image energy to the noise field energy at some point $(\mathcal{E}, \mathcal{N})$ in the filter output plane is maximized.

The instantaneous signal image energy at point $(\mathcal{E}, \mathcal{N})$ of the filter output in the absence of noise is given by

$$|S(\mathcal{E}, \mathcal{N})|^2 = |F(x, y) \circledast H(x, y)|^2 \qquad (19.2\text{-}3)$$

with $x = \mathcal{E}$ and $y = \mathcal{N}$. By the convolution theorem

$$|S(\mathcal{E}, \mathcal{N})|^2 = \left| \int\int_{-\infty}^{\infty} \mathcal{F}(\omega_x, \omega_y) \mathcal{H}(\omega_x, \omega_y) \exp\{i(\omega_x \mathcal{E} + \omega_y \mathcal{N})\} \, d\omega_x \, d\omega_y \right|^2$$

$$(19.2\text{-}4)$$

where $\mathcal{F}(\omega_x, \omega_y)$ is the Fourier spectrum of $F(x, y)$. The additive input noise component $N(x, y)$ is assumed to be stationary, independent of the signal image, and described by its noise power-spectral density $W_N(\omega_x, \omega_y)$. From Eq. 1.10-8 the total noise power at the filter output is

$$N = \int\int_{-\infty}^{\infty} W_N(\omega_x, \omega_y) |\mathcal{H}(\omega_x, \omega_y)|^2 \, d\omega_x \, d\omega_y \qquad (19.2\text{-}5)$$

Then, forming the signal-to-noise ratio one obtains

$$\frac{|S(\mathcal{E}, \mathcal{N})|^2}{N} = \frac{\left| \int\int_{-\infty}^{\infty} \mathcal{F}(\omega_x, \omega_y) \mathcal{H}(\omega_x, \omega_y) \exp\{i(\omega_x \mathcal{E} + \omega_y \mathcal{N})\} \, d\omega_x \, d\omega_y \right|^2}{\int\int_{-\infty}^{\infty} W_N(\omega_x, \omega_y) |\mathcal{H}(\omega_x, \omega_y)|^2 \, d\omega_x \, d\omega_y}$$

$$(19.2\text{-}6)$$

This ratio is found to be maximized when the filter transfer function is of the form (5, 8)

$$\mathcal{H}(\omega_x, \omega_y) = \frac{\mathcal{F}^*(\omega_x, \omega_y) \exp\{-i(\omega_x \mathcal{E} + \omega_y \mathcal{N})\}}{\mathcal{W}_N(\omega_x, \omega_y)} \qquad (19.2\text{-}7)$$

If the input noise power-spectral density is white with a flat spectrum $\mathcal{W}_N(\omega_x, \omega_y) = n_w/2$, the matched filter transfer function reduces to

$$\mathcal{H}(\omega_x, \omega_y) = \frac{2}{n_w} \mathcal{F}^*(\omega_x, \omega_y) \exp\{-i(\omega_x \mathcal{E} + \omega_y \mathcal{N})\} \qquad (19.2\text{-}8)$$

and the corresponding filter impulse response becomes

$$H(x, y) = \frac{2}{n_w} F^*(\mathcal{E} - x, \mathcal{N} - y) \qquad (19.2\text{-}9)$$

In this case the matched filter impulse response is an amplitude scaled version of the complex conjugate of the signal image field rotated by 180°.

For the case of white noise the filter output can be written as

$$F_O(x, y) = \frac{2}{n_w} F_U(x, y) \circledast F^*(\mathcal{E} - x, \mathcal{N} - y) \qquad (19.2\text{-}10\text{a})$$

or

$$F_O(x, y) = \frac{2}{n_w} \int\limits_{-\infty}^{\infty}\!\!\int F_U(\alpha, \beta) F^*(\alpha + \mathcal{E} - x, \beta + \mathcal{N} - y)\, d\alpha\, d\beta$$

$$(19.2\text{-}10\text{b})$$

If the matched filter offset $(\mathcal{E}, \mathcal{N})$ is chosen to be zero, the filter output

$$F_O(x, y) = \frac{2}{n_w} \int\limits_{-\infty}^{\infty}\!\!\int F_U(\alpha, \beta) F^*(\alpha - x, \beta - y)\, d\alpha\, d\beta \qquad (19.2\text{-}11)$$

is then seen to be proportional to the mathematical correlation between the input image field and the complex conjugate of the signal image field. Ordinarily, the parameters $(\mathcal{E}, \mathcal{N})$ of the matched filter transfer function are set to be zero so that the origin of the output plane becomes the point of no translational offset between $F_U(x, y)$ and $F(x, y)$.

If the unknown image $F_U(x, y)$ consists of the signal image translated by distances $\Delta x, \Delta y$ plus additive noise as defined by

$$F_U(x, y) = F(x + \Delta x, y + \Delta y) + N(x, y) \qquad (19.2\text{-}12)$$

the matched filter output for $\mathscr{E} = 0$, $\mathscr{N} = 0$ will be

$$F_O(x, y) = \frac{2}{n_W} \int\limits_{-\infty}^{\infty}\!\!\int [F(\alpha + \Delta x, \beta + \Delta y) + N(\alpha, \beta)] F^*(\alpha - x, \beta - y) \, d\alpha \, d\beta$$

(19.2-13)

A correlation peak will occur at $x = \Delta x$, $y = \Delta y$ in the output plane, thus indicating the translation of the input image relative to the reference image. Hence the matched filter is translation invariant. It is, however, not invariant to rotation of the image to be detected.

It is possible to implement the general matched filter of Eq. 19.2-7 as a two-stage linear filter with transfer function

$$\mathscr{H}(\omega_x, \omega_y) = \mathscr{H}_A(\omega_x, \omega_y)\mathscr{H}_B(\omega_x, \omega_y)$$

(19.2-14)

The first stage, called a whitening filter, has a transfer function chosen such that noise $N(x, y)$ with a power spectrum $\mathscr{W}_N(\omega_x, \omega_y)$ at its input results in unit energy white noise at its output. Thus

$$\mathscr{W}_N(\omega_x, \omega_y)|\mathscr{H}_A(\omega_x, \omega_y)|^2 \equiv 1$$

(19.2-15)

The transfer function of the whitening filter may be determined by a spectral factorization of the input noise power-spectral density into the product (7)

$$\mathscr{W}_N(\omega_x, \omega_y) = \mathscr{W}_N^+(\omega_x, \omega_y)\mathscr{W}_N^-(\omega_x, \omega_y)$$

(19.2-16)

such that the following conditions hold:

$$\mathscr{W}_N^+(\omega_x, \omega_y) = [\mathscr{W}_N^-(\omega_x, \omega_y)]^*$$

(19.2-17a)

$$\mathscr{W}_N^-(\omega_x, \omega_y) = [\mathscr{W}_N^+(\omega_x, \omega_y)]^*$$

(19.2-17b)

$$\mathscr{W}_N(\omega_x, \omega_y) = |\mathscr{W}_N^+(\omega_x, \omega_y)|^2 = |\mathscr{W}_N^-(\omega_x, \omega_y)|^2$$

(19.2-17c)

The simplest type of factorization is the spatially noncausal factorization

$$\mathscr{W}_N^+(\omega_x, \omega_y) = \sqrt{\mathscr{W}_N(\omega_x, \omega_y)} \exp\{i\theta(\omega_x, \omega_y)\}$$

(19.2-18)

where $\theta(\omega_x, \omega_y)$ represents an arbitrary phase angle. Causal factorization of the input noise power-spectral density may be difficult if the spectrum does not factor into separable products. For a given factorization the whitening filter transfer function may be set to

$$\mathscr{H}_A(\omega_x, \omega_y) = \frac{1}{\mathscr{W}_N^+(\omega_x, \omega_y)}$$

(19.2-19)

The resultant input to the second-stage filter is $F_1(x, y) + N_W(x, y)$ where $N_W(x, y)$ represents unit energy white noise and

$$F_1(x, y) = F(x, y) \circledast H_A(x, y) \tag{19.2-20}$$

is a modified image signal with a spectrum

$$\mathscr{F}_1(\omega_x, \omega_y) = \mathscr{F}(\omega_x, \omega_y)\mathscr{H}_A(\omega_x, \omega_y) = \frac{\mathscr{F}(\omega_x, \omega_y)}{W_N^+(\omega_x, \omega_y)} \tag{19.2-21}$$

From Eq. 19.2-8, for the white noise condition, the optimum transfer function of the second-stage filter is found to be

$$\mathscr{H}_B(\omega_x, \omega_y) = \mathscr{F}_1^*(\omega_x, \omega_y) \exp\{-i(\omega_x \mathscr{E} + \omega_y \mathscr{N})\} \tag{19.2-22a}$$

or

$$\mathscr{H}_B(\omega_x, \omega_y) = \frac{\mathscr{F}^*(\omega_x, \omega_y)}{W_N^-(\omega_x, \omega_y)} \exp\{-i(\omega_x \mathscr{E} + \omega_y \mathscr{N})\} \tag{19.2-22b}$$

Calculation of the product $\mathscr{H}_A(\omega_x, \omega_y)\mathscr{H}_B(\omega_x, \omega_y)$ shows that the optimum filter expression of Eq. 19.2-7 can be obtained by the whitening filter implementation.

The basic limitation of the normal matched filter as defined by Eq. 19.2-7 is that the correlation output between an unknown image field and an image signal to be detected is primarily dependent on the energy of the images rather than their spatial structure. For example, consider a signal image in the form of a bright hexagonally shaped object against a black background. If the unknown image field contains a circular disk of the same brightness and area as the hexagonal object, the correlation function resulting will be very similar to the correlation function produced by a perfect match. In general, the normal matched filter provides relatively poor discrimination between objects of different shape, but of similar size or energy content. This drawback of the normal matched filter is overcome somewhat with the derivative matched filter (8), which makes use of the edge structure of an object to be detected.

The transfer function of the pth-order derivative matched filter is given by

$$\mathscr{H}_p(\omega_x, \omega_y) = \frac{(\omega_x^2 + \omega_y^2)^p \mathscr{F}^*(\omega_x, \omega_y) \exp\{-i(\omega_x \mathscr{E} + \omega_y \mathscr{N})\}}{W_N(\omega_x, \omega_y)}$$

$$\tag{19.2-23}$$

where p is an integer. If $p = 0$, the normal matched filter

$$\mathscr{H}_0(\omega_x, \omega_y) = \frac{\mathscr{F}^*(\omega_x, \omega_y) \exp\{-i(\omega_x \mathscr{E} + \omega_y \mathscr{N})\}}{W_N(\omega_x, \omega_y)} \tag{19.2-24}$$

is obtained, With $p = 1$ the filter

$$\mathcal{H}_1(\omega_x, \omega_y) = (\omega_x^2 + \omega_y^2)\mathcal{H}_0(\omega_x, \omega_y) \qquad (19.2\text{-}25)$$

is called the Laplacian matched filter. Its impulse response function is

$$H_1(x, y) = \left[\frac{\partial^2}{\partial x^2} + \frac{\partial^2}{\partial y^2}\right] \circledast H_0(x, y) \qquad (19.2\text{-}26)$$

In the general case since the pth-order derivative matched filter transfer function can be written as

$$\mathcal{H}_p(\omega_x, \omega_y) = (\omega_x^2 + \omega_y^2)^p \mathcal{H}_0(\omega_x, \omega_y) \qquad (19.2\text{-}27)$$

Thus the derivative matched filter may be implemented by cascaded operations consisting of a generalized derivative operator whose function is to enhance the edges of an image, followed by a normal matched filter.

19.3. MATCHED FILTERING OF STOCHASTIC IMAGE FIELDS

In the preceding section the ideal image $F(x, y)$ to be detected in the presence of an additive noise field was assumed deterministic. If the state of $F(x, y)$ is not known exactly, but only statistically, the matched filtering concept can be extended to the detection of a stochastic image field in the presence of noise (13). Even if $F(x, y)$ is known deterministically, it is often useful to consider it as a random field with mean $E\{F(x, y)\} = F(x, y)$. Such a formulation provides a mechansim for incorporating a priori knowledge of the spatial correlation of an image field in its detection. Conventional matched filtering, as defined by Eq. 19.2-7, completely ignores the spatial relationships between the pixels of an observed image field.

For purposes of analysis let the observed unknown field

$$F_U(x, y) = F(x, y) + N(x, y) \qquad (19.3\text{-}1a)$$

or

$$F_U(x, y) = N(x, y) \qquad (19.3\text{-}1b)$$

be composed of an ideal image $F(x, y)$, which is a sample of a two-dimensional stochastic process with known moments, plus a noise field $N(x, y)$ independent of the image field, or be composed of noise alone. The unknown field is convolved with the matched filter impulse response $H(x, y)$ to produce an output field modeled as

$$F_O(x, y) = F_U(x, y) \circledast H(x, y) \qquad (19.3\text{-}2)$$

The stochastic matched filter is designed so that it maximizes the ratio of the average squared signal energy without noise to the variance of the filter output. This is simply a generalization of the conventional signal-to-noise ratio of Eq. 19.2-6. In the absence of noise the expected signal energy at some point $(\mathcal{E}, \mathcal{N})$ in the output field is

$$|S(\mathcal{E}, \mathcal{N})|^2 = |E\{F(x, y) \circledast H(x, y)\}|^2 \qquad (19.3\text{-}3)$$

By the convolution theorem and linearity of the expectation operator,

$$|S(\mathcal{E}, \mathcal{N})|^2 = \left| \int\int_{-\infty}^{\infty} E\{\mathcal{F}(\omega_x, \omega_y)\} \mathcal{H}(\omega_x, \omega_y) \exp\{i(\omega_x\mathcal{E} + \omega_y\mathcal{N})\} \, d\omega_x \, d\omega_y \right|^2$$

$$(19.3\text{-}4)$$

The variance of the matched filter output under the assumption of stationarity and signal and noise independence is

$$N = \int\int_{-\infty}^{\infty} [\mathcal{W}_F(\omega_x, \omega_y) + \mathcal{W}_N(\omega_x, \omega_y)] |\mathcal{H}(\omega_x, \omega_y)|^2 \, d\omega_x \, d\omega_y$$

$$(19.3\text{-}5)$$

where $\mathcal{W}_F(\omega_x, \omega_y)$ and $\mathcal{W}_N(\omega_x, \omega_y)$ are the image signal and noise power spectral densities, respectively. This generalized signal-to-noise ratio, which is of similar form to the specialized case of Eq. 19.2-6, is maximized when

$$\mathcal{H}(\omega_x, \omega_y) = \frac{E\{\mathcal{F}^*(\omega_x, \omega_y)\} \exp\{-i(\omega_x\mathcal{E} + \omega_y\mathcal{N})\}}{\mathcal{W}_F(\omega_x, \omega_y) + \mathcal{W}_N(\omega_x, \omega_y)} \qquad (19.3\text{-}6)$$

Note that when $F(x, y)$ is deterministic, Eq. 19.3-6 reduces to the matched filter transfer function of Eq. 19.2-7.

The stochastic matched filter is often modified by replacement of the mean of the ideal image to be detected by a replica of the image itself. In this case for $\mathcal{E} = \mathcal{N} = 0$

$$\mathcal{H}(\omega_x, \omega_y) = \frac{\mathcal{F}^*(\omega_x, \omega_y)}{\mathcal{W}_F(\omega_x, \omega_y) + \mathcal{W}_N(\omega_x, \omega_y)} \qquad (19.3\text{-}7)$$

A special case of common interest occurs when the noise is white, $\mathcal{W}_N(\omega_x, \omega_y) = n_w/2$, and the ideal image is regarded as a first-order nonseparable Markov process, as defined by Eq. 1.9-17, with power spectrum

$$\mathcal{W}_F(\omega_x, \omega_y) = \frac{2}{\alpha^2 + \omega_x^2 + \omega_y^2} \qquad (19.3\text{-}8)$$

where $\exp(-\alpha)$ is the adjacent pixel correlation. For such processes the resultant modified matched filter transfer function becomes

$$\mathcal{H}(\omega_x, \omega_y) = \frac{2(\alpha^2 + \omega_x^2 + \omega_y^2)\mathcal{F}^*(\omega_x, \omega_y)}{4 + n_W(\alpha^2 + \omega_x^2 + \omega_y^2)} \tag{19.3-9}$$

At high spatial frequencies and low noise levels, the modified matched filter defined by Eq. 19.3-9 becomes equivalent to the Laplacian matched filter of Eq. 19.2-25.

19.4. MATCHED FILTERING OF DISCRETE IMAGES

A matched filter for object detection can be defined for discrete as well as continuous images. One approach is to perform discrete linear filtering using a discretized version of the matched filter transfer function of Eq. 19.2-7 following the techniques outlined in Section 11.4. Alternatively, the discrete matched filter can be developed by a vector-space formulation (13, 14). The latter approach, presented in this section, is advantageous because it permits a concise analysis for nonstationary image and noise arrays. Also, image boundary effects can be dealt with accurately.

Consider an observed image vector

$$\mathbf{f}_U = \mathbf{f} + \mathbf{n} \tag{19.4-1a}$$

or

$$\mathbf{f}_U = \mathbf{n} \tag{19.4-1b}$$

composed of a deterministic image vector $\mathbf{f}$ plus a noise vector $\mathbf{n}$, or noise alone. The discrete matched filtering operation is implemented by forming the inner product of $\mathbf{f}_U$ with a matched filter vector $\mathbf{m}$ to produce the scalar output

$$f_O = \mathbf{m}^T \mathbf{f}_U \tag{19.4-2}$$

Vector $\mathbf{m}$ is chosen to maximize the signal-to-noise ratio. The signal power in the absence of noise is simply

$$S = (\mathbf{m}^T \mathbf{f})^2 \tag{19.4-3}$$

and the noise power is

$$N = E\{(\mathbf{m}^T \mathbf{n})(\mathbf{m}^T \mathbf{n})^T\} = \mathbf{m}^T \mathbf{K}_n \mathbf{m} \tag{19.4-4}$$

where $\mathbf{K}_n$ is the noise covariance matrix. Hence the signal-to-noise ratio is

$$\frac{S}{N} = \frac{\mathbf{m}^T \mathbf{f}}{\mathbf{m}^T \mathbf{K}_n \mathbf{m}} \tag{19.4-5}$$

The optimal choice of $\mathbf{m}$ can be determined by differentiating the signal-to-noise ratio of Eq. 19.4-5 with respect to $\mathbf{m}$ and setting the result to zero. These operations lead directly to the relation

$$\mathbf{m} = \left[\frac{(\mathbf{m}^T \mathbf{K}_n \mathbf{m})}{(\mathbf{m}^T \mathbf{f})} \right] \mathbf{K}_n^{-1} \mathbf{f} \qquad (19.4\text{-}6)$$

where the term in the bracket is a scalar, which may be normalized to unity. The matched filter output

$$f_O = \mathbf{f}^T \mathbf{K}_n^{-1} \mathbf{f}_U \qquad (19.4\text{-}7)$$

reduces to simple vector correlation for white noise. In the general case the noise covariance matrix may be spectrally factored into the matrix product

$$\mathbf{K}_n = \mathbf{K}\mathbf{K}^T \qquad (19.4\text{-}8)$$

with $\mathbf{K} = \mathbf{E}\mathbf{\Lambda}_n^{1/2}$ where $\mathbf{E}$ is a matrix composed of the eigenvectors of $\mathbf{K}_n$ and $\mathbf{\Lambda}_n$ is a diagonal matrix of the corresponding eigenvalues (14). The resulting matched filter output

$$f_O = [\mathbf{K}^{-1}\mathbf{f}]^T [\mathbf{K}^{-1}\mathbf{f}_U] \qquad (19.4\text{-}9)$$

can be regarded as vector correlation after the unknown vector $\mathbf{f}_U$ has been "whitened" by premultiplication by $\mathbf{K}^{-1}$.

Extensions of the previous derivation for the detection of stochastic image vectors are straightforward. The signal energy of Eq. 19.4-3 becomes

$$S = (\mathbf{m}^T \mathbf{n}_f)^2 \qquad (19.4\text{-}10)$$

where $\mathbf{n}_f$ is the mean vector of $\mathbf{f}$ and the variance of the matched filter output is

$$N = \mathbf{m}^T \mathbf{K}_f \mathbf{m} + \mathbf{m}^T \mathbf{K}_n \mathbf{m} \qquad (19.4\text{-}11)$$

under the assumption of independence of $\mathbf{f}$ and $\mathbf{n}$. The resulting signal-to-noise ratio is maximized when

$$\mathbf{m} = (\mathbf{K}_f + \mathbf{K}_n)^{-1} \mathbf{n}_f \qquad (19.4\text{-}12)$$

Vector correlation of $\mathbf{m}$ and $\mathbf{f}_U$ to form the matched filter output can be performed directly using Eq. 19.4-2 or alternatively, according to Eq. 19.4-9 where $\mathbf{K} = \mathbf{E}\mathbf{\Lambda}^{1/2}$ and $\mathbf{E}$ and $\mathbf{\Lambda}$ denote the matrices of eigenvectors and eigenvalues of $(\mathbf{K}_f + \mathbf{K}_n)$, respectively (14). In the special, but common, case of white noise and a separable, first-order Markovian covariance matrix, the whitening operations can be performed using an efficient Fourier domain processing algorithm developed for Wiener filtering (15).

19.5. IMAGE REGISTRATION

In many image processing applications it is necessary to form a pixel-by-pixel comparison of two images of the same object field obtained from different sensors, or of two images of an object field taken from the same sensor at different times. To form this comparison it is necessary spatially to register the images and thereby correct for relative translational shifts magnification differences, and rotational shifts, as well as geometrical and intensity distortions of each image. Often it is possible to eliminate or minimize many of these sources of misregistration by proper static calibration and compensation of the image sensor. However, in some applications misregistration detection and subsequent correction must be performed dynamically for each pair of images.

Consideration is given here to the task of registering images subject to translational differences. The results can be applied to the detection of rotational and magnification differences by increasing the dimensionality of the problem, or by a proper transformation of coordinates (e.g., a rotational shift is equivalent to a translational shift in polar coordinates).

19.5.1. Correlation Registration

A classical technique for registering a pair of functions is to form a correlation measure between the functions and determine the location of the maximum correlation (16, 17). In applying this technique to two dimensions, let $F_1(j, k)$ and $F_2(j, k)$ represent two discrete images to be registered. In its simplest form, the correlation measure is defined as

$$R(m, n) = \frac{\sum_{j=1}^{J} \sum_{k=1}^{K} F_1(j, k) F_2(j - m, k - n)}{\left[\sum_{j=1}^{J} \sum_{k=1}^{K} F_1^2(j, k) \right]^{1/2} \left[\sum_{j=1}^{J} \sum_{k=1}^{K} F_2^2(j - m, k - n) \right]^{1/2}}$$

$$(19.5-1)$$

where (j, k) are indices in a $J \times K$ pixel window area W that is located within an $M \times N$ point search area S. Figure 19.5-1 illustrates the relationship between the search and window areas. In general, the correlation function must be computed for all $(M - J + 1)(N - K + 1)$ possible translations of the window area within the search area to determine its maximum value and obtain a misregistration estimate.

There are two basic problems with this simple correlation measure. First, the correlation function may be rather broad, making detection of the peak difficult. It should be noted that the simple correlation measure ignores the

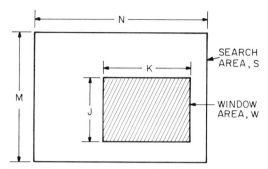

FIGURE 19.5-1. Correlation registration search and window areas.

spatial relationship of points within each image. Second, image noise may mask the peak correlation. Both problems can be alleviated by extending the correlation measure to consider the statistical properties of each image function $F_1(j, k)$ and $F_2(j, k)$.

The statistical correlation measure is defined as

$$R_s(m, n) = \frac{\sum\limits_{j=1}^{J} \sum\limits_{k=1}^{K} G_1(j, k)G_2(j-m, k-n)}{\left[\sum\limits_{j=1}^{J} \sum\limits_{k=1}^{K} G_1^2(j, k)\right]^{1/2}\left[\sum\limits_{j=1}^{J} \sum\limits_{k=1}^{K} G_2^2(j-m, k-n)\right]^{1/2}}$$

$$(19.5\text{-}2)$$

where the arrays $G_i(j, k)$ are obtained by the convolution operation

$$G_i(j, k) = F_i(j, k) \circledast D_i(j, k) \qquad (19.5\text{-}3)$$

with spatial filter impulse response functions $D_i(j, k)$. The impulse response functions are chosen to maximize the peak correlation when the pair of images are in best register. The design problem can be solved by recourse to the theory of matched filtering of discrete arrays developed in the previous section. Accordingly, let $\mathbf{f}_1$ denote the vector of column-scanned elements of $F_1(j, k)$ in the window area and let $\mathbf{f}_2(m, n)$ represent the elements of $F_2(j, k)$ over the window area for a given registration shift (m, n). There are a total of $M \cdot N$ vectors $\mathbf{f}_2(m, n)$. The elements of $\mathbf{f}_1$ and $\mathbf{f}_2(m, n)$ are usually highly correlated spatially. Hence, following the techniques of stochastic matches filtering, the first processing step should be to whiten each vector by premultiplication with whitening filter matrices $\mathbf{H}_1$ and $\mathbf{H}_2$ according to the relations

$$\mathbf{g}_1 = [\mathbf{H}_1]^{-1}\mathbf{f}_1 \qquad (19.5\text{-}4a)$$

$$\mathbf{g}_2(m, n) = [\mathbf{H}_2]^{-1}\mathbf{f}_2(m, n) \qquad (19.5\text{-}4b)$$

where $\mathbf{H}_1$ and $\mathbf{H}_2$ are obtained by a factorization of the image covariance matrices

$$\mathbf{K}_1 = \mathbf{H}_1\mathbf{H}_1^T \qquad (19.5\text{-}5a)$$

$$\mathbf{K}_2 = \mathbf{H}_2\mathbf{H}_2^T \qquad (19.5\text{-}5b)$$

The factorization matrices may be expressed as

$$\mathbf{H}_1 = \mathbf{E}_1\mathbf{\Lambda}_1^{1/2} \qquad (19.5\text{-}6a)$$

$$\mathbf{H}_2 = \mathbf{E}_2\mathbf{\Lambda}_2^{1/2} \qquad (19.5\text{-}6b)$$

where $\mathbf{E}_1$ and $\mathbf{E}_2$ contain eigenvectors of $\mathbf{K}_1$ and $\mathbf{K}_2$, respectively, and $\mathbf{\Lambda}_1$ and $\mathbf{\Lambda}_2$ are diagonal matrices of the corresponding eigenvalues of the covariance matrices.

The statistical correlation measure can then be obtained by the normalized inner-product computation

$$R_s(m, n) = \frac{\mathbf{g}_1^T\mathbf{g}_2(m, n)}{[\mathbf{g}_1^T\mathbf{g}_1]^{1/2}[\mathbf{g}_2^T(m, n)\mathbf{g}_2(m, n)]^{1/2}} \qquad (19.5\text{-}7a)$$

It can be shown that the statistical correlation function can also be computed by the alternative relation

$$R_s(m, n) = \frac{[(\mathbf{K}^T)^{-1}\mathbf{f}_1]^T\mathbf{f}_2}{\{[(\mathbf{K}^T)^{-1}\mathbf{f}_1]^T[(\mathbf{K}^T)^{-1}\mathbf{f}_1][\mathbf{f}_2^T(m, n)][\mathbf{f}_2(m, n)]\}} \qquad (19.5\text{-}7b)$$

where $\mathbf{K} = \mathbf{H}_2\mathbf{H}_1^T$. Computation by Eq. 19.5-7a requires whitening of $\mathbf{f}_1$ and all $M \cdot N$ versions of $\mathbf{f}_2$, while Eq. 19.5-7b only requires a single matrix multiplication $\mathbf{G}\mathbf{f}_1$ where $\mathbf{G} = (\mathbf{K}^T)^{-1}$. Clearly, the second formulation is preferable to the first if all computations are performed by standard vector-space arithmetic.

Computation of the processing matrix $\mathbf{G}$ requires computation of two sets of eigenvectors and eigenvalues of the covariance matrices of the two images to be registered over the window area. If the window area contains $J \times K$ pixels, the covariance matrices $\mathbf{K}_1$ and $\mathbf{K}_2$ will each be $(J \cdot K) \times (J \cdot K)$ matrices. For example, if $J = K = 16$, the covariance matrices $\mathbf{K}_1$ and $\mathbf{K}_2$ are each of dimension 256×256. Computation of the eigenvectors and eigenvalues for such matrices, in general, is numerically difficult for all but the largest of computers. However, in special cases the computation can be simplified appreciably (14). For example if the images are modeled as separable Markov sources and there is no observational noise, the convolutional operators of Eq. 19.5-3 reduce to the statistical edge detection mask of Eq. 17.4-6 given by

$$\mathbf{D}_i = \begin{bmatrix} \rho^2 & -\rho(1+\rho^2) & \rho^2 \\ -\rho(1+\rho^2) & (1+\rho^2)^2 & -\rho(1+\rho^2) \\ \rho^2 & -\rho(1+\rho^2) & \rho^2 \end{bmatrix} \qquad (19.5\text{-}8)$$

where ρ denotes the adjacent pixel correlation. If the images are spatially uncorrelated, $\rho = 0$, and the convolution operation is not required. At the other extreme, if $\rho = 1$, then

$$\mathbf{D}_i = \begin{bmatrix} 1 & -2 & 1 \\ -2 & 4 & -2 \\ 1 & -2 & 1 \end{bmatrix} \qquad (19.5\text{-}9)$$

This operator is a form of the Laplacian operator. Thus, when the images are highly correlated, the statistical correlation measure concentrates on the edge outline comparison between the two scenes.

Figure 19.5-2 provides computer simulation results of the performance of the statistical correlation measure for registration of natural scenes. In the simulation the tank image has been offset horizontally by three pixels

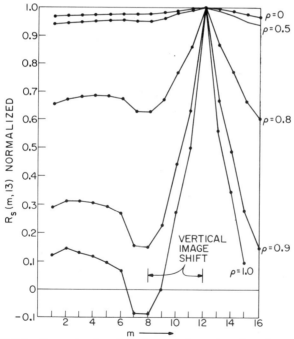

FIGURE 19.5-2. Example of statistical correlation misregistration detection.

and vertically by four pixels. The pair of images have then been correlated in a window area of 16×16 pixels over a search area of 32×32 pixels. The curves in Figure 19.5-2 represent the normalized statistical correlation measure taken through the peak of the correlation function. It should be noted that for $\rho = 0$, corresponding to the conventional correlation measure, it is relatively difficult to distinguish the peak of $R_S(m, n)$. For $\rho = 0.9$ or greater, $R_S(m, n)$ peaks sharply at the correct point.

19.5.2. Sequential Registration

A common criticism of the correlation measure form of image registration is the great amount of computation that must be performed if the window and search areas are large. With the correlation measure technique, no decision can be made until the correlation array $R_S(m, n)$ is computed for all (m, n). Furthermore, the amount of computation of $R_S(m, n)$ is the same for all amounts of misregistration. These deficiencies of the standard correlation measure have led to the search for sequential algorithms that could inherently provide a misregistration estimate with fewer computations.

A method of sequential test has been proposed by Barnea and Silverman (18). The basic form of this algorithm is deceptively simple. The error

$$\mathcal{E}_S = \sum_j \sum_k |F_1(j, k) - F_2(j - m, k - n)| \tag{19.5-10}$$

is accumulated for pixel values in a window area. If the error exceeds a predetermined threshold value before all $J \times N$ points in the window area are examined, then it is assumed that the test has failed for the particular window, and a new window is checked. If the error grows slowly, then the number of points examined when the threshold is finally exceeded is recorded and denoted as a rating of the test window. Eventually, when all test windows have been examined, the window with the largest rating is assumed to be the proper registration window. The highest rating possible is equal to the number of window points $J \times K$. It should be noted that only a relatively small number of computations is necessary for windows that correspond to a gross misregistration.

There are several extensions to the sequential test algorithm that have been proposed to speed its convergence and improve its reliability (18). A natural extension is a hybrid system employing a sequential test algorithm to discard gross misregistration points followed by a statistical correlation measure for the remaining test points. Such a system could provide the performance advantages of the statistical correlation measure with the speed advantages of the sequential test.

REFERENCES

1. R. O. Duda and P. E. Hart, *Pattern Classification and Scene Analysis*, Wiley-Interscience, New York, 1973, 276–284.

2. W. H. Highleyman, "An Analog Method for Character Recognition," *IRE Trans. Electronic Computers*, **EC-10**, 3, September 1961, 502–510.

3. L. N. Kanal and N. C. Randall, "Recognition System Design by Statistical Analysis," Proceedings ACM National Conference, 1964.

4. J. H. Munson, "Experiments in the Recognition of Hand-Printed Text: Part I—Character Recognition," Proceedings Fall Joint Computer Conference, December 1968, 1125–1138.

5. G. L. Turin, "An Introduction to Matched Filters," *IRE Trans. Inf. Theory*, **IT-6**, 3, June 1960, 311–329.

6. C. E. Cook and M. Bernfeld, *Radar Signals*, Academic Press, New York, 1965.

7. J. B. Thomas, *An Introduction to Statistical Communication Theory*, Wiley, New York, 1965, 187–218.

8. H. C. Andrews, *Computer Techniques in Image Processing*, Academic Press, New York, 1970, 55–71.

9. L. J. Cutrona, E. N. Leith, C. J. Palermo, and L. J. Porcello, "Optical Data Processing and Filtering Systems," *IRE Trans. Information Theory*, **IT-6**, 3, June 1960, 386–400.

10. A. Vander Lugt, F. B. Rotz, and A. Kloester, Jr., "Character-Reading by Optical Spatial Filtering," in *Optical and Electro-Optical Information Processing*, J. Tippett et al., Eds., MIT Press, Cambridge, Mass., 1965, 125–141.

11. A. Vander Lugt, "Signal Detection by Complex Spatial Filtering," *IEEE Trans. Inf. Theory*, **IT-10**, 2, April 1964, 139–145.

12. A. Kozma and D. L. Kelly, "Spatial Filtering for Detection of Signals Submerged in Noise," *Appl. Opt.*, **4**, 4, April 1965, 387–392.

13. A. Arcese, P. H. Mengert, and E. W. Trombini, "Image Detection Through Bipolar Correlation," *IEEE Trans. Inf. Theory*, **IT-16**, 5, September 1970, 534–541.

14. W. K. Pratt, "Correlation Techniques of Image Registration," *IEEE Trans. Aerospace and Electronic Systems*, **AES-10**, 3, May 1974, 353–358.

15. W. K. Pratt and F. Davarian, "Fast Computational Techniques for Pseudoinverse and Wiener Image Restoration," *IEEE Trans. Computers*, **C-26**, 6 June, 1977, 571–580.

16. W. Meyer-Eppler and G. Darius, "Two-Dimensional Photographic Autocorrelation of Pictures and Alphabet Letters," in *Proceedings 3rd London Symposium on Information Theory*, C. Cherry, Ed., Academic Press, New York, 1956, 34–36.

17. P. F. Anuta, "Digital Registration of Multispectral Video Imagery," *Soc. Photo-Optical Instr. Engineers J.*, **7**, September 1969, 168–178.

18. D. I. Barnea and H. F. Silverman, "A Class of Algorithms for Fast Image Registration," *IEEE Trans. Computers*, **C-21**, 2, February 1972, 179–186.

20 IMAGE UNDERSTANDING SYSTEMS

Image understanding may be regarded as a descriptive process in which an image field or array is examined in order to generate some nonpictorial description or representation of the image. At the simplest level an image understanding system may simply provide a cue that an image contains a specific object or perhaps an unexpected object. At the other extreme the system may generate a very general verbalized description of a scene in the sense that a human viewer would write a paragraph about the contents of a particular picture. Systems that perform relatively simple image description tasks for narrow classes of images have been constructed. Research is presently underway to develop generalized, programmable systems that can process wide classes of imagery for a variety of tasks.

20.1. PATTERN RECOGNITION SYSTEMS

Many image analysis tasks can be successfully performed by the classical pattern recognition system shown in Figure 20.1-1 (1–4). Pattern recognition systems are designed to classify an input pattern—an image or portion of an image—into one of several categories. For example, in an Earth resources imagery application a picture of agricultural fields may be broken into small blocks, and each block classified according to the crop type, wheat, corn, cotton, etc. Each input image block may be regarded as a point in a pattern space of all possible amplitude patterns. For an $N \times N$ pixel block in which each pixel amplitude is quantized to B levels, the dimension of the pattern space $B^{N \cdot N}$ can be enormous even for relatively small blocks and coarse quantization. Therefore it is usually neces-

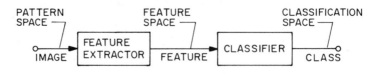

FIGURE 20.1-1. Pattern recognition system.

sary to perform a dimensionality reduction by feature extraction. Typical features include edge points, texture, and Fourier components. These features can also be regarded as points in some N-dimensional pattern space. A pattern recognition classifier is designed by measuring features of representative imagery whose correct classification is known. This feature set, called prototype data, is then mapped in pattern space. Figure 20.1-2 contains an example in which two features, for example, average luminance and texture, are measured for each block. Hopefully, the prototype features will tend to cluster into groups according to desired classes. If this does occur, then decision boundaries are established to separate features of unknown data into proper classes.

In its early days of development, pattern recognition was viewed by many as a solution to almost all image analysis problems. This optimism was subsequently tempered by two limitations of the pattern recognition approach. First, the inherent dimensionality of imagery is enormous, and in many cases the number of potential classifications is quite large. As a result the processing required by a pattern recognizer is often prohibitive. A more fundamental limitation is that an image description by classification may not be appropriate. For example, guidance information obtained from visual sensors may be required for an industrial robot. Another example is structural analysis of scene, for example, body A lies above and to the right of body B, and so on. Although there are many applications in which classical pattern recognition fails in an image analysis environment, the concept should not be dismissed entirely. There may be many subtasks in an image analysis system that can be performed well by pattern recognition.

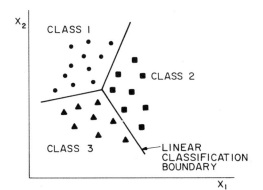

FIGURE 20.1-2. Example of prototype classification for two features.

20.2. IMAGE UNDERSTANDING SYSTEM MODELS

A variety of models have been proposed for image understanding systems. Examination of these models indicates that they contain the same set of broadly defined processing and manipulating elements: feature extraction, symbolic representation, and semantic interpretation. The models differ primarily in the organization of the elements, the nature of element control, and the degree of artificial intelligence and knowledge employed.

Figure 20.2-1 contains a block diagram of a hierarchical image understanding model that employs "bottom-up" processing. In the first stage of the model primitive features such as pixel amplitude, edge point location, textural descriptors, and the like are extracted from an observed image. Point and spatial processing may also be incorporated in this stage to reduce noise and interference effects or to enhance the features to be subsequently extracted. Next, the feature set is passed on to the symbolic representation stage, which forms a grouping of the features into symbols. For example, edge points are grouped into line segments or closed curves. Regions of common amplitude or texture are combined to form segments of similar attribute. The symbol set is then manipulated by the semantic interpretation stage to produce some desired scene description. Scene descriptions are clearly application dependent. In some cases the desired description may merely be an indication of absence or presence of a suspected object in a scene, or perhaps that the object is moving up, down, right, or left in the image frame. At the other extreme the description might entail the writing of a detailed report on the contents of a scene for photointerpretation purposes. The semantic interpreter attempts to recognize and label the structures represented by its input symbols utilizing a priori knowledge of the scene or class of scenes under examination as a guide. This knowledge is incorporated in visual models of images to be processed. Scene knowledge may vary from a very simple-minded object description that a suspected object should appear brighter than its background, to quite complex scene descriptions involving web structure rela-

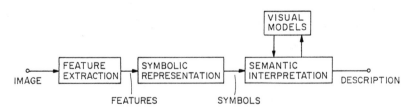

FIGURE 20.2-1. Hierarchical image understanding model—bottom-up approach.

tions of interconnectivity constraints on the scene parts. A semantic interpreter must examine the symbols of an image symbol set to determine their
spatial interrelationships, and then verify the detected relationships with
the visual model. For example, large blue regions detected at the top of a
scene adjacent to large greenish regions at the bottom of a scene might be
interpreted as sky and grass, respectively. On completion of the scene
interpretation, the various parts of the scene are labeled to form the image
description.

The term "bottom-up" applied to the image understanding model of
Figure 20.2-1 indicates both the data and control flow in the model. Each
stage independently performs its processing or manipulation task and
passes its output on to the next stage. The key to success of the approach is
a reduction in dimensionality from stage to stage. The feature set should be
smaller than the number of pixels in the input image, and the symbol set
should be smaller than the feature set. This sequential reduction in dimensionality is vital because the relative processing complexity is generally
greater at each succeeding stage. Hierarchical bottom-up image understanding systems can be successfully developed for limited application
domains in which the description task is relatively simple and the range of
input imagery is narrow. Difficulties quickly arise when either condition is
violated.

Another large class of image understanding systems are based on the
hierarchical "top-down" model of Figure 20.2-2. In this model operation is
goal directed; the interpretation stage is guided in its structural analysis by
trial or test descriptions of a scene. The matched filter of Chapter 19 is the
most common example of a top-down system. In matched filtering or
template matching a search is instituted for a specific object or structure
within a scene. The result of the search is an indication of the presence or
absence of the object, or some probability of its presence. Scene descriptions are obtained by sequentially searching for objects in a scene, based on

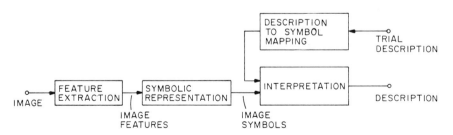

FIGURE 20.2-2. Hierarchical image understanding model—top-down approach.

previous successes and failures, and then interpreting the relationship between detected objects. In the matched filtering example the interpretation is normally performed at the pixel level by cross correlation of an object template with an observed image field. Interpretation can be performed at a higher level in the chain by correlating image features or symbols rather than pixels. Higher-level interpretation is potentially advantageous because of the reduced dimensionality at the feature or symbol level.

Hierarchical image understanding systems suffer from a lack of adaptability. They are usually designed for specific tasks on restricted types of images. Adaptation to other tasks and different types of images often requires a massive system redesign. Another drawback of the hierarchical approach is the large amount of processing required. Furthermore, much of this processing is often wasted in the generation of features and symbols that are not required for the analysis of a particular scene. One means of avoiding these problems is to establish a central monitor that can view the overall performance of the image understanding system and then issue commands to the various system elements to modify their operation to maximize system performance and efficiency. Minsky and Papert (5, p. 10) have proposed an alternative philosophy embodied in a heterarchical organization in which the image understanding system is goal directed, possesses visual knowledge, and exercises distributed control. Figure 20.2-3 contains a block diagram of an image understanding system that achieves heterarchical operation by distributed feedback control. If the semantic interpretation stage in the model experiences difficulty in working with its input symbol set, control can be fed back to the symbolic representation stage requesting a new set of symbols. This action in turn may cause a feedback control command to the feature extraction stage requesting a modified set of features. Direct feedback control is also possible between the semantic interpreter and feature extractor when needed. This model organization provides an important auxiliary benefit in addition to flexibility. The

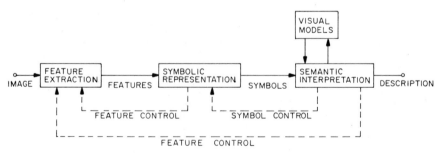

FIGURE 20.2-3. Heterarchical image understanding model.

dimensionality of the feature and symbol sets can be kept at minimum levels because the sets can be restructured on command.

Reddy and Newell (6) have proposed another image understanding system configuration called the blackboard model. In the blackboard model, described by the simplified example of Figure 20.2-4, the various system elements communicate with a common data storage: the blackboard. Whenever any element performs a task, its output is put into data storage for all other elements to access independently. The individual elements can either be directed by a central control, or they can be imbued with sufficient intelligence and autonomy to produce results for the common goal of the system as needed.

Finally, mention should be made of the "frames" theory proposed by Minsky (5, p. 211, 7). Minsky postulates that when a person views a scene, the scene is perceived in relation to a replica or structure of the scene, called a frame, that is stored in human memory. These frames are, in essence, memory snapshots of previously viewed scenes. A person can easily visualize familiar faces, places, and events, for example, the living room of one's home. In the context of image understanding a frame is a data structure consisting of a network of nodes and relations. The higher levels of the network are fixed, for it is on this basis that the frame is selected from memory. Lower network levels in the frame contain slots that are filled in during the viewing of a scene provided that the scene contents satisfy certain expectations. In the living room example the sofa may be expected to be along the right wall. If it is, the pertinent perceived details of the sofa are placed in the frame slots. If the sofa has been moved to the left side of the room—the unexpected has occurred—that portion of the frame dealing with the sofa location, called a subframe, must be updated. Frames theory has not reached the stage of model development, the concept is presently a guide, seemingly quite useful, to the future development of such a model.

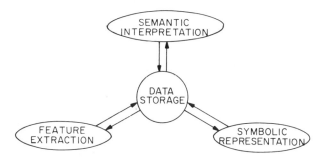

FIGURE 20.2-4. Blackboard image understanding model.

The discussion of models presented in this section is obviously quite cursory. Presently existing models are somewhat more structured than the presentation might indicate, but for the most part image understanding models remain relatively incomplete and undetailed. In the following sections specific approaches to the design of image understanding systems are described.

20.3. SYNTACTIC METHODS

Students in elementary school spend many hours diagramming sentences into their parts: nouns, pronouns, verbs, adverbs, adjectives, prepositions, and articles. Surprisingly enough, there is a link between this dreary exercise and scene analysis; formal linguistic methods of natural language analysis have been employed for structural or syntactical image analysis.*
Formal definitions of a language and its constituents are listed below.

Formal Language Definitions

Syntax—description of a language.
Language—set of sentences constructed according to a set of rules.
Sentence—collection of terminal symbols.
Terminal symbol—element of a sentence.
Nonterminal symbol—element of production rule (syntactic rule).
Alphabet—any finite set of symbols.
Grammar—collection of terminal symbols, nonterminal symbols, production rules, and start symbols.
Production rule—rule for replacement of nonterminal symbol with another nonterminal symbol or with a terminal symbol.
Top-down parse—sequence of production rules that produces a sentence from a nonterminal goal symbol.
Bottom-up parse—sequence of production rules that produces a nonterminal goal symbol from a sentence.

As an example of this structure consider the simple sentence

$$S = \text{MIKE} \# \text{PAINTED} \# \text{THE} \# \text{PICTURE} \qquad (20.3\text{-}1)$$

where $\#$ explicitly denotes a space. The terminal symbols employed in the

---

* Material in this section draws upon the tutorial work of R. H. Anderson (8). References 2 and 9–12 also contain useful surveys of the subject.

writing of this sentence are

$$T = \{\text{MIKE,PAINTED,THE,PICTURE}, \# \} \qquad (20.3\text{-}2)$$

The associated set of nonterminal symbols is defined as

$$N = \{\langle\text{sentence}\rangle, \langle\text{noun phrase}\rangle, \langle\text{verb phrase}\rangle, \langle\text{noun}\rangle, \langle\text{verb}\rangle, \langle\text{article}\rangle\}$$
$$(20.3\text{-}3)$$

Nonterminal symbols are employed in the generation of sentences but do not appear as a final (terminal) result of the language. A sentence can be generated by a set of production rules. In this example the production rules are:

$$\langle\text{sentence}\rangle \rightarrow \langle\text{noun phrase}\rangle \# \langle\text{verb phrase}\rangle$$

$$\langle\text{noun phrase}\rangle \rightarrow \langle\text{noun}\rangle$$

$$\langle\text{noun phrase}\rangle \rightarrow \langle\text{article}\rangle \# \langle\text{noun}\rangle$$

$$\langle\text{verb phrase}\rangle \rightarrow \langle\text{verb}\rangle \# \langle\text{noun phrase}\rangle$$

$$\langle\text{noun}\rangle \rightarrow \text{MIKE}$$

$$\langle\text{noun}\rangle \rightarrow \text{PICTURE}$$

$$\langle\text{verb}\rangle \rightarrow \text{PAINTED}$$

$$\langle\text{article}\rangle \rightarrow \text{THE}$$

Figure 20.3-1 illustrates the generation of the sentence of Eq. 20.3-1 by a procedure called top-down parsing. At each stage in the process replacement rules are employed to move from the goal symbol $\langle$sentence$\rangle$ to a string of terminal symbols by replacing the right part of a production rule with its left. At the final stage the string of generated symbols is compared to the input sentence of Eq. 20.3-1. If a match exists, the parse is accomplished; otherwise the process must "backtrack" and change the ordering of replacement rules until a match is found or all possibilities are exhausted. The bottom-up parsing procedure described in Figure 20.3-1b begins with the input sentence of Eq. 20.3-1 and attempts transformations that will yield the goal symbol $\langle$sentence$\rangle$ under control of the production rules. Again, combinations of production rule application must be tried until success or exhaustion results. The efficiency of parsing algorithms has been studied by Griffiths and Petrick (13).

The syntactic method of analyzing alphabetic character strings to determine if a string is valid can be carried over to image analysis. Immediate problems arise in the extension of the syntactic approach

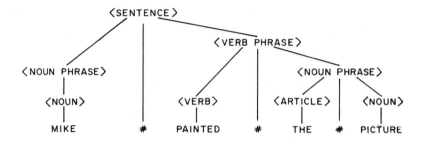

(a) TOP DOWN GENERATION

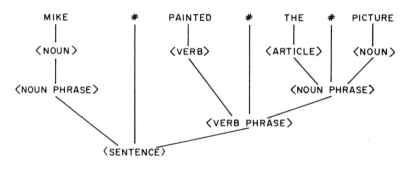

(b) BOTTOM UP ANALYSIS

FIGURE 20.3-1. Examples of sentence generation and analysis.

to two dimensions. First, there are no obvious choices for primative terminal elements. What is the picture analog of an alphabetic character? Second, the two dimensionality of images causes problems in the development of production rules. What is the picture analog of string concatenation?

Figure 20.3-2 contains an example of top-down parsing of a stylized scene into macro terminal symbols: SKY, SUN, DOOR, ROOF, and so on. Suppose that this scene is to be analyzed to determine if it contains a house. From the parsing tree a house is defined by a triangular shaped roof and a side, which in turn is composed of a window and a door. Conceptually, the house can be recognized by searching the scene for WINDOW, DOOR, FRONT terminal symbols and checking their spatial relationships to determine if these terminal symbols form a nonterminal SIDE symbol. then the search must be resumed to detect the ROOF symbol and check its structural relationship to the SIDE symbol. If all the production rules are

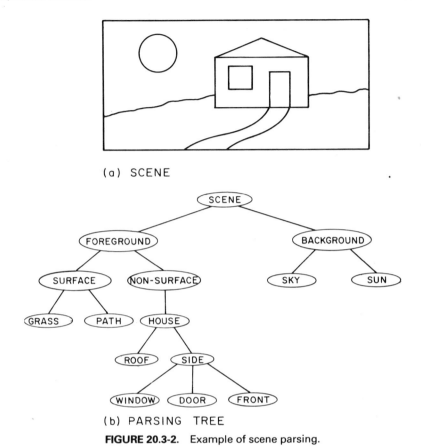

(a) SCENE

(b) PARSING TREE

FIGURE 20.3-2. Example of scene parsing.

satisfied, the house is deemed present in the scene. This example serves to illustrate problems associated with two-dimensional syntactic image analysis. The success of the procedure is predicated on detection of fairly complex macro terminal symbols. The number of macro symbols can be quite large if the class of scenes is generalized. If the macro symbols cannot be detected reliably, it will be necessary to parse the scene further to obtain more primitive terminal symbols such as line and region segments. This rapidly leads to an explosion in dimensionality. Furthermore, as symbol dimensionality grows, the set of production rules multiplies rapidly. The formidability of these problems has limited use of syntactic methods to the analysis of simple, well-structured images.

The beginning of syntactic scene analysis applications traces back to work on the symbolic representation of cursive script by Grimsdale (14) and Eden (15). Narasimhan (16, 17) has pioneered the application of the syntactic method to more general classes of imagery with specific emphasis on bubble-chamber photographs. In Narasimhan's model, terminal symbols, called basic sets, consist of local line segments, line junctions, and line ends. Bottom-up processing is employed to analyze strings of terminal symbols detected in a photograph. Terminal symbols are connected according to a set of grammar rules to form nonterminal symbols and string phrases such as straight lines, open curves, U bends, and circular arcs. Newly constructed phrase strings are further connected to form sentences.

Shaw (18, 19) has developed a Picture Description Language based upon syntactic concepts. In this language terminal symbols are line segments possessing a head and a tail that are connected according to the simple operators

$(A+B)$ head of A connected to tail of B

$(A \times B)$ tail of A connected to tail of B

$(A * B)$ head of A connected to head of B and
tail of A connected to tail of B

$(\tilde{A})$ reverse head and tail assignments

The composite structures produced by these operators are assigned heads and tails. Figure 20.3-3 gives an example of the generation of several stick letters from a set of straight line primitives. Shaw has used the picture description language for top-down analysis of spark-chamber photographs.

Ledley (20, 21) has applied syntactical methods to computer classification of chromosones. In the classification system the closed boundary of a chromosone is classified into one of several shape categories. Figure 20.3-4 contains an example for five categories. The result of shape categorization is a string of terminal signals that is parsed according to a set of production rules. The data parse is then compared to the parse description of prototype chromosones to perform the classification.

The work of Narisimhan, Shaw, and Ledley has proved that syntactic methods are feasible for image analysis tasks for "simple" images. Whether syntactic techniques can be successfully extended to general classes of images remains an open question.

20.4. RELATIONAL METHODS

The parsing tree described in the previous section only provides a crude description of a scene in terms of the connectivity of its terminal and nonterminal symbols. Further information is often available. It may be

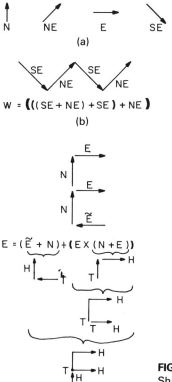

$$W = (((SE + NE) + SE) + NE)$$

(b)

$$E = (\tilde{E} + N) + (E \times (N + E))$$

FIGURE 20.3-3. Example of stick letter parsing with Shaw's picture description language. (a) Compass direction lines. (b) Parse of stick letter *W*. (c) Parse of stick letter *E*.

(c)

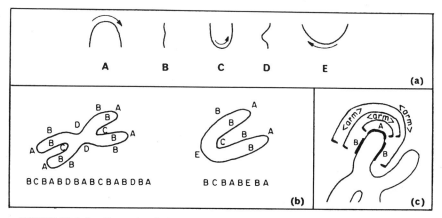

A B C D E

(a)

BCBABDBABCBABDBA

BCBABEBA

⟨arm⟩ ⟨arm⟩ ⟨arm⟩

(b)   (c)

FIGURE 20.3-4. Example of chromosone syntactical classification by Ledley (21).

579

known, for example, that object *A* is above object *B*, and that region *C* surrounds both objects. Information of this nature can be specified in a relational graph in which lines connecting parsing tree symbols are labeled with the type of connectivity and spatial relationship between symbols. Figure 20.4-1 provides an example. Arrows on the connecting lines indicate the sense of the relation, for example, ROOF is above SIDE. A relational graph with such indications is called a directional graph. Little more can be said about relational methods in general terms. Attention is now directed to specific approaches to image understanding systems utilizing these relational principles both implicitly and explicitly.

The relational approach to image understanding traces back to the pioneering work of Roberts (22), who developed a complete software system for analysis of scenes containing polyhedral objects possessing planar faces. Polyhedral objects form a logical starting point for scene analysis because they are relatively easy to define and the spatial relationships between polyhedral objects are well-structured. Roberts' analysis system begins with a line-drawing representation of a polyhedral solid that is stored as a list of straight line segments defined by the Cartesian coordinates of their endpoints. This list is searched to detect connected line

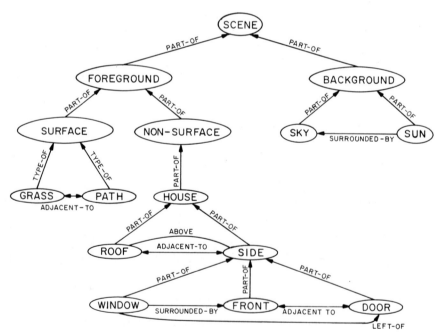

FIGURE 20.4-1.   Example of a directional graph.

segments that form polygons. Figure 20.4-2 illustrates the three types of polygons that a scene may contain: convex, concave, and boundary. In the next stage of the process the set of polygon break points is matched against sets of break points of primitive object models in order to form a decomposition of the original object as shown in the example of Figure 20.4-3. If a primitive object model is found to be a part of the original object, that part is eliminated from the original object by deletion and insertion of appropriate line segments in the line list. The process continues until the original object matches one of the primitive object models. The matching process takes into consideration translation, rotation, and scale changes of the primitive object models in relation to the original object parts.

Roberts' concept of decomposing a complex polyhedral object into primitive objects spawned a line of research into what has now been called blocks world scene analysis. Guzman (23) and Falk (24) have followed with

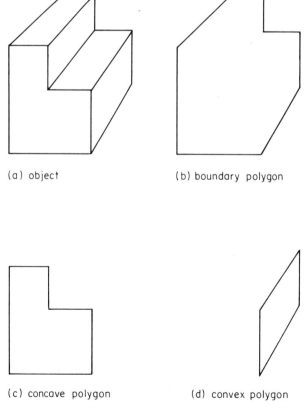

(a) object   (b) boundary polygon

(c) concave polygon   (d) convex polygon

FIGURE 20.4-2.   Polygon composition of a polygonal object.

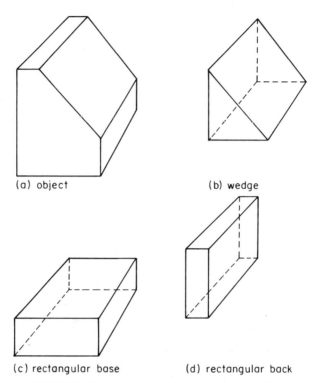

(a) object   (b) wedge

(c) rectangular base   (d) rectangular back

FIGURE 20.4-3. Decomposition of polyhedral object.

investigations of scenes containing multiple occluding objects and scenes described by imperfect line drawings. Heuristic rules have been applied over local areas in their systems to segment planar surfaces from a line representation of a scene. Winston (5, p. 5) has introduced learning methods by which information obtained from analyzed scenes is used to augment the set of visual scene models. Models are stored in directed graph network data structures consisting of simple adjacency and support relations between objects. Figure 20.4-4 provides an example of the directed graph of an arch and several examples of arch formation. A key element of Winston's work is the knowledge gained by near-miss situations. In the arch example a near-miss can infer that two support objects are not allowed to be adjacent.

Line-drawing representations of polyhedral objects are highly constrained in the real world; some combinations of straight lines and vertices are not permissable in a line drawing of a physical polyhedral object, Clowes (25) and Huffman (26) have developed procedures for determining if a line drawing represents valid or invalid (nonsense) objects. Waltz (5, p.

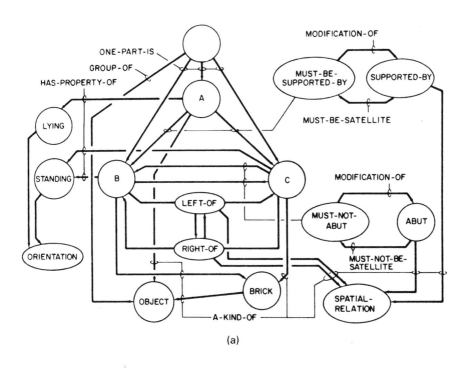

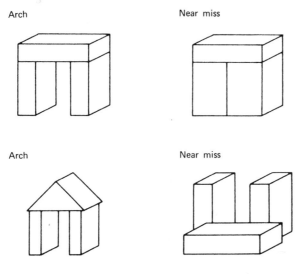

(b)

FIGURE 20.4-4. Example of directed graph of an arch (5). (a) Directed graph. (b) Examples.

583

19) has pursued this approach establishing the 11 categories of Figure 20.4-5 for labeled edge lines. If two or more lines meet in a vertex, certain physical restrictions must be met. For example, at an L-type junction the shadow gradients across the two lines must be in the same direction. Analysis of the number of labelings that are combinatorially possible reveals that the vast majority are physically illegal. The total number of valid vertices is only a few thousand for polyhedral objects. Waltz's system begins by labeling lines emanating from each vertex. A "filter" program then checks the consistency of line labels of interconnected vertices, and deletes inconsistent labels. Next, nonunique labels are reconciled by recourse to a set of combination rules. This number can be further constrained when the type of adjacent vertices is analyzed.

The blocks world analysis techniques mentioned previously possess a common feature; the starting point is either an abstract line drawing or a line drawing extracted from a real scene. Shirai (5, p. 93, 27) has taken an

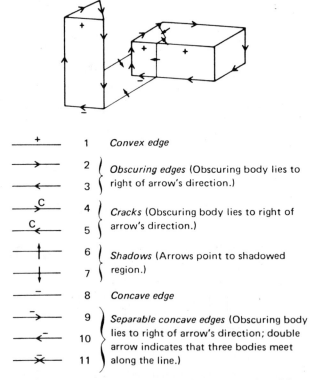

— + —	1	*Convex edge*
— → —	2	*Obscuring edges* (Obscuring body lies to
— ← —	3	right of arrow's direction.)
— C→ —	4	*Cracks* (Obscuring body lies to right of
— C← —	5	arrow's direction.)
— ┼ —	6	*Shadows* (Arrows point to shadowed
— ┼ —	7	region.)
— − —	8	*Concave edge*
— → —	9	*Separable concave edges* (Obscuring body
— ← —	10	lies to right of arrow's direction; double arrow indicates that three bodies meet
— ⤫ —	11	along the line.)

FIGURE 20.4-5.   Categorization of polyhedral lines (5).

alternative approach to polyhedral scene analysis in which real scenes are analyzed directly as arrays of picture points. Shirai's program is the first to attempt heterarchical analysis of meaningful scenes. Knowledge of the type of objects to be encountered is utilized to guide an edge detector search of faint concave edges and creases.

Important steps have been taken by Horn (5, p. 115) and Binford, Agin, and Nevatia (28–30) toward the analysis of scenes containing curved solid objects. Horn has utilized the shading of illuminated smoothly curved objects to deduce their physical shape. The work of Binford, Agin, and Nevatia has been directed toward three-dimensional shape descriptions of objects using medial axis skeletons and linked conical cross-sectional structures.

One of the first attempts at analyzing reasonably complex real-world scenes by the relational approach was performed by Brice and Fennema (31). The first stage of their system is composed of a region growing segmenter. Next, the boundary of each detected region is fitted by line segments. The analyzer stage then utilizes semantic knowledge to group regions and recognize objects. As an example, in an office scene semantic knowledge consists of the facts: floor is low in the scene; wall is high in the scene; a painting is surrounded by wall. Barrow and Popplestone (32) have also developed a scene analysis system based on region growing segmentation. In their system feature vectors are measured for each segmented region using features such as shape, thinness, size, and relation to neighboring segments, that is, above, below, left-of, and so on. The feature vector of each region is then matched to the feature vector sets of regions in a visual model of the class of scenes to be analyzed. Matching difficulties are sometimes caused by shadows and occlusions.

One of the immediate problems that arises in the analysis of natural scenes is the overabundance of image features and symbols. This massive amount of data coupled with the combinatorially vast number of possible interrelationships simply overwhelms data structures and renders tree searching futile. Kelly (33) has introduced the important concept of planning in scene analysis as a means of limiting the dimensionality of tree searches. In Kelly's analysis scheme features and symbols are first extracted from a reduced resolution version of a scene. Objects are then recognized and labeled to produce a hypothesis model of the scene. This model then serves as a guide to search regions in the full resolution picture for feature and symbol extraction. Following along the theme of Kelly's planner, Tenenbaum et al. (34) have proposed an analysis system involving two phases: aquisition and validation. In the acquisition phase an image is examined for gross characteristics based on a visual model utilizing contextual information to guide a search. For example, in an office scene the search is initially directed toward the detection of a planar surface in the middle height range of the picture that is suspected of being the top surface of a desk. The search then continues on the planar surface for objects of interest, which are analyzed and tentatively recognized. In the validation phase more sophisticated processing is performed to extract hopefully more reliable features and symbols in the vicinity of hypothesized objects. This information is analyzed to determine if the acquisition hypothesis is valid. In this manner precious information processing resources can be allocated more efficiently.

On reaching this point in the section it is obvious that the presentation is merely a highly abridged survey of research results in the image understanding field. In the conglomerate progress has been made, but it is difficult at this juncture to sift important principles from interesting but non-general ideas. Clearly, much work remains in this vital area of image processing.

REFERENCES

1. H. C. Andrews, *Introduction to Mathematical Techniques in Pattern Recognition*, Wiley-Interscience, New York, 1972.

2. R. O. Duda and P. E. Hart, *Pattern Classification and Scene Analysis*, Wiley-Interscience, New York, 1973.

3. K. Fukunaga, *Introduction to Statistical Pattern Recognition*, Academic Press, New York, 1972.

4. W. S. Meisel, *Computer-Oriented Approaches to Pattern Recognition*, Academic Press, New York, 1972.

5. P. H. Winston, *The Psychology of Computer Vision*, McGraw-Hill, New York, 1975.

6. R. Reddy and A. Newell, "Image Understanding: Potential Research Approaches," ARPA Image Understanding Workshop, Washington D.C., March 1975.

7. P. H. Winston, *Artificial Intelligence*, Addison-Wesley, New York, 1977.

8. R. H. Anderson, "Two-Dimensional Compiler Notes," unpublished short course notes, University of Southern California, July 1969.

9. R. A. Kirsch, "Computer Interpretation of English Text and Picture Patterns," *IEEE Trans. Electronic Computers*, **EC-13**, 4, August 1964, 363–376.

10. W. F. Miller and A. C. Shaw, "Linguistic Methods in Picture Processing—A survey," Proceedings Fall Joint Computer Conference, December 1968, 279–290.

11. R. Narasimhan, "On the Description, Generation, and Recongnition of Classes in Pictures," in *Automatic Interpretation and Classification of Images*, A. Graselli, Ed., Academic Press, New York, 1969, 1–42.

12. K. S. Fu and P. H. Swain, "On Syntactic Pattern Recognition," in *Software Engineering*, Vol. 2, J. T. Tou, Ed., Academic Press, New York, 1971, 155-182.

13. T. V. Griffiths and S. R. Petrick, "On the Relative Efficiencies of Context-Free Grammar Recognizers," *Commun. ACM*, **8**, 5, May 1965, 289–300.

14. R. L. Grimsdale, "Automatic Pattern Recognition—New Morphological System Using a Digital Computer," *Wireless World*, **65**, November 1959, 499–501.

15. M. Eden, "Handwriting and Pattern Recognition," *IRE Trans. Inf. Theory*, **IT-8**, 2, February 1962, 160–166.

16. R. Narasimhan, "Labelling Schemata and Syntactic Description of Pictures," *Information and Control*, **7**, June 1964, 151–179.

17. R. Narasimhan, "Syntax-Directed Interpretation of Classes of Pictures," *Commun. ACM*, **9**, 3, March 1966, 166–173.

18. A. C. Shaw, "A Formal Picture Description Scheme as a Basis for Picture Processing Systems," *Information and Control*, **14**, 1, January 1969, 9–52.

19. A. C. Shaw, "Parsing of Graph-Representable Pictures," *JACM*, **17**, 3, July 1970, 453–481.

20. R. S. Ledley, "High-Speed Automatic Analysis of Biomedical Pictures," *Science*, **146**, 3641, October 9, 1964, 216–223.

21. R. S. Ledley et al., "FIDAC: Film Input to Digital Automatic Computer and Associated Syntax-Directed Pattern-Recognition Programming System," in *Optical and Electro-Optical Information Processing*, J. T. Tippett et al., Eds., MIT Press, Cambridge, Mass., 1965.

22. L. G. Roberts, "Machine Perception of Three-Dimensional Solids," in *Optical and Electro-Optical Information Processing*, J. T. Tippett et al., Eds., MIT Press, Cambridge, Mass., 159–197.

23. A. Guzman, "Decomposition of a Visual Scene into Three-Dimensional Bodies," Proceedings Fall Joint Computer Conference, Vol. 33, 1968, 291–304.

24. G. Falk, "Interpretation of Imperfect Line Data as a Three-Dimensional Scene," *Artificial Intelligence*, **3**, 2, 1972, 101-144.

25. M. Clowes, "On Seeing Things," *Artificial Intelligence*, **4**, 1, 1971, 79–116.

26. D. A. Huffman, "Impossible Objects as Nonsense Sentences," in *Machine Intelligence*, Vol. 6, B. Meltzer and D. Mitchie, Eds., University Press, Edinburgh, 1971, 295–323.

27. Y. Shirai, "A Context Sensitive Line Finder for Recognition of Polyhedra," *Artificial Intelligence*, **4**, 2, 1973, 95–119.

28. T. O. Binford and G. J. Agin, "Computer Description of Curved Objects," 3rd International Joint Conference on Artificial Intelligence, Menlo Park, Calif., 1973, 629–640.

29. R. Nevatia and T. O. Binford, "Structural Descriptions of Complex Objects," 3rd International Joint Conference on Artificial Intelligence, Menlo Park, Calif., 1973, 641–657.

30. R. Nevatia, *Structured Descriptions of Complex Curved Objects for Recognition and Visual Memory*, Springer-Verlag, New York, 1977.

31. C. R. Brice and C. L. Fennema, "Scene Analysis Using Regions," *Artificial Intelligence*, **1**, 1970, 205–206.

32. H. G. Barrow and R. J. Popplestone, "Relational Descriptions in Picture Processing," in *Machine Intelligence*, B.Meltzer and D. Mitchie, Eds., University Press, Edinburgh, 1971, 377–396.

33. M. D. Kelly, "Visual Identification of People by Computer," Stanford University Report AIM-130, 1970.

34. J. M. Tenenbaum, J. M. Garvey, S. Weyl, and H. C. Wolf, "An Interactive Facility for Scene Analysis Research," Stanford Research Institute, Technical Report 87, 1974.

6 IMAGE CODING

During the past 20 years there has been an extensive effort toward the development of digital image coding systems for television and facsimile transmission. The design objective of these coding systems generally has been the representation of images with acceptable fidelity and with as small a number of code bits as possible. Reducing the number of code bits permits: (a) individual images to be transmitted faster; (b) more parallel television channels to be transmitted through a communication link; (c) a reduction of transmitter power requirements; or (d) more compact image storage.

Psychophysical experiments indicate that a human only comprehends visual information at a rate of about 50 bits per second. Also, information-theoretic studies show that most natural imagery is highly redundant. Nevertheless, conventional television coding systems present about 50 million bits per second to the viewer. Clearly, there is a substantial potential for improvement by image coding.

Chapters 21, 22, and 23 provide descriptions of image coding techniques. A performance analysis of image coding systems is presented in Chapter 24.

21 ANALOG PROCESSING IMAGE CODING

This chapter contains a classification of image coding techniques and an operational description of commercial television systems. Descriptions and analyses are presented for image coding methods that can be utilized for analog or sampled data transmission.

21.1. CLASSIFICATION OF IMAGE CODING TECHNIQUES

Digital image coding systems may be classified in a number of ways as indicated in Table 21.1-1. Coding systems may be classified as to the type of imagery to be coded: pictorial or nonpictorial images. Pictorial images are natural scenes of objects or two-dimensional displays that are normally viewed by a human observer, while nonpictorial images are two-dimensional arrays of data, such as radar range versus velocity data, that are not normally viewed by an observer. Another classification is photometric

TABLE 21.1-1. Classification of image coding systems

Type of imagery
Pictorial
Nonpictorial
Photometric content
Monochrome
Color
Multispectral
Amplitude scale
Binary
Continuous tone
Type of signal processing
Analog
Digital
Processing dimensionality
Line-scan processing
Intraframe processing
Interframe processing

(a) ANALOG PROCESSING CODER

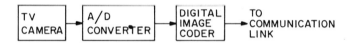

(b) DIGITAL PROCESSING CODER

FIGURE 21.1-1. Image compression coders.

type: monochrome, color, or multispectral imagery. Some coding systems are designed to process only binary valued imagery such as computer graphics data or pure black or white facsimile data, while others accept continuous tone images. Still another logical classification, shown in Figure 21.1-1, is based on the type of signal processing: analog versus digital. In an analog system the analog signal voltage from a scanning sensor is processed such that the processed signal analog bandwidth is reduced compared to a normally scanned video signal, and therefore sampling can be performed at a reduced rate. In a digital processing system, the analog image signal is immediately digitized, and attempts are made to recode the data to reduce the number of required code bits. Finally, there are coding systems that process individual scan lines, systems that process areas of an image, and systems that process sequences of frames of continuous motion imagery such as real-time television.

In the following chapters operational descriptions of image coding systems are presented. References 1–7 provide a comprehensive listing of information on these systems.

21.2. COMMERCIAL TELEVISION SYSTEMS

Closed-circuit monochrome television transmission was first demonstrated in 1925, independently, by Baird and Jenkins (8). In 1928 Baird gave the first demonstration of sequential color television in which red, green, and blue image fields were sequentially transmitted. During the following year Ives and Johnsrud demonstrated a simultaneous color television transmission system (9). Baird is credited with the first radio broadcast of monochrome television over a transatlantic communication link in 1928. Radio frequency transmission of color television was first accomplished by

Goldmark in 1940 (10, 11). Since these early experiments many television transmission methods and systems have been proposed and investigated. At present there are three world-wide television system standards: the National Television System Committee (NTSC), the Phase Alternating Line (PAL), and the Sequential Couleur a Memoire (SECAM) (12). North America and Japan employ the NTSC system; SECAM is utilized in France, Eastern Europe, and Russia; and PAL is the standard for the United Kingdom, the remainder of Europe, South America, and Africa.

21.2.1. NTSC System (13–15)

The National Television System Committee is a group formed in the United States in 1940 by the Radio Manufacturer's Association (subsequently changed to the Radio, Electronic, and Television Manufacturer's Association, RETMA) to formulate standards for monochrome television broadcast service. In 1950 the NTSC was reformed to investigate proposed color television systems and recommend a standard system for United States broadcast television.

In the monochrome version of the NTSC television system, a television camera performs electrooptical line-by-line scanning of a scene. Each complete image scan, called a frame, is divided into even and odd fields composed of even and odd line scans. A frame contains 525 scan lines; the frame time is 1/30 sec, and each field scan period is 1/60 sec. The choice of a 60-Hz frame rate is motivated by the 60-Hz alternating current power lines employed in the United States. If the frame rate is set at any other value, sum and difference beat signals generated from interference of the field oscillator signal and stray electrical and magnetic fields emanating from transmitter and receiver power supplies will lead to visual degradation patterns. At the end of each scan line a horizontal synchronization (synch) pulse is transmitted, and a vertical synch signal is transmitted at the end of each field. Figure 21.2-1 contains a sketch of a typical video signal waveform. The composite analog video signal is passed through a low-pass electrical filter with a half-power bandwidth of about 4.0 MHz before amplitude modulation of a transmission carrier. At the receiver, after carrier demodulation, the synch signals are extracted from the composite video to drive the horizontal and vertical deflection circuits of the television display.

The frequency spectrum of a television signal is not continuous, but rather is composed of discrete spectral components as a result of the line and frame scanning processes. Figure 21.2-2 illustrates an idealized video signal frequency spectrum for a stationary picture (15, p. 8–65). The

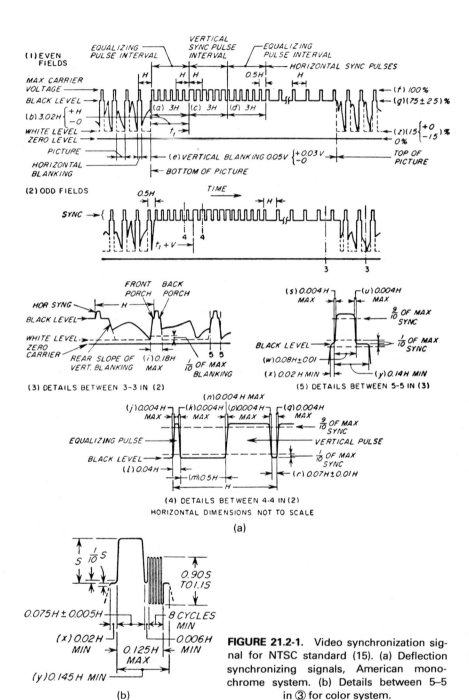

FIGURE 21.2-1. Video synchronization signal for NTSC standard (15). (a) Deflection synchronizing signals, American monochrome system. (b) Details between 5–5 in ③ for color system.

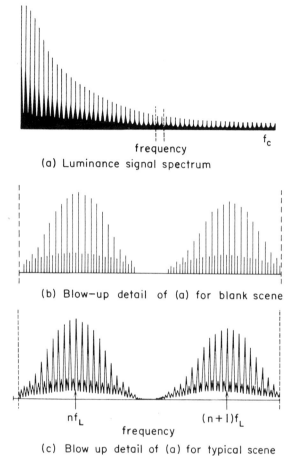

(a) Luminance signal spectrum

(b) Blow-up detail of (a) for blank scene

(c) Blow up detail of (a) for typical scene

FIGURE 21.2-2. Luminance signal spectrum, adapted from (15).

spectrum consists of a series of spectral clusters separated by the line scanning frequency of 15,750 Hz. As shown in Figure 21.2-2*b*, each line cluster is itself composed of spectral components separated by the field scanning frequency 60 Hz. These field harmonics alternate in amplitude because of the 2:1 line interlacing. If a scene contains object motion, the individual lines of the video signal spectrum become broadened, as shown in Figure 21.2-2*c*.

In a color television system the camera provides simultaneous red, green, and blue line scans of a scene; these are combined to form the scene luminance according to the relation

$$Y = 0.299R + 0.587G + 0.114B \qquad (21.2\text{-}1)$$

The luminance signal is then transmitted along with two chrominance signals I and Q that are linear functions of the color difference signals $R - Y$ and $B - Y$. The $G - Y$ color difference signal can be generated from

$$G - Y = -0.581(R - Y) - 0.394(B - Y) \qquad (21.2\text{-}2)$$

and the R, G, B signals can then be reconstructed by adding Y to each color difference. The color differences are normalized to form the signals

$$U = \frac{R - Y}{1.14} = 0.877(R - Y) \qquad (21.2\text{-}3a)$$

$$V = \frac{B - Y}{2.03} = 0.493(B - Y) \qquad (21.2\text{-}3b)$$

This normalization, which is a standard for the NTSC, PAL, and SECAM systems, was chosen to limit the maximum excursion of the composite color television signal to the arbitrary value of 1.33 times the excursion of the monochrome television signal. In the NTSC system the I and Q chrominance signals are formed by

$$I = U \cos(33°) - V \sin(33°) \qquad (21.2\text{-}4a)$$

$$Q = U \sin(33°) + V \cos(33°) \qquad (21.2\text{-}4b)$$

Alternatively, the Y, I, and Q signals can be directly related to the R, G, B camera signals by

$$Y = 0.299R + 0.587G + 0.114B \qquad (21.2\text{-}5a)$$

$$I = 0.596R - 0.274G - 0.322B \qquad (21.2\text{-}5b)$$

$$Q = 0.211R + 0.523G + 0.312B \qquad (21.2\text{-}5c)$$

Figure 21.2-3 describes NTSC video signal coding processing. For transmission the luminance signal is filtered to a bandwidth of about 4.0 MHz,

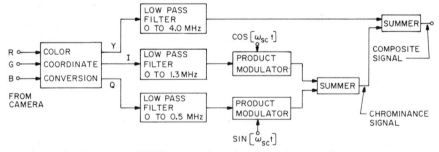

FIGURE 21.2-3. NTSC composite color video signal coding process.

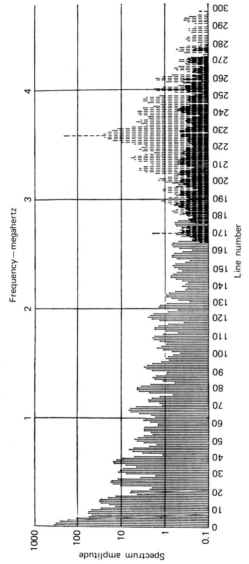

FIGURE 21.2-4. Composite luminance/chrominance spectrum (15).

597

while the I and Q signals are bandlimited to about 1.3 and 0.5 MHz, respectively. This rather severe bandlimiting of I and Q at the transmitter affects the frequency spectrum of the reconstructed R, G, B signals at the receiver, of course, but the degradation to a human viewer has proved minimal because of the poor spatial frequency response of the human visual system to colored light (16). In the next stage of transmitter processing the I and Q signals amplitude modulate subcarrier signals that are 90° out of phase with respect to each other. The modulated subcarrier signals are then summed together with the luminance signal. Figure 21.2-4 contains a sketch of the envelope of the energy distribution of the luminance signal and the combined chrominance signal. As discussed previously, the frequency spectrum of a raster-scanned video signal has a line structure with a rather sparse energy distribution between lines. Thus by frequency shifting the combined chrominance signal by a frequency deviation of one-half the line frequency, the luminance and chrominance signals can be summed in a nonoverlapping comb-like fashion. In this manner the chrominance signals can be combined with the luminance signal to form a color video signal whose bandwidth is the same as a conventional monochrome television signal. Horizontal and vertical synch signals are then combined with the color video signal during the horizontal and vertical retrace intervals to produce a composite color video signal. At the receiver the color video signal is reconstructed by a stripping of its synch components. A color signal demodulation circuit separates the Y, I, Q signals, which are converted to R, G, B drive signals for display according to the relations

$$R = 1.000\,Y + 0.956I + 0.621Q \tag{21.2-6a}$$

$$G = 1.000\,Y - 0.272I - 0.647Q \tag{21.2-6b}$$

$$B = 1.000\,Y - 1.106I + 1.703Q \tag{21.2-6c}$$

21.2.2. SECAM System (17)

One of the major objections to the NTSC television system is the requirement for quadrature modulation of the chrominance component. The quadrature modulation process is subject to phase detection errors, and subsequently to severe chrominance shifts (18). This difficulty motivated the development of the French SECAM television system. In the SECAM system during each line scan the luminance signal Y is transmitted along with one of the chrominance signals $R - Y$ or $B - Y$ on an alternate line basis. At the decoder the alternate line chrominance signals are stored and repeated during each line display. The single chrominance signal to be transmitted is modulated onto a subcarrier and added to the luminance signal in an interleaved fashion similar to the NTSC modulation process. The French SECAM system transmits 625 lines at a 50-Hz frame rate with 2:1 line interlacing.

21.2.3. PAL System (19)

In the PAL system, which is closely related to the NTSC system, the composite signal is formed as

$$C = Y + U \sin \omega_{SC}t + kV \cos \omega_{SC}t \qquad (21.2\text{-}7)$$

where ω_{SC} is the subcarrier angular frequency, U and V are the normalized color difference signals of Eq. 21.2-3, and the factor k assumes the value of plus one every other scan line and minus one for the remaining lines. The sign alternation results in a reversal of transmission phase errors from line to line. The corresponding chromaticity errors, which are in opposite directions in color space, tend to be averaged by the viewer. Throughout Europe the PAL system scanning standard is 625 lines at a 50-Hz frame rate with a 2:1 line interlace. In several South American countries, which have adopted PAL, the frame rate is 60 Hz to conform to local power frequency.

21.3. MODULATION BANDWIDTH REDUCTION TECHNIQUES

It has long been recognized that the frequency spectrum of a normally scanned television signal is not continuous, but rather contains a train of discrete components separated by regions of little signal energy. This is the basis for the development of an experimental monochrome television bandwidth reduction system, called frequency interlace (20), in which the television spectrum is halved by folding over the upper half of the spectrum onto the lower half and interleaving the spectral components. Figure 21.3-1 illustrates the folding and interleaving process. The spectral folding can be performed by conventional modulation and filtering methods; reconstruction requires some form of comb filter to extract the interleaved components. If the reconstruction process is not performed accurately, a low-frequency line crawling effect will result in the displayed image. The frequency interlace system is conceptually simple to implement; however, the reduction in analog transmission bandwidth is limited to a factor of 2 to 1.

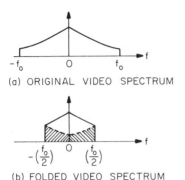

(a) ORIGINAL VIDEO SPECTRUM

(b) FOLDED VIDEO SPECTRUM   **FIGURE 21.3-1.** Spectrum interlace technique.

21.4. SPATIAL RESOLUTION AND FRAME RATE REDUCTION TECHNIQUES

One of the simplest means of bandwidth reduction is to reduce the inherent bandwidth requirements of an image sensor by limiting its spatial resolution and frame repetition rate. The extent to which spatial resolution and frame rate can be reduced is often a difficult decision involving factors of visual image quality or photometric imaging accuracy.

21.4.1. Spatial Resolution Reduction

If an imaging system is required to extract photometric samples over some specified field of view with some specified angular resolution, then computation of the minimum spatial resolution of the imaging system is a straightforward matter. However, if an imaging system must record objects with a certain guaranteed level of legibility, recognizability, or detectability, the specification of spatial resolution is not so well established. Chapter 7, which discussed image quality measures, provides some guidance for such decisions.

As indicated in Section 21.2, a variety of resolution standards have been developed for commercial and national television systems throughout the world. Digital image processing systems often are designed for 256, 512, 1024, . . . lines since such binary numbers make full use of digital registers. Also, binary size images can make efficient use of fast computational algorithms such as the fast Fourier transform.

In many imaging applications fine resolutions is not required over the entire area of an image. Certain regions of an image may be known to be of greatest significance, or perhaps certain regions can be isolated by an operator to be of importance. Maier and Gardenhire (21) have developed an image coding technique for facsimile transmission of photographs based on the concept of variable spatial resolution. In this system, called the Redundant Area Coding System (REARCS), an operator examines each photograph to be transmitted and outlines regions to be coded at fine and coarse resolution. The coarsely scanned regions serve to establish the context of the scene for the finely scanned regions. Figure 21.4-1 contains examples of pictures coded by a simulation of the REARCS coding system. It should be noted that the REARCS technique requires transmission of boundary information about each region as well as the pixel sample values. Simulation tests have indicated that compression ratios of about 8:1 are possible in many applications.

Variable spatial resolution can also be used as a means of bandwidth reduction for facsimile and television transmission systems when an object of interest is constrained to lie within the center region of an image. In such cases resolution at the periphery of an image can be reduced in comparison to the resolution at its center since it is known that the object of interest will always be reproduced with high resolution. Also, it is known that peripheral vision resolution is degraded from foveal vision for a human observer. Figure 21.4-2 contains an example of variable spatial resolution scanning in which the image is divided into four zones. Resolution in the center zone is set at the finest level; resolution in the first ring is set at one-half the finest resolution; resolution in the second ring is set at one-fourth the finest resolution, and so on. In this example the total number of

(a) (b)

FIGURE 21.4-1. Example of redundant area coding for a 1024×1024 pixel image: 64:1 subsampling of background; 8:1 cosine transform coding of 256×256 pixel window; total compression ratio 44.5:1. Photographs provided by W. H. Chen and C. Reader, Ford Aerospace Corp., Palo Alto, California. (a) Original. (b) Coded.

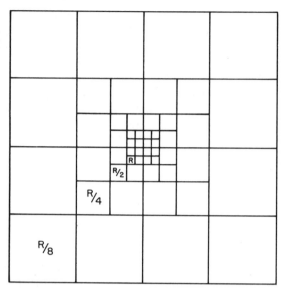

FIGURE 21.4-2. Example of variable spatial resolution.

pixels in the variable spatial resolution image is

$$N_R = 16(R) + 12\left(\frac{R}{2}\right) + 12\left(\frac{R}{4}\right) + 12\left(\frac{R}{8}\right) = 26.5R \qquad (21.4\text{-}1)$$

where R denotes the number of pixels in the highest resolution block. If the image were scanned at its finest resolution, it would contain $N_F = (32 \times 32)R$ pixels. Therefore, the bandwidth reduction factor is $N_F/N_R = 38.6$.

It is known that the spatial resolution acuity of a viewer is substantially degraded for moving objects: a viewer cannot easily focus to the fine detail of a moving object unless the movement is regular; rapidly moving objects are often blurred as a result of poor temporal response of the image sensor and display (22). In a real-time television system it is possible spatially to sample objects moving within a frame with a coarser grid than for stationary objects without any apparent loss of image quality (23–26). Unfortunately, the principle is much more easily stated than implemented. A fundamental problem is that of detecting when an object is moving and with what rate it is moving. Presumably, the spatial resolution for moving objects should be set inversely proportional to the object's velocity.

Seyler and Budrikis have performed experiments with real-time television systems which indicate that a human viewer requires a relatively long time (700–800 msec) to adapt to the content of a new scene (27). During this time the resolution of transmitted images can be reduced substantially without noticeable impairment.

21.4.2. Frame Rate Reduction

The illusion of motion in a picture can be maintained at rates considerably lower than the United States standard of 30 frames per second. However, with normal television, low frame rates lead to picture flicker. The effect of flicker can be made unobjectionable for low-frame-rate television by a multiple display of frames at a high field rate (28, 29). This, of course, requires some type of frame storage system at the receiver.

With a frame storage unit employed in a system, the lower limit of the field frequency is determined by the effect of image breakup for moving objects in a scene. Baldwin (28) has performed experiments to determine whether a lower frame rate would be acceptable from the standpoint of image breakup. In these experiments a 24-frame-per-second motion picture was made of various moving objects. Then a lower-frame-rate intermediate was made by discarding some of the frames of the original movie. The remaining frames were repeated to produce a 24-frame-per-second film. The simplest reconstruction was to print each frame of the intermediate two or more times as needed. Other more complicated methods of frame combinations were also attempted. In some scenes, such as a conversation closeup, 12 frames per second proved satisfactory, but in another scene of a train moving across the screen, some jerkiness was evident at the same frame rate. At lower frame rates, all scenes showed more motion breakup. The more complicated ways of frame combining showed only a slight improvement over the simplest method of frame repetition.

Conventional television standards allow almost 18% of the horizontal line time and about 6% of the vertical interval for blanking purposes (15, p. 2–22). The lowering of these blanking times could result in a bandwidth reduction, but with some picture degradation. For slow-scanned television it is possible to realize some small savings in bandwidth by this means.

21.5. PICTURE INTERLACE TECHNIQUES

The 2-to-1 line interlacing ratio used in conventional television was adopted because it provided a simple means of obtaining a 2-to-1 bandwidth reduction without objectionable flicker or image breakup. For television systems utilizing frame storage at the receiver, flicker is not a consideration. In such systems the only possible attribute of interlacing is its ability to provide a mechanism of bandwidth reduction without appreciable image breakup.

21.5.1. Line Interlace

The way in which bandwidth is generally reduced by 2-to-1 line interlacing is to scan every other line of a picture during one field, and scan the remaining lines in the next field. The field rate of the interlaced system is set at the frame rate of the noninterlaced system. To extend the 2-to-1 line interlace technique, for example, every fourth or eighth line would be scanned during a single field. Two points that must be considered for line interlacing systems are the effects of image breakup and picture disturbances attributable to the interlacing process.

In noninterlaced television the motion of an object within a scene will cause the reproduced image of the object to be blurred and to jump in discrete steps through the picture. When interlacing is added to the system, and there is no physical storage of fields at the receiver display, or if the frame rate is so low that the persistence of the eye is negligible beyond a single field presentation, then the image jump and blur of the displayed image will not be affected by the interlacing. However, the static and dynamic resolution of the scene will be reduced by the interlace factor because only a fraction of the total lines of a picture will be displayed at any one time.

For a system with field storage in which past fields are repeatedly displayed until new fields are available, the resolution of the picture will theoretically be the same as that for noninterlaced television. In actual practice it is difficult accurately to space the interlaced lines of fields so that some "pairing" of adjacent lines tends to occur. This causes an effective reduction in resolution.

The image jump of noninterlaced television will be reduced by the interlace ratio for objects moving perpendicular to the lines. However, for these objects the image will be broken up by the line interlacing. As a result of storage in the system, the image will be smeared out over several lines. This phenomenon is illustrated in Figure 21.5-1, in which adjacent fields are shown added to the previous frame. In the case of noninterlaced television, every line of a field is replaced every field period. The 2-to-1 interlaced system replaces a line every other field period but displays each field every period. Thus one-half of the lines in the line interlaced system represent "stale" data. The circular object moving down the picture in the noninterlaced system moves in discrete jumps between fields. The same object reproduced by the interlaced system appears to be spread out spatially since some of the lines behind the movement of the object are

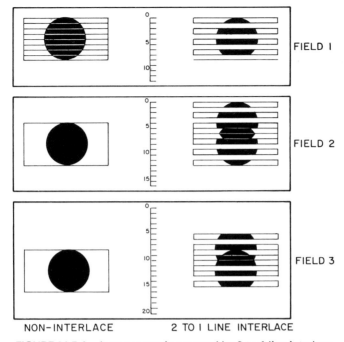

NON-INTERLACE   2 TO I LINE INTERLACE

FIGURE 21.5-1. Image smearing caused by 2-to-1 line interlace.

erased one field late. The same phenomena exists for higher-order line interlacing.

The other problem inherent in line interlacing is the effect of line crawling disturbances attributable to the sequential display of fields. An illustration of line interlace crawling effects is given in Figure 21.5-2 for 2-to-1 and 3-to-1 line interlacing. The lines numbered 1, 2, and 3 represent individual scanning lines of the first, second, and third fields, respectively. Consider the 3-to-1 interlace of Figure 21.5-2*b*. After field 3 is traced out, field 1 appears. Visually, the number 1 lines appear one line

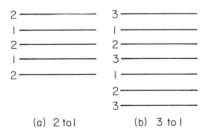

(a) 2 to I   (b) 3 to I

FIGURE 21.5-2. Individual scanning lines for interlacing ratios of 2 to 1 and 3 to 1.

spacing below and two line spacings above the number 3 lines. The optical illusion that results is that the number 3 lines have shifted slightly down to form the number 1 lines. The latter, in turn, appear to shift slightly down to create the number 2 lines, and so on. The direction of drift is independent of the actual direction of vertical scan. For a standard interlacing ratio of 2 to 1, as in Figure 21.5-2a, the drift illusion is absent because the number 1 lines and number 2 lines are equally separated. The drift illusion can possibly be reduced by a pseudorandom line-scanning process.

21.5.2. Dot Interlace

The basic 2-to-1 line interlace technique of conventional commercial television can be extended in the horizontal direction of a picture as well as in the vertical direction (30–31). Conceptually, a picture frame is divided into several fields of picture elements or dots that are sequentially transmitted. Usually the fields are chosen to be nonoverlapping. A bandwidth reduction can be achieved by transmitting each field at the normal television frame rate. For example, if a frame is divided into 16 nonoverlapping fields, the equivalent frame rate will be one-sixteenth of the normal frame rate, resulting in a $16:1$ bandwidth reduction. Deutsch (30) has reported a 16-to-1 dot interlace system incorporating reduced resolution and reduced frame rate that achieves transmission over bandwidths as low as 10 kHz.

Figure 21.5-3 illustrates the dot pattern of a single field for several dot interlace systems. Included in the figure for reference are the dot patterns of noninterlace, line interlace, and vertical interlace television. The addition of line interlace to a dot interlace system is not generally worthwhile because of the problems of image breakup and line crawling mentioned previously.

The bandwidth reduction achieved for each system in Figure 21.5-3 is relative to the noninterlace television system at a fixed scan rate of R element positions per second. For the 2-to-1 dot interlace system there is only one way to arrange the dots in the basic pattern block shown by heavy lines, and only one way to place the dot pattern of the next field. The 4-to-1, 8-to-1, 16-to-1, and higher-order dot interlace systems provide many possibilities for the dot pattern arrangement and the dot field presentation sequence. The selection of a dot pattern and field presentation sequence for these systems determines the degree of optical disturbance in a reproduced picture.

The dot interlace system of bandwidth reduction is subject to two types of optical disturbances in a displayed picture: patterning and dot crawl. Patterning is the optical illusion of a false texture in a picture resulting from the arrangement of dots within a frame. It is present when some of the dots

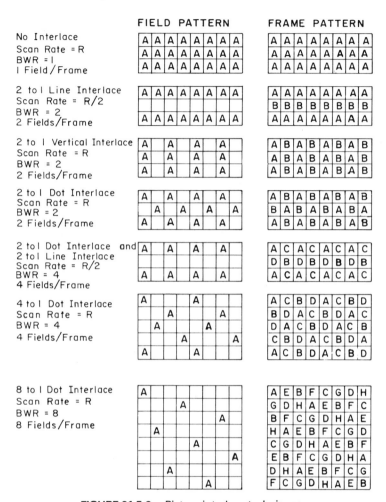

FIGURE 21.5-3. Picture interlace techniques.

are not displayed in a field period. The crawling effect is an optical illusion in which lines or dots of a picture appear to crawl across the display because of stroboscopic effects in the presentation of successive fields. It is possible to minimize these disturbing effects by properly ordering the successive presentations of picture fields with the content of each field judiciously arranged. From the standpoint of implementation it is desirable to force a repetitive structure on the dot patterns and field presentation sequences. However, such structure must not be allowed to create patterning and dot crawl effects.

· As an example, consider a dot interlace coding system in which each frame is divided into 16 nonoverlapping fields. The field pattern repeats over a 16-by-16 block of pixels. Figure 21.5-4 illustrates several dot pattern layouts for a 16-to-1 dot interlace. The patterns labeled Random 1 and Random 2 were chosen from a random number table with the restriction that the first element be at the origin and that each row and column be occupied by only one dot. The modulus patterns, which can be easily generated by interconnected counters, locate dots by counting from the origin along each row and folding over the count at the end of each row. If the modulus count results in a doubly occupied row or column, the column count is indexed by one. These cases are indicated by ×s in each block. The modulus 6 pattern subjectively appears to give an even distribution of dots without much noticeable structure.

The field pattern for subsequent fields could be any other nonoverlapping dot pattern. However, the simplest design approach is to utilize a dot pattern for each field that is a translated version of the basic dot pattern of

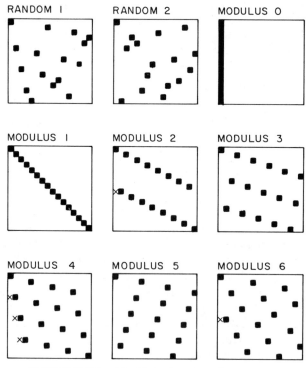

FIGURE 21.5-4. 16×16 dot interlace dot patterns.

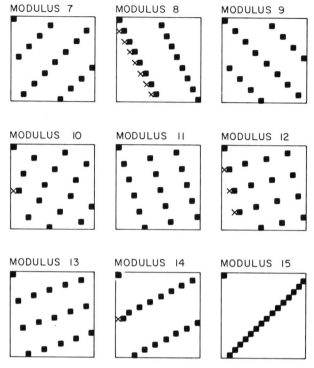

FIGURE 21.5-4. *Continued.*

the first field. In this regard the dot patterns of Figure 21.5-4 can be regarded as field presentation charts with the horizontal index specifying the location of the origin element of the basic pattern and the vertical index specifying the field number. It is clearly not a good strategy to use a modulus pattern with a low factor because of the obvious field presentation patterning. Also the use of the same modulus for the dot pattern and field presentation sequence should be avoided for the same reason.

With a dot interlace system the resolution of still scenes is reduced by the interlace ratio unless the eye, display tube persistence, or an external memory provide some degree of field storage. For moderately low-frame-rate television systems, the eye and display tube persistence are inadequate storage mechanisms, and an external memory must be relied on for field storage. With a memory used in the receiver system each field that is not being replaced by "fresh" data may be taken from the memory and displayed on the monitor every display frame. Thus full resolution for still scenes is possible for complete storage of fields. However, this storage has a detrimental effect on the reproduction of moving objects in a scene since the field storage will cause the smearing of an image of a moving object. The degree of smearing is directly proportional to the number of fields stored in the memory, but the number of stored fields also determines the resolution for still scenes. Thus there is a compromise between the number of stored fields and the system resolution. Other compromises are the increase of patterning effects and the decrease of the dot crawl disturbance with the degree of field storage. Still another compromise is the matter of background suppression of dots that are not renewed from the memory during each display frame. If they are left solid black or white, another form of disturbance will be present. In summary, it may be concluded that the dot interlace technique provides a relatively simple means of bandwidth reduction for applications in which image motion is not great and some amount of artificial smearing of moving objects can be tolerated.

21.6. VARIABLE VELOCITY SCANNING

In the variable-velocity scanning method of bandwidth compression (33–37), the camera scanning velocity varies with picture detail in such a manner as to provide a fast scan where low detail exists and slow scan for high detail. In general, variable-velocity scanning depends on the fact that most of the picture information of interest to a human observer lies in the edges (high-frequency transitions) of the picture. In a single line scan for normal television the average probability of occurrence for an edge is far less than that for a steady-state region. If the scanning velocity is modified to spend more time transmitting an edge and less time transmitting a steady-state region, the edge information is spread out over time, the redundant information (steady-state levels) is reduced in time, and the resulting video bandwidth can be reduced. The entire video information is retained in this signal, and with the velocity information at the receiver, the modified video signal may be recovered and appropriately processed to obtain the original television signal. In principle, the velocity information may be recovered from the modified video signal so that an additional channel for a velocity signal is not needed.

In the block diagram of a variable velocity scanning method, shown in Figure 21.6-1, the camera scan velocity V is determined by the feedback relation

$$V = \frac{dx}{dt} = V_M - K\left|\frac{de}{dt}\right| \qquad (21.6-1)$$

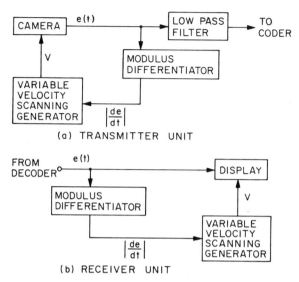

FIGURE 21.6-1. Variable-velocity scanning system.

where x is the distance along a scan line, e is the camera output voltage, V_M is the maximum scan velocity, and K is a constant. Because

$$\frac{de}{dt} = V \left| \frac{de}{dx} \right| \qquad (21.6\text{-}2)$$

then

$$V = \frac{V_M}{1 + K \left| \dfrac{de}{dx} \right|} \qquad (21.6\text{-}3)$$

Now let

$$\eta = \frac{V_M}{V_N} \qquad (21.6\text{-}4)$$

represent the ratio of the maximum to normal scan velocities. The ratio of the average time required to scan a television line of length L with variable velocity scanning compared to the time required for a scan at the normal rate of V_N is given by

$$\frac{T}{T_N} = \frac{1 + (\eta - 1)D_F}{\eta} \qquad (21.6\text{-}5)$$

where D_F is an image detail factor defined by

$$D_F = \frac{1}{L} \int_0^L \left| \frac{de}{dx} \right| dx \qquad (21.6\text{-}6)$$

For a checkerboard brightness pattern, $D_F = 1$ and no gain is possible, while in the other extreme for a blank picture $D_F = 1/\eta$, as expected. Measurements indicate that D_F lies in the range of 3–5% for natural imagery (35). The ratio T/T_N is a measure of the average time reduction for scanning television lines. By appropriately sampling the velocity-modulated television signal and redistributing the samples over the time period T_N, a bandwidth reduction may be achieved. For example, for $D_F = 0.05$ and $\eta = 10$, a 7:1 bandwidth reduction can be obtained.

Because of the differentiation operation in the variable-velocity scanning system, the video signal-to-noise ratio must be about 60 dB (4) to prevent line length errors caused by camera noise. Standard television usually operates with a signal-to-noise ratio of about 30 dB. There is another major drawback of the variable velocity coding system. In order to achieve a high bandwidth reduction, the system is designed to pass the highest frequency that occurs when a full-amplitude checkerboard is scanned. A low-amplitude checkerboard pattern actually results in a higher-frequency video signal. Such signals are filtered at the transmitter unit, thus degrading high-frequency, low-amplitude detail. This degradation coupled with the high video signal-to-noise ratio requirements has limited the usefulness of the coding system.

21.7. MULTIPLEX CODING TECHNIQUES

Telephone voice multiplexing systems have been developed in which a few transmission channels service many voice sources such that only active voice sources are transmitted at any instant. As a result of the large number of pauses in human speech, such systems can be designed so that the probability of overload is quite small. Telephone multiplexing systems of this type depend on an irregular and sparse data flow from each channel and a lack of correlation between sources.

The voice multiplexing concept has been extended to image transmission (39–41). In the simplest system designed for black or white facsimile data, N image lines are simultaneously scanned from N different documents. If a one bit, indicating a black dot against a white background, is encountered in only one channel, a binary code word designating the channel number is transmitted; if no ones are generated, a null code word is transmitted.

Consequently, at each pixel point one of $N+1$ code words is transmitted. For a uniform length code word of $\log_2(N+1)$ bits, where N is appropriately chosen as $7, 15, 31, \ldots$, the compression factor becomes

$$C = \frac{N}{\log_2(N+1)} \qquad (21.7\text{-}1)$$

Thus for $N = 7$, a compression of $2.3:1$ will be realized. The drawback of this scheme, of course, is the error effect that occurs when multiple channels generate simultaneous ones. Those channels that are not serviced suffer a black to white dot reversal error. Computer simulation tests (39) for typewritten pages indicate that about 35% of the ones will be deleted for $N = 7$ channels with a probability of occurrence of black dots of about 10%. However, even at this relatively high black deletion rate, the probability of alphanumeric character error is only 4% without contextual detection.

Huang and Tretiak (42) have suggested another approach to image multiplexing in which N different black or white facsimile images are each scanned with a different pseudorandom dot scanner. The image data from the N channels sequentially enters a logical OR gate that produces a one output if any of its inputs is a one. At the receiver, the transmitted data sequence is directed to all N receiver channels, which are each pseudorandomly scanned for display in correspondence with their appropriate transmitter channels. A one bit appearing at the output of a source channel will be directed to the proper display point in its receiver channel, but it will also be displayed as an error point in all other $N-1$ receiver channels. Because the erroneous black dots are pseudorandomly distributed spatially, they produce a "snow-like" effect in a displayed image. Easily readable results have been obtained with up to four multiplexed sources (42). The error effect can be substantially reduced by a posteriori noise filtering that eliminates isolated black points within an image.

REFERENCES

1. T. S. Huang, "PCM Picture Transmission," *IEEE Spectrum*, **2**, 12, December 1965, 57–60.
2. Special Issue on Redundancy Reduction, *Proc. IEEE*, **55**, 3, March 1967.
3. T. S. Huang, W. F. Schreiber, and O. J. Tretiak, "Image Processing," *Proc. IEEE*, **59**, 11, November 1971, 1586–1609.
4. Special Issue on Signal Processing for Digital Communications, *IEEE Trans. Commun. Tech.*, **COM-19**, 6, Part I, December 1971.
5. Special Issue on Digital Picture Processing, *Proc. IEEE*, **60**, 7, July 1972.

6. T. S. Huang and O. J. Tretiak, Eds., *Picture Bandwidth Compression*, Gordon and Breach, New York, 1972.

7. A. Habibi and G. S. Robinson, "A Survey of Digital Picture Coding," *IEEE Computer*, **7**, 5, May 1974, 21–34.

8. J. C. Wilson, *Television Engineering*, Pitman, London, 1937.

9. H. E. Ives and A. L. Johnsrud, "Television in Colors by a Beam Scanning Method," *J. Opt. Soc. Am.*, **20**, January 1930, 11–21.

10. P. C. Goldmark et al., "Color Television—Part I," *Proc. IRE*, **30**, 4, April 1942, 162–182.

11. P. C. Goldmark et al., "Color Television—Part II," *Proc. IRE*, **31**, 9, September 1943, 465–578.

12. F. C. McLean, "Worldwide Color Television Standards," *IEEE Spectrum*, **3**, 6, June 1966, 59–60.

13. G. M. Glassford, *Fundamentals of Television Engineering*, McGraw-Hill, New York, 1955.

14. K. McIlwain and C. E. Dean, Eds., *Principles of Color Television*, Wiley, New York, 1956.

15. D. G. Fink, Ed., *Television Engineering Handbook*, McGraw-Hill, New York, 1957.

16. K. McIlwain, "Requisite Color Bandwidth for Simultaneous Color-Television Systems," *Proc. IRE*, **40**, August 1952, 909–912.

17. W. F. Bailey and C. J. Hirsch, "Quadrature Cross Talk in NTSC Color Television," *Proc. IRE*, **42**, January 1954, 84–90.

18. H. de France, "The Sequential-Simultaneous Colour Television System," *Acta Electronics*, **2**, 1957–1958, 392–397.

19. B. Townsend, *PAL Colour Television*, Cambridge University Press, Cambridge, England, 1970.

20. E. A. Howson and D. A. Bell, "Reduction of Television Bandwidth by Frequency Interlace," *J. Brit. IRE*, **20**, 2, February 1960, 127–136.

21. J. L. Maier and L. Gardenhire, "Redundant Area Coding System (REARCS)," Proceedings of the International Telemetering Conference, Los Angeles, California, Vol. 8, October 1972, 301–314.

22. B. G. Haskell, F. W. Mounts, and J. C. Candy, "Interframe Coding of Videotelephone Pictures," *Proc. IEEE*, **60**, 7, July 1972, 792–800.

23. A. J. Seyler, "The Coding of Visual Signals to Reduce Channel-Capacity Requirements," *Proc. Inst. Elec. Eng.*, **109**, Part C, September 1962, 676–684.

24. R. F. W. Pease and J. O. Limb, "Exchange of Spatial and Temporal Resolution in Television Coding," *Bell Syst. Tech. J.*, **50**, 1, January 1971, 191–200.

25. J. O. Limb and R. F. W. Pease, "A Simple Interframe Coder for Video Telephony," *Bell. Syst. Tech. J.*, **50**, 6, July–August 1971, 1877–1888.

26. J. C. Candy et al., "Transmitting Television as Clusters of Frame-to-Frame Differences," *Bell Syst. Tech. J.*, **50**, 6, July–August 1971, 1889–1917.

27. A. J. Seyler and Z. L. Budrikis, "Detail Perception After Scene Changes in Television Image Presentations," *IEEE Trans. Inf. Theory*, **IT-11**, 1, January 1965, 31–43.

28. M. W. Baldwin, "Demonstration of Some Visual Effects of Using Frame Storage in Television Transmission," IRE Convention Record, 1958, 107.

29. R. C. Brainard, F. W. Mounts, and B. Prasada, "Low Resolution TV: Subjective Effects of Frame Repetition and Picture Replenishment," *Bell Syst. Tech. J.*, **46**, 1, January 1967, 261–271.

30. S. Deutsch, "Pseudo-Random Dot Scan Television Systems," *IEEE Trans. Broadcasting*, **BC-11**, 1, July 1965, 11–21.

31. G. G. Gouriet, "Dot Interlaced Television," *Electronic Eng.*, **24**, 290, April 1952, 166–171.

32. J. Haantjes and K. Teer, "Multiplex Television Transmission: Subcarrier and Dot Interlace Systems," *Wireless Eng.*, Part I, **31**, September 1954, 215–233; Part II, **31**, October 1954, 266–273.

33. E. E. Wright, "Velocity Modulation in Television," Proc. Phys. Soc. (London), **46**, July 1934, 512–514.

34. L. H. Bedford and O. S. Puckle, "A Velocity Modulation Television System," *J. IEE*, **75**, 1934, 63.

35. E. C. Cherry and G. G. Gouriet, "Some Possibilities for the Compression of Television Signals by Recoding," *Proc. IEE*, **100**, Part II, 1953, 3–18.

36. M. P. Beddoes, "Experiments with Slope Feedback Coder for TV Compression," *IRE Trans. Broadcasting*, **BC-7**, 2, March 1961, 12–28.

37. M. P. Beddoes, "Two Channel Method for Compressing Bandwidth of Television Signals," *Proc. IEE*, **110**, 2, February 1963, 369–374.

38. M. D. Prince and M. A. Honnel, "TV Image Reproduction by Use of Velocity-Modulation Principles," *Proc. IRE*, **39**, 3, March 1951, 265–268.

39. D. Seitzer, F. Class, and P. Stucki, "An Experimental Approach to Video Bandwidth Compression by Multiplexing," *IEEE Trans. Commun. Tech.*, **COM-17**, 5, October 1969, 564–568.

40. P. Stucki, "Limits of Instantaneous Priority Multiplexing Applied to Black-and-White Pictures," *IEEE Trans. Commun. Tech.*, **COM-19**, 2, April 1971, 169–177.

41. F. Class, "Video Bandwidth Compression by Multiplexing: Experimental Results," *IEEE Trans. Commun. Tech.*, **COM-19**, 3, June 1971, 371–372.

42. T. S. Huang and O. J. Tretiak, "A Pseudorandom Multiplex System for Facsimile Transmission," *IEEE Trans. Commun. Tech.*, **COM-16**, 3, June 1968, 436–438.

22 DIGITAL POINT PROCESSING IMAGE CODING

This chapter presents an analysis of digital image coding methods that utilize point processing. Pulse code modulation, statistical, frame replenishment, and predictive coding methods are described. A design analysis for linear predictive image coding systems is also included.

22.1. PULSE CODE MODULATION CODING

In a basic pulse code modulation (PCM) image coding system the continuous video signal is sampled and quantized. Each quantized sample is then assigned a constant-length group of code bits, called a code word. A bit rate reduction can obviously be achieved by reducing the number of quantization levels. For an imaging system whose quality is assessed by some analytic measure, the number of quantization levels is taken as the smallest value that satisfies the measure of image quality. With a subjective assessment of image quality, the number of quantization levels must be kept large enough to prevent a noticeable gray scale contouring effect caused by a jump in the reconstructed image luminance between quantization levels in a region where the original image is slowly changing in luminance. For monochrome images, 50 or more levels are usually required to prevent noticeable gray scale contouring. Consequently, in a PCM monochrome image coder the image luminance is usually quantized from 64 to 256 levels corresponding to a 6–8 bit per pixel code (1–4). Basic PCM color image coders usually assign from 6 to 8 bits each to the red, green, and blue tristimulus values. Several rather simple digital image coding techniques have been developed in which the number of quantization levels can be reduced significantly, as compared to conventional PCM coding, without severe gray scale contouring.

22.1.1. Companding Quantization

In Chapter 6 optimum values for quantization decision and reconstruction levels were determined for the minimization of the mean-square quantization error of the variable or variables to be quantized. It was found that, in general, the decision and reconstruction levels should be spaced non-linearly on the variable amplitude scale. Companding quantization described in Chapter 6 is an equivalent alternative to nonlinear quantization. In a companding quantizer, as shown in Figure 22.1-1, the input variable undergoes a nonlinear transformation, followed by uniform quantization, followed in turn by a nonlinear inverse transformation.

If quantization levels are to be chosen to minimize the visual effect of gray scale contouring in monochrome images, then the placement of the quantization decision and reconstruction levels should be set so that each step represents an equal-length increment of the lightness metric described in Section 7.3. Equivalently, the lightness scale, which relates image luminance to perceived luminance, should be linearly quantized, rather than the luminance itself, by the companding operation in which the point transform is the lightness function (4). This procedure can also be extended to color image quantization by utilizing the geodesic color measure as a companding function. Another approach to image quantization is to convert the image luminance or tristimulus values to the signal space of the human visual system before uniform quantization (5). The companding function is then equivalent to the model for the human visual system, described in Chapter 2, for monochrome or color vision.

Computer simulations of monochrome image quantization for a variety of lightness functions are presented in Figure 22.1-2. In these simulations the luminance signal of an image has been uniformly quantized to 12 bits by a precision image scanner, and the resultant digital image has been rescaled and requantized within the computer to simulate companding quantization with 8 quantization levels. These experiments indicate that

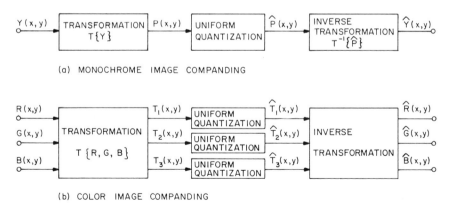

(a) MONOCHROME IMAGE COMPANDING

(b) COLOR IMAGE COMPANDING

FIGURE 22.1-1.   Companding image quantization.

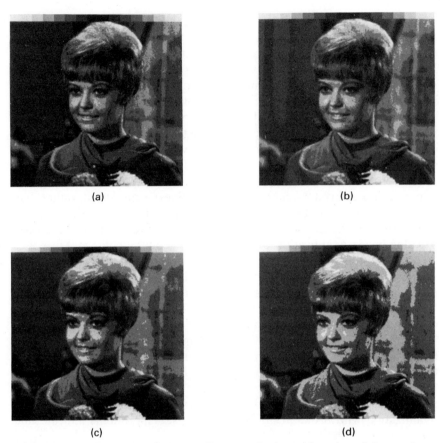

FIGURE 22.1-2. Examples of companding quantization with various lightness functions for eight level quantization. (a) Without companding. (b) Log companding. (c) Square-root companding. (d) Cube-root companding.

the gray scale contouring effect is reduced somewhat by lightness companding, and that nearly equivalent results are obtained with all of the lightness functions. Frei (6) has reported a reduction of about $2:1$ in the number of quantization levels required to obtain equivalent visual results for the quantization of color images with and without companding based on a color vision model.

22.1.2. Pseudonoise Quantization

The visual effect of gray scale contouring can be minimized considerably by adding low-amplitude pseudonoise to the video signal amplitude before quantization and synchronously subtracting the noise from the quantized video after the quantizer (7–12). This process, called Roberts' modulation after its developer (7), permits quantization with as few as 3 bits per sample without particularly noticeable gray scale contouring. However, there is an increase in the mean-square error in the quantization process, and an introduction of a "snow-like" visual degradation to the image.

Figure 22.1-3 contains a block diagram for the analysis of the pseudonoise quantization method. An image sample x, representing the image intensity or some function of the intensity, is combined with a pseudonoise signal n_T and the sum z is fed to the linear quantizer. The pseudonoise signal has a uniform probability density

$$p(n_T) = \frac{1}{\Delta} \qquad (22.1\text{-}1)$$

for $|n_T| \le \Delta/2$, where Δ is the spacing between reconstruction levels. Another uniformly distributed source n_R is then subtracted from the quantizer output w. In the pseudonoise quantization system n_T and n_R are obtained from pseudorandom number generators, which can be synchronized to give identical but random outputs.

The basic concept of pseudonoise quantization is illustrated in Figure 22.1-4. In Figure 22.1-4a the original image signal is assumed to be composed of an image line segment linearly increasing in magnitude. As the image signal crosses a decision level, the reconstruction jumps from one reconstruction level to another. It is these jumps that are particularly visible to the eye and give the appearance of gray scale contouring. A uniformly distributed pseudonoise signal shown in Figure 22.1-4b is added to the original image signal and quantized as seen in Figure 22.1-4d. The effect of the additive pseudonoise is to cause a "dithering" of the reconstructed image signal about the value it would assume if there were no noise added before quantization. This dithering spreads out the quantization steps. Next, as illustrated in Figure 22.1-4e, the pseudonoise signal that was originally added to the original image signal before quantization is now subtracted from the quantizer output. This operation tends to restore

FIGURE 22.1-3. Pseudonoise quantization system.

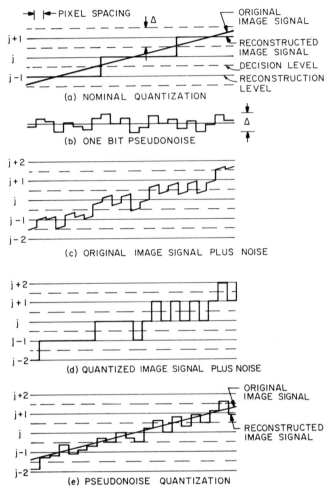

FIGURE 22.1-4. Example of pseudonoise quantization.

the reconstructed image signal to the average value it would have had if no noise had been present in the quantization system. As can be seen from the example, the abrupt jumps in the image level have been replaced by smaller jumps generally occurring at each pixel.

Following Roberts' analysis, the overall system performance can be measured by the mean-square error between the input and output as defined by

$$\mathscr{E} = \int_0^1 \int_0^1 (x - y)^2 p(x, y) \, dx \, dy \qquad (22.1\text{-}2)$$

where it is assumed that the image sample amplitude is normalized to the range 0 to 1 and $p(x, y)$ is the joint probability density of the system input and output variables. The amount of apparent noise added to the image as a result of the introduction of pseudonoise in the quantization process can be measured by the variance of the output about its conditional mean value averaged over all possible inputs. This quantization error variance is defined as

$$V = \int_0^1 \int_0^1 (y - \bar{y}_x)^2 p(x, y) \, dx \, dy \qquad (22.1\text{-}3)$$

where

$$\bar{y}_x = \int_0^1 y p(y \mid x) \, dy \qquad (22.1\text{-}4)$$

is the conditional output mean. Finally, the deviation of the conditional mean value of the output about the input is measured as

$$D = \int_0^1 \int_0^1 (x - \bar{y}_x)^2 p(x, y) \, dx \, dy \qquad (22.1\text{-}5)$$

For quantization without pseudonoise, the mean-square quantization error is a minimum and the variance of the output is zero. By adding a small amount of noise n_T and n_R, the error and output noise variance V will be increased somewhat, but the tonal deviation D will be reduced. Subjectively better images are then obtained as a result of the eye's ability spatially to average small luminance deviations. Performance results for pseudonoise quantization are summarized in Table 22.1-1 for quantization of an image with a uniformly distributed amplitude. In each case the error measures are normalized by the mean-square error $\mathscr{E}(\text{PCM})$ obtained without pseudonoise quantization.

TABLE 22.1-1. Pseudonoise quantization performance results for uniform input density.

	Normalized Mean-Square Error	Normalized Quantization Error Variance	Deviation
PCM	1	0	1
One bit postquantizer noise	2	1	1
One bit prequantizer noise	$2 - 2^{-b}$	$2(1 - 2^{-b})$	2^{-b}
One bit prequantizer noise minus one bit postquantizer noise	$1 + 2^{-b}$	1	2^{-b}

22.1.3. Improved Gray Scale Quantization

In 1966 Bisignani, Richards, and Whelan (13) introduced a new technique of image quantization called Improved Gray Scale (IGS) quantization. In the IGS system, deterministic low-level luminance perturbations generated from the previous pixel scanned along a line are added to pixels to be quantized in order to diminish the effect of gray-scale contouring. For 6-bit quantization a "construction" code word is formed as the modulo 8 sum of the pixel code word and the three least significant bits of the previous construction code word. The addition is inhibited if the 3 most significant pixel bits are all ones. The 3 most significant bits of the construction code word are then transmitted resulting in a 2:1 bit rate reduction. Table 22.1-2 gives an example of the coding algorithm. The last column of the table contains the pixel values that would be reconstructed if an ordinary 3-bit code were to be employed. The IGS code provides a display with only

TABLE 22.1-2. Example of 3-bit improved gray scale quantization system (13).

Pixel	Pixel Value	Pixel Code	Construction Code	XMTR Code	Display Pixel Value	Standard 3-Bit Pixel Value
0^a	—		000 000	—		
1	12	001 100	001 100	001	8	8
2	12	001 100	010 000	010	16	8
3	13	001 101	001 101	001	8	8
4	13	001 101	010 010	010	16	8
5	10	001 010	001 100	001	8	8
6	13	001 101	010 001	010	16	8
7	9	001 001	001 010	001	8	8
8	9	001 001	001 011	001	8	8
9	15	001 111	010 010	010	16	8
10	13	001 101	001 111	001	8	8
11	19	010 011	011 010	011	24	16
12	38	100 110	101 000	101	40	32
13	40	101 000	101 000	101	40	40
14	24	011 000	011 000	011	24	24
15	10	001 010	001 010	001	8	8
16	10	001 010	001 100	001	8	8
17	10	001 010	001 110	001	8	8
18	10	001 010	010 000	010	16	8
19	10	001 010	001 010	001	8	8
20	10	001 010	001 100	001	8	8
21	10	001 010	001 110	001	8	8

^{a} Initial condition.

3 bits, but the displayed value fluctuates more rapidly, and therefore tends to spread out the gray scale contours by spatial averaging of the eye. The mean-square error of the reconstruction is increased somewhat compared to straight PCM coding. Pictures processed by the IGS system have diminished contouring but exhibit a small-scale graininess.

22.1.4. Coarse–Fine Quantization System

In the coarse–fine quantization system, also developed by Bisignani, Richards, and Whelan (13, 14), the original image is linearly quantized with 64 levels and binary coded with 6 bits per pixel. The 3 most significant bits form the coarse information, and the 3 least significant bits are the fine information. If the image is changing in luminance such that there is a change in the coarse bits, they are transmitted directly as absolute levels. On the other hand, if the coarse bits are not changing, the fine bits are transmitted as relative levels to be combined with the previous coarse bits to reconstruct a 6-bit pixel for display. It should be noted that only 3 bits are transmitted for each pixel. The actual decison as to whether a pixel should be coarsely or finely represented is somewhat more complicated than described above. The decision is based on a set of ad hoc rules utilizing the states of the past three pixels (13, 14). The highly adaptive nature of the coarse–fine quantization system renders it difficult to characterize analytically. Subjective testing has shown that the quantized images are equivalent in quality to 6-bit PCM images, except at edge regions where some gray scale contouring is noticeable.

Figure 22.1-5 contains examples of 3-bit PCM, pseudonoise quantization, improved gray scale quantization, and coarse–fine quantization. The gray scale contouring effect noticeable in the PCM coded image is not apparent in the other three pictures. However, the three systems have introduced some spatial degradation. In the pseudonoise quantized picture the degradation appears as additive noise, while with the IGS and coarse–fine systems, more localized degradation is noticeable.

22.1.5. Split-Band Quantization

In the split-band quantization system (15) the line-scanned television signals are split into low- and high-frequency components by electrical filters. The low-frequency signals are quantized and coded with 5–6 bits while the high-frequency components are coded with only 3 bits under the assumption that the eye will tolerate larger brightness errors in quickly varying image signals. The system is easily implemented; however, the compression ratio is small, and there is some visible degradation.

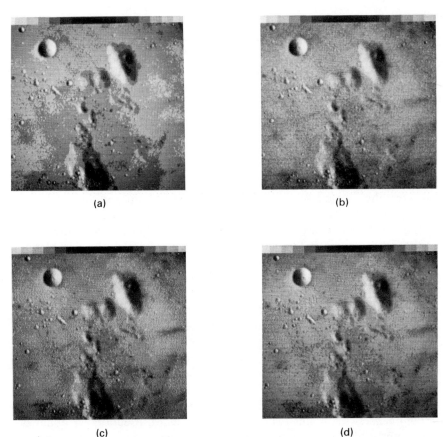

(a)   (b)

(c)   (d)

FIGURE 22.1-5.   Quantization reduction coding techniques for coding at 3.0 bits/pixel. (a) PCM. (b) Pseudonoise. (c) Improved gray scale. (d) Coarse–fine.

22.1.6. PCM Quantization Error Reduction

PCM image coding is normally performed on a pixel-by-pixel basis. However, because pixel values are spatially correlated, a reduction in quantization error can be realized by the vector quantization techniques outlined in Chapter 6. Optimal vector quantization entails the specification of a set of decision regions D_j and a vector of reconstruction levels $\mathbf{r}_j$ for a set of J pixels arranged in a vector $\mathbf{f}$. Determination of the optimal decision regions is generally too formidable a computational task to consider. Hence only rectangularly shaped decision regions are usually utilized. For a fixed set of decision regions the vector of optimal reconstruction levels is obtained from

$$\mathbf{r}_j = \frac{\int_{D_j} \mathbf{f} p(\mathbf{f})\, d\mathbf{f}}{\int_{D_j} p(\mathbf{f})\, d\mathbf{f}} \qquad (22.1\text{-}6)$$

where $p(\mathbf{f})$ is the joint probability density of pixel amplitudes. Huhns (16) has developed an iterative solution to Eq. 22.1-6 in which the reconstruction level of a pixel is determined from the decision level states of its four nearest neighbors (left, right, up, down). In this solution the joint probability density of the five pixels involved in the restoration is modeled as a correlated joint Rayleigh density. Figure 22.1-6 presents a comparison of image reconstructions by standard PCM coding and with the vector

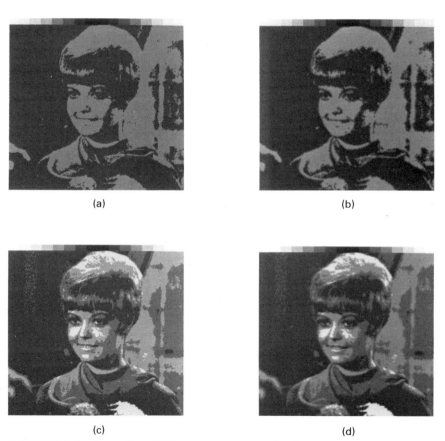

(a)   (b)

(c)   (d)

FIGURE 22.1-6. Examples of PCM vector reconstruction for quantization error reduction (16). 1 bit per pixel: (a) standard PCM; (b) vector reconstruction. 2 bits per pixel: (c) standard PCM; (d) vector reconstruction.

reconstruction process. In all cases the gray scale contouring effect is substantially dimiminished and the mean-square error is reduced. Gray scale contouring can also be reduced by spatially smoothing a reconstructed image by low-pass convolutional processing or Fourier domain filtering. However, this operation causes a reduction in small-scale image detail.

22.2. STATISTICAL CODING TECHNIQUES

Statistical measurements of the brightness distribution of digital images and subsequent entropy calculations indicate that natural images contain a large amount of redundancy. In this context redundancy can be defined as the total number of bits that are required for straight PCM coding minus the entropy of the entire image. As an example consider a monochrome picture containing $N \times N$ pixels. If each pixel brightness level is quantized to B levels, then a total of

$$T = B^{N^2} \tag{22.2-1}$$

different pictures could be represented. Not all of these T pictures normally occur with equal likelihood. Let p_i denote the probability of occurrence of the ith possible picture. The entropy of the picture source, which is a measure of the minimal number of code bits required to code the picture, is then

$$H = - \sum_{i=1}^{T} p_i \log_2 p_i \tag{22.2-2}$$

In a PCM image coder the number of quantization levels per pixel is usually chosen to be

$$B = 2^b \tag{22.2-3}$$

where b is an integer (about 6 to 8). PCM coding then requires a total of

$$N_B = bN^2 \tag{22.2-4}$$

bits to code each of the N^2 pixels with a constant length code word of b bits. For natural images the entropy H is many orders of magnitude less than the number of PCM code bits N_B, which, of course, indicates the gross inefficiency of PCM image coding.

The obvious question is then whether there exist statistical coding techniques that can code pictures with as few bits as the entropy limit. The answer is affirmative, in the theoretical sense, but practical achievement of such a coder is not feasible at present. Consider the following straightforward solution to the optimum coding problem. Each of the T possible images has associated with it a probability of occurrence p_i. The general strategy is to assign code words of relative short length to those pictures with the highest probability of occurrence, and to assign longer-length code words to less likely occurring pictures. An optimum coding procedure, known as Huffman coding (1), produces codes whose average length approaches the normalized entropy limit H/N^2 quite closely. Assume that these code words can be generated and stored in a code book. Then, when each picture is generated, the coding procedure is simply to look up the corresponding code word in the table and transmit it. The decoder performs the reverse operation of entering the table with the code word and determining the corresponding picture that should be displayed. While this coding procedure is both straightforward and optimal, its dimensionality turns out to be staggering. For example, if a picture contains 256×256 pixels with each pixel quantized to 256 levels, the total number of possible pictures that could be generated is about 10 raised to the power 158,000! Clearly this number is much too large for any practical code table look-up procedure. One might then consider breaking up the picture into smaller blocks, of say 4×4 pixels, and applying the table look-up procedure. However, even in this case the number of possible block images is about 10 to the 40th power, and still too large for practical implementation. There is one other major difficulty with this coding procedure: the probability of occurrence p_i for each possible picture must be known to develop the appropriate code word. In practice, it is difficult to measure or estimate the a priori probabilities. Failure to utilize the proper probabilities usually degrades the performance of the coding technique quite severely.

Although the outlook for optimal statistical coding does indeed appear bleak, it has proved possible to eliminate at least some image redundancy by suboptimal coding techniques, and achieve a worthwhile reduction in image transmission channel requirements. The following sections describe several methods of statistical image coding. Many of the techniques are strictly information preserving, that is, they do not introduce any image degradation. Other methods permit a small, controlled amount of degradation in order to achieve a greater bandwidth reduction. Some of the statistical coding methods to be described have potential uses as subsystems of other image coding systems.

22.1.1. Single Pixel Coding

The simplest type of statistical image coder is one in which each pixel, in effect, is individually assigned a code group from a code book based on its quantized amplitude. For efficient coding the code assignment should be such that pixel values with a high likelihood of occurrence should be assigned code groups with a small number of bits; conversely, rarely occurring pixel values should be assigned longer code groups. If this process is performed efficiently, the average length of a code group will be equal to the single pixel entropy of the image.

As a starting point for code development it is necessary to model, estimate, or measure the probabilities of occurrence of each pixel value for the class of images to be encoded. Suppose that the probability that a quantized pixel amplitude is equal to the nth reconstruction level r_n is given by

$$P(n) = \Pr\{F(j, k) = r_n\} \qquad (22.2\text{-}5)$$

In the coding process a code word of $b(n)$ bits is assigned to each quantization level resulting in an average code length

$$L_c = \sum_{n=0}^{L-1} P(n)b(n) \qquad (22.2\text{-}6)$$

The efficiency E_f of the code is the ratio of the single pixel entropy $H\{F(j, k)\}$ to the average code word length. Thus

$$E_f = \frac{H\{F(j, k)\}}{L_c} \qquad (22.2\text{-}7)$$

There are several high-efficiency codes that can be employed for single pixel image coding. Appendix 3 describes two of these codes: the Shannon–Fano code and the Huffman code. The latter is the most efficient of all possible source codes. In general, these codes are variable length, and thus it becomes necessary to provide a data buffer storage unit to collect the variable-bit-rate code bits and transmit them at some slower average rate. There is one other general problem associated with the utilization of statistical source codes. The codes are matched to an assumed set of source probabilities. If the actual source probabilities differ from the assumed source probabilities, the performance of the coder can be degraded drastically. In fact, a mismatched coder can result in an increased bit requirement compared to constant word length PCM.

For typical natural monochrome images quantized to 64 levels, the single pixel entropy ranges from about 4 to 6 bits per pixel. This relatively small amount of redundancy as compared to 6 bit per pixel constant word length PCM coding is seldom worth the penalty of increased implementation requirements and the general difficulties associated with variable code lengths.

22.2.2. Previous Pixel Coding

Since adjacent pixels along an image line are highly correlated in natural images, there is a high degree of redundancy between pixel pairs along a line. For natural monochrome images quantized to 64 levels the previous pixel entropy is on the order of 2–3 bits. This represents a significant amount of redundancy compared to a constant word length PCM code of 6 bits per pixel. A statistical coder to take advantage of the previous pixel redundancy is simple in principle. For each of the L quantized levels of a previous pixel there is an associated conditional probability distribution $P(j/k)$ and a corresponding code. Thus, in operation, the coder references the kth (quantized value of previous pixel) codebook, and selects the jth (quantized value of present pixel) code word from the codebook. It is therefore necessary to store L^2 codewords, or to provide an algorithm for generating the codewords, for each pair (j, k). For 64 quantization levels the codebook would contain 4096 entries. In many applications a coder of this complexity is not feasible.

Although there generally is a significant increase in image redundancy when considering the coding of pixels in pairs, a law of diminishing returns soon takes over. Typically, coding pixels in triplets rather than pairs provides an additional one-half bit per pixel in redundancy removed, but requires a codebook of L^3 entries. It should also be noted that a channel error in a pixel code affects not only that reconstructed pixel, but all other pixels subsequently coded along the image line. This error propagation effect can be limited by transmitting an actual pixel value periodically along a line.

A variant of previous pixel coding is to code the differnces in pixel values after coding the first pixel along a line (18–20). If each pixel has L quantization levels then the pixel difference may assume $2L-1$ values. Since the probability of occurrence of large differences is relatively small, it is possible to simplify the coder considerably without a great loss in performance. The coding strategy is as follows: small differences receive individual code words; if the difference exceeds some specified level, the actual pixel value is coded and appended to a prefix code that distinguishes the total code word from the coded differences. Table 22.2-1 illustrates a Shannon–Fano code for coding pixel differences. Codes of this type may have efficiencies as high as 90%, and yet are feasible to implement (18). Thus far the statistical codes that have been discussed have all been information preserving. However, statistical coders need not be purely information preserving. Table 22.2-2 illustrates a technique of pixel difference coding in which pixel differences with a deviation of plus or minus one quantization level receive a unique code word.

TABLE 22.2-1. Example of pixel difference coding with no errors

Pixel Difference, D	Code Word
0	1
+1	0100
−1	0101
+2	0110
−2	0111
+3	00100
−3	00101
+4	00110
−4	00111
$|D| \geq 5$	000 + 6 bit pixel

TABLE 22.2-2. Example of pixel difference coding with one level error

Pixel Difference, D	Code Word
0 ± 1	1
3 ± 1	0100
6 ± 1	0101
-3 ± 1	0110
-6 ± 1	0111
9 ± 1	00100
12 ± 1	00101
-9 ± 1	00110
-12 ± 1	00111
15 ± 1	0001000
18 ± 1	0001001
21 ± 1	0001010
24 ± 1	0001011
-15 ± 1	0001100
-18 ± 1	0001101
-21 ± 1	0001110
-24 ± 1	0001111
$|D| \geq 26$	0000 + 8 bit pixel

As mentioned previously, one of the major problems associated with statistical coders is that they are efficient only if the codes are well matched to the source probabilities. Rice and Plaunt (21) have developed an adaptive statistical image coding system in which the source probability distribution is continuously examined during coding, and one of a set of statistical codes is chosen to best match the source.

22.3. RUN CODING

Run coding (22–30) is a relatively simple coding technique in which the amplitudes of adjacent pixels along a line are compared. If a significant change in detail (edge) occurs, a run is said to exist. Either a function of the amplitude of the brightness of the pixel at the end of the run, or a function of the amplitude of the difference signal, is transmitted along with an indication of the location of the run end. If the location of the end of the run is determined by counting the number of elements from the beginning of the line to the occurrence of the end of the run, the system is called run-end coding. The location of the end of a run can also be specified in terms of the relative distance from the previous end. This system is denoted as run-length coding.

For a digital transmission system the amplitude and position of a run are transmitted as a group of code bits. If the amplitude and position of the runs are to be transmitted as they occur in a continuously scanned image, a reduction of the transmission signal power density will be possible, but the bandwidth will be unchanged. To achieve a bandwidth reduction it is necessary to gather the runs of a picture, and redistribute them in a transmission time sequence at a rate that is equal to the average rate of their occurrence. This can be accomplished with a memory at the sensor that stores the amplitude and position of runs, or by using a variable-scan-rate system that generates runs at a fixed rate (31).

The run-end coding system has the disadvantage of requiring a large fixed number of bits to describe each run position as a point along a line composed of several hundred pixels. The run-length coding system requires shorter groups of bits to specify the position of a run on the average. However, the variable length of the position code presents some problems in encoding. A variation of the position encoding method is to limit the length of the position code describing the run length to a uniform fixed length. If no natural run ends within the maximum run-length interval, a "pseudo" run is formed and transmitted. The pseudo run signifies a run of zero amplitude (i.e., no run end). This technique has the disadvantage of requiring a larger number of runs to code a picture because the number of position bits used for a run will be larger than is necessary to code many runs, and also since pseudo runs will have to be occasionally transmitted. However, a judicious choice of the length of the maximum run length based on signal statistics can minimize the coding system redundancy.

22.3.1. Run-Length Coding Analysis (32–36)

A simple but reasonably accurate model for the analysis of a run-length coding system is to assume that the probability p of encountering an edge at a given pixel is independent from pixel to pixel. Then letting Z represent the number of pixels in a run ($Z = 1$ designates two adjacent edges), the probability distribution of runs between natural edges is given by the geometric distribution

$$P\{Z = j\} = q^{i-1}p \tag{22.3-1}$$

where $q = 1 - p$. The expected natural run length is found to be

$$E\{Z\} = \frac{1}{p} \tag{22.3-2}$$

The entropy of a run is given by

$$H\{Z\} = - \sum_{j=1}^{\infty} q^{i-1}p \log_2 \{q^{i-1}p\} = \frac{-[q \log_2 q + p \log_2 p]}{p} \tag{22.3-3}$$

Now suppose that the runs are terminated to a maximum length of M pixels. The probability distribution of runs is then

$$P\{Z_M = j\} = q^{i-1}p + q^M\delta(j - M) \tag{22.3-4}$$

for $1 \le j \le M$. The expected run length now becomes

$$E\{Z_M\} = \sum_{j=1}^{M} jq^{i-1}p + Mq^M = \frac{1}{p} + Mq^M \tag{22.3-5}$$

and the corresponding entropy of runs is

$$H\{Z_M\} = -\frac{(1 - q^{M-1})(p \log_2 p + q \log_2 q)}{p} \tag{22.3-6}$$

Figure 22.3-1 contains a plot of the average edge run length as a function of the probability of edge occurrence. For a given value of p there is a value of the pseudo run length that maximizes the entropy per edge run. However, the factor of importance is not the entropy per run, but rather the entropy per pixel as given by

$$H\{E\} = \frac{H\{Z_M\}}{E\{Z_M\}} \tag{22.3-7}$$

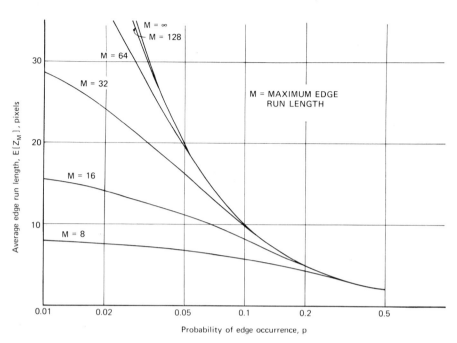

FIGURE 22.3-1. Average run length.

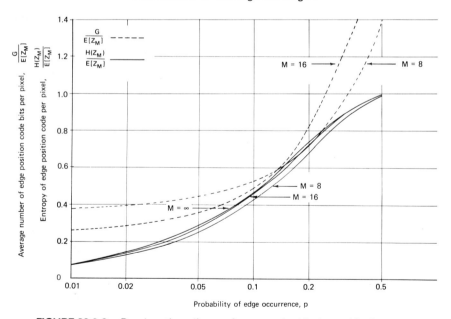

FIGURE 22.3-2. Run-length coding performance for black or white images.

The entropy per pixel plotted in Figure 22.3-2 as a function of the probability of an edge occurrence for $M = 8$, 16, and infinity, clearly indicates that there is only a small penalty in increased pixel entropy caused by the restriction of run lengths. Figure 22.3-2 also contains a plot of the average number of bits

$$L_c = \frac{G}{E\{Z_M\}} \qquad (22.3\text{-}8)$$

required to code a run with a constant-word-length G bit code where $M = 2^G$ bits. In the region of practical interest $(0.1 \le p \le 0.2)$, the figure shows that constant-word-length run coding closely approaches the run entropy.

Now consideration is given to the coding of the edge amplitude information. For a simple system in which the pixel value following each significant brightness change is to be coded, the total coding entropy is given by

$$H\{E + A\} = \frac{H\{F(j, k)\} + H\{Z_M\}}{E\{Z_M\}} \qquad (22.3\text{-}9)$$

The value of the total entropy is obviously dependent on the number of pixel quantization levels because the entropy $H\{F(j, k)\}$ depends on this factor. However, the entropy of an edge run and the average run length are even more sensitive to the number of quantization levels through the probability of an edge occurrence. For more than 16 quantization levels the edge probability generally becomes so large that the coding process is rendered useless.

It is of interest to examine the coding performance of the run-length coding scheme for practical fixed-length codes for edge run lengths and edge amplitude values. If A and G bits are allotted to each edge amplitude and run length, respectively, the average pixel code word length becomes

$$L_c = \frac{A + G}{E\{Z_M\}} \qquad (22.3\text{-}10)$$

Figure 22.3-3 contains a plot of the average number of edge code bits per pixel for $A = 3$ bits and a pseudo run length of $M = 2^G$. The heavy line indicates the minimum average number of code bits per pixel as a function of edge probability for an optimum choice of run length. For an edge probability of 0.1 an average of less than 1.0 bits per pixel is required compared to a straight PCM coding of 3.0 bits per pixel.

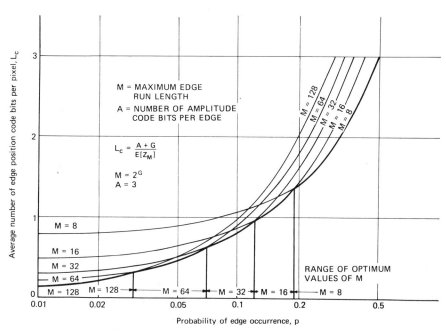

FIGURE 22.3-3.   Run-length coding performance for monochrone images.

Run-length coding is most practical for images with few required gray scales. If the image is a black or white facsimile signal, it is only necessary to code the changes in level after the first pixel value along a line is coded. The entropy per pixel for this case is simply the edge-run entropy as given by Figure 22.3-2. For black or white images it is often preferable to code the black and white runs with different codes if their respective expected run lengths differ markedly. Compression ratios of up to about 5:1 have been reported for black or white one-dimensional facsimile coding systems. Two-dimensional extensions of the run-length coding concept (37–39) yield compression factors of about 10:1.

22.3.2. Bit-Plane Coding

In constant-word-length PCM coding of an image, the code words may be conceptually organized into planes corresponding to their pixel position with the most significant bits occupying the lower plane. It has been found that in most natural images the lower-plane bits seldom change, while the upper-plane bits fluctuate almost randomly. A bandwidth reduction is possible, in principle, by run-length coding the bit state transitions in each bit plane. However, simulation tests indicate that the bandwidth reduction obtainable is usually much less than $2:1$ (40, 41).

22.4. FRAME-REPLENISHMENT CODING

A large potential television bandwidth reduction exists in the removal of spatial redundancy between adjacent frames of television pictures. In most scenes there is relatively little change in detail between adjacent frames. Thus by only transmitting the change in detail referenced to an initially transmitted frame, a significant bandwidth compression may be realized. The basic problem with this concept is the development of a method of obtaining the frame detail difference signal consistent with the picture scanning and transmitting processes, and with a modest amount of signal storage and processing equipment.

If pixel differences are formed between adjacent frames, it is found that a majority of the elements are virtually unchanged. This observation has led to the development of a frame-to-frame coding technique by Mounts called frame-replenishment coding (42–45). Figure 22.4-1 contains a block diagram of the frame-replenishment coding system. In operation each camera frame is digitized with 8 bits and the first frame of the sequence is digitally stored in a reference frame memory. In subsequent frames each

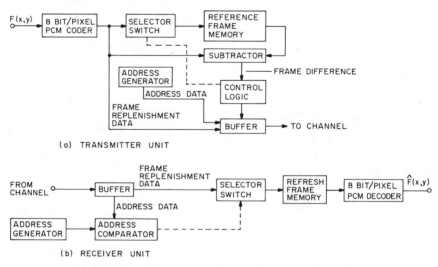

(a) TRANSMITTER UNIT

(b) RECEIVER UNIT

FIGURE 22.4-1.   Frame replenishment image coding system.

digitized pixel is compared to its counterpart in the frame memory. If a significant difference exists, the new pixel value replaces the stored value in the frame memory, and is also placed in a buffer memory for transmission. It is also necessary to identify the position of the significant change along the line by its horizontal code coordinate. The first pixel along each line is also coded to provide a line count. An improvement in coding efficiency can be obtained by coding frame differences in clusters rather than individually.

One of the major drawbacks of the frame-replenishment system is the requirement of a large-capacity buffer to accommodate long bursts of frame differences associated with prolonged image motion. This requirement can be alleviated somewhat by adapting the frame difference threshold value to the buffer fullness. If the buffer is nearly empty, the replenishment sensitivity can be set low; conversely, if the buffer is close to capacity, the replenishment sensitivity can be raised. Alternatively, it is possible spatially to subsample moving image areas to reduce buffer size requirements. Simulations of a frame-replenishment system have been reported (45) at coding rates of about 1.0 bits per pixel with quality rated as excellent except for periods of violent motion.

22.5. PREDICTIVE CODING

In a predictive image coding system, as shown in Figure 22.5-1, the value of each scanned pixel is predicted based on some previous history of scanned elements. Then the predicted estimate is subtracted from the

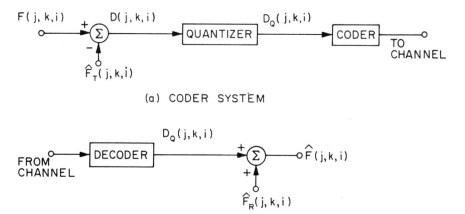

(a) CODER SYSTEM

(b) DECODER SYSTEM

FIGURE 22.5-1. Predictive image coding system.

actual pixel value, and the difference signal is then quantized coded and transmitted. At the receiver the quantized difference signal is used to form a reconstruction of the image signal. A bandwidth reduction is possible by coarsely quantizing the difference signal to be transmitted. As the bibliography at the end of this chapter attests, there has been considerable effort toward the development of predictive image coding systems. The following sections trace this development from the invention of the basic concept to the present research in adaptive predictive coding systems.

22.5.1. Deltamodulation

The simplest form of a predictive data encoder is the deltamodulation system illustrated in Figure 22.5-2 (46). In this system a bandlimited analog video signal is fed to a differencing device. If the difference signal is positive, a pulse generator produces a positive pulse of a given step size at the sampling instant; otherwise a negative pulse is produced. The positive and negative pulses are then represented as binary bits and transmitted. At the same time the pulses are fed back to an integrator that produces a stepwise representation of the input signal. The deltamodulation receiving system sequentially receives the image code bits and reconstructs the positive and negative code pulses. These pulses are then integrated to reconstruct the video signal. A low-pass filter removes spurious high-frequency components of the reconstructed signal. In this version of the deltamodulation coding system the prediction is based only on the previous pixel along a line, and the pixel difference signal is quantized to only two levels.

The invention of the basic two-level deltamodulation system for signal coding is generally credited to the Philips Research Laboratories of the Netherlands in 1952 (47). In 1961 Salaman (48) described a deltamodulation system for television signals. Balder and Kramer (49) developed one of the first experimental deltamodulation video transmission systems. In their system two types of integrating networks were studied. The simplest was a single RC (resistor–capacitor) integrating network and the other consisted of cascaded RC networks with different time constants. Their

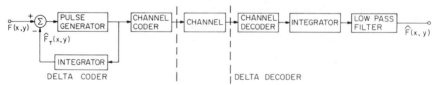

FIGURE 22.5-2. Deltamodulation image coding system.

experimental results are indicative of the performance realizable with simple two-level deltamodulation systems. With the single integrating network the sampling rate was set at 20 times the highest frequency of the video signal, which is 10 times the Nyquist sampling rate. Since 1 bit is required per sample for deltamodulation, 10 bits per Nyquist sample are required for transmission. This is greater than the 6–8 bits per pixel normally required for PCM transmission so that a bandwidth increase results from use of the single integrator deltamodulation coder. The cascaded integration network system required a sampling rate of 8 times the highest video frequency (4 times the Nyquist rate) to maintain adequate quality and resulted in coding at an average rate of 4 bits per pixel.

Figure 22.5-3 illustrates typical waveforms in a deltamodulation system. This figure indicates a basic problem of the deltamodulation system: if the quantizer step size is kept small to minimize quantization error, video slopes with fast rise times cannot be accurately followed unless the sampling rate is very high. Thus for a fixed sampling rate there is a tradeoff between quantization error and slope overload.

Figure 22.5-4 contains photographs of a computer simulation of deltamodulation image coding. When the reconstruction level is set at 2.5% of the peak image amplitude, the coded image exhibits considerable slope overload. At the other extreme a reconstruction level of 10% results in a high degree of granularity error. A reconstruction level of 5% provides a reasonable compromise between slope overload and granularity errors.

A deltamodulation coder inherently behaves as a differentiator of an input image signal, and therefore an integrator circuit in the decoder is required to reconstruct the average luminance value of the input image. Since the channel delta pulses are integrated at the receiver, any channel

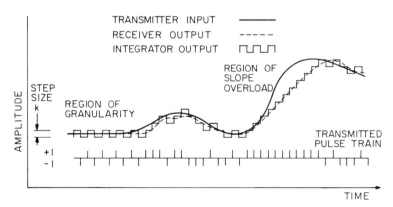

FIGURE 22.5-3. Typical signals in a deltamodulation coding system.

(a)   (b)

(c)   (d)

FIGURE 22.5-4. Examples of deltamodulation image coding, 1.0 bits per pixel. $q =$ reconstruction level. (a) Original. (b) $q = 2.5\%$, MSE $= 5.71\%$. (c) $q = 5.0\%$, MSE $= 2.58\%$. (d) $q = 10.0\%$, MSE $= 3.35\%$.

errors produce cumulative luminance errors along an image line. Inose and Yasuda (50) have proposed the delta-sigma modulator image coding system of Figure 22.5-5 as a means of circumventing the requirement for a receiver integrator. In the delta-sigma system of Figure 22.5-5a an integrator is placed before a delta coder and a differentiator follows the delta decoder. This conceptual system can be reduced to the simplified system of Figure 22.5-5b by commuting the position of the linear system elements. The delta-sigma modulator has been shown to be a special case of a 1-bit direct feedback coder (51).

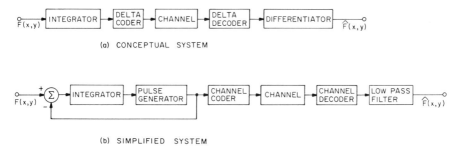

(a) CONCEPTUAL SYSTEM

(b) SIMPLIFIED SYSTEM

FIGURE 22.5-5. Delta-sigma modulation image coding system.

One means of reducing slope overload without increasing quantization error is to permit the deltamodulation system to assume more than two levels. Multilevel deltamodulators do indeed achieve better performance, but at the cost of additional complexity. It should also be noted that a multilevel deltamodulator is really a special case of a differential PCM coder to be discussed next. Another method of improving the performance of a deltamodulator is to adapt the reconstruction levels to the state of the video signal. Adaptive linear predictive systems are considered in a subsequent section.

22.5.2. Differential Pulse Code Modulation

The general concept of linear predictive coding has developed from an invention by Cutler (52) of the differential pulse code modulation (DPCM) system. In Cutler's original 1952 patent it was proposed that integrators be employed to predict the present sample based on the previous sample value along a line, and that the difference between the present sample and its estimate be quantized and coded for transmission.

Figure 22.5-6 contains a block diagram of the DPCM image coding system. In such a system the continuous image signal is spatially sampled, and the difference between an actual pixel and its estimate is quantized and coded for transmission. Usually the difference signal is quantized to eight levels and coded with a 3- or 4-bit code (53, 54). Thus the bandwidth reduction is from the 6–8 bits per pixel of conventional PCM to 3 bits per pixel for DPCM. In a basic DPCM coder the prediction is based on the quantized difference signal of the previously scanned pixel along an image line. At the receiver the decoded difference signal is reconstructed and combined with an estimate from a predictor identical to the one at the transmitter to provide a reconstruction of the original image.

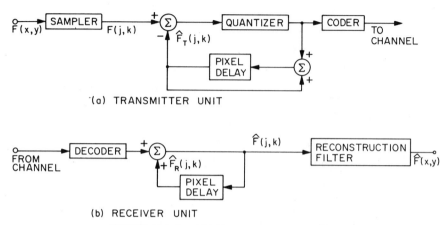

(a) TRANSMITTER UNIT

(b) RECEIVER UNIT

FIGURE 22.5-6. DPCM image coding system.

In 1958 Graham (55) proposed the use of a tapered quantizer scale in which the quantization levels between the input and output variables are placed nonlinearly. Figure 22.5-7 illustrates typical quantization scales for DPCM and deltamodulation. With a tapered quantizer the subjective quality of the reconstructed image is improved substantially. However, in most applications it has been found that at least eight quantization levels are still required.

A sampled image input signal lies within some maximum to minimum brightness range. Therefore its estimate should be limited to the same range. If the input sample is at its maximum value at a given pixel point, the analog difference signal must either be zero or negative. At the other extreme if the input is at its minimum value, the difference signal is zero or positive. In either case the full range of the bipolar quantization scale would not be used. Musmann (56) has proposed a folding quantizer scale, as shown in Figure 22.5-8, in which the unnecessary positive (negative) reconstruction levels are utilized on the lower (upper) side of the scale.

Subjectively, individual images coded with a well-designed 3-bit, 8-level DPCM coder appear to be about the same quality as 5–6 bit PCM images, except for some error in the vicinity of the edges (57). If DPCM coded images are displayed at real-time television rates, the edge errors tend to be correlated from frame to frame, and an image degradation called "edge busyness" is noted. This edge busyness is manifested as a sparkling effect near edge boundaries.

In an eight-level DPCM coder the probability of occurrence of the quantized difference signals is not uniform; small differences are more numerous than large differences. It is therefore possible to employ a

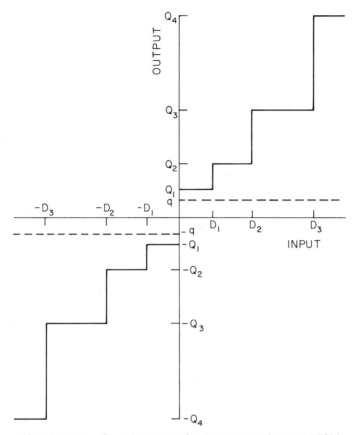

FIGURE 22.5-7. Quantizer scales for deltamodulation and DPCM.

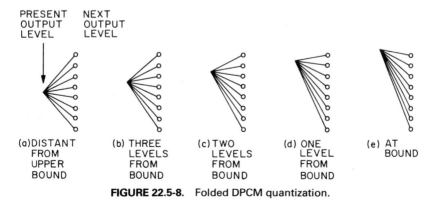

PRESENT NEXT
OUTPUT OUTPUT
LEVEL LEVEL

(a) DISTANT FROM UPPER BOUND (b) THREE LEVELS FROM BOUND (c) TWO LEVELS FROM BOUND (d) ONE LEVEL FROM BOUND (e) AT BOUND

FIGURE 22.5-8. Folded DPCM quantization.

variable-length statistical code, such as a Huffman code, rather than a 3-bit constant-length code, and achieve a greater coding compression. Simulation studies indicate that an average coding rate of about 2.5 bits per pixel can be achieved with a variable-length Huffman code (58, 59). Such a code, however, has the disadvantage of requiring a data buffer storage unit.

Computer simulation photographs of images coded by DPCM are contained in Figure 22.5-9. In this simulation the quantizer was set according to the scale of Figure 22.5-6 for three values of the lowest quantization level. Subjectively, the setting of $Q_1 = 2.5\%$ appears to be a good compromise between slope overload and granularity errors.

Brainard and Candy (60, 61) have studied the application of a direct feedback coder to image coding. This coder, which is a simplification of the

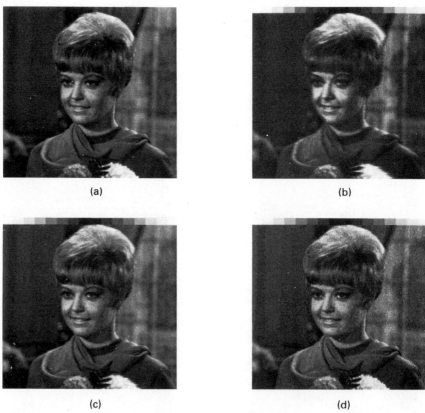

(a)   (b)

(c)   (d)

FIGURE 22.5-9. Examples of DPCM image coding, 3.0 bits per pixel. Q_1 is lowest reconstruction level. (a) Original. (b) $Q_1 = 0.5\%$, MSE $= 1.31\%$. (c) $Q_1 = 1.0\%$, MSE $= 0.33\%$. (d) $Q_1 = 5.0\%$, MSE $= 1.66\%$.

noise feedback coder proposed by Kimme and Kuo (62), contains a differentiating pre-emphasis filter, an integrating amplifier, and a leaky integrator deemphasis filter. The purported advantage of the direct feedback coder over a DPCM coder is the greater degree of design freedom in choosing the frequency transfer functions of the three filters to minimize quantization error. However, in simulation tests (61) there was no perceptible improvement for well-designed coders utilizing tapered quantizers.

22.5.3. Spatial Predictive Coders

Harrison (63) in 1952 extended the basic DPCM concept by forming the prediction signal from a linear combination of several previously scanned pixels along a scan line and from previous lines. Both theoretical and

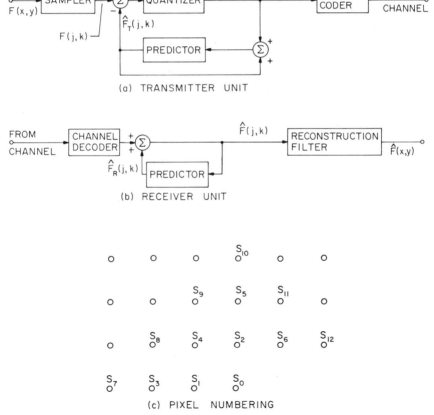

(a) TRANSMITTER UNIT

(b) RECEIVER UNIT

(c) PIXEL NUMBERING

FIGURE 22.5-10. Spatial predictive image coding system.

experimental studies have found that the mean-square error measure and subjective quality can be improved by utilizing more information in the prediction (64, 65). Figure 22.5-10 contains a generalized block diagram for the spatial predictive coding system and a numbering convention for pixels utilized in the prediction. Details of the predictor design are described in Section 22.6. A standard DPCM coder, which utilizes the previously scanned pixel (S_1) along an image line as the basis of its prediction of S_0, is often referred to as a first-order predictor. Following this nomenclature a second-order predictor would utilize the two previously scanned pixels along a line $(S_1$ and $S_3)$, or perhaps the previous pixel along the line (S_1) and the nearest pixel from the previous line (S_2). A third-order predictor might employ (S_1, S_2, S_4) as the basis for its prediction. Pixel S_6 is often used for prediction in standard raster-scanned imaging systems because S_6 provides a good indication of vertical edge structure. Studies to be described in Section 22.6 indicate that the pixel measurements that should be employed for minimum coding error correspond to the pixel neighbors with the highest statistical correlation to the pixel to be estimated. Furthermore, following this strategy, it is found that the coding error reduction diminishes rapidly for more than a third-order prediction system.

The drawback of a higher-order linear predictive image coder is primarily implementation complexity. For example, in a third-order predictive system utilizing pixel positions S_1, S_2, and S_4 to estimate S_0, storage is required for the three quantized differences $S_1 - \hat{S}_1$, $S_2 - \hat{S}_2$, $S_4 - \hat{S}_4$. Also, the complexity of the predictor is increased somewhat as compared to a DPCM coder.

22.5.4. Adaptive Predictive Coders

As mentioned previously, in a basic deltamodulation image coder, there is a compromise between granularity and slope overload error. Both of these error effects can be reduced somewhat by adapting the quantization levels to the image content. If the image brightness along a line is changing rapidly, the reconstruction levels should be increased to reduce slope overload, and if the image brightness is relatively constant, the reconstruction levels should be decreased to reduce granularity error. This technique is the basis of several adaptive deltamodulation and DPCM image coding systems (66–75). Winkler (66, 67) has proposed a deltamodulation quantization algorithm in which the quantization step size is doubled if three sequential delta code bits of the same polarity are encountered, and the quantization step size is halved if the delta code reverses state. Jayant (76), on the basis of a theoretical study, has concluded that the step size should be increased by a factor of $\frac{3}{2}$:1 and decreased by a factor of $\frac{2}{3}$:1. It is possible, in principle, to extend the concept of DPCM coders in which all eight quantization levels are adaptively set. Difficulties with this approach are the additional complexity of the coder and possible system instability.

Another approach to adaptive predictive coding is the dual-mode DPCM/deltamodulation coder in which the coder operates in either a DPCM mode or a deltamodulation mode. If the image brightness is relatively smooth over several samples, the image data are coded by deltamodulation, and if the brightness changes abruptly, the coder switches to 3-bit DPCM until the image activity once again reduces to a smooth level. A simple mode-switch algorithm is to switch from delta to DPCM after three identical sequential delta states. The reverse switch from DPCM to delta occurs when the DPCM coder is in its idling mode between the $+Q_1$ to $-Q_1$ or $-Q_1$ to $+Q_1$ states. The advantage of this mode-switch algorithm is its simplicity; switching is based on the previous history of channel code bits, and therefore no additional accounting code bits are necessary. Unfortunately, there is a three-pixel delay in switching from delta to DPCM, which may result in considerable slope overload error at an edge. Frei, Schinder, and Vettiger (75) have proposed a more sophisticated dual-mode coder in which the image is sampled at three times its normal rate in order to detect delta to DPCM transitions more accurately. The mode switching from delta to DPCM is described in Table 22.5-1. If three similar delta states are encountered in the oversampled mode, a 5-bit code group, as indicated in the table, is transmitted. Otherwise, a majority logic decision is made on the delta states to transmit a "1" code bit if 2 out

TABLE 22.5-1.   Oversampled dual-mode transmission logic

ΔM mode			Transmission code					
$+q$	$+q$	$+q$	1	1	1	(1	0)	← Marker bits
$+q$	$+q$	$-q$	1					
$+q$	$-q$	$-q$	1					
$-q$	$+q$	$+q$	1					
$-q$	$-q$	$+q$	0					
$-q$	$+q$	$-q$	0					
$+q$	$-q$	$-q$	0					
$-q$	$-q$	$-q$	0	0	0	(0	1)	← Marker bits

After 3 sequential delta "ones" insert a "zero" marker bit

$$\cdots 1 \quad 1 \quad 1 \quad \underline{0} \cdots$$

After 3 sequential delta "zeros" insert a "one" marker bit

$$\cdots 0 \quad 0 \quad 0 \quad \underline{1} \cdots$$

of 3 of the delta states are positive; a "0" code bit is transmitted in the opposite case. The DPCM to delta switch is based on observation of the idling condition: $+Q_1$ to $-Q_1$ or $-Q_1$ to $+Q_1$. Experimental studies with a real-time television dual-mode coder have shown that subjective quality equivalent to 3-bit DPCM can be obtained at an average bit rate of about 2.0 bits per pixel. Possible disadvantages of the method are its coder–decoder complexity plus increased sensitivity to channel errors as compared to PCM. Also, the coding is variable length so that a data buffer is required. Figure 22.5-11 contains photographs of computer simulations of the simple dual-mode coder and the oversampled dual-mode coder. Subjectively, the dual-mode coders perform substantially better than the adaptive delta coders but require twice the bit rate. The simple dual-mode coder exhibits some slope overload errors in the vicinity of edges. Such errors are much less apparent in the oversampled dual-mode coder image.

22.5.5. Color Image Predictive Coding

There are two basic approaches to the application of predictive coding to color television: direct coding of the composite color television signal, and coding of the color tristimulus values. Teacher and Yutz (77) have investigated deltamodulation coding of the NTSC composite signal and concluded that the poor high-frequency response of deltamodulation leads to unacceptable amplitude and phase distortion errors in the chrominance subcarrier at reasonable sampling rates.

(a)   (b)

FIGURE 22.5-11.   Examples of adaptive spatial linear predictive coding. (a) Dual-mode 2 bits per pixel. (b) Oversampled dual-mode 2 bits per pixel.

Bhushan (78) has studied deltamodulation coding on the R-G-B components of color television. Limb, Rubinstein, and Walsh (79) have investigated DPCM coding of the tristimulus signals

$$Y = 0.299R_N + 0.587G_N + 0.114B_N \qquad (22.5\text{-}1a)$$

$$C_1 = (R_N - Y)\frac{\cos\theta}{1.14} - (B_N - Y)\frac{\sin\theta}{2.03} \qquad (22.5\text{-}1b)$$

$$C_2 = (R_N - Y)\frac{\sin\theta}{1.14} + (B_N - Y)\frac{\cos\theta}{2.03} \qquad (22.5\text{-}1c)$$

where R_N, G_N, B_N are the NTSC receiver phosphor tristimulus values and θ is a parameter of the coordinate conversion. Acceptable image quality for a video telephone application was obtained by setting $\theta = 22°$ and allocating 12, 6, and 4 quantization levels to the DPCM differences signals of the Y, C_1, and C_2 channels, respectively. In addition, the C_1 and C_2 chrominance signals were only coded along every other line with line averaging used to fill in the missing chrominance lines at the decoder. In another approach Habibi (80) has proposed a coding scheme in which the luminance signal is DPCM coded by standard means and the NTSC I and Q chrominance signal are separately coded by adaptive deltamodulation.

22.5.6. Differential Frame Coding

It is possible to extend the technique of predictive coding to utilize the redundancy between frames (81). Since there is a high degree of redundancy between frames for most real-time imaging applications, the performance of such a predictive coder should be quite effective. However, there has been little effort to develop a generalized predictive coder because of the inherent problems of storing a sequence of frames. Mounts (82) has implemented a frame-to-frame differential PCM predictive coder that derives its prediction signal from a previous frame only. The performance of this coder is about the same as for a differential PCM coder using the previous pixel along a line: 3.0 bits per pixel. The frame differential coder is subject to a "temporal overload" error analogous to the slope overload error of DPCM. If a scene contains large-area, high-contrast objects that are moving, the edges of such reproduced objects are not sharp, but rather increase in steps equal to the largest quantizer. There has been some effort to combine frame-to-frame differential PCM with the frame-replenishment technique described in Section 22.4 (82).

Computer simulation studies have been performed (83) to evaluate the performance of spatio-temporal DPCM coders. Good quality results appear achievable at coding rates of about 2.0 bits per pixel, but, of course, frame storage is required.

22.6. DESIGN OF LINEAR PREDICTIVE IMAGE CODERS

In the design of a linear predictive coder the design variables are the number and location of previous pixels to be used in the prediction, the weighting to be assigned to these pixels, and the number and placement of the quantization levels. The nonlinear character of the quantizer usually creates analytic difficulties in seeking an optimum design to minimize the reconstruction error of the coder. Most designs are directed toward determining an optimum prediction without quantization error, and then optimally designing the quantizer to minimize its error (84–88). This design philosophy will be followed here.

In a predictive image coding system, as shown in Figure 22.6-1, a predictor generates an estimate, $\hat{F}_T(j, k, i)$, of an actual pixel value $F(j, k, i)$ based on the values of previously scanned pixels in the present frame or past frames. The difference $D(j, k, i)$ between the estimate and

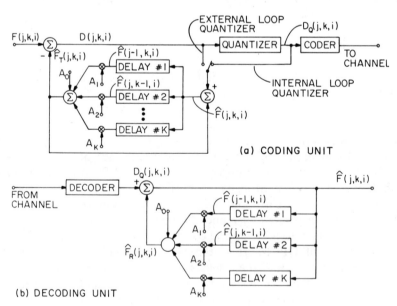

(a) CODING UNIT

(b) DECODING UNIT

FIGURE 22.6-1. Linear predictive image coding system with feedback prediction.

the actual pixel value

$$D(j, k, i) = F(j, k, i) - \hat{F}_T(j, k, i) \qquad (22.6\text{-}1)$$

is quantized, coded, and transmitted over the channel. At the receiver the decoded quantized prediction difference is combined with the pixel estimate to reconstruct a pixel value

$$\hat{F}(j, k, i) = D_Q(j, k, i) + \hat{F}_R(j, k, i) \qquad (22.6\text{-}2)$$

If the quantizer in Figure 22.6-1 is removed, the pixel reconstruction $\hat{F}(j, k, i)$ becomes identically equal to the actual pixel value $F(j, k, i)$ regardless of the accuracy of the estimate $\hat{F}_R(j, k, i)$. A bandwidth reduction can be achieved only by quantizing and coding the prediction difference. Typically, the prediction difference is quantized with from 2 to 16 levels, and coded with from 1 to 4 bits.

The estimator producing the pixel estimate $\hat{F}_T(j, k, i)$ at the transmitter system has available, in theory, all of the previously scanned pixels in the present and past frames plus the quantized prediction differences $D_Q(j, k, i)$ of these pixels. The receiver system has available all previously reconstructed pixels and all quantized prediction differences of these pixels.

There are two principal methods of prediction that could be employed in a predictive coder: feedforward and feedback prediction. A feedforward prediction system forms an estimate by taking a linear combination of previously scanned pixels obtained from a storage unit. A major problem associated with feedforward prediction is that the decoding unit does not have access to the recorded history of scanned pixels available to the coding unit: the decoder only has access to reconstructed pixels whose values are subject to quantization error. Consequently, the transmitter pixel estimate $\hat{F}_T$ and the receiver pixel estimate $\hat{F}_R$ will differ and the system will ultimately become unstable. This problem can be eliminated by feedback prediction.

In the feedback prediction image coding system of Figure 22.6-1, the transmitter estimate is formed by taking a linear combination of previously generated prediction differences. The output of delay line number 1 corresponds to the prediction difference of the left-hand neighbor, and the output of delay line number 2 corresponds to the neighbor above. The weighting constants A_k are usually chosen to minimize the variance of the prediction difference. If the quantizer is placed external to the feedback loop, summation of the previous pixel estimate $\hat{F}_T$ and the difference signal D produces an exact replica of the actual pixel value with a one-pixel delay. Next, the difference signal is quantized and coded for transmission. At the receiver the quantized difference D_Q is added to the receiver estimate $\hat{F}_R$ to produce the reconstructed pixel $\hat{F}$. If there were no quantization of the difference signal, the transmitter and receiver pixel estimates would be identical and the pixel reconstruction $\hat{F}$ would be an identically delayed version of the actual pixel value F. Quantization of the difference signal causes errors in the reconstruction $\hat{F}$ as compared to F. Furthermore, these errors may accumulate because the transmitter and receiver estimates will not be identical if the quantizer is placed outside the feedback loop. Error accumulation can be eliminated by including the quantizer in the coder prediction loop, and thereby forcing the transmitter and receiver estimates to be identical because the transmitter and receiver predictors are both driven by the same quantized prediction signal. For this configuration, the feedback loop can be designed to minimize the quantization error as well as prediction difference signal variance.

Consideration is now given to the specification of the predictor weighting constants. With reference to Figure 22.5-10, let $S_1, S_2, \ldots, S_K$ represent the values of K previously scanned pixels that are to be used in the prediction of a pixel of value S_0. The pixels employed in the prediction may lie along the same line or along previously scanned lines. In the design of the coder the pixels S_k are assumed to be samples of a stochastic process with known first- and second-order moments.

Neglecting quantization, the linear estimate of S_0 is given by

$$\hat{S}_0 = A_0 + A_1 S_1 + A_2 S_2 + \cdots + A_K S_K \qquad (22.6\text{-}3)$$

where the A_k are prediction weighting constants. A prediction difference is then defined as

$$D = S_0 - \hat{S}_0 \qquad (22.6\text{-}4)$$

In most designs the prediction weighting constants are chosen to minimize the mean-square prediction difference

$$D_P \equiv E\{D^2\} = E\{[S_0 - \hat{S}_0]^2\} \qquad (22.6\text{-}5)$$

The rationale for this performance measure is that the measure is tractable, correlates reasonably well with subjective evaluation, and, as will be found later, the quantization error is directly proportional to the mean-square prediction difference. Minimization of the mean-square prediction difference can be performed by taking the partial derivative of D_P with respect to each weighting value A_k and setting the result to zero. Thus let

$$\frac{\partial D_P}{\partial A_k} = \frac{\partial E\{[S_0 - (A_0 + A_1 S_1 + A_2 S_2 + \cdots + A_K S_K)]^2\}}{\partial A_k} = 0$$

$$(22.6\text{-}6)$$

On differentiation one obtains

$$E\{S_0\} = E\{\hat{S}_0\} = A_0 + A_1 E\{S_1\} + A_2 E\{S_2\} + \cdots + A_K E\{S_K\}$$
(22.6-7a)

$$E\{S_0 S_k\} = A_1 E\{S_1 S_k\} + A_2 E\{S_2 S_k\} + \cdots + A_K E\{S_K S_k\}$$
(22.6-7b)

for $1 \le k \le K$. The optimum weighting values A_k are then found from the simultaneous solution of the $K+1$ linear equations of Eq. 22.6-7 in terms of the means $E\{S_k\}$ and the cross moments $E\{S_j S_k\}$ between all of the pixels involved in the prediction. Using the optimal values of the A_k, the minimum mean-square prediction difference is found to be

$$(\sigma_P^2)_{\min} = E\{S_0^2\} - A_0 E\{S_0\} - \sum_{k=1}^{K} A_k E\{S_0 S_k\} \qquad (22.6\text{-}8)$$

It is found that, in general, as K approaches infinity, the sequence of prediction differences becomes uncorrelated (89). If the sequence of pixels is a sample of an Nth-order autoregressive process, then only N previously scanned pixels need to be used in the prediction to achieve complete decorrelation (88). Employing more than N pixels, in this case, will not improve the prediction accuracy.

Table 22.6-1 contains a listing of predictor weighting coefficients for a two-dimensional Markov process with correlation function

$$R(j_1, j_2; k_1, k_2) = \exp\left\{-\sqrt{\alpha_C (j_1 - j_2)^2 + \alpha_R (k_1 - k_2)^2}\right\} \quad (22.6\text{-}9)$$

where k_i are row indices, j_i are column indices, and α_R and α_C are row and column scaling constants. Figure 22.6-2 contains a plot of the mean-square prediction difference as a function of predictor order for several predictive coding systems. These curves indicate that the mean-square prediction difference reduces to almost its minimum value for a fourth-order predictor.

In typical predictive image coding systems it has been found that the prediction difference amplitude can be well modeled by a two-sided exponential (Laplacian) density of the form

$$p(D) = \frac{\alpha}{2} \exp\left\{-\alpha |D|\right\} \qquad (22.6\text{-}10)$$

where $\alpha = \sqrt{2}/\sigma_p$ and σ_p is the standard deviation of the prediction difference signal. The common analytic approach to the design of the quantizer is to select the $J+1$ decision levels d_j and the J reconstruction

TABLE 22.6-1. Weighting coefficients and mean-square prediction difference for several linear predictive coding systems. $\alpha_R = 9.28 \times 10^{-4}$, $\alpha_C = 16.7 \times 10^{-4}$, $\exp\{-\alpha_C\} = 0.960$, $\exp\{-\alpha_R\} = 0.970$.

Weighting Coefficient	1st Order hor.	1st Order ver.	2nd Order hor.	2nd Order hor./ver.	3rd Order hor.	3rd Order hor./ver./dia.	3rd Order geom.	4th Order geom.	5th Order geom.	6th Order geom.
A_1	0.970	0.960	0.970	0.595	0.970	0.628	0.970	0.652	0.650	0.602
A_2				0.394		0.443	0.960	0.439	0.449	0.243
A_3			0.000		0.000		0.941	-0.033	-0.032	-0.018
A_4						-0.081		-0.071	-0.065	-0.020
A_5									-0.015	-0.093
A_6										0.279
A_7					0.000					
	5.910%	7.840%	5.910%	4.406%	5.910%	4.337%	4.391%	4.371%	4.370%	3.960%

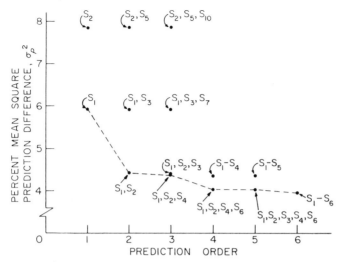

FIGURE 22.6-2. Mean-square prediction difference for linear predictive coding systems as a function of predictor order.

levels r_j to minimize the mean-square quantization error. Following this approach, the decision and reconstruction levels may be computed according to the Max algorithm of Eq. 6.1-11. Decision and reconstruction levels for a unit variance Laplacian density are listed in Table 6.1-1. Alternatively, a companding quantizer may be employed in which the prediction difference undergoes a nonlinear transformation to produce the variable

$$z(D) = \frac{D_m [1 - \exp(-\sqrt{2/D_m}(D/3\sigma_P))]}{[1 - \exp(-\sqrt{2D_m}/3\sigma_P)]} \qquad \text{for } D \geq 0$$

$$(22.6\text{-}11a)$$

$$z(-D) = -z(D) \qquad \text{for } D < 0$$

$$(22.6\text{-}11b)$$

The variable $z(D)$ is then linearly quantized to produce reconstruction levels $z_Q(D)$, which, in turn, undergo another nonlinear transformation resulting in the reconstruction levels

$$D_Q = \left[\sqrt{\frac{D_m}{2}} 3\sigma_P \right] \ln \left[1 - \frac{z_Q(D)}{D_m} \left(1 - \exp \left(-\frac{\sqrt{2D_m}}{3\sigma_P} \right) \right) \right] \qquad \text{for } z_Q(D) \geq 0$$

$$(22.6\text{-}12a)$$

$$D_Q = -D_Q \qquad \text{for } z_Q(D) < 0$$

$$(22.6\text{-}12b)$$

In these equations the factor D_m represents the maximum reconstruction level of the prediction difference D, as determined by the Max algorithm. It is possible to utilize the factor D_m as a quantization variable, at the expense of a larger mean-square error, but possibly improved subjective performance. If D_m is set at a small level, more quantization levels will be assigned to small prediction differences and the fine detail of the reconstruction will be improved, but large-magnitude edge rendition will be degraded. On the other hand, D_m can be increased to improve edge rendition at the penalty of poorer fine-detail resolution.

The exponential model of Eq. 22.6-10 for the probability density of the difference signal is clearly valid only when the image pixel value is sufficiently far from its upper and lower bounds so that severe clipping of the reconstructed image does not occur. Musmann (7) has proposed an improved quantization scheme in which quantization decision and reconstruction levels are determined from the conditional probability density $p(D\,|\,S_1, S_2, \ldots, S_K)$. Furthermore, the probability density model is parametrized to reflect the nearness of the actual pixel to the upper or lower bounds. Construction of a quantizer based on a high-order conditional density is not feasible because of the dimensionality involved.

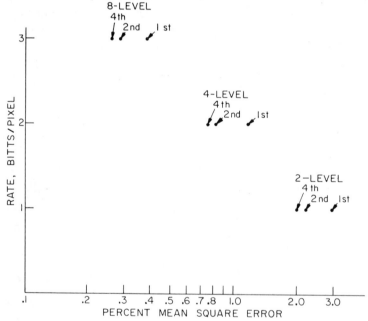

FIGURE 22.6-3. Theoretical mean-square error as a function of coding rate for predictive coding systems.

However, a variable quantizer to adapt to the nearness to the bound can be implemented with only moderate complexity.

Referring to Eq. 6.1-12, the mean-square quantization error can be expressed in terms of the probability density of the prediction difference signal as

$$\mathscr{E} = \sigma_P^2 - \sum_{j=0}^{J-1} r_j^2 \int_{d_j}^{d_{j+1}} p(D)\, dD \qquad (22.6\text{-}13)$$

where σ_P^2 represents the variance of the prediction difference signal, as specified by Eq. 22.6-8, and d_j and r_j are quantization decision and reconstruction levels, respectively. For the Laplacian density model of Eq. 22.6-10 the error expression reduces to

$$\mathscr{E} = \sigma_P^2 - \sum_{j=J/2}^{J-1} r_j^2 [\exp\{-\alpha d_j\} - \exp\{-\alpha d_{j+1}\}] \qquad (22.6\text{-}14)$$

for an even number of reconstruction levels. Figure 22.6-3 contains a plot of coding rate versus mean-square error coding distortion for several predictive coding systems.

REFERENCES

1. W. M. Goodall, "Television Transmission by Pulse Code Modulation," *Bell Syst. Tech. J.*, **30**, January 1951, 33–49.

2. R. L. Cabrey, "Video Transmission over Telephone Cable Pairs by Pulse Code Modulation," *Proc. IRE*, **48**, 9, September 1960, 1546–1561.

3. L. H. Harper, "PCM Picture Transmissions," *IEEE Spectrum*, **3**, June 1966, 146.

4. F. Kretz, "Subjectively Optimal Quantization of Pictures," *IEEE Trans. Commun.* (Concise Paper), **COM-23**, 11, November 1975, 1288–1292.

5. T. G. Stockham, "Intra-Frame Encoding for Monochrome Images by Means of a Psychophysical Model Based on Nonlinear Filtering of Multiplied Signals," in *Picture Bandwidth Compression*, T. S. Huang and O. J. Tretiak, Eds., Gordon and Breach, New York, 1972, 415–442.

6. W. Frei (private communication).

7. L. G. Roberts, "Picture Coding Using Pseudo-Random Noise," *IRE Trans. Inf. Theory*, **IT-8**, 2, February 1962, 145–154.

8. B. Lippel, M. Kurland, and A. H. Marsh, "Ordered Dither Patterns for Coarse Quantization of Pictures," *Proc. IEEE*, **59**, 3, March 1971, 429–431.

9. B. Lippel and M. Kurland, "The Effect of Dither on Luminance Quantization of Pictures," *IEEE Trans. Commun. Tech.*, **COM-19**, 6, December 1971, 879–889.

10. J. E. Thompson and J. J. Sparkes, "A Pseudo-Random Quantizer for Television Signals," *Proc. IEEE*, **55**, 3, March 1967, 353–355.

11. J. E. Thompson, "A 36-MBIT/S Television Codec Employing Pseudorandom Quantization," *IEEE Trans. Commun. Tech.*, **COM-19**, 6, December 1971, 872–879.

12. J. O. Limb, "Design of Dither Waveforms for Quantized Visual Signals," *Bell Syst. Tech. J.*, **48**, 7, September 1969, 2555–2583.

13. W. T. Bisignani, G. P. Richards, and J. W. Whelan, "The Improved Grey Scale and the Coarse–Fine PCM Systems: Two New Digital TV Bandwidth Reduction Techniques," *Proc. IEEE*, **54**, 3, March 1966, 376–390.

14. G. P. Richards and W. T. Bisignani, "Redundancy Reduction Applied to Coarse–Fine Encoded Video," *Proc. IEEE*, **55**, 10, October 1967, 1707–1717.

15. E. R. Kretzmer, "Reduced-Alphabet Representation of Television Signals," *IRE Convention Record*, Part 4, 1956, 140–147.

16. M. N. Huhns, "Optimum Restoration of Quantized Correlated Signals," University of Southern California, Image Processing Institute, Report USCIPI 600, August 1975.

17. D. A. Huffman, "A Method for the Construction of Minimum-Redundancy Codes," *Proc. IRE*, **40**, 9, September 1952, 1098–1101.

18. L. D. Davisson and R. L. Kutz, "A Real Time Programmable Data Compression System," Proceedings International Telemetering Conference, 1971.

19. L. D. Davisson and R. L. Kutz, "An Operational Data Compression System Using Minicomputers," National Telemetering Conference Record, Houston, Texas, December 1972, 34A-1 to 34A-4.

20. C. L. May and D. J. Spencer, "Data Compression for Earth Resources Satellites," Proceedings International Telemetering Conference, Los Angeles, California, Vol. 8, October 1972, 352–362.

21. R. F. Rice and J. R. Plaunt, "Adaptive Variable-Length Coding for Efficient Compression of Spacecraft Television Data," *IEEE Trans. Commun. Tech.*, **COM-19**, 6, December 1971, 889–898.

22. A. E. Laemmel, "Coding Processes for Bandwidth Reduction in Picture Transmission," Microwave Institute, Polytechnic Institute of Brooklyn, Report R 246–251, August 1951.

23. G. G. Gouriet, "Bandwidth Compression of a Television Signal," *Proc. IEE*, **104**, Part B, 15, May 1957, 265–272.

24. W. S. Michel, "Statistical Encoding for Text and Picture Communication," *Commun. Electron.*, **35**, March 1958, 33–36.

25. I. I. Tsukkerman, "The Transmission of the Coordinates of a Televised Image," *Radio Eng.*, **13**, 4, July 1958, 93–105.

26. W. F. Schreiber and C. F. Knapp, "TV Bandwidth Reduction by Digital Coding," *IRE National Convention Record*, **6**, Part 4, 1958, 88–89.

27. W. F. Schreiber, C. F. Knapp, and N. D. Kay, "Synthetic Highs: An Experimental TV Bandwidth Reduction System," *J. Soc. Motion Picture and Television Engineers*, **68**, August 1959, 525–537.

28. B. Julesz, "A Method of Coding TV Signals Based on Edge Detection," *Bell Syst. Tech. J.*, **38**, 4, July 1959, 1001–1020.

29. E. C. Cherry, M. P. Barton, and M. H. Kubba, "An Experimental Study Possible Bandwidth Compression of Visual Image Signals," *Proc. IEEE*, **51**, 11, November 1963, 1507–1517.

30. A. H. Robinson and C. Cherry, "Results of a Prototype Television Bandwidth Compression Scheme," *Proc. IEEE*, **55**, 3, March 1967, 356–364.

31. W. K. Pratt, "Stop-Scan Edge Detection System for Interplanetary Television Transmission," IRE National Symposium on Space Electronics and Telemetry, October 1962.

32. J. Capon, "A Probabilistic Model for Run-Length Coding of Pictures," *IRE Trans. Inf. Theory*, **IT-5**, 4, December 1959, 157–163.

33. W. K. Pratt, "Coding Compression of a Television Bandwidth Reduction System," *Proc. IEEE (Correspondence)*, **54**, 6, June 1966, 914–916.

34. S. W. Golomb, "Run Length Encodings," *IEEE Trans. Inf. Theory*, **IT-12**, 3, July, 1966, 399–401.

35. W. W. Happ, "Coding Schemes for Run-Length Information, Based on Poisson Distribution," National Telemetering Conference Record, April 1969, 257–261.

36. J. O. Limb, "Efficiency of Variable Length Binary Encoding," UMR Mervin J. Kelly Communications Conference, Rolla, Missouri, October 1970, 13.3-1 to 13.3-9.

37. C. G. Beaudette, "An Efficient Facsimile System for Weather Graphics," in *Picture Bandwidth Compression*, T. S. Huang and O. J. Tretiak, Eds., Gordon and Breach, New York, 1972, 217–220.

38. T. S. Huang, "Run-Length Coding and Its Extensions," in *Picture Bandwidth Compression*, T. S. Huang and O. J. Tretiak, Eds., Gordon and Breach, New York, 1972, 221–266.

39. H. E. White, M. D. Lippman, and K. H. Powers, "Dictionary Look-Up Encoding of Graphics Data," in *Picture Bandwidth Compression*, T. S. Huang and O. J. Tretiak, Eds., Gordon and Breach, New York, 1972, 265–281.

40. J. W. Schwartz and R. C. Barker, "Bit-Plane Encoding: A Technique for Source Encoding," *IEEE Trans. Aerospace Electron. Syst.*, **AES-2**, 4, July 1966, 385–392.

41. D. R. Spencer and T. Huang, "Bit-Plane Encoding of Continuous-Tone Pictures," Symposium on Computer Processing in Communications, Polytechnic Institute of Brooklyn, New York, April 1969.

42. A. J. Seyler, "The Coding of Visual Signals to Reduce Channel-Capacity Requirements," *Proc. IEE*, **109**, C, September 1962, 676–684.

43. F. W. Mounts, "A Video Encoding System Using Conditional Picture-Element Replenishment," *Bell Syst. Tech. J.*, **48**, 7, September 1969, 2545–2555.

44. J. C. Candy, M. A. Franke, B. G. Haskell, and F. W. Mounts, "Transmitting Television as Clusters of Frame-to-Frame Differences," *Bell Syst. Tech. J.*, **50**, 6, July–August 1971, 1889–1917.

45. B. G. Haskell, F. W. Mounts, and J. C. Candy, "Interframe Coding of Videotelephone Pictures," *Proc. IEEE*, **60**, 7, July 1972, 792–800.

46. H. R. Schindler, "Delta Modulation," *IEEE Spectrum*, **7**, October 1970, 69–78.

47. F. De Jager, "Deltamodulation: A Method of PCM Transmission Using a One-Unit Code," *Philips Res. Rep.*, **7**, 1952, 442–466.

48. R. G. Salaman, "Digital Television Encoding," Seventh National Communication Symposium Record, 1961, 274–279.

49. J. C. Balder and C. Kramer, "Video Transmission by Delta Modulation Using Tunnel Diodes," *Proc. IRE*, **50**, 4, April 1962, 428–431.

50. H. Inose and Y. Yasuda, "A Unit Bit Coding Method by Negative Feedback," *Proc. IEEE*, **51**, 11, November 1963, 1524–1535.

51. R. C. Brainard and J. C. Candy, "Direct-Feedback Coders: Design and Performance with Television Signals," *Proc. IEEE*, **57**, 5, May 1969, 776–786.

52. C. C. Cutler, "Differential Quantization of Communication Signals," Patent 2-605-361, Application June 1950, Issuance July 1952.

53. J. B. Millard and H. I. Maunsell, "Digital Encoding of Video Signals," *Bell Syst. Tech. J.*, **50**, 2, February 1971, 459–479.

54. R. P. Abbott, "A Differential Pulse-Code-Modulation Coder for Videotelephony Using Four Bits per Sample," *IEEE Trans. Commun. Tech.*, **COM-19**, 6, December 1971, 907–913.

55. R. E. Graham, "Predictive Quantizing of Television Signals," *IRE WESCON Convention Record*, Part 4, 1958, 142–157.

56. H. H. Bauch et al., "Picture Coding," *IEEE Trans. Commun.*, **COM-20**, 9, September 1974, 1158–1167.

57. J. O. Limb, "Source-Receiver Encoding of Television Signals," *Proc. IEEE*, **55**, 3, March 1967, 364–379.

58. J. O. Limb, "Adaptive Encoding of Picture Signals," in *Picture Bandwidth Compression*, T. S. Huang and O. J. Tretiak, Eds., Gordon and Breach, New York, 1972, 341–382.

59. M. C. Chow, "Variable-Length Redundancy Removal Coders for Differentially Coded Video Telephone Signals," *IEEE Trans. Commun. Tech.*, **COM-19**, 6, December 1971, 922–926.

60. R. C. Brainard, "Subjective Evaluation of PCM Noise-Feedback Coder for Television," *Proc. IEEE*, **55**, 3, March 1967, 346–353.

61. R. C. Brainard and J. C. Candy, "Direct-Feedback Coders: Design and Performance with Television Signals," *Proc. IEEE*, **57**, 5, May 1969, 776–786.

62. E. G. Kimme and F. F. Kuo, "Synthesis of Optimal Filters for a Feedback Quantization System," *IEEE Trans. Circuit Theory*, **CT-10**, 3, September 1963, 405–413.

63. C. W. Harrison, "Experiments with Linear Prediction in Television," *Bell Syst. Tech. J.*, **31**, 4, July 1952, 746–783.

64. J. B. O'Neal, "Predictive Quantizing Systems (Differential Pulse Code Modulation) for the Transmission of Television Signals," *Bell Syst. Tech. J.*, **45**, 5, May–June 1966, 689–721.

65. D. J. Connor, R. F. W. Pease, and W. G. Scholes, "Television Coding Using Two-Dimensional Spatial Prediction," *Bell Syst. Tech. J.*, **50**, March 1971, 1049–1063.

66. M. R. Winkler, "High Information Delta Modulation," *IEEE International Convention Record*, Part 8, 1963, 260–265.

67. M. R. Winkler, "Pictorial Transmission with HIDM," *1965 IEEE International Convention Record*, Part 1, 1965, 285–291.

68. R. H. Bosworth and J. C. Candy, "A Companded One-Bit Coder for Television Transmission," *Bell Syst. Tech. J.*, **48**, 5, May–June 1969, 1459–1479.

69. J. C. Candy, "Refinement of a Delta Modulator," in *Picture Bandwidth Compression*, T. S. Huang and O. J. Tretiak, Eds., Gordon and Breach, New York, 1971, 323–339.

70. E. F. Brown, "Sliding-Scale Operation of Differential Type PCM Codes for Television," in *Picture Bandwidth Compression*, T. S. Huang and O. J. Tretiak, Eds., Gordon and Breach, New York, 1972, 303–322.

71. G. W. Aughenbough, J. D. Irwin, and J. B. O'Neal, "Delayed Differential Pulse Code Modulation," Proceedings 2nd Annual Princeton Conference, October 1970, 125–130.

72. C. C. Cutler, "Delayed Encoding: Stabilizer for Adaptive Coders," *IEEE Trans. Commun. Tech.*, **COM-19**, 6, December 1971, 898–907.

73. W. Kamunski and E. F. Brown, "An Edge-Adaptive Three-Bit Ten-Level Differential PCM Coder for Television," *IEEE Trans. Commun. Tech.*, **COM-19**, 6, December 1971, 944–947.

74. P. Kaul and L. Golding, "A DPCM Code Using Edge Coding and Line Replacement," NTC '72 Record, IEEE Publication No. 72 CHO 601-5-NTC, Houston, Texas, December 1972, 34B-1 to 34B-6.

75. A. H. Frei, H. R. Schindler, and P. Vettiger, "An Adaptive Dual-Mode Coder/Decoder for Television Signals," *IEEE Trans. Commun. Tech.*, **COM-19**, 6, December 1971, 933–944.

76. N. S. Jayant, "Adaptive Delta Modulation with One-Bit Memory," *Bell Syst. Tech. J.*, **49**, 3, March 1970, 321–342.

77. C. F. Teacher and R. W. Yutz, "Secure Color Video Techniques," Def. Doc. Center, AD 462528, Philco Corporation, Blue Bell, Pennsylvania, February 1965.

78. A. K. Bhushan, "Transmission and Coding of Color Pictures," in *Picture Bandwidth Compression*, T. S. Huang and O. J. Tretiak, Eds., Gordon and Breach, New York, 1972, 697–725.

79. J. O. Limb, C. B. Rubenstein, and K. A. Walsh, "Digital Coding of Color Picturephone Signals by Element-Differential Quantization," *IEEE Trans. Commun. Tech.*, **COM-19**, 6, December 1971, 992–1006.

80. A. Habibi, "Delta Modulation and DPCM Coding of Color Signals," Proceedings of the International Telemetering Conference, Los Angeles, California, Vol. 8, October 1972, 333–343.

81. B. A. Haskell, F. W. Mounts, and J. C. Candy, "Interframe Coding of Videotelephone Pictures," *Proc. IEEE*, **60**, 7, 792–800.

82. F. W. Mounts, "Frame-to-Frame Digital Processing of TV Pictures to Remove Redundancy," in *Picture Bandwidth Compression*, T. S. Huang and O. J. Tretiak, Eds., Gordon and Breach, New York, 1972, 653–673.

83. J. A. Roese, W. K. Pratt, and G. S. Robinson, "Interframe Transform Coding and Predictive Coding Methods," IEEE International Communications Conference, San Francisco, California, June 1975.

84. J. B. O'Neal, "Delta Modulation Quantizing Noise Analytical and Computer Simulation Results for Gaussian and TV Input Signals," *Bell Syst. Tech. J.*, **45**, 1, January 1966, 117–142.

85. J. B. O'Neal, "Predictive Quantizing System (Differential Pulse Code Modulation) for the Transmission of Television Signals," *Bell Syst. Tech. J.*, **45**, 5, May–June 1966, 689–721.

86. J. B. O'Neal, "A Bound on Signal-to-Quantizing Noise Ratios for Digital Encoding Systems," *Proc. IEEE*, **55**, 3, March 1967, 287–292.

87. J. B. O'Neal, "Entropy Coding in Speech and Television Differential PCM Systems," *IEEE Trans. Inf. Theory*, **IT-17**, 6, November 1971, 758–761.

88. A. Habibi, "Comparison of Nth Order DPCM Encoder with Linear Transformation and Block Quantization Techniques," *IEEE Trans. Commun. Tech.*, **COM-19**, 6, December 1971, 948–957.

89. A. Papoulis, *Probability, Random Variables, and Stochastic Processes*, McGraw-Hill, New York, 1965.

90. H. H. Bauch et al., "Picture Coding," *IEEE Trans. Commun. Tech.*, **COM-20**, 9, September 1974, 1158–1167.

23 DIGITAL SPATIAL PROCESSING IMAGE CODING

Digital image coding techniques based on spatial coding concepts are considered in this chapter. Interpolative, transform, feature, and symbolic coding techniques are described.

23.1. INTERPOLATIVE CODING TECHNIQUES

Interpolative coding systems are based on numerical representation or approximation techniques whereby a sequence or plane of pixel values is "fitted" by continuous functions. There are two basic interpolation processes that can be applied to image coding: source interpolation and destination interpolation.

23.1.1. Source Interpolation

In source interpolative coding systems the luminance values of an image are approximated by continuous functions within some permissible error band (1–5). Interpolation may be performed along a scan line or over areas of an image.

Figure 23.1-1a illustrates the operation of a zero-order interpolator. In this example an error tolerance band is established about each pixel value, and maximal length horizontal line segments are fitted within the error band without any constraints as to the start and stop coordinates. Each pixel is spanned by a horizontal line segment. The vertical coordinate and sample spacing length of each horizontal line segment is then transmitted. At the receiver pixel values are reconstructed to the amplitude of the horizontal line segment. This type of interpolation permits the greatest amount of freedom possible in fitting the horizontal line segments to the image data, and thus provides the most efficient representation in terms of minimizing the horizontal line lengths. However, the computation involved in the line fitting process is often excessive. Figure 23.1-1b describes a simplified zero-order interpolator in which the horizontal line segments are restricted to begin at a pixel sample value and to end at a sample time. This

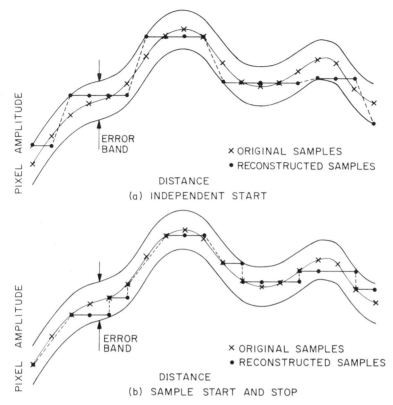

FIGURE 23.1-1. Zero-order interpolation.

simplified form of a first-order interpolator is equivalent to a run-length encoder that codes luminance values between edges.

The operation of several first-order interpolators is presented in Figure 23.1-2. In the interpolator of Figure 23.1-2*a* straight line segments spanning all pixel values are fitted within the error tolerance without restrictions as to the start and stop coordinates of the line segments. The computational task of line segment fitting can be simplified somewhat by anchoring the starting point of a line segment to the stopping point of the previous line segment, as shown in Figure 23.1-2*b*. A still simpler version, described in Figure 23.1-2*c*, restricts the start and stop line segment coordinates to pixel values. This type of interpolator is often called a fan interpolator.

Higher-order polynomial functions, such as cubic spline functions, can be utilized for interpolative coding, but the computation involved in the

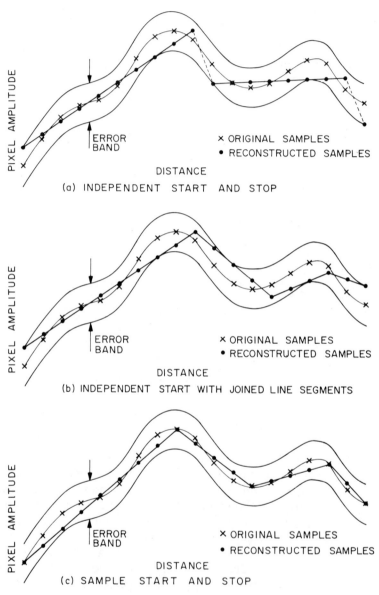

PIXEL AMPLITUDE

ERROR
BAND

× ORIGINAL SAMPLES
• RECONSTRUCTED SAMPLES

DISTANCE

(a) INDEPENDENT START AND STOP

PIXEL AMPLITUDE

ERROR
BAND

× ORIGINAL SAMPLES
• RECONSTRUCTED SAMPLES

DISTANCE

(b) INDEPENDENT START WITH JOINED LINE SEGMENTS

PIXEL AMPLITUDE

ERROR
BAND

× ORIGINAL SAMPLES
• RECONSTRUCTED SAMPLES

DISTANCE

(c) SAMPLE START AND STOP

FIGURE 23.1-2. First-order interpolation.

interpolation process grows rapidly with the degree of the fitting polynomial. Two-dimensional versions of zero- and first-order interpolators can also be formulated. But again, the attendant implementation task is formidable.

There have been some analytical studies (6, 7) of zero- and first-order interpolation for very simple interpolation algorithms. However, analysis for the general algorithms with few constraints is a formidable task. Simulation studies (2, 3) indicate that monochrome image coding down to about 1.0 bits per pixel with a relatively low peak error can be achieved with first-order interpolation, but the coding systems are generally quite complex (8).

23.1.2. Destination Interpolation

A 2-to-1 bandwidth reduction can be obtained simply by transmitting only odd-numbered lines of an image frame, and then artificially generating the even lines by interpolation functions at the receiver. Alternatively, the original image can be sampled in a checkerboard pattern, and the missing pixels can be interpolated at the receiver by a two-dimensional interpolation function. A television processing system utilizing this type of destination interpolation has been developed by Gabor and Hill (9).

Higher-order bandwidth reduction can be achieved by spatially subsampling an image and interpolating the subsamples at the receiver (10). Subsampling can be achieved simply by discarding image samples according to some specified pattern, that is, only transmit the upper left corner pixel of each 4×4 group. However, this strategy leads to aliasing error if the original image is sampled at the Nyquist rate or lower. A better approach is to bandlimit the original image by analog or discrete processing and then resample at the appropriate lower rate. If the subsamples are Nyquist samples, two-dimensional sinc or Bessel interpolation waveforms, as defined in Section 4.1, will provide perfect interpolation. However, as mentioned repeatedly, this type of interpolation is difficult to implement. Practical alternatives discussed in Section 4.3 include zero-order, spline function, and bilinear interpolation.

Figure 21.3-3 contains several computer simulation examples of destination interpolation image coding. In Figures 21.3-3b and 21.3-3c the original 256×256-pixel image has been subsampled by sample deletion to produce a 64×64 array of samples that have been interpolated by zero-order and bilinear interpolation. The examples of Figures 21.3-3d and 21.3-3e are the same except that the 64×64-pixel array of subsamples has been obtained by averaging the pixels in the original image in 4×4 blocks prior to extraction. The aliasing error effect noticeable with the sample deletion strategy is greatly diminished by the sample averaging technique.

(a)

(b)

(c)

(d)

(e)

FIGURE 23.1-3. Examples of destination interpolation image coding—16:1 reduction. (a) 256×256 original. 4×4 interpolation with sample deletion: (b) zero order; (c) bilinear. 4×4 interpolation with 4×4 sample averaging: (d) zero order; (e) bilinear.

23.2. TRANSFORM IMAGE CODING

Transform image coding represents a radical departure from the classical forms of image coding such as PCM, predictive, and interpolative coding in which the image signal is directly coded. The transform image coding process is indirect. A unitary mathematical transform is performed on the image data to produce a set of transform coefficients, which are then quantized and coded for transmission. Transform coding has proved to be an effective and practical means of coding for monochrome, color, and multispectral images for both still pictures and real-time television.

23.2.1. Transform Monochrome Image Coding

In 1968 the concept of coding and transmitting the two-dimensional Fourier transform of a monochrome image, rather than the image itself, was introduced (11, 12). The basic concept of the Fourier transform coding process is that for most natural images may of the transform coefficients are of relatively low magnitude. These coefficients often can be discarded entirely, or coded with a small number of code symbols with only negligible image distortion. Pratt, Andrews, and Kane (13) found in 1969 that the Hadamard transform could be utilized in place of the Fourier transform with a considerable decrease in computational requirements for many applications (14,15). Investigations then began into application of the discrete Karhunen–Loeve (16) and Haar transforms for image coding (17, 18). The Karhunen–Loeve transform, also known as the Hoetelling transform, provides minimum mean-square error coding performance, but unfortunately requires statistical knowledge of the image source and does not possess a fast computational algorithm. On the other hand, the Haar transform has the attribute of an extremely efficient computational algorithm, but usually results in a relatively large coding error. Shibata and Enomoto introduced orthogonal transforms containing a "slant" basis vector for data of vector lengths of four and eight in 1971 (19). The slant vector, a discrete sawtooth waveform decreasing in uniform steps over its length, is suitable for efficiently representing gradual brightness changes in an image line. Pratt, Chen, and Welch subsequently developed a generalized slant transform algorithm for larger size vectors and arrays (20). Ahmed has shown that the cosine transform, which possesses a fast algorithm, approaches the efficiency of the Karhunen–Loeve transform for Markov process image data (21). Jain has suggested a sine transform with similar properties (22).

The basic premise of a monochrome image transform coding system is that the two-dimensional transform of an image has an energy distribution more suitable for coding than the spatial domain representation (23). As a result of the inherent pixel-to-pixel correlation of natural monochrome images, the energy in the transform domain tends to be clustered into a relatively small number of transform samples. Figure 23.2-1 contains displays of the magnitude of transform coefficients for several unitary transforms. To achieve a bandwidth reduction, low-magnitude transform samples can be discarded in an analog transmission system, or grossly quantized in a digital transmission system, without introducing serious image degradation.

Figure 23.2-2 contains a block diagram of a transform coding system for monochrome images. In operation a two-dimensional transform is taken of the image pixels over the entire image, or repeatedly over subsections of the image called blocks. Let $F(j, k)$ denote a block of pixels. For a two-dimensional unitary transform that is orthogonally separable, the transform coefficients are described by

$$\mathscr{F}(u, v) = \sum_{j=1}^{N} \sum_{k=1}^{N} F(j, k) A_C(j, u) A_R(k, v) \qquad (23.2\text{-}1)$$

where $A_R(k, v)$ and $A_C(j, u)$ represent the row and column kernels, respectively. Alternatively, the block of pixels may be described by the matrix **F**. Then in vector-space form the matrix of transform coefficients is given by

$$\mathscr{F} = \mathbf{A}_C \mathbf{F} \mathbf{A}_R \qquad (23.2\text{-}2)$$

Next, the transform domain samples are operated on by a sample selector that decides which samples are to be transmitted. For an analog communication system the selected samples are redistributed uniformly in time and transmitted by analog modulation, while for a digital communication link, the selected samples are quantized, coded, and transmitted in binary form. At the receiver the incoming data is decoded, and an inverse transform is performed to reconstruct the original image.

There are two basic strategies of sample selection: zonal sampling and threshold sampling (24). In zonal sampling the reconstruction is made with a subset of transform samples lying in certain prespecified geometric zones, usually the low-frequency coefficients. For analog transmission the amplitude of each component in the zone is transmitted, while for digital transmission each component in a zone is quantized and assigned a binary code word. The number of quantization levels is usually made proportional to the estimated variance of the component, and the number of code bits made proportional to its expected probability of occurrence. With threshold sampling the image reconstruction is made with a subset of the

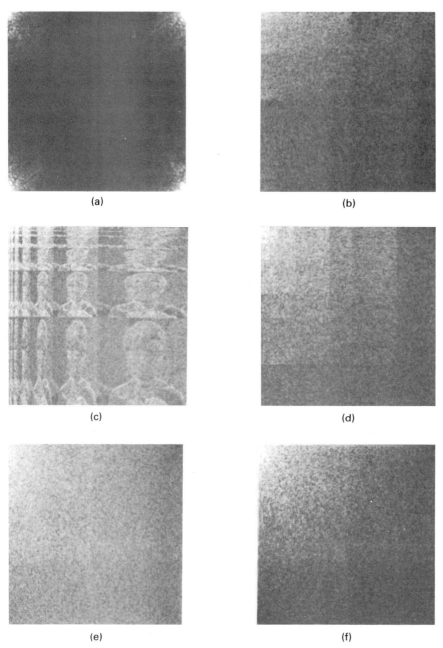

FIGURE 23.2-1. Transform domain logarithm magnitude displays of GIRL picture, 256×256 coefficients. (a) Fourier. (b) Hadamard. (c) Haar. (d) Slant. (e) Cosine. (f) Sine.

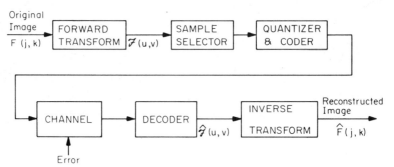

FIGURE 23.2-2.   Transform monochrome image coding system.

samples that are larger than a specified threshold. Since the locations of the significant samples must be communicated, threshold sampling is usually employed only in digital links.

Zonal Sampling

The sample selection process for two zones can be analyzed conveniently by defining a transform domain sampling function $\mathscr{T}(u, v)$, which takes on the value unity for samples to be transmitted and zero for samples to be discarded. The reconstructed image then becomes

$$\hat{F}(j, k) = \sum_{u} \sum_{v} \mathscr{F}(u, v)\mathscr{T}(u, v)A_C(u, j)A_R(k, v) \qquad (23.2\text{-}3)$$

There are several types zones that could logically be employed for zonal sampling; for example, a rectangular, elliptical, or triangular zone. Both analytic and experimental studies (24) have indicated that the optimum zone for a mean-square error criterion is the so-called maximum variance zone in which $\mathscr{T}(u, v)$ is chosen to be unity for those transform samples having the largest variance for a given covariance model of the original image.

For purposes of analysis of transform zonal coding, in the general case of multiple zones, it is convenient to regard the pixels of an image or image block as an N-element vector $\mathbf{f}$, which is a sample of a random process with zero mean and known covariance matrix $\mathbf{K}_f$ (25). This vector undergoes a linear transformation defined by the $N \times N$ − element operator matrix $\mathbf{A}$. The N-element vector $\mathscr{f}$ denotes the one-dimensional transformation of $\mathbf{f}$ as given by

$$\mathscr{f} = \mathbf{Af} \qquad (23.2\text{-}4)$$

Figure 23.2-3 contains a diagram illustrating the generation of the spectral components of a signal and the selection or truncation of these components. The complete vector of spectral components $\mathcal{f}$ is operated on by a $P \times Q$ ($P < Q$) selection matrix $\mathbf{S}$ that extracts certain elements from $\mathcal{f}$ and records them in a P-element vector $\mathcal{f}_T$. The selection matrix contains a unit element at $S(i, j)$ to transfer the jth element of $\mathcal{f}$ to the ith element of $\mathcal{f}_T$. In the system of Figure 23.2-3 the vector $\mathcal{f}_T$ is multiplied by the $Q \times P$ matrix $\mathbf{S}^T$, which transfers $\mathcal{f}_T$ to the proper elements of the transform domain estimate vector $\hat{\mathcal{f}}$ and fills the remaining elements with zeros. In effect, the matrix product $\mathbf{S}^T\mathbf{S}$ replaces the discarded spectral components of $\mathcal{f}$ with zeros. An inverse unitary transform $\mathbf{A}^{-1}$ then reconstructs an estimate

$$\hat{\mathbf{f}} = \mathbf{A}^{-1}\mathbf{S}^T\mathbf{S}\mathbf{A}\mathbf{f} \qquad (23.2\text{-}5)$$

of the signal vector $\mathbf{f}$. The mean-square error $\mathcal{E}$ between the signal vector and its estimate is defined by

$$\mathcal{E} = \text{tr}\,[E\{(\mathbf{f}-\hat{\mathbf{f}})(\mathbf{f}-\hat{\mathbf{f}})^{*T}\}] \qquad (23.2\text{-}6)$$

Substitution of Eq. 23.2-5 into Eq. 23.2-6 gives

$$\mathcal{E} = \text{tr}\,[(\mathbf{I}-\mathbf{A}^{-1}\mathbf{S}^T\mathbf{S}\mathbf{A})\mathbf{K}_f(\mathbf{I}-\mathbf{A}^{-1}\mathbf{S}^T\mathbf{S}\mathbf{A})^{*T}] \qquad (23.2\text{-}7a)$$

or

$$\mathcal{E} = \text{tr}\,[\mathbf{A}^{-1}(\mathbf{I}-\mathbf{S}^T\mathbf{S})\mathbf{K}_{\mathcal{f}}(\mathbf{I}-\mathbf{S}^T\mathbf{S})^{*T}\mathbf{A}] \qquad (23.2\text{-}7b)$$

recognizing that for unitary matrices the correlation matrix in the spatial domain $\mathbf{K}_f$ is related to the correlation matrix in the transform domain $\mathbf{K}_{\mathcal{f}}$ by

$$\mathbf{K}_{\mathcal{f}} = \mathbf{A}\mathbf{K}_f\mathbf{A}^{-1} \qquad (23.2\text{-}8)$$

For square matrices $\text{tr}\,\{\mathbf{X}\ \mathbf{Y}\} = \text{tr}\,\{\mathbf{Y}\ \mathbf{X}\}$. Hence it can be easily shown that

$$\mathcal{E} = \text{tr}\,[\mathbf{K}_{\mathcal{f}}(\mathbf{I}-\mathbf{S}^T\mathbf{S})] \qquad (23.2\text{-}9)$$

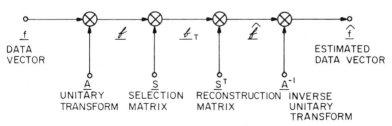

FIGURE 23.2-3. Zonal transform coding operations.

Equation 23.2-9 indicates the simple result that the mean-square error for transform zonal coding is equal to the mean-square energy of the discarded transform coefficients. Thus the mean-square error per pixel can be expressed as

$$\mathcal{E} = \frac{1}{N^2} \sum_u \sum_v E\{\mathcal{F}^2(u, v)\}[1 - \mathcal{T}(u, v)] \tag{23.2-10}$$

where the selection operator $\mathcal{T}(u, v)$ is unity for kept components and zero for discarded components. Hence the mean-square error performance of a unitary transform is determined by its degree of cumulative energy packing. In this regard it has been shown (26, 27) that the Karhunen–Loeve (KL) transform results in the smallest mean-square error for all unitary transforms.

Figure 23.2-4 contains a plot of mean-square error versus block size determined by evaluation of Eq. 23.2-10 for a transform zonal sampled

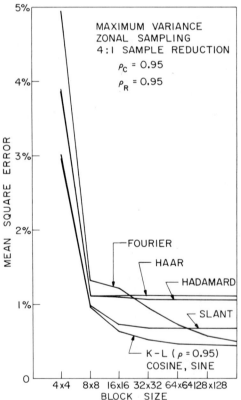

FIGURE 23.2-4. Zonal sampling mean-square error performance of image transforms as a function of block size.

image field statistically model as a first-order two-dimensional Markov process. In this plot the 25% of the transform coefficients with the largest variances have been selected, and the remainder discarded. From the figure it is seen that the Karhunen–Loeve transform provides the lowest mean-square error. For a first-order Markov process the mean-square error obtained by the cosine transform of even size or by the sine transform is nearly identical to that of the optimal KL transform. Also to be noted from Figure 23.2-4 is that, except for the Fourier transform, the rate of decrease in mean-square error for large block sizes becomes quite small after a block size of about 16×16 is reached. The mean-square error level of the Fourier transform converges relatively slowly to that of the KL transform for large block sizes. Figure 23.2-5 shows reconstructions of images for maximum variance zonal sampling in 16×16 blocks for several transforms. Subjectively, the performance rating of these transforms appears to be in accord with the mean-square error estimates of Figure 23.2-4.

Zonal Coding

In the zonal transform coding system a set of zones is established in each transform block. Transform samples in each zone are then quantized with the same number of quantization levels set proportional to the expected variance of the transform coefficients. For a constant-word-length code, $N_B(u, v)$ code bits are assigned to each coefficient, resulting in

$$L(u, v) = 2^{N_B(u, v)} \tag{23.2-11}$$

quantization levels. A total of

$$N_B = \sum_u \sum_v N_B(u, v) \tag{23.2-12}$$

bits are then required to code the picture. The bit assignment $N_B(u, v)$ for each coefficient is set either according to the log-variance relation

$$N_B(u, v) = \frac{N_B}{N^2} + 2 \log_{10}[V_{\mathscr{F}}(u, v)] - \frac{2}{N^2} \sum_{a=1}^{N} \sum_{b=1}^{N} \log_{10}[V_{\mathscr{F}}(a, b)] \tag{23.2-13}$$

derived in Eq. 6.2-11, where $V_{\mathscr{F}}(u, v)$ is the variance of a transform coefficient, or by the sequential bit assignment algorithm described in Chapter 6. If N_B is set low, some coefficients will be assigned no quantization levels, and will therefore be discarded in a manner similar to zonal

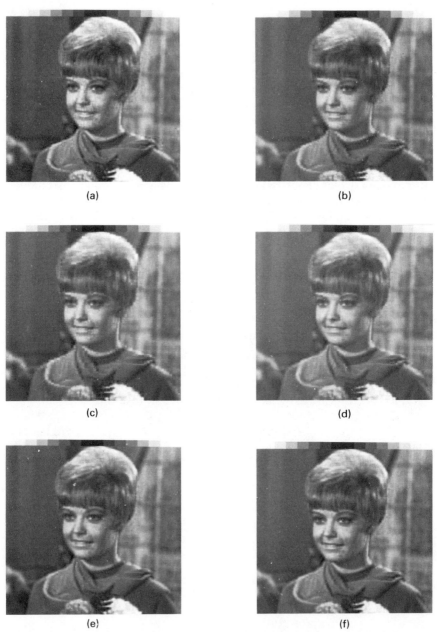

FIGURE 23.2-5. Examples of transform zonal sampling in 16×16 pixel blocks. $4:1$ sample reduction. (a) Fourier. (b) Hadamard. (c) Haar. (d) Slant. (e) Cosine. (f) Karhunen-Loeve.

sampling. Figure 23.2-6 illustrates a typical bit assignment for coding in 16×16 pixel blocks.

8	8	8	7	7	7	5	5	4	4	4	4	4	4	4	4
8	8	7	6	5	5	3	3	3	3	3	2	2	2	2	2
8	7	6	4	4	4	3	3	2	2	2	2	2	2	2	2
7	6	4	3	2	2	2	2	1	1	1	1	0	0	0	0
7	5	4	2	2	2	2	1	1	1	0	0	0	0	0	0
7	5	4	2	2	2	1	1	0	0	0	0	0	0	0	0
5	3	3	2	2	1	1	0	0	0	0	0	0	0	0	0
5	3	3	2	1	1	0	0	0	0	0	0	0	0	0	0
4	3	2	1	1	0	0	0	0	0	0	0	0	0	0	0
4	3	2	1	1	0	0	0	0	0	0	0	0	0	0	0
4	3	2	1	0	0	0	0	0	0	0	0	0	0	0	0
4	3	2	1	0	0	0	0	0	0	0	0	0	0	0	0
4	2	2	0	0	0	0	0	0	0	0	0	0	0	0	0
4	2	2	0	0	0	0	0	0	0	0	0	0	0	0	0
4	2	2	0	0	0	0	0	0	0	0	0	0	0	0	0
4	2	2	0	0	0	0	0	0	0	0	0	0	0	0	0

FIGURE 23.2-6. Typical bit assignments for transform zonal coding in 16×16 pixel blocks at a rate of 1.5 bits per pixel.

For a given number of quantization levels $L(u, v)$ the optimum placement of the quantization decision and reconstruction levels to minimize the mean-square reconstruction error is given by the Max quantization strategy of Chapter 6. Referring to Eq. 6.1-11, the quantization decision levels $\mathscr{D}_j(u, v)$ and reconstruction levels $\mathscr{R}_j(u, v)$ are determined from simultaneous solution of the equations

$$\mathscr{R}_j(u, v) = 2\mathscr{D}_j(u, v) - \mathscr{R}_{j-1}(u, v) \qquad (23.2\text{-}14a)$$

$$\mathscr{R}_j(u, v) = \frac{\int_{\mathscr{D}_j}^{\mathscr{D}_{j+1}} \mathscr{F}(u, v) p[\mathscr{F}(u, v)] \, d\mathscr{F}}{\int_{\mathscr{D}_j}^{\mathscr{D}_{j+1}} p[\mathscr{F}(u, v)] \, d\mathscr{F}} \qquad (23.2\text{-}14b)$$

where $p[\mathscr{F}(u, v)]$ represents the scalar probability density of a transform coefficient at spatial frequency (u, v). This probability density is usually modeled as the Rayleigh density of Eq. 10.12-2 for transform coefficients corresponding to constant basis functions. The Gaussian density of Eq. 10.12-1 provides an accurate model for the remaining transform coefficients. With this quantization and coding strategy, the resultant mean-square error, as derived in Eq. 6.1-12, becomes

$$\mathscr{E} = \sum_{u=0}^{N-1} \sum_{v=0}^{N-1} \left[E\{\mathscr{F}^2(u, v)\} - \sum_{j=0}^{L(u,v)} \mathscr{R}_j^2(u, v) \right.$$
$$\left. \cdot P\{\mathscr{D}_j(u, v) \le \mathscr{F}(u, v) < \mathscr{D}_{j+1}(u, v)\} \right] \qquad (23.2\text{-}15)$$

where $P[\,\cdot\,]$ denotes the probability that the amplitude of a transform coefficient lies between two adjacent decision levels. No exact closed-form solution of Eq. 23.2-15 has been found. Figure 23.2-7 contains a plot of the mean-square error, as computed from Eq. 23.2-15, for several transforms for coding of a two-dimensional Markov array with an average of 1.5 bits per pixel. Simulation results for zonal coding in 16×16 pixel blocks are presented in Figure 23.2-8. It is possible to achieve a slightly lower mean-square error for a given channel rate by employing Huffman coding of the quantized coefficients rather than constant-word-length coding, but the coder will be much more complex to implement.

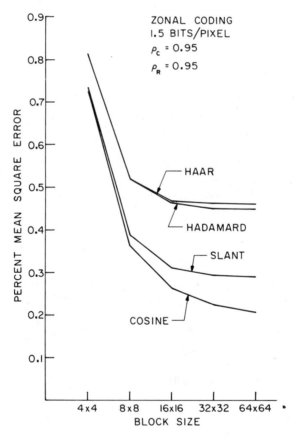

FIGURE 23.2-7.   Zonal coding mean-square error performance of image transforms as a function of block size.

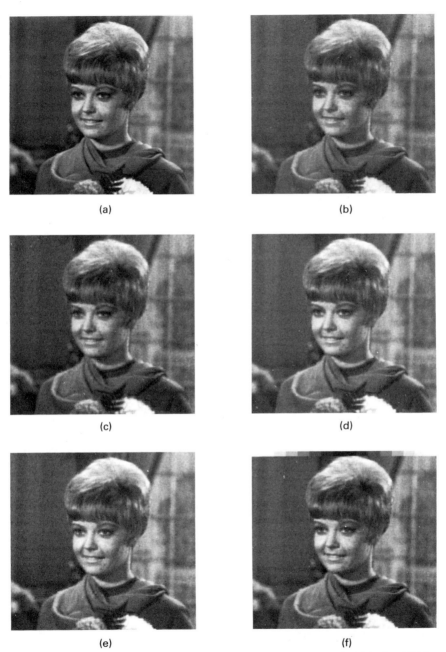

FIGURE 23.2-8. Examples of transform zonal coding in 16×16 pixel blocks, 1.5 bits per pixel. (a) Original. (b) Hadamard. (c) Haar. (d) Slant. (e) Cosine. (f) Karhunen-Loeve.

677

Threshold Coding

In a threshold coding system each sample whose magnitude is greater than a given threshold level is quantized with a fixed number of levels and its amplitude is coded. It is necessary to code the position of each significant sample in the transform plane. A simple, but quite efficient, technique for position coding is to code the number of nonsignificant samples between significant samples. This run length coding scheme can be implemented as follows:

1. The first sample along each line is coded regardless of its magnitude. A position code word of all zeros or all ones affixed to the amplitude provides a line synchronization code group;
2. The amplitude of the second run-length code word is the coded amplitude of the next significant sample. The position code is the binary count of the number of samples of the significant sample from the previous significant sample;
3. If a significant sample is not encountered after scanning the maximum run length of samples, the position and amplitude code bits are set to all ones to indicate a maximum run length.

The advantage of including a line synchronization code group is that it becomes unnecessary to code the line number, and the propagation of channel errors over more than one line is prevented.

Figure 23.2-9 contains simulation results for threshold coding. As expected, because the coding process is adaptive, its performance is somewhat better than the simpler zonal coding process. With standard threshold coding the number of coefficients, and therefore the number of code bits, transmitted is image dependent. A variation of threshold coding, called *N*-largest coding (28), has been developed for communication links in which the transmission bit rate and picture transmission rate is fixed. With this coding algorithm the *N*-largest coefficients in a block are coded regardless of their values. In effect, the threshold is adaptively set for each block to achieve the desired transmission rate.

23.2.2. Adaptive Transform Coding

With the monochrome transform image coding systems described in the previous section the quantizer scale is set before operation to minimize either the expected subjective error or mean-square error. The performance of a basic transform coder can often be improved substantially by monitoring the gray scale activity or short-term statistical changes within an image, and then adaptively rescaling the quantizer in an appropriate manner.

(a)

(b)

(c)

(d)

FIGURE 23.2-9. Hadamard and slant transform threshold coding in 16×16 pixel blocks, quantized transform. (a) Hadamard transform 2.0 bits per pixel. (b) Hadamard transform 1.15 bits per pixel. (c) Slant transform 2.0 bits per pixel. (d) Slant transform 1.15 bits per pixel.

One of the desirable properties of an image transform for purposes of coding is its ability to produce a sequence of nearly uncorrelated coefficients from a highly correlated image field. If this process is performed well, one might expect that knowledge of the neighboring coefficients would not be useful in the quantization of a particular coefficient because the coefficients are nearly uncorrelated. However, it must be remembered that the coefficients are still statistically dependent even though nearly uncorrelated. Thus there is some theoretical basis for adaptive transform coefficient quantization and reconstruction.

Andrews and Tescher (29) have developed an adaptive Fourier transform quantization technique in which the magnitude and phase of each coefficient are adaptively coded. The probability density of the phase $\Phi(u, v)$ is modeled as a uniform density, and the density of the magnitude $\mathcal{M}(u, v)$ is modeled as a Rayleigh density. The number of quantum levels for the phase and magnitude components is set proportional to the variance factor $V_{\mathscr{F}}(u, v)$ with the restriction that the number of phase levels is twice as large as the number of magnitude levels. Since the statistical mean $\bar{\mathcal{M}}(u, v)$ of the coefficient magnitude

$$E\{\mathcal{M}(u, v)\} = \bar{\mathcal{M}}(u, v) = \frac{\pi}{2} V_{\mathscr{F}}(u, v) \qquad (23.2\text{-}16)$$

is proportional to its variance $V_{\mathscr{F}}(u, v)$, estimation of the sample mean of each coefficient provides an estimate of its variance parameter. The estimate of the sample mean $\bar{\mathcal{M}}(u, v)$ is taken as the average of the quantized magnitudes of four neighboring previously quantized coefficients according to the formula

$$\bar{\mathcal{M}}(u, v) = \hat{\mathcal{M}}(u, v-1) + \hat{\mathcal{M}}(u-1, v-1) + \hat{\mathcal{M}}(u-1, v)$$
$$+ \hat{\mathcal{M}}(u-1, v+1) \qquad (23.2\text{-}17)$$

This adaptive coding technique has also been extended to the coding of Hadamard transform coefficients. Simulation results exhibit lower mean-square error and better subjective quality than obtained by nonadaptive coding.

Tasto and Wintz (30, 31) have studied an adaptive transform coding system in which image blocks are classified into three categories according to luminance activity, and blocks of each category are matched to the category statistics. The categories chosen are:

1. Blocks with a significant amount of detail;
2. Lighter than average blocks with little detail;
3. Darker than average blocks with little detail.

Similar methods have been developed by Chen (32) and by Cox and Tescher (33). Simulation of these adaptive methods has shown that an additional compression factor of $2:1$ can be obtained over a well-designed nonadaptive coder; however, adaptive coders are generally quite complex to implement.

23.2.3. Transform Color Image Coding

Figure 23.2-10 contains a block diagram of a transform color image coding system (34). In this system the color image is represented by three source tristimulus signals $R(j, k)$, $G(j, k)$, $B(j, k)$ that specify the red, green, and blue content of a pixel at coordinate (j, k) according to the National Television System Commission (NTSC) receiver phosphor primary system. The source tristimulus signals are then converted to a new three-dimensional space $Y(j, k)$, $I(j, k)$, $Q(j, k)$, which specify the luminance and the chrominance information of the image pixel according to the NTSC television transmission primary system. The conversion is defined by

$$\begin{bmatrix} Y(j, k) \\ I(j, k) \\ Q(j, k) \end{bmatrix} = \begin{bmatrix} 0.299 & 0.587 & 0.114 \\ 0.596 & -0.274 & -0.322 \\ 0.211 & -0.523 & 0.312 \end{bmatrix} \begin{bmatrix} R(j, k) \\ G(j, k) \\ B(j, k) \end{bmatrix} \quad (23.2\text{-}18)$$

The reason for transform coding the Y, I, Q signals rather than the $R\,G\,B$ signals is that the Y, I, Q signals are reasonably well uncorrelated, and most of the color image energy is compacted into the Y plane. This permits a more efficient design of the quantizers. Table 23.2-1 compares the energy distribution of the $R\,G\,B$ and $Y\,I\,G$ color planes. The converted signals then individually undergo a two-dimensional transform, which results in three transform domain planes $\mathcal{Y}(u, v)$, $\mathcal{I}(u, v)$, $\mathcal{Q}(u, v)$ obtained from

$$\mathcal{Y} = \mathbf{AYA}^T \quad (23.2\text{-}19a)$$

$$\mathcal{I} = \mathbf{AIA}^T \quad (23.2\text{-}19b)$$

$$\mathcal{Q} = \mathbf{AQA}^T \quad (23.2\text{-}19c)$$

where $\mathbf{A}$ is the transform matrix. Note that since the coordinate conversion and spatial transformation are linear operations, their order may be

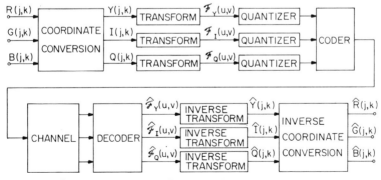

FIGURE 23.2-10. Transform color image coding system.

reversed. Next, the transform samples are quantized with the number of quantum levels made proportional to the expected variance of each pixel, and with the quantization level spacing allowed to be variable to minimze the mean-square quantization error. The quantized samples $\hat{\mathcal{Y}}(u, v)$, $\hat{\mathcal{I}}(u, v)$, and $\hat{\mathcal{Q}}(u, v)$ are then coded and transmitted over a channel. At the receiver the channel output is decoded and inverse transforms are taken to obtain

$$\hat{\mathbf{Y}} = \mathbf{A}^T \hat{\mathcal{Y}} \mathbf{A} \qquad (23.2\text{-}20a)$$

$$\hat{\mathbf{I}} = \mathbf{A}^T \hat{\mathcal{I}} \mathbf{A} \qquad (23.2\text{-}20b)$$

$$\hat{\mathbf{Q}} = \mathbf{A}^T \hat{\mathcal{Q}} \mathbf{A} \qquad (23.2\text{-}20c)$$

Finally, an inverse coordinate conversion results in the reconstructed tristimulus signals

$$\begin{bmatrix} \hat{R}(j, k) \\ \hat{G}(j, k) \\ \hat{B}(j, k) \end{bmatrix} = \begin{bmatrix} 1.000 & 0.956 & 0.621 \\ 1.000 & -0.272 & -0.647 \\ 1.000 & -1.106 & 1.703 \end{bmatrix} \begin{bmatrix} \hat{Y}(j, k) \\ \hat{I}(j, k) \\ \hat{Q}(j, k) \end{bmatrix} \qquad (23.2\text{-}21)$$

TABLE 23.2-1. Energy compaction of coordinate conversions

Test Image	Coordinate System	Percentage of σ_1^2	Percentage of σ_1^2	Percentage of σ_3^2
Girl	RGB	45.14	35.41	19.45
	YIQ	78.32	17.54	4.14
	$K_1K_2K_3$	85.84	12.10	2.06
Couple	RGB	51.55	31.09	17.36
	YIQ	84.84	13.81	1.35
	$K_1K_2K_3$	92.75	6.46	0.79

The coordinate conversion from the R, G, B color space to the YIQ color space can be considered along with the spatial transforms as a three-dimensional transformation. The coordinate conversion provides an energy compaction between color planes, and the spatial transforms provide an energy compaction within the color planes. Adopting this philosophy, the optimal three-dimensional transform would be a Karhunen–Loeve transformation which completely decorrelates the $3N^2$ color image components. It has been shown (34) that the Y, I, Q coordinate conversion provides almost as high an energy compaction for color images as does a Karhunen–Loeve color coordinate conversion. This result is verified by the color image energy distribution of the two color images described in Table 23.2-1.

In order optimally to design the transform color image coder it is necessary to specify some analytic measure of color image fidelity; unfortunately, no standard fidelity measures exist. As a rational alternative, the design procedure usually selected is to design the transform domain quantization system to minimize the mean-square error between the YIQ and $\hat{Y}\hat{I}\hat{Q}$ color planes as defined by

$$\mathscr{E} = \frac{1}{3N^2}\sum_j\sum_k\{[Y(j,k)-\hat{Y}(j,k)]^2+[I(j,k)-\hat{I}(j,k)]^2$$
$$+[Q(j,k)-\hat{Q}(j,k)]^2\} \tag{23.2-22}$$

Several variations of the quantization procedure have been investigated. A highly effective implementation has been found to be:

1. Model the row and column covariance matrices of R, G, B as first-order Markov processes and compute the variances of the elements of Y, I, Q;
2. Model the probability density of the constant basis vector component of $\mathscr{Y}$ by a Rayleigh density, and the probability of the other basis vector components of $\mathscr{Y}, \mathscr{I}, \mathscr{Q}$ by Gaussian densities with variances computed in (1);
3. Assign

$$L_Y(u,v)=2^{N_Y(u,v)} \tag{23.2-23a}$$

$$L_I(u,v)=2^{N_I(u,v)} \tag{23.2-23b}$$

$$L_Q(u,v)=2^{N_Q(u,v)} \tag{23.2-23c}$$

quantization levels to each transform component where the number of bits alloted to each component is made proportional to the logarithm of its variance computed in (1);
4. The total number of bits alloted to a color image is set at

$$N_B = N_{BY} + N_{BI} + N_{BQ} \tag{23.2-24}$$

where

$$N_{BY} = \sum_{u=1}^{N}\sum_{v=1}^{N} N_Y(u,v) \tag{23.2-25a}$$

$$N_{BI} = \sum_{u=1}^{N}\sum_{v=1}^{N} N_I(u,v) \tag{23.2-25b}$$

$$N_{BQ} = \sum_{u=1}^{N}\sum_{v=1}^{N} N_Q(u,v) \tag{23.2-25c}$$

5. For a given value of N_B select trial values of N_{BY}, N_{BI}, N_{BQ} then compute quantization levels from (3), and with the probability density models of (2), perform a variable spacing quantization of each transform component using the Max quantization rule;

6. For representative color images compute the mean-square error, and by iterative search techniques, determine optimum bit allocations for transform planes.

It should be noted that the above procedure need not be performed dynamically for every color image to be coded. The optimization need only be performed for typical color images to be coded to obtain a quantization scale that can be designed into the quantizer hardware.

Figure 23.2–11 contains a plot of the mean-square error versus N_{BI} for several values of N_{BY} and a fixed value N_B for the girl image. The optimum average bit allocation for this test image is found to be $N_{BY} = 1.25$, $N_{BI} =$

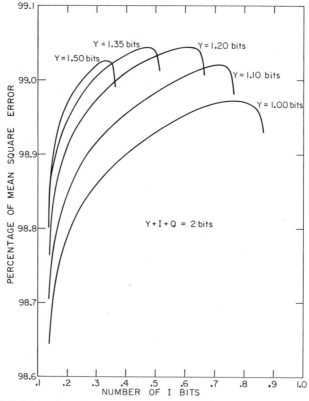

FIGURE 23.2-11.   Quantization error for various color plane bit assignments.

0.55, $N_{BQ} = 0.20$. The optimum allocation does not change appreciably for other images or total bit allotments.

Figure 23.2-12 provides results of a computer simulation of the slant transform image coding system for coding at an average rate of 2.0 bits per pixel. Monochrome photographs of the R, G, B and Y, I, Q components of a color image are shown in Figure 23.2-12a and 23.2-12b. It should be noted that visually the R, G, B components are highly correlated. Figure 23.2-12c, containing photographs of the log magnitude of each transform plane for transformation in 16×16 pixel blocks, illustrates the spatial energy compaction within each plane. Reproductions of Y, I, Q and R, G, B after zonal coding are shown in Figure 23.2-12d and 23.2-12e, respectively. The R, G, B reconstructions exhibit some degradation as a result of the coding process, but the visual effect of the degradation is much less visible in the color reconstruction because of the spatial frequency limitations of the human visual system.

Another approach to transform color image coding, explored by Enomoto and Shibata (35), is to transform code the composite color television signal composed of the luminance component frequency interleaved with the chrominance components. The Fourier frequency spectrum of the composite signal contains a concentration of a signal energy about the chrominance subcarrier frequency. Therefore, the high-frequency or -sequency transform coefficients tend to be large and should be assigned more quantization levels than for a monochrome television signal. Good quality coding has been obtained at coding rates of 3.0 to 4.0 bits per pixel with this technique.

23.2.4. Transform Interframe Coding

In most natural television imagery there is a great deal of correlation in the temporal direction between frames as well as spatial correlation. Three-dimensional transform coding can be utilized to provide decorrelation and energy compaction between frames and within each frame.

Let $F(j, k, i)$ denote a block of $J \times K \times I$ pixels extracted from a sequence of I image frames. The separable three-dimensional unitary transform of this block is defined as

$$\mathscr{F}(u, v, w) = \sum_{j=1}^{J} \sum_{k=1}^{K} \sum_{i=1}^{I} F(j, k, i) A_C(j, u) A_R(k, v) A_T(i, w)$$

$$(23.2\text{-}26)$$

where $A_C(j, u)$, $A_R(k, v)$, and $A_T(i, w)$ are the column, row, and temporal transform kernels, respectively. In an interframe transform coding system each coefficient is coded following a zonal sampling, zonal coding, or

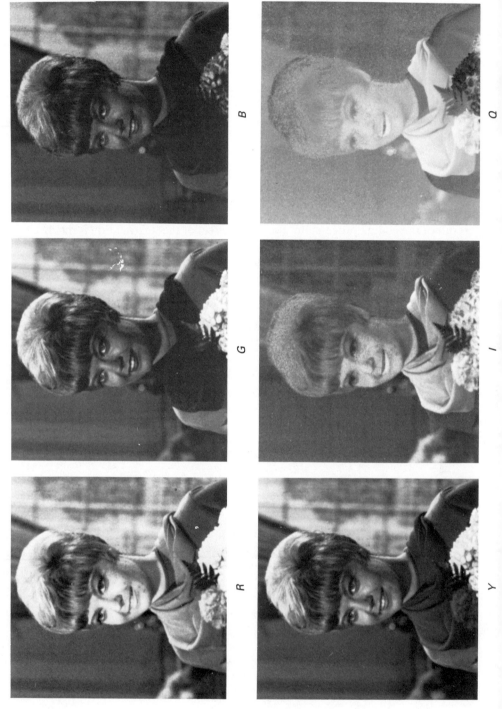

B

Q

G

I

R

Y

686

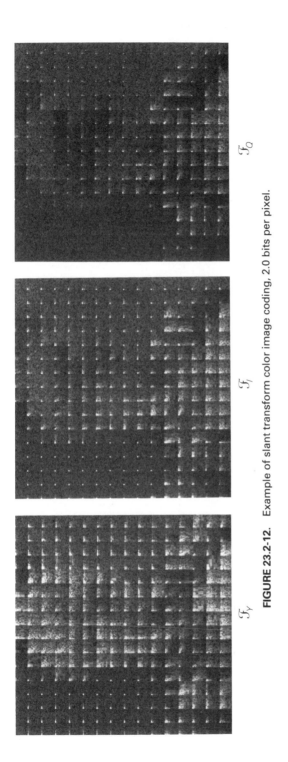

$\mathcal{F}_Y$ $\mathcal{F}_I$ $\mathcal{F}_Q$

FIGURE 23.2-12. Example of slant transform color image coding, 2.0 bits per pixel.

687

$\hat{a}$
0.20 bits per pixel.

$\hat{i}$
0.55 bits per pixel.

$\hat{y}$
1.25 bits per pixel.

688

$\hat{B}$

$\hat{G}$

FIGURE 23.2-12. (*Continued*)

$\hat{R}$

threshold coding strategy using design techniques similar to those of two dimensional transform coding. The reconstructed transform coefficients at the receiver $\hat{\mathcal{F}}(u, v, w)$ are then inverse transformed to produce a reconstructed pixel block $\hat{F}(j, k, i)$.

Any unitary transform can be utilized for the temporal direction of interframe transform coding provided that the frame dimension I is compatable with the transform, for example, $I = 2, 4, 8, \ldots$. The Fourier transform phase-shifting property may be potentially useful for image coding. Since the Fourier transform of a scene containing a translated object differs from the transform of the original scene only by a phase shift of each transform coefficient, it is theoretically possible to perform transform coding on the magnitude and phase of the original scene, and then subsequently code only the phase changes of coefficients in following frames. The mean-square error ranking of the various unitary transforms for interframe transform coding is the same as for two-dimensional coding. Figures 23.2-13 and 23.2-14 contain curves of the theoretical mean-square coding error for interframe coding of a three-dimensional Markov process source as a function of block size for zonal sampling and zonal coding strategies (36).

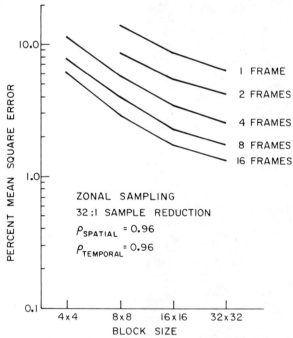

FIGURE 23.2-13. Zonal sampling mean-square error performance as a function of block size for interframe cosine transform coding.

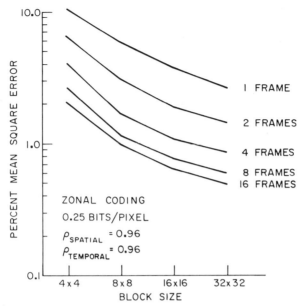

FIGURE 23.2-14. Zonal coding mean-square error performance as a function of block size for interframe cosine transform coding.

Tescher and Andrews (29) have investigated use of Fourier and Hadamard transforms for interframe image coding. In the systems studied each frame was transform coded over its entire area and a sequence of four spatial transform planes was transform coded in the temporal direction. On a sequence of picture telephone images, computer simulations with the Fourier transform resulted in coding at about 0.25 bits per pixel with about 2.0% mean-square error, and at 0.5 bits per pixel with about 1.0% mean-square error. Coding results obtained with the Hadamard transform were not as good as for the Fourier transform.

Roese et al. (37) have studied three-dimensional Fourier and Cosine transform coding over $16 \times 16 \times 16$ cubes of pixels for imagery containing camera and subject motion. Excellent results, as indicated in Figure 23.2-15, have been obtained at coding rates down to 0.25 bits per pixel.

23.3. TRANSFORM CODING QUANTIZATION ERROR REDUCTION

In transform image coding one of the major coding techniques is to transmit only those transform coefficients that lie in some geometrical zone in the transform domain; these are usually the low-frequency components.

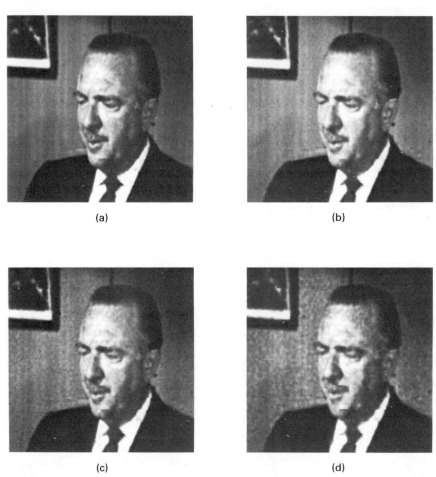

(a)   (b)

(c)   (d)

FIGURE 23.3-15. Examples of cosine transform interframe coding—frame No. 16. (a) 1.0 bits per pixel per frame, NMSE = 0.16%. (b) 0.5 bits per pixel per frame, NMSE = 0.30%. (c) 0.25 bits per pixel per frame, NMSE = 0.49%. (d) 0.1 bits per pixel per frame, NMSE = 0.88%.

At the receiver it has been common practice to insert zeros for missing components before the inverse transformation operation. It is possible, however, to utilize knowledge of the correlation of the received transform coefficients to estimate the missing coefficients rather than arbitrarily setting their values to zero. This coefficient restoration process is called spectrum extrapolation (38). Another coding algorithm employed for transform coding is to allocate a number of quantization levels to coefficients based on their expected variance. This quantization process, of course, introduces error. Normally, in transform coding the quantization error is simply accepted. Since, however, the quantized coefficients are correlated, it is possible to perform a type of spectral interpolation to reduce quantization error (39).

Spectrum Extrapolation

Figure 23.3-1 contains a diagram describing the transform zonal coding process for image reconstruction by spectral extrapolation. In the zonal coding process the image vector $\mathbf{f}$ is transformed by a unitary matrix $\mathbf{A}$ resulting in the vector of transform coefficients $\mathbf{\mathcal{f}}$. Multiplication by the $P \times Q$ ($P < Q$) selection matrix $\mathbf{S}$ results in the $P \times 1$ truncated vector $\mathbf{\mathcal{f}}_T$ of transform samples. At the decoder the vector $\mathbf{\mathcal{f}}_T$ is multiplied by a restoration matrix $\mathbf{W}$ that generates an estimate of the discarded spectral coefficients. An inverse unitary transform $\mathbf{A}^{-1}$ then reconstructs an estimate $\hat{\mathbf{f}}$ of the image vector $\mathbf{f}$. The estimator matrix $\mathbf{W}$ is chosen to minimize the mean-square error between the image vector and its estimate. The optimum choice of $\mathbf{W}$ can be found by forcing the dynamic error $(\mathbf{f} - \hat{\mathbf{f}})$ to be orthogonal to the observation $\mathbf{f}_T$. Thus by setting

$$E\{(\mathbf{f}-\hat{\mathbf{f}})\mathbf{\mathcal{f}}_T^{*T}\} = \mathbf{0} \tag{23.3-1}$$

one obtains

$$E\{(\mathbf{f} - \mathbf{A}^{-1}\mathbf{W}\mathbf{S}\mathbf{f})(\mathbf{S}\mathbf{A}\mathbf{f})^{*T}\} = \mathbf{0} \tag{23.3-2}$$

This leads directly to the optimum solution

$$\mathbf{W} = \mathbf{A}\mathbf{K}_f\mathbf{A}^{-1}\mathbf{S}^T[\mathbf{S}\mathbf{A}\mathbf{K}_f\mathbf{A}^{-1}\mathbf{S}^T]^{-1} \tag{23.3-3}$$

provided that the matrix inverse exists. Analysis of the structure of $\mathbf{W}$ indicates that it copies the elements of $\mathbf{\mathcal{f}}_T$ into the appropriate elements of $\hat{\mathbf{\mathcal{f}}}$; the remaining elements of $\hat{\mathbf{\mathcal{f}}}$ are, in general, obtained by a linear combination of the elements of $\mathbf{\mathcal{f}}_T$. In essence, the estimator linearly

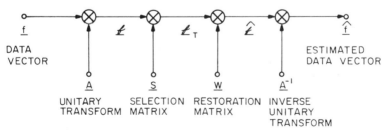

FIGURE 23.3-1. Transform spectrum extrapolation operation.

extrapolates the values of the observation of known spectral components to determine the unknown spectral values. The usual alternative to spectrum extrapolation, described by Eq. 23.2-5, is simply to set the values of the discarded spectral components to zero by multiplying f_T by $\mathbf{S}^T$, and then to perform an inverse transformation.

When the optimal restoration matrix of Eq. 23.3-3 is employed for spectral estimation, the resulting mean-square error is found to be

$$\mathscr{E}_O = \mathrm{tr}[\mathbf{K}_f \, (\mathbf{I}_N - \mathbf{WS})] \qquad (23.3\text{-}4)$$

Figure 23.3-2 contains a plot of the mean-square error of estimated spectral components for the Haar and Hadamard transforms. In this example

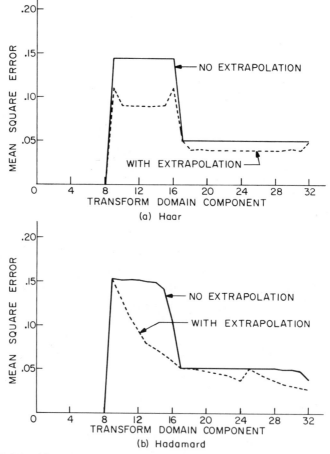

FIGURE 23.3-2.   Mean-square error reduction by spectrum extrapolation for Haar and Hadamard transforms. Markov process with $\rho = 0.95$, $N = 32$, $M = 8$.

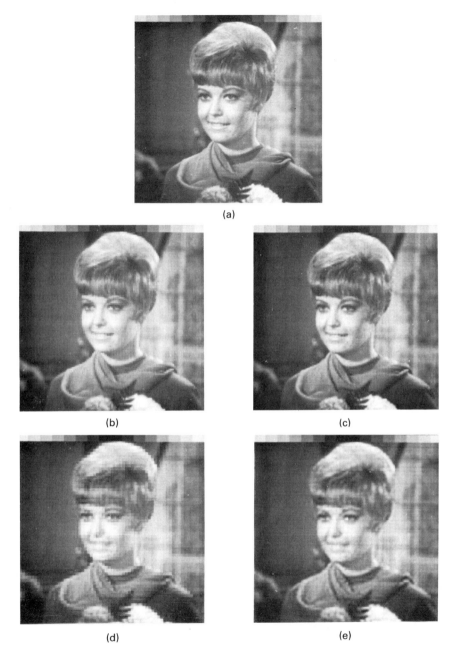

FIGURE 23.3-3. Hadamard transform spectrum extrapolation examples. (a) Original. (b) 4 : 1 zonal selection. (c) 4 : 1 zonal selection spectrum extrapolation. (d) 10 : 1 zonal selection. (e) 10 : 1 zonal selection spectrum extrapolation.

the data are assumed to be generated by a first-order Markov process with a correlation factor of $\rho = 0.95$. Computer simulation experiments have been performed to evaluate the spectrum extrapolation process for image coding. In the experiment illustrated in Figure 23.3-3 the original image of Figure 23.3-3a has been Hadamard transformed in 16×16 blocks, and the coefficients lying outside of a 5×5 low-sequency zone have been set to zero before the inverse transformation resulting in Figure 23.3-3b. In Figure 23.3-3c the coefficients outside the zone have been extrapolated assuming the image to be a sample of a first-order Markov process. The improvement in subjective quality is readily apparent from the photographs.

Spectrum Interpolation

With a variable quantization level assignment algorithm for transform coding, the vector of transform coefficients f is examined element by element, and a vector of code symbols **d** is formed to denote the decision band occupied by an element. Normally the reconstruction is performed on an element-by-element basis, that is, the kth decision symbol $d(k)$ reconstructs the kth coefficient $\hat{f}(k)$ for $k = 1, 2, \ldots, N^2$ coefficients. Spectrum interpolation utilizes the vector **d** to generate the reconstructed vector $\hat{f}$ following the vector quantization procedure derived in Section 6.2. First, a decision region D_j in the N^2-dimensional space of transform coefficients is determined according to the state of the received decision level vector **d**. Then the reconstructed vector of transform coefficients is found from solution of the equation

$$\hat{f} = \frac{\int_{D_i} f p(f) \, df}{\int_{D_i} p(f) \, df} \tag{23.3-5}$$

where $p(f)$ represents the joint probability density of transform coefficients. Evaluation of Eq. 23.3-5 is quite difficult except for a few special cases. If the joint density is Gaussian and the quantization is not too gross, Eq. 23.3-5 can be reduced to a closed-form approximate solution (40). An approximate recursive solution has been obtained by Huhns for the Gaussian case for an arbitrary quantization scale (39).

23.4. HYBRID TRANSFORM/DPCM CODING

Transform and predictive image coding systems both operate according to the same principle: the decorrelation of a naturally correlated image field to produce a sequence of variables that are then individually quantized and coded. For transform coding the sequence of decorrelated variables is produced by projection of the image data to a new vector space, while predictive coding entails feedback prediction and differencing. Transform coding and DPCM coding have comparative advantages and disadvantages. Two-dimensional transform coding provides a lower mean-square error reconstruction than predictive coding at low coding rates; however, a transform coder is usually much more complex to implement than a DPCM coder. Habibi (41) has proposed a hybrid transform/DPCM image coding method that possesses many of the theoretical attributes of two-dimensional transform coding, but is simpler to implement.

Figure 23.4-1 contains a descriptive block diagram of an intraframe hybrid transform/DPCM image coder. In operation, a one-dimensional transform is taken along each image line of the $N \times N$ image block $F(j, k)$ yielding a sequence of transform coefficients

$$\mathcal{f}_j(v) = \sum_{k=0}^{N-1} F(j, k)A(k, v) \qquad (23.4\text{-}1)$$

where $A(k, v)$ is the transform kernel. Transform coefficients then enter a bank of DPCM coders that perform previous element predictive coding along columns of the original image. In practice, a single adaptive DPCM coder could be time shared between columns. The DPCM coder forms the difference signal

$$d(v) = \mathcal{f}_j(v) - \hat{\mathcal{f}}_j(v) \qquad (23.4\text{-}2)$$

with the transform coefficient estimate being formed by a weighting of the coefficient from the previous line according to the equation

$$\hat{\mathcal{f}}_j(v) = a_j \hat{\mathcal{f}}_{j-1}(v) \qquad (23.4\text{-}3)$$

where a_j is a weighting constant. The quantized difference signals from the DPCM coders are then coded and time multiplexed for transmission. At the receiver DPCM decoding is first performed to produce the reconstructed transform coefficients $\hat{\mathcal{f}}_j(v)$. Next, an inverse transformation is performed to obtain the reconstructed image field as given by

$$F(j, k) = \sum_{v=0}^{N-1} \mathcal{f}_j(v)B(k, v) \qquad (23.4\text{-}4)$$

where $B(k, v)$ is the inverse transform kernel.

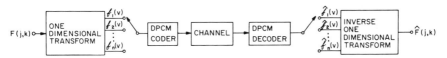

FIGURE 23.4-1. Hybrid transform/DPCM monochrome image coding system.

For a given transform the design variables of the hybrid coder are the number and placement of the quantization levels. One design procedure is to model the image field as a two-dimensional stochastic process with known covariance function. The one-dimensional transform coefficients are then modeled as Gaussian variates, and the DPCM difference signals as variates with an exponential distribution whose variances are directly related to the variances of the transform coefficients. Then Max's algorithm can be utilized to select quantization reconstruction and decision levels to minimize the mean-square reconstruction error.

Figure 23.4-2 illustrates the mean-square error of hybrid transform-DPCM coding as a function of average source rate for several transforms. As expected, the hybrid cosine transform system provides best performance, but the performance difference with other transforms is not great. Figure 23.4-3 contains several pictures coded by the hybrid transform-DPCM coding technique. Subjectively, the performance is quite good down to coding rates of about 1.0 bits per pixel, and in some applications, the results may be adequate at coding rates as low as 0.5 bits per pixel.

The concept of hybrid transform/DPCM coding has been applied to interframe coding by Roese et al. (37, 42). One approach is to perform a one-dimensional transform along each line and perform DPCM between the corresponding coefficients of sequential frames. Better performance is obtained with two-dimensional transforms within a frame and DPCM

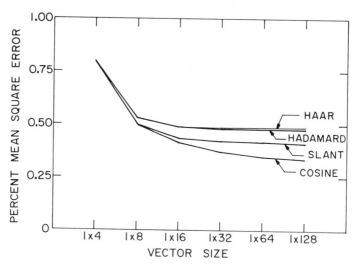

FIGURE 23.4-2.   Intraframe hybrid transform/DPCM mean-square error performance of image transforms as a function of block size.

(a)   (b)

(c)

FIGURE 23.4-3. Examples of hybrid transform/DPCM intraframe image coding at 1.0 bits/pixel and vector length 16. (a) Hadamard/DPCM. (b) Cosine/DPCM. (c) Karhunen-Loeve/DPCM.

coding of the interframe coefficients. Figure 23.4-4 provides examples of adaptive hybrid interframe coding utilizing a cosine transform in 16×16 pixel blocks.

23.5. FEATURE CODING

In the perception of a scene a human observer does not perform a quantitative analysis of the luminance or tristimulus values at each pixel point. Rather, it seems that an observer searches for distinguishing image features

(a)

(b)

(c)

(d)

FIGURE 23.4-4.   Examples of cosine transform/DPCM adaptive interframe coding—
frame No. 16. (a) 1.0 bits per pixel per frame. NMSE = 0.022%. (b) 0.5 bits per pixel per
frame. NMSE = 0.067%. (c) 0.25 bits per pixel per frame. NMSE = 0.186%. (d) 0.1 bits
per pixel per frame. NMSE = 0.625%.

such as edges or textural regions, and somehow mentally forms these
features into recognizable groupings. These symbolic groupings are then
compared at some level to an enormous memory bank of stored image
representations to interpret the scene. Under this assumption it is logical to
consider the efficient coding of pictorial features rather than pixel arrays.
Image coding techniques based on the coding of luminance contours,
edges, and texture regions have been proposed.

23.5.1. Luminance Contour Coding

A quantized image may be considered to be composed of layers of planes each of constant gray level. The image may then be represented by the boundaries or contours of the gray levels in each plane. Figure 23.5-1 illustrates the contours of a typical region within an image.

Wintz, Wilkins, and Gattis (43–45) have investigated methods of tracing image contours by a computer and efficiently encoding the contour traces for transmission. The basic premise of contour coding as a means of bandwidth compression is that an image will contain a relatively small number of contours compared to its total number of pixels. Furthermore, it is hoped that it will be more efficient to code the perimeters of the pixel areas of constant gray level than the pixel values themselves. Computer simulations have indicated that by statistical coding of the contours it is possible to achieve a 7:1 compression for black or white images and a 1.5:1 compression of images with 16 to 32 gray levels (46). Contour coding is a rather complex process, however, and suited only for rather low picture transmission rates.

A clever method of coding binary image boundaries has been developed by Freeman (47, 48). The coding method does not necessarily seek to produce an efficient code in the sense of minimizing the number of code bits required to describe a boundary, but rather provides a code that possesses some manipulative properties. That is, if the code for a boundary is known, it is possible to compute measures of the bounded region such as area, maximum height, maximum width, perimeter, and so on.

A chain code example is illustrated in Figure 23.5-2. Each chain is composed of line segments connecting adjacent pixels in a horizontal, vertical, or diagonal direction. A vertical line connecting four pixels, for example, would have the code 222. In the example of Figure 23.5-2 a closed boundary is chain coded from an arbitrary starting point, which is the pixel closest to the lower left corner of the picture.

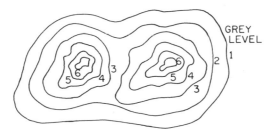

FIGURE 23.5-1. Example of gray level contours.

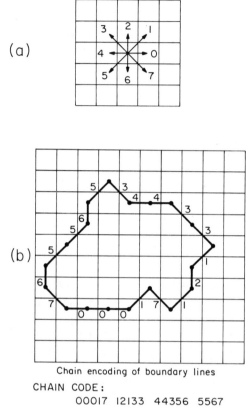

Chain encoding of boundary lines
CHAIN CODE:
00017 12133 44356 5567
FIGURE 23.5-2. Example of basic chain coding (48).

Completely enclosed boundary regions can be coded with a simple modification to the basic chain coding procedure. The outer boundary is first chain coded in a normal manner. When this boundary has been closed, a code group 0401 is inserted in the chain code, and an "invisible line" connecting the two boundaries is encoded. When the second boundary is reached, the code group 0402 is inserted in the chain code to indicate the end of the invisible line. The inner boundary is then chain coded in a normal manner. The prefix 04 of the "invisible chain follows" code group 0401 and the "visible chain follows" code group 0402 normally designates the rarely occurring event of a right shift followed by a left shift. This legitimate event is then coded as 0404. The prefix 04 is also used with other suffix codes to indicate a variety of special cases such as gray scale and color coding.

23.5.2. Edge Coding

It is well known that a human observer depends heavily on the recognition of edges for visual image interpretation. Furthermore, testing has indicated that, although a human viewer possesses a high degree of sensitivity to edge positional errors, moderately large amplitude errors can be tolerated. These experimental observations have served as the basis of several one- and two-dimensional edge coding schemes (49, 52).

In 1958 Schreiber, Knapp, and Kay (49, 50) introduced an edge coding technique called synthetic highs in which a scanned video signal is divided into its high- and low-frequency components by electrical filters. Figure 23.5-3 illustrates the frequency components of a pulse element of a video signal. In the coding system the low-frequency component is sampled at its Nyquist rate, which is much less than the Nyquist rate of the original video signal. The high-frequency signal is not directly sampled; edge amplitude values of the image signal are detected and transmitted by some suitable coding method. At the receiver the high-frequency component of the original video signal is synthesized by a tapped delay line circuit and added to the decoded low-frequency component. For digital transmission a bandwidth reduction is possible because the low-frequency signal can be sampled at a reduced rate, and the edges, which occur relatively infrequently, can be grossly quantized. In practice, the performance of the synthetic highs system is limited by difficulties of reliable edge detection in the presence of video signal noise.

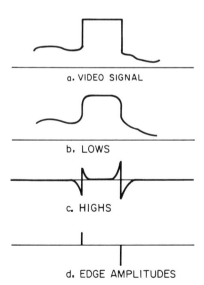

a. VIDEO SIGNAL

b. LOWS

c. HIGHS

d. EDGE AMPLITUDES   **FIGURE 23.5-3.** Video signal components.

Graham (51) has extended the synthetic highs concept to two dimensions. In this coding system the lows signal can be obtained by two-dimensional low-pass filtering or by image sampling with a large aperture. Edge points can be isolated by gradient or Laplacian edge detection followed by a boundary linking process. Simulation studies indicate that coding can be obtained down to about 0.25 bits per pixel on images with little detail. The major drawback of the system is implementation complexity.

23.5.3. Texture Coding

Many images can be segmented into disjoint regions each of reasonably constant texture. It is also possible to synthesize textural regions. Hence,

(a)   (b)

(c)   (d)

FIGURE 23.5-4. Example of texture coding. (a) TANK. (b) TANK outline. (c) Reconstruction with gray background. (d) Reconstruction with texture background.

for image coding applications, one could conceivably code the texture measures of a texture segmented image, and then synthesize the texture in each region at the decoder. Figure 23.5-4 provides a computer simulation example of the process. Research is presently underway on both the efficient analysis and synthesis of texture.

23.6. SYMBOLIC CODING

Transform coding techniques represent an image as a weighted set of two-dimensional unitary basis functions. This concept can be generalized to include image representation by weighted amounts of any two-dimensional patterns or symbols.

23.6.1. Area Character Coding

Altemus and Schaphorst (53) have investigated a form of symbolic pattern coding for binary images, called area character coding. In this system an

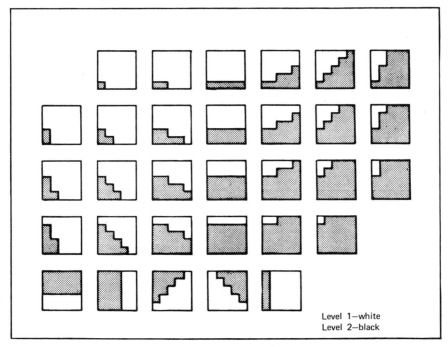

FIGURE 23.6-1. Vocabulary of characters.

image is divided into 5×5 blocks, and the black or white patterns are compared to a vocabulary of the 31 patterns shown in Figure 23.6-1. If a pattern matches an entry, a 5-bit code is transmitted; if no pattern match is found, the 25 block pixel values are transmitted along with a 5-bit prefix code to distinguish the event. Compression ratios of about $10:1$ have been reported for sparse facsimile documents (53). The extension to gray scale imagery is not favorable because of the large number of patterns that may exist.

23.6.2. SVD Coding

The matrix singular value decomposition (SVD) technique, described in Section 5.2, can be applied to image coding. From Eqs. 5.2-1 and 5.2-3 the SVD transform relations of an image matrix $\mathbf{F}$ are given by

$$\Lambda^{1/2} = \mathbf{U}^T \mathbf{F} \mathbf{V} \qquad (23.6\text{-}1a)$$

$$\mathbf{F} = \mathbf{U}\Lambda^{1/2}\mathbf{V}^T \qquad (23.6\text{-}1b)$$

where $\mathbf{U}$ and $\mathbf{V}$ are unitary matrices containing eigenvectors of $\mathbf{FF}^T$ and $\mathbf{F}^T\mathbf{F}$, respectively, and Λ is a diagonal matrix whose terms are the corresponding eigenvalues. The SVD transform of Eq. 23.6-1b may be regarded as a symbolic representation of an image block F in terms of a set of basis plane luminance patterns $\mathbf{u}_j \mathbf{v}_j^T$ according to the relation of Eq. 5.2-6 given by

$$\mathbf{F} = \sum_{j=1}^{N} \lambda^{1/2}(j)\mathbf{u}_j \mathbf{v}_j^T \qquad (23.6\text{-}2)$$

where $\lambda(j)$ is the jth diagonal element of Λ and $\mathbf{u}_j$ and $\mathbf{v}_j$ are column eigenvectors of $\mathbf{U}$ and $\mathbf{V}$, respectively. For most natural images the singular values $\lambda(j)$ drop off in magnitude quite rapidly, and therefore the series expansion can be truncated without much error. This process is analogous to zonal sampling for unitary transform coding. The remaining singular values must then be individually quantized and coded for transmission. It is also necessary to code the eigenvectors $\mathbf{u}_j$ and $\mathbf{v}_j$ because they are image dependent.

  Andrews and Patterson (54) have evaluated the SVD image coding method for images coded in 16×16 blocks using a minimum mean-square error coding strategy for the singular values and eigenvectors. Simulation results indicate that coding at 2.0 bits per pixel can be achieved with about a 1.0% error. This performance is somewhat poorer than for conventional transform coding.

REFERENCES

1. L. W. Gardenhire, "Redundancy Reduction, the Key to Adaptive Telemetry," National Telemetering Conference, Los Angeles, California, 1964.

2. C. M. Kortman, "Redundancy Reduction: A Practical Method of Data Compression," *Proc. IEEE*, **55**, 3, March 1967, 253–263.

3. D. Hochman, H. Katzman, and D. R. Weber, "Application of Redundancy Reduction to Television Bandwidth Compression," *Proc. IEEE*, **55**, 3, March 1967, 263–267.

4. C. A. Andrews, J. M. Davies, and G. R. Schwarz, "Adaptive Data Compression," *Proc. IEEE*, **55**, 3, March 1967, 267–277.

5. C. M. Kortman, "Data Compression by Redundancy Reduction," *IEEE Spectrum*, **4**, March 1967, 133–139.

6. L. Ehrman, "Analysis of Some Redundancy Removal Bandwidth Compression Techniques," *Proc. IEEE*, **55**, 3, March 1967, 278–287.

7. L. D. Davisson, "Data Compression Using Straight Line Interpolation," *IEEE Trans. Inf. Theory*, **IT-14**, 3, May 1968, 390–394.

8. S. A. Sheldahl, "Comparison of Hardware Requirements for Polynomial Data Compressions," Proceedings National Telemetering Conference, Washington, D.C., 1968.

9. D. Gabor and P. C. J. Hill, "Television Bandwidth Compression by Contour Interpolation," *Proc. IEE*, **108**, Part B, 39, May 1961, 634, 303–315.

10. H. C. Andrews, "Digital Interpolation of Discrete Images," *IEEE Trans. Computers*, **C-25**, 2, February 1976, 196–202.

11. H. C. Andrews and W. K. Pratt, "Fourier Transform Coding of Images," Hawaii International Conference on System Science, January 1968, 677–679.

12. G. B. Anderson and T. S. Huang, "Piecewise Fourier Transformation for Picture Bandwidth Compression," *IEEE Trans. Commun.* **COM-20**, 3, June 1972, 488–491.

13. H. C. Andrews, J. Kane, and W. K. Pratt, "Hadamard Transform Image Coding," *Proc. IEEE*, **57**, 1, January 1969, 58–68.

14. W. K. Pratt and H. C. Andrews, "Application of Fourier–Hadamard Transformation to Bandwidth Compression," in *Picture Bandwidth Compression*, T. S. Huang and O. J. Tretiak, Eds., Gordon and Breach, New York, 1972, 515–554.

15. J. W. Woods and T. S. Huang, "Picture Bandwidth Compression by Linear Transformation and Block Quantization," in *Picture Bandwidth Compression*, T. S. Huang and O. J. Tretiak, Eds., Gordon and Breach, New York, 1972, 555–573.

16. A. Habibi and P. A. Wintz, "Image Coding by Linear Transformation and Block Quantization," *IEEE Trans. Commun. Tech.*, **COM-19**, 1, February 1971, 50–63.

17. H. C. Andrews, *Computer Techniques in Image Processing*, Academic Press, New York, 1970.

18. K. R. Rao, M. A. Narasimhan, and K. Revuluri, "Image Data Processing by Hadamard-Haar Transforms," *IEEE Trans. Computers*, **C-23**, 9, September 1975, 888–896.

19. H. Enomoto and K. Shibata, "Orthogonal Transform Coding System for Television Signals," *IEEE Trans. Electromagnetic Compatibility*, Special Issue on Walsh Functions, **EMC-13**, 3, August 1971, 11–17.

20. W. K. Pratt, W. H. Chen, and L. R. Welch, "Slant Transform Image Coding," *IEEE Trans. Commun.*, **COM-22**, 8, August 1974, 1075–1093.

21. N. Ahmed, T. Natarajan, and K. R. Rao, "On Image Processing and a Discrete Cosine Transform," *IEEE Trans. Computers*, **C-23**, 1, January 1974, 90–93.

22. A. K. Jain, "A Fast Karhunen–Loeve Transform for Finite Discrete Images," Proceedings National Electronics Conference, Chicago, Illinois, October 1974, 322–328.

23. H. C. Andrews and W. K. Pratt, "Transform Image Coding," in *Proceedings Computer Processing in Communications*, Polytechnic Press, New York, 1969, 63–84.

24. P. A. Wintz, "Transform Picture Coding," *Proc. IEEE*, **60**, 7, July 1972, 809–823.

25. W. K. Pratt, "Transform Coding Spectrum Extrapolation," Proceedings Hawaii Systems Science Conference, January 1974.

26. H. P. Kramer and M. V. Mathews, "A Linear Coding for Transmitting a Set of Correlated Signals," *IRE Trans. Inf. Theory*, **IT-2**, September 1956, 41–46.

27. J. J. Y. Huang and P. M. Schulteiss, "Block Quantization of Correlated Gaussian Random Variables," *IEEE Trans. Commun. Syst.*, **CS-11**, 3, September 1963, 289–296.

28. J. J. Reis, R. T. Lynch, and J. Butman, "Haar Transform Video Bandwidth Reduction System for RPVs," Proceedings SPIE Conference on Advances in Image Transmission Techniques, San Diego, California, August 1976.

29. H. C. Andrews and A. G. Tescher, "The Role of Adaptive Phase Coding in Two and Three Dimensional Fourier and Walsh Image Compression," Proceedings Walsh Function Symposium, Washington, D.C., March 1974.

30. M. Tasto and P. A. Wintz, "A Bound on the Rate-Distortion Function and Application to Images," *IEEE Trans. Inf. Theory*, **IT-18**, 1, January 1972, 150–159.

31. M. Tasto and P. A. Wintz, "Image Coding by Adaptive Block Quantization," *IEEE Trans. Commun. Tech.*, **COM-19**, 6, December 1971, 957–972.

32. W. Chen, "Adaptive Coding of Color Images Using Cosine Transform," Proceedings International Communications Conference, Philadelphia, June 1976, 47-7 to 47-13.

33. R. V. Cox and A. G. Tescher, "Channel Rate Equalization Techniques for Adaptive Transform Coders," Proceedings SPIE Conference on Advances in Image Transmission Techniques, San Diego, August 1976.

34. W. K. Pratt, "Spatial Transform Coding of Color Images," *IEEE Trans. Commun. Tech.*, **COM-19**, 6, December 1971, 980–982.

35. H. Enomoto and K. Shibata, "Orthogonal Transform Coding System for Television Signals," Applications of Walsh Function Symposium, Washington, D.C., 1971, 11–17.

36. J. A. Rose and W. K. Pratt, "Theoretical Performance Models for Interframe Transform and Hybrid Transform/DPCM Coders," Proceedings SPIE Conference on Advances in Image Transmission Techniques, San Diego, August 1976.

37. J. A. Roese et al., "Interframe Transform Coding and Predictive Coding Methods," IEEE International Communications Conference, San Francisco, California, June 1975.

38. W. K. Pratt, "Transform Image Coding Spectrum Extrapolation," Proceedings Hawaii Systems Science Conference, January 1974.

39. M. N. Huhns, "Optimum Restoration of Quantized Correlated Signals," University of Southern California, Image Processing Institute, USCIPI 600, August 1975.

40. R. E. Curry, *Estimation and Control with Quantized Measurements*, M.I.T. Press, Cambridge, Mass., 1970.

41. A. Habibi, "Hybrid Coding of Pictorial Data," *IEEE Trans. Computers*, **COM-22**, 5, May 1974, 614–624.

42. J. A. Roese, W. K. Pratt, and G. S. Robinson, "Interframe Cosine Transform Image Coding," *IEEE Trans. Commun.*, **COM-25**, 11, November 1977.

43. J. L. Gattis and P. A. Wintz, "Automated Techniques for Data Analysis and Transmission," Purdue University, School of Engineering, Report TR-EE-37, August 1971.

44. L. C. Wilkins and P. A. Wintz, "A Contour Tracing Algorithm for Data Compression of Two Dimensional Data," Purdue University, School of Engineering, Report TR-EE-69-3, January 1969.

45. P. A. Wintz and L. C. Wilkins, "Studies on Data Compression, Part I: Picture Coding by Contours, Part II: Error Analysis of Run-Length Codes," Purdue University, School of Engineering, Report TR-EE-70-17, September 1970.

46. L. C. Wilkins and P. A. Wintz, "Image Coding By Coding Contours," Proceedings International Conference on Communications, San Franciso, Vol. 1, 1970.

47. H. Freeman, "On the Encoding of Arbitrary Geometric Configurations," *IRE Trans. Electronic Computers*, **EC-10**, 2, June 1961, 260–268.

48. H. Freeman, "Boundary Encoding and Processing," in *Picture Processing and Psychopictorics*, B. S. Lipkin and A. Rosenfeld, Eds., Academic Press, New York, 1970, 241–266.

49. W. F. Schreiber and C. F. Knapp, "TV Bandwidth Reduction by Digital Coding," *IRE National Convention Record*, **6**, Part 4, 1958, 88–89.

50. W. F. Schreiber, C. F. Knapp, and N. D. Kay, "Synthetic Highs: An Experimental TV Bandwidth Reduction System," *J. Soc. Motion Picture and Television Engineers*, **68**, August 1959, 525–537.

51. D. N. Graham, "Image Transmission by Two-Dimensional Contour Coding," *Proc. IEEE*, **55**, 3, March 1967, 336–346.

52. W. F. Schreiber, T. S. Huang, and O. J. Tretiak, "Contour Coding of Images," in *Picture Bandwidth Compression*, T. S. Huang and O. J. Tretiak, Eds., Gordon and Breach, New York, 1972, 443–448.

53. W. C. Altemus and R. A. Schaphorst, "Data Conversion Equipment," Philco Corporation Report No. ASD TDR 62-392, AD 275 514, May 1962.

54. H. C. Andrews and C. L. Patterson, "Singular Value Decomposition (SVD) Image Coding," *IEEE Trans. Commun.*, **COM-24**, 4, April 1976, 425–432.

24 IMAGE CODING
PERFORMANCE ANALYSIS

Chapter 24 is devoted to a performance assessment of the major image coding methods described in Part 6. The effects of channel errors are determined both theoretically and experimentally. Theoretical rate-distortion bounds are established for several image coding techniques, and the predicted and measured performance of practical image coding systems is compared to these bounds.

24.1. CHANNEL ERROR MODELS (1–4)

If digital images are to be transmitted over a communication channel subject to transmission errors, consideration should be given to the effect of channel errors and means of source and channel coding to combat such error effects. The problem is many faceted: it depends on the type of images to be transmitted and their use, the error criterion, the methods of source and channel coding, and the statistical model for the communication channel.

Several statistical models have been utilized to predict the performance of digital communication channels. The simplest and most widely employed model is the binary symmetric channel (BSC) model in which the state of a transmitted bit is reversed with probability p and left unchanged with probability $1-p$. In a BSC bit errors are assumed independent of one another. Burst error channels, in which errors occur in clumps, are also encountered in practice. In order to simplify the analysis of such channels, the error bursts are often assumed to be of fixed length and independent. That is, an error burst of M bits is assumed to occur with probability p according to a BSC model. The analysis of channel error effects on image transmission presented in this chapter is limited to the simple binary symmetric channel.

Consider an $N \times 1$ binary number k that represents a single linearly quantized image amplitude component. This input to the binary symmetric channel is defined as

$$k = \sum_{i=0}^{N-1} k_i 2^i \qquad (24.1\text{-}1)$$

where $k_i \in \{0, 1\}$. The channel output is given by

$$h = \sum_{i=0}^{N-1} h_i 2^i \tag{24.1-2}$$

where $h_i \in \{0, 1\}$, and the channel error is defined as $\mathcal{E} = h - k$. In analyzing the effects of channel errors on image transmission the prime interest is the expected luminance or color shift and the variance of the shift rather than the average luminance or color of an image point. Therefore the statistics of interest of a single image component are the first and second conditional moments of the output binary number.

The probability distribution of an output number h conditioned on the input number k is given by the geometric distribution

$$P\{h|k\} = p^{[N-M\{h,k\}]}(1-p)^{M\{h,k\}} \tag{24.1-3}$$

where $M\{h, k\}$ is the number of bit matches between h and k obtained from

$$M\{h, k\} = \sum_{i=0}^{N-1} [h_i k_i + (1-h_i)(1-k_i)] \tag{24.1-4}$$

For no channel errors $P\{h, k\} = \delta(h - k)$, and for $p = 0.5$ the output number is uniformly distributed, $P\{h, k\} = 2^{-N}$. The latter case is of interest in predicting the convergence point of an error shift.

The conditional mean of the output number can be expressed in terms of the conditional mean of each bit of the output number as

$$E\{h|k\} = \sum_{i=0}^{N-1} 2^i E\{h_i|k_i\} \tag{24.1-5}$$

During transmission the channel input bit k_i is reversed in state to $1 - k_i$ with probability p and kept in the same state k_i with probability $1 - p$. Therefore, the conditional mean of the channel output is

$$E\{h_i|k_i\} = p(1 - k_i) + (1 - p)k_i \tag{24.1-6}$$

On summing the series

$$E\{h|k\} = (1 - 2p)k + p(2^N - 1) \tag{24.1-7}$$

The conditional second moment of the output number is given by

$$E\{h^2|k\} = E\left\{ \left[\sum_{i=0}^{N-1} h_i 2^i \right]^2 \Big| k \right\} = \sum_{i=0}^{N-1} \sum_{j=0}^{N-1} 2^{i+j} E\{h_i h_j | k_i k_j\} \tag{24.1-8}$$

For $i \neq j$

$$E\{h_i h_j | k_i k_j\} = (1-p)^2 k_i k_j + (1-p)pk_i(1-k_j) + p(1-p)(1-k_i)k_j \\ + p^2(1-k_i)(1-k_j) \tag{24.1-9}$$

and for $i = j$

$$E\{h_i^2|k_i\} = (1-p)k_i^2 + p(1-k_i)^2 \qquad (24.1\text{-}10)$$

Then on summation of the series

$$E\{h^2|k\} = [k(1-2p) + p(2^N-1)]^2 + \left(\frac{4N-1}{3}\right)p(1-p) \quad (24.1\text{-}11)$$

and the conditional variance becomes

$$\sigma^2\{h|k\} = \left(\frac{4^N-1}{3}\right)p(1-p) \qquad (24.1\text{-}12)$$

There are other representations in addition to the simple binary code that could be employed for signal representation. In most applications the optimum code will be the code that minimizes the variance of the error given in Eq. 24.1-12. Huang et al. (3), who have investigated this problem, did not find any code, including the gray or reflected binary code, that provided a smaller error variance than the straight binary code.

24.2. PCM MONOCHROME IMAGE CODING CHANNEL ERROR EFFECTS (4)

Figure 24.2-1 contains a model for the analysis of channel errors for monochrome luminance transmission. The luminance signal Y, assumed normalized to a range $[0, 1]$, is linearly quantized between 0 and $2^N - 1$ according to the relation

$$Y_T = Y(2^N - 1) \qquad (24.2\text{-}1)$$

and then rounded to its nearest integer value. After passing through the binary symmetric channel the coded luminance value Y_T' is rescaled to yield

$$Y' = \frac{Y_T'}{2^N - 1} \qquad (24.2\text{-}2)$$

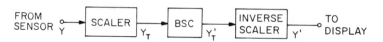

FIGURE 24.2-1.   Model for analysis of luminance channel errors.

The nth conditional moment of Y' with respect to the transmitted luminance component Y_T can be obtained by direct computation of

$$E\{(Y')^n|Y_T\} = \sum_{Y_T'=0}^{2^N-1} [Y'\{Y_T'\}]^n P\{Y_T'|Y_T\} \qquad (24.2\text{-}3)$$

where the conditional probability distribution is given by Eq. 24.1-3. However, since the forward and inverse scaling operations are linear, the conditional moments of the luminance shift can be easily obtained in terms of the conditional moments of the BSC. The conditional mean luminance shift is

$$E\{Y'|Y_T\} = \frac{E\{Y_T'|Y_T\}}{2^N-1} \qquad (24.2\text{-}4)$$

Also, from Eq. 24.1-7

$$E\{Y'|Y_T\} = \frac{(1-2p)Y_T}{2^N-1} + p \qquad (24.2\text{-}5)$$

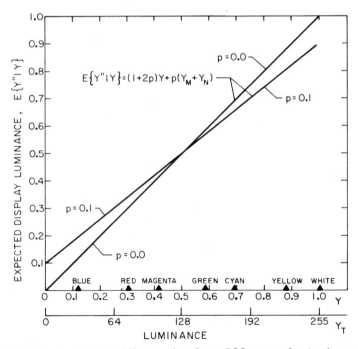

FIGURE 24.2-2. Luminance shift resulting from BSC errors for luminance transmission.

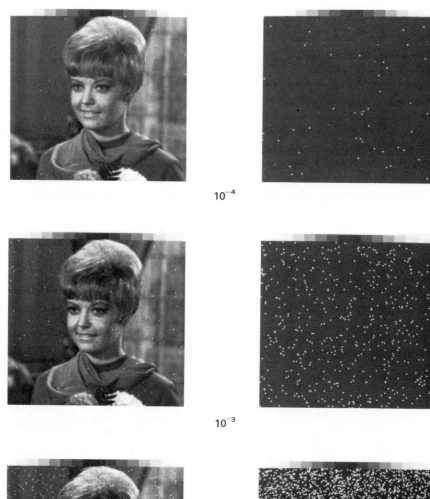

10^{-4}

10^{-3}

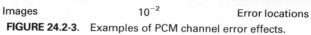

Images 10^{-2} Error locations
FIGURE 24.2-3. Examples of PCM channel error effects.

714

Similarly, from Eq. 24.1-12, the variance in the luminance shift is found to be

$$\sigma^2\{Y'|Y_T\} = \left(\frac{4^N - 1}{3}\right)\frac{p(1-p)}{(2^N - 1)^2} = \left(\frac{2N+1}{3}\right)p(1-p) \quad (24.2\text{-}6)$$

Figure 24.2-2 contains a plot of the mean luminance shift as a function of the coded luminance value Y_T and the corresponding input luminance Y. The mean luminance shift is away from high contrast values toward a midgray level.

Several examples of PCM channel error effects for monochrome images are presented in Figure 24.2-3. PCM channel errors are often described as "salt and pepper" noise because of the discrete appearance of erroneous black pixels in white surrounds and white pixels in black backgrounds. Subjectively, PCM channel errors are usually tolerable down to error rates of 10^{-3} (1, 5).

24.3 PCM COLOR IMAGE CODING CHANNEL ERROR EFFECTS (4)

In the evaluation of the effect of channel errors on the transmission of color images, two cases have been considered: transmission of tristimulus values and transmission of the luminance plus two chromaticity values. For both cases channel errors are referenced to the image luminance Y and the Uniform Chromaticity Scale (UCS) chromaticity values u, v. Figure 24.3-1 defines the two transmission systems.

24.3.1. Tristimulus Channel Input

In the tristimulus transmission system of Figure 24.3-1a the source tristimulus values (R, G, B), normalized to a range $[0, 1]$, are linearly converted to a set of transmission tristimulus values

$$\begin{bmatrix} T_1 \\ T_2 \\ T_3 \end{bmatrix} = \begin{bmatrix} m_{11} & m_{12} & m_{13} \\ m_{21} & m_{22} & m_{23} \\ m_{31} & m_{32} & m_{33} \end{bmatrix} \begin{bmatrix} R \\ G \\ B \end{bmatrix} \quad (24.3\text{-}1)$$

where the m_{ij} are constants. Each tristimulus component T_i is then linearly quantized over its maximum T_{iM}, and its minimum T_{iN} values to a binary number between 0 and $2^N - 1$ according to the relation

$$T_{iT} = \left(\frac{T_i - T_{iN}}{T_{iM} - T_{iN}}\right)(2^N - 1) \quad (24.3\text{-}2)$$

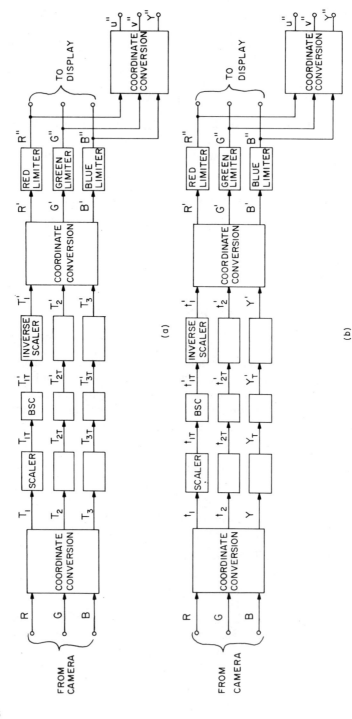

FIGURE 24.3-1. Models for analysis of channel errors. (a) $T_1 T_2 T_3$ transmission. (b) Y, $t_1 t_2$ transmission.

where T_{iT} is truncated to its lowest integer value. The received tristimulus components T'_{iT} are then inversely scaled to obtain

$$T'_i = \left(\frac{T_{iM} - T_{iN}}{2^N - 1}\right) T'_{iT} + T_{iN} \qquad (24.3\text{-}3)$$

Next, a coordinate conversion is made to produce the received red, green, blue trisimulus values (R', G', B'). As a result of channel errors, the values of (R', G', B') may exceed the display system range $[0, 1]$, and hence it is necessary to limit their values to produce display tristimulus values (R'', G'', B'') corresponding to physically reproducible colors.

In Figure 24.3-1 the display (R'', G'', B'') tristimulus values are converted to the Uniform Chromaticity Scale (UCS) luminance value Y'' and chromaticity coordinates (u'', v'') according to the relations

$$Y'' = \lambda_1 R'' + \lambda_2 G'' + \lambda_3 B'' \qquad (24.3\text{-}4)$$

$$u'' = \frac{\eta_1 R'' + \eta_2 G'' + \eta_3 B''}{\eta_4 R'' + \eta_5 G'' + \eta_6 B''} \qquad (24.3\text{-}5)$$

$$v'' = \frac{\eta_7 R'' + \eta_8 G'' + \eta_9 B''}{\eta_4 R'' + \eta_5 G'' + \eta_6 B''} \qquad (24.3\text{-}6)$$

where the λ_k and η_k are constants for a conversion from the R, G, B coordinate system to UCS coordinates.

Color shifts are then determined by evaluation of the conditional moments of Y'', u'', and v''. The nth conditional moment of u'' with respect to the transmitted color components $\{M\} = \{T_{1T}, T_{2T}, T_{3T}\}$ can be obtained by direct computation of

$$E\{(u'')^n|M\} = \sum_{T'_{1T}=0}^{2^N-1} \sum_{T'_{2T}=0}^{2^N-1} \sum_{T'_{3T}=0}^{2^N-1} [u''\{T'_{1T}, T'_{2T}, T'_{3T}\}]^n P\{T'_{1T}|T_{1T}\}$$

$$\cdot P\{T'_{2T}|T_{2T}\}P\{T'_{3T}|T_{3T}\} \qquad (24.3\text{-}7)$$

Similar expressions are obtained for $E\{(v'')^n|M\}$ and $E\{(Y'')^n|M\}$.

The conditional distributions $P\{T'_{iT}|T_{iT}\}$ can be computed from Eq. 24.1-3, and the function u'' (or v'' or Y'') in the summations can be evaluated for all combinations of T_{iT}. Unfortunately, direct computation of the conditional moments for large N is usually quite lengthy.

If the channel error probability is small, the conditional probability distributions $P\{T'_{iT}|T_{iT}\}$ will be narrowly distributed about their mean values. In such an instance the probabilities that (R', G', B') exceed their respective limits will be quite small. It is then possible to obtain the conditional means of u'', v'', and Y'' in approximate form (5, p. 212) by neglecting the limiters and writing expressions for u'' and Y'' directly in terms of the channel output variables T'_{iT}. Thus

$$u'' \approx \frac{a_1 T'_{1T} + a_2 T'_{2T} + a_3 T'_{3T} + a_4}{a_5 T'_{1T} + a_6 T'_{2T} + a_7 T'_{3T} + a_8} \tag{24.3-8}$$

$$v'' \approx \frac{a_9 T'_{1T} + a_{10} T'_{2T} + a_{11} T'_{3T} + a_{12}}{a_5 T'_{1T} + a_6 T'_{2T} + a_7 T'_{3T} + a_8} \tag{24.3-9}$$

$$Y'' \approx a_{13} T'_{1T} + a_{14} T'_{2T} + a_{15} T'_{3T} + a_{16} \tag{24.3-10}$$

where

$$a_1 = \beta_1 (T_{1M} - T_{1N})$$

$$a_2 = \beta_2 (T_{2M} - T_{2N})$$

$$a_3 = \beta_3 (T_{3M} - T_{3N})$$

$$a_4 = (2^N - 1)(\beta_1 T_{1N} + \beta_2 T_{2N} + \beta_3 T_{3N})$$

$$a_5 = \beta_4 (T_{1M} - T_{1N})$$

$$a_6 = \beta_5 (T_{2M} - T_{2N})$$

$$a_7 = \beta_6 (T_{3M} - T_{3N})$$

$$a_8 = (2^N - 1)(\beta_4 T_{1N} + \beta_5 T_{2N} + \beta_6 T_{3N})$$

$$a_9 = \beta_7 (T_{1M} - T_{1N})$$

$$a_{10} = \beta_8 (T_{2M} - T_{2N})$$

$$a_{11} = \beta_9 (T_{3M} - T_{3N})$$

$$a_{12} = (2^N - 1)(\beta_7 T_{1N} + \beta_8 T_{2N} + \beta_9 T_{3N})$$

$$a_{13} = \frac{\gamma_1 (T_{1M} - T_{1N})}{2^N - 1}$$

$$a_{14} = \frac{\gamma_2 (T_{2M} - T_{2N})}{2^N - 1}$$

$$a_{15} = \frac{\gamma_3 (T_{3M} - T_{3N})}{2^N - 1}$$

$$a_{16} = \gamma_1 T_{1N} + \gamma_2 T_{2N} + \gamma_3 T_{3N}$$

The β_k and γ_k are constants for a conversion from the transmission-tristimulus coordinate system to the UCS coordinates. Now, expanding u'', v'', and Y'' in a Taylor series about their mean values and keeping terms of up to second order, one obtains approximate expressions for the mean values of the displayed chromaticity and luminance components. Thus*

$$E\{u''|M\} = \frac{a_1 E\{T'_{1T}|T_{1T}\} + a_2 E\{T'_{2T}|T_{2T}\} + a_3 E\{T'_{3T}|T_{3T}\} + a_4}{a_5 E\{T'_{1T}|T_{1T}\} + a_6 E\{T'_{2T}|T_{2T}\} + a_7 E\{T'_{3T}|T_{3T}\} + a_8}$$

$$+ \tfrac{1}{2}\sigma^2\{T'_{1T}|T_{1T}\}\left[\frac{\partial^2 u''}{\partial T'^2_{1T}}\right] + \tfrac{1}{2}\sigma^2\{T'_{2T}|T_{2T}\}\left[\frac{\partial^2 u''}{\partial T'^2_{2T}}\right]$$

$$+ \tfrac{1}{2}\sigma^2\{T'_{3T}|T_{3T}\}\left[\frac{\partial^2 u''}{\partial T'^2_{3T}}\right] \qquad (24.3\text{-}11)$$

and

$$E\{Y''|M\} = a_{13} E\{T'_{1T}|T_{1T}\} + a_{14} E\{T'_{2T}|T_{2T}\} + a_{15} E\{T'_{3T}|T_{3T}\} + a_{16} \qquad (24.3\text{-}12)$$

where $E\{T'_{iT}|T_{iT}\}$ and $\sigma^2\{'_{iT}|T_{iT}\}$ are the conditional mean and variance of each channel output as given by Eqs. 24.1-7 and 24.1-12. In a similar manner the conditional variances of u'' and Y'' are found to be

$$\sigma^2\{u''|M\} \approx \sigma^2\{T'_{1T}|T_{1T}\}\left[\frac{\partial u''}{\partial T'_{1T}}\right]^2$$

$$+ \sigma^2\{T'_{2T}|T_{2T}\}\left[\frac{\partial u''}{\partial T'_{2T}}\right]^2 + \sigma^2\{T'_{3T}|T_{3T}\}\left[\frac{\partial u''}{\partial T'_{3T}}\right]^2 \qquad (24.3\text{-}13)$$

and

$$\sigma^2\{Y''|M\} \approx a_{13}^2 \sigma^2\{T'_{1T}|T_{1T}\} + a_{14}^2 \sigma^2\{T'_{2T}|T_{2T}\} + a_{15}^2 \sigma^2\{T'_{3T}|T_{3T}\} \qquad (24.3\text{-}14)$$

24.3.2. Luminance/Chromaticity Channel Input

The exact analysis to obtain the conditional moments of u'', v'', and Y'' for transmission of the luminance and chromaticities of a color is similar to the analysis of the previous section. By direct computation the nth conditional moments are found to be

$$E\{(u'')^n|M\} = \sum_{t'_{1T}=0}^{2^N-1} \sum_{t'_{2T}=0}^{2^N-1} \sum_{Y'_T=0}^{2^N-1} [u''\{t'_{1T}, t'_{2T}, Y'_T\}]^n$$

$$\cdot P\{t'_{1T}|t_{1T}\}P\{t'_{2T}|t_{2T}\}P\{Y'_T|Y_T\} \qquad (24.3\text{-}15)$$

---

* The equation for v'' is of similar form to that for u''.

and similarly for $E\{(v'')^n|M\}$ and $E\{(Y'')^n|M\}$, with u'', v'', and Y'' evaluated for all combinations of the received luminance and chromaticity values. Again, as in the previous section, approximations can be made for a low channel error probability. In this case the effects of limiting can be neglected, and equations for u'', v'', Y'' can be expressed directly in terms of the received channel variables t_{iT}, Y. Hence

$$u'' \approx \frac{a_1 t'_{1T} + a_2 t'_{2T} + a_3}{a_4 t'_{1T} + a_5 t'_{2T} + a_6} \tag{24.3-16}$$

$$v'' \approx \frac{a_7 t'_{1T} + a_8 t'_{2T} + a_9}{a_4 t'_{1T} + a_5 t'_{2T} + a_6} \tag{24.3-17}$$

$$Y'' \approx a_{10} Y'_T + a_{11} \tag{24.3-18}$$

where

$$a_1 = \alpha_1(t_{1M} - t_{1N})$$

$$a_2 = \alpha_2(t_{2M} - t_{2N})$$

$$a_3 = (\alpha_1 t_{1N} + \alpha_2 t_{2N} + \alpha_3)(2^N - 1)$$

$$a_4 = \alpha_4(t_{1M} - t_{1N})$$

$$a_5 = \alpha_5(t_{2M} - t_{2N})$$

$$a_6 = (\alpha_4 t_{1N} + \alpha_5 t_{2N} + \alpha_6)(2^N - 1)$$

$$a_7 = \alpha_1(t_{1M} - t_{1n})$$

$$a_8 = \alpha_8(t_{2M} - t_{2N})$$

$$a_9 = (\alpha_7 t_{1N} + \alpha_8 t_{2N} + \alpha_9)(2^N - 1)$$

$$a_{10} = \frac{Y_M - Y_N}{2^N - 1}$$

$$a_{11} = Y_N$$

where the α_k are constants for a conversion from the transmission chromaticities to UCS chromaticities. It should be noted that the chromaticities u'', v'' are independent of the received luminance value Y'_T, and likewise Y'' is independent of the received chromaticities t'_{1T}, t'_{2T} only if there is no limiting. Making a Taylor series expansion, to an accuracy of second-order moments, the conditional means of u'' and Y'' are found to be

$$E\{u''|M\} = \frac{a_1 E\{t'_{1T}|t_{1T}\} + a_2 E\{t'_{2T}|t_{2T}\} + a_3}{a_4 E\{t'_{1T}|t_{1T}\} + a_5 E\{t'_{2T}|t_{2T}\} + a_6}$$

$$+ \tfrac{1}{2}\sigma^2\{t'_{1T}|t_{1T}\}\left[\frac{\partial^2 u''}{\partial t'^2_{1T}}\right] + \tfrac{1}{2}\sigma^2\{t'_{2T}|t_{2T}\}\left[\frac{\partial^2 u''}{\partial t'^2_{2T}}\right] \qquad (24.3\text{-}19)$$

and

$$E\{Y''|M\} = a_{10}\{Y'_T|Y_T\} + a_{11} \qquad (24.3\text{-}20)$$

Similarly, the conditional variance of u'' and Y'' are

$$\sigma^2\{u''|M\} = \sigma^2\{t'_{1T}|t_{1T}\}\left[\frac{\partial u''}{\partial t'_{1T}}\right]^2 + \sigma^2\{t'_{2T}|t_{2T}\}\left[\frac{\partial u''}{\partial t'_{2T}}\right]^2 \qquad (24.3\text{-}21)$$

and

$$\sigma^2\{Y''|M\} = a^2_{10}\sigma^2\{Y'_T|Y_T\} \qquad (24.3\text{-}22)$$

24.3.3. Evaluation

Luminance and chromaticity shifts have been predicted for the following color coordinate transmission systems: the United States NTSC television receiver primary system for which the transmitted color components are the red, green, and blue source tristimulus values; the NTSC transmission system in which Y, I, Q tristimulus values are formed from linear combinations of the R, G, B signals (the Y signal is the luminance and the I, Q tristimulus values carry the hue and saturation information); and the CIE uniform chromaticity scale system for which the U, V, W, tristimulus values are linear combinations of the R, G, B signals (the V signal is the luminance). Figure 24.3-2 contains a plot of the mean luminance shift of several test colors as a function of their actual luminance values for transmission of (RGB), (YIQ), (Yrg), and (Yuv) color coordinates. Each color component is coded with 6 bits and the channel error probability is $p = 0.1$. The plotted points have been obtained by direct evaluation of equations similar to Eqs. 24.3-7 and 24.3-15. For purposes of comparison, Figure 24.3-2 also contains two solid lines that indicate the expected luminance shift as predicted by Eq. 24.2-5, which is the approximation for no red, green, or blue limiting. The approximation is exact for (RGB) transmission, because there can be no signal limiting in this case. It has been

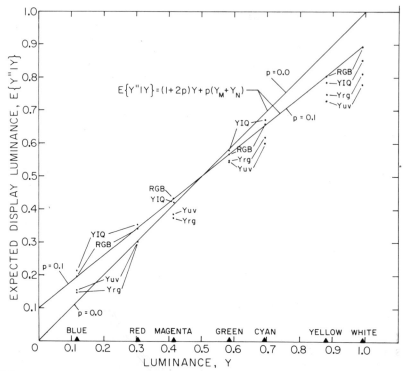

FIGURE 24.3-2. Luminance shift resulting from BSC errors for color transmission.

found that the approximation is quite close for a channel error probability of $p = 0.001$ or smaller. In general, the effect of channel errors is to shift the displayed luminance toward a midgray level. For most of the test colors the mean luminance shift is less for transmission of tristimulus values than for transmission of luminance/chromaticity components.

The shift in u, v chromaticity coordinates as a result of channel errors is illustrated in Figures 24.3-3a to 24.3-3d for seven test colors and four transmission systems under consideration. The tail of each arrow indicates the chromaticity of the transmitted color and the arrowhead indicates the mean value of the chromaticity of the received color. Crosses specify the expected standard deviation of the color. In all examples the probability of bit error is $p = 0.1$, and each color component is coded with 6 bits. For R, G, B transmission the effect of channel errors is seen to be a desaturation of a transmitted color toward white. This result is intuitively reasonable. On the average, each R, G, B tristimulus value will change by the same percentage amount toward its own midvalue of one-half. In the limit for a channel with a bit error probability of $p = 0.5$, the expected value of each received R, G, B tristimulus value is one-half, regardless of its transmitted value. Hence the received color becomes a midluminance gray. With Y, I, Q, transmission channel errors also tend to desaturate a transmitted color toward white. In the limit for $p = 0.5$ the expected values of the received I and Q signals are zero and the received color is achromatic. The mean color shift for Y, r, g transmission is to a yellowish hue. To explain this effect consider again the situation in which $p = 0.5$. The expected values of r and g are each one-half. Hence the blue chromaticity value b obtained at the receiver from $b = 1 - r - g$ is constrained to zero. Equal amounts of red and green thus produce yellow. Finally, for Y, u, v transmission, the mean color shift is towards magenta. The reason for this color shift is that the u and v chromaticity coordinates are strongly dependent on the red and blue tristimulus values, respectively. As the channel error probability increases, the values of u and v each approach one-half, causing the red and blue contributions to the received color to increase and the green contribution to decrease.

Experiments have been performed to verify the analytic predictions. Digital color images were subjected to transmission through a computer-simulated binary symmetric channel with an error rate of $p = 0.01$. In all examples the mean color shift was as predicted by the chromaticity diagrams. Subjectively, the least image degradation occurred for transmission of the R, G, B source tristimulus values. In this case the mean color shift is toward a gray desaturation. For all other color coordinate transmission systems the color shift is away from gray to a primary complementary color.

24.4. DPCM IMAGE CODING CHANNEL ERROR EFFECTS

In a predictive image coding system each reconstructed pixel is formed by the summation of the receiver prediction estimate and the received quantized prediction difference generated at the coder. The receiver prediction estimate is also formed from the received prediction difference. If a channel error occurs, the next reconstructed pixel will be in error, and this error will cause all subsequent receiver prediction errors to differ from the corresponding transmitter prediction estimates. As a consequence, channel error effects persist along image lines until they are corrected or perhaps offset by subsequent channel errors. To minimize the propagation effects of channel errors, predictive coding systems are usually reset at the beginning of each scan line by transmitting the PCM code of the first pixel along the scan line. This pixel value is then employed as the first pixel estimate at both the transmitter and receiver.

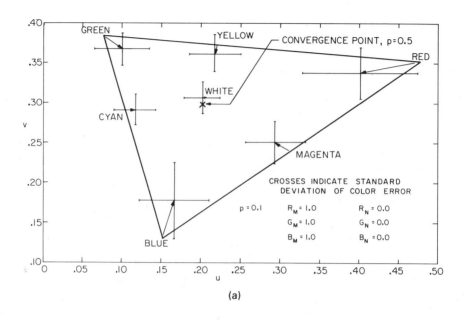

(a)

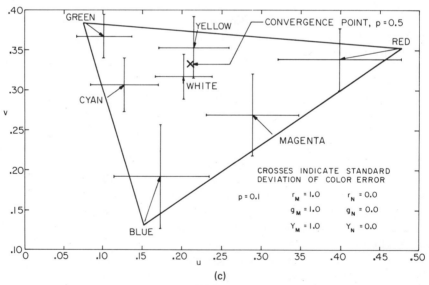

(c)

FIGURE 24.3-3. Chromaticity shifts resulting from BSC errors. (a) Chromaticity shift for *R, G, B* transmission. (b) Chromaticity shift for *Y, I, Q* transmission. (c) Chromaticity shift for *Y, r, g* transmission. (d) Chromaticity diagram for *Y, u, v* transmission.

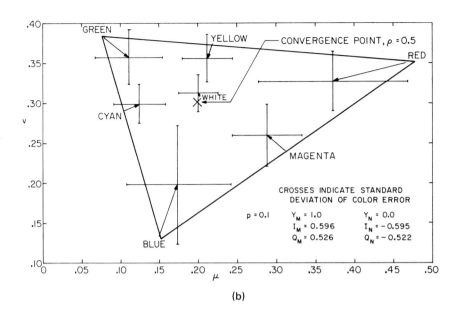

(b)

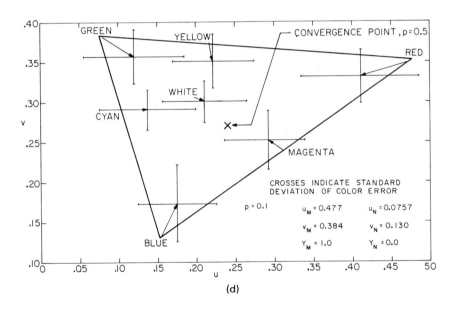

(d)

FIGURE 24.3-3. (*Continued*)

Figure 24.4-1 contains an example of channel error effects for DPCM coding using a 3-bit binary code for reconstruction levels. The coder employs error resetting at the beginning of each scan line. In this simulation the previous pixel prediction weighting factor A_k is set at 0.9. As a result of this "leaky integration," the error streaks tend to diminish along the line length. Further decreasing of the prediction weighting factors tends to reduce the persistence of DPCM errors, but the source coding performance in the absence of channel errors suffers.

Examples of predictive coding errors for fourth-order spatial prediction are given in Figure 24.4-2. Error propagation proceeds both horizontally and vertically from the error point, but visually the error effects appear less obstrusive than for a DPCM coder operating at the same channel error rate.

A common means of DPCM error correction is periodically to transmit the transmitter prediction estimate along a scan line as an 8-bit PCM code, and to ulitilize this esimate in place of the internally generated prediction estimate at the receiver (7). Error propagation is then limited to the period between prediction updates. PCM errors in the prediction updates must also be taken into consideration. Another approach to DPCM error correction is sequentially to examine each received prediction difference. If the difference signal differs substantially from its previous pixel neighbor, then it is assumed that the signal is in error and the previous difference signal is substituted for the received signal. Although this procedure avoids large-magnitude channel error effects, valid large-scale DPCM differences along edges are erroneously lost, thereby degrading the resolution of the reconstructed picture.

(a)

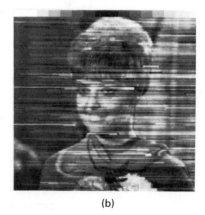
(b)

FIGURE 24.4-1.   Channel error effects for DPCM image coding with 3 bit code. (a) 10^{-4}.
(b) 10^{-2}.

(a)   (b)

FIGURE 24.4-2. Channel error effects for linear predictive coding with a fourth order spatial predictor and a 3-bit code. (a) 10^{-4}. (b) 10^{-2}.

24.5. TRANSFORM IMAGE CODING CHANNEL ERROR EFFECTS

Channel errors affect transform coded images in a much different manner than PCM or DPCM coded images. Since a reconstructed image is a weighted linear combination of its transform coefficients, the effect of erroneous coefficients is averaged over all pixels of the reconstructed image. However, from the converse viewpoint, a single erroneous transform coefficient affects all reconstructed pixels.

Figure 24.5-1 illustrates the effect of channel errors for zonal and threshold coded pictures for a slant transform. As expected, the effect of channel errors is much more deleterious for threshold coding than for zonal coding because of errors in the threshold position code.

24.6. PERFORMANCE RATING

Part 6 of this book has described quite a large number of image coding systems. A comprehensive rating of these systems is quite difficult because of the many factors involved in assessing their performance and implementation complexity. With modern signal processing and storage technology, implementation complexity has ceased to be such a dominant limitation in the construction of image coding systems. It is now feasible to consider systems requiring multiple frames of storage and reasonably

$$10^{-4}$$

$$10^{-3}$$

Zonal coding $\qquad 10^{-2} \qquad$ Threshold coding

FIGURE 24.5-1. Channel error effects for slant transform coding in 16×16 pixel blocks at 1.5 bits per pixel.

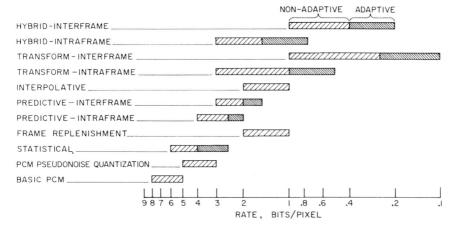

FIGURE 24.6-1.   Coding rate of image coding systems.

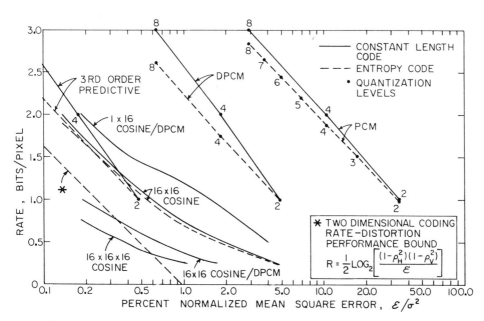

FIGURE 24.6-2.   Rate versus mean-square error relations for image coding systems.

complex processing for operation at real-time television rates. Consequently, in this section attention is limited to a performance comparison of image coding systems.

Figure 24.6-1 contains a chart comparing the coding rates of several adaptive and nonadaptive coding systems. As obviously expected, interframe coders outperform intraframe coders, and adaptive coders are better than nonadaptive coders. However, further generalizations are difficult to make because the chart does not include any information about coding error. Figure 24.6-2 presents the theoretical coding rate versus mean-square error performance of several coding systems for nonadaptive operation. A rate-distortion performance bound is also included in the figure. Theoretical performance estimates for adaptive image coders are not available. In Figure 24.6-2 the image source correlation is assumed to be separable and Markovian with equal horizontal, vertical, and temporal correlation factors of $\rho_H = \rho_V = \rho_T = 0.95$. Each system has been optimally designed to achieve a minimum mean-square coding error for coding of the statistical source. Table 24.6-1 contains design parameters for the coding systems.

In summary, it can be said that the field of image coding has reached a stage of maturity in the last few years. Several practical image coding methods are now available for the image transmission and storage applications. Sufficient information is now available on the theoretical and subjective coding performance to permit a rational choice between competitive coding systems as a function of implementation complexity.

TABLE 24.6-1. Coding system parameters

System	Statistical Model	Block Size	Coding Strategy
PCM	Rayleigh	1×1	Constant length code
Linear predictive	Laplacian	1×1	Constant length code
Intraframe transform	d.c. Rayleigh a.c. Gaussian	16×16	Zonal coding, constant length code
Intraframe hybrid DPCM/transform	Laplacian	1×16	Zonal coding, constant length code
Interframe transform	d.c. Rayleigh a.c. Gaussian	$16 \times 16 \times 16$	Zonal coding, constant length code
Interframe hybrid DPCM/transform	Laplacian	$16 \times 16 \times 1$	Zonal coding, constant length code

REFERENCES

1. T. S. Huang and M. T. Chikhaoui, "The Effect of BSC on PCM Picture Quality," *IEEE Trans. Inf. Theory*, **IT-13**, 2, April 1967, 270–273.

2. I. T. Young and J. C. Mott-Smith, "On Weighted PCM," *IEEE Trans. Inf. Theory (Correspondence)*, **IT-11**, 4, October 1965, 596–597.

3. T. S. Huang, O. J. Tretiak, B. Prasada, and Y. Yamaguchi, "Design Considerations in PCM Transmission of Low-Resolution Monochrome Still Pictures," *Proc. IEEE*, **55**, 3, March 1967, 331–335.

4. W. K. Pratt, "Digital Color Image Coding and Transmission," University of Southern California, Electronic Sciences Laboratory, USCEE Report 403, June 1971.

5. J. M. Knight, "Maximum Acceptable Bit Error Rates for PCM Analog and Digital TV Systems," Prroceedings National Telemetering Conference, 1962, 1–9.

6. A. Papoulis, *Probability, Random Variables, and Stochastic Processes*, McGraw-Hill, New York, 1965.

7. R. J. Arguello, H. R. Sellner, and J. A. Stuller, "The Effect of Channel Errors in the Differential Pulse-Code Modulation Transmission of Sampled Imagery," *IEEE Trans. Commun. Tech.*, **COM-19**, 6, December 1971, 926–933.

8. R. L. Katz and J. A. Sciulli, "The Performance of an Adaptive Image Data Compression System in the Presence of Noise," *IEEE Trans. Inf. Theory*, **IT-14**, 2, March 1968, 273–279.

9. H. C. Andrews and W. K. Pratt, "Transform Image Coding," in *Computer Processing in Communications*, Vol. XIX, Polytechnic Press, Brooklyn, New York, 1969, 63–84.

10. G. B. Anderson and T. S. Huang, "Errors in Frequency-Domain Processing of Images," Proceedings Spring Joint Computer Conference, Vol. 34, Boston, Massachusetts, 1969, 173–185.

1 APPENDIX

SELECTED REFERENCES

BOOKS

N. Ahmed and K. R. Rao, *Orthogonal Transforms for Digital Signal Processing*, Springer-Verlag, New York, 1975.

H. C. Andrews, with contributions by W. K. Pratt and K. Caspari, *Computer Techniques in Image Processing*, Academic Press, New York, 1970.

H. C. Andrews, *Introduction to Mathematical Techniques in Pattern Recognition*, Wiley–Interscience, New York, 1972.

H. C. Andrews and B. R. Hunt, *Digital Image Restoration*, Prentice-Hall, Englewood Cliffs, N.J., 1977.

M. Born and E. Wolf, *Principles of Optics*, Pergamon Press, New York, 1970.

W. T. Cathey, *Optical Information Processing and Holography*, Wiley, New York, 1974.

G. C. Cheng, Ed., Pictorial Pattern Recognition, Thompson, Washington, D.C., 1968.

T. N. Cornsweet, *Visual Perception*, Academic Press, New York, 1970.

R. O. Duda and P. E. Hart, *Pattern Classification and Scene Analysis*, Wiley–Interscience, New York, 1973.

R. M. Evans, W. T. Hanson, and W. L. Brewer, *Principles of Color Photography*, Wiley, New York, 1953.

D. G. Fink, Ed., *Television Engineering Handbook*, McGraw-Hill, New York, 1957.

K. Fukunaga, *Introduction to Statistical Pattern Recognition*, Academic Press, New York, 1972.

J. W. Goodman, *Introduction to Fourier Optics*, McGraw-Hill, New York, 1968.

A. Grasselli, *Automatic Interpretation and Classification of Images*, Academic Press, New York, 1969.

F. A. Graybill, *Introduction to Matrices with Applications in Statistics*, Wadsworth, Belmont, Calif., 1969.

H. F. Harmuth, *Transmission of Information by Orthogonal Functions*, 2nd ed., Springer-Verlag, New York, 1972.

T. S. Huang and O. J. Tretiak, Eds., *Picture Bandwidth Compression*, Gordon and Breach, New York, 1972.

T. S. Huang, Ed., *Topics in Applied Physics: Picture Processing and Digital Filtering*, Vol. 6, Springer-Verlag, New York, 1975.

R. W. G. Hunt, *The Reproduction of Colour*, Wiley, New York, 1957.

S. Kaneff, Ed., *Picture Language Machines*, Academic Press, New York, 1970.

B. S. Lipkin and A. Rosenfeld, *Picture Processing and Psychopictorics*, Academic Press, New York, 1970.

C. E. Mees, *The Theory of Photographic Process*, Macmillan, New York, 1966.

W. S. Meisel, *Computer-Oriented Approaches to Pattern Recognition*, Academic Press, New York, 1972.

R. Nevatia, *Structured Descriptions of Complex Curved Objects for Recognition and Visual Memory*, Springer-Verlag, New York, 1977.

A. V. Oppenheim and R. W. Schaefer, *Digital Signal Processing*, Prentice-Hall, Englewood Cliffs, N.J., 1975.

A. Papoulis, *Systems and Transforms with Applications in Optics*, McGraw-Hill, New York, 1968.

K. Preston, Jr., *Coherent Optical Computers*, McGraw-Hill, New York, 1972.

L. R. Rabiner and B. Gold, *Theory and Application of Digital Signal Processing*, Prentice-Hall, Englewood Cliffs, N.J., 1975.

A. Rosenfeld, *Picture Processing by Computer*, Academic Press, New York, 1969.

A. Rosenfeld and A. C. Kak, *Digital Image Processing*, Academic Press, New York, 1976.

J. T. Tippett et al., Eds., *Optical and Electro-Optical Information Processing*, MIT Press, Cambridge, Mass., 1965.

P. H. Winston, Ed., *The Psychology of Computer Vision*, McGraw-Hill, New York, 1975.

P. H. Winston, *Artificial Intelligence*, Addison-Wesley, New York, 1977.

G. Wyszecki and W. S. Stiles, *Color Science*, Wiley, New York, 1967.

SPECIAL ISSUES

Special Issue on Redundancy Reduction, *Proc. IEEE*, **55**, 3, March 1967.

Special Issue on Digital Communications, *IEEE Commun. Tech.*, **COM-19**, 6, Part I, December 1971.

Special Issue on Digital Picture Processing, *Proc. IEEE*, **60**, 7, July 1972.

Special Issue on Two-Dimensional Signal Processing, *IEEE Trans. Computers*, **C-21**, 7, July 1972.

Special Issue on Digital Image Processing, *IEEE Computer*, **7**, 5, May 1974.

Special Issue on Digital Signal Processing, *Proc. IEEE*, 63, 4, April 1975.

REVIEW PAPERS

H. C. Andrews, A. G. Tescher, and R. P. Kruger, "Image Processing by Digital Computer," *IEEE Spectrum*, **9**, 7, July 1972, 20–32.

H. C. Andrews, "Digital Image Restoration: A Survey," *IEEE Computer*, **7**, 5, May 1975, 36–45.

A. Habibi and G. S. Robinson, "A Survey of Digital Picture Coding," *IEEE Computer*, **7**, 5, May 1974, 21–34.

T. S. Huang, "PCM Picture Transmission," *IEEE Spectrum*, 2, 12, December 1965, 57–60.

T. S. Huang, "Image Enhancement—A Review," *Opto-Electronics*, **1**, February 1969.

T. S. Huang, "Digital Holography," *Proc. IEEE*, **59**, 9, September 1971, 1335–1346.

T. S. Huang, W. F. Schreiber, and O. J. Tretiak, "Image Processing," *Proc. IEEE*, **59**, 11, November 1971, 1586–1609.

B. R. Hunt, "Digital Image Processing," *Proc. IEEE*, **63**, 4, April 1975, 693–708.

2 APPENDIX

COLOR COORDINATE CONVERSION

There are two basic methods of specifying a color in the three primary system: by its three tristimulus values (T_1, T_2, T_3), and by its chromaticity coordinates (t_1, t_2) and its luminance (Y). Given either one of these representations, it is possible to convert from one primary system to another.

CASE 1. TRISTIMULUS TO TRISTIMULUS CONVERSION

Let (T_1, T_2, T_3) represent the tristimulus values in the original coordinate system and $(\tilde{T}_1, \tilde{T}_2, \tilde{T}_3)$ represent the tristimulus values in a new coordinate system. The conversion between systems is given by

$$\tilde{T}_1 = m_{11}T_1 + m_{12}T_2 + m_{13}T_3 \tag{1}$$

$$\tilde{T}_2 = m_{21}T_1 + m_{22}T_2 + m_{23}T_3 \tag{2}$$

$$\tilde{T}_3 = m_{31}T_1 + m_{32}T_2 + m_{33}T_3 \tag{3}$$

where the m_{ij} are the coordinate conversion constants. Exhibit 1 lists the conversion matrices for several common coordinate systems.

CASE 2. TRISTIMULUS TO LUMINANCE/CHROMINANCE CONVERSION

Let

$$t_1 \equiv \frac{T_1}{T_1 + T_2 + T_3} \tag{4}$$

$$t_2 \equiv \frac{T_2}{T_1 + T_2 + T_3} \tag{5}$$

EXHIBIT 1. Tristimulus conversion matrices

Output Tristimulus Value	Input Tristimulus Value														
	R_c	G_c	B_c	R_N	G_N	B_N	X	Y	Z	U	V	W	Y	I	Q
R_c	1.000	0.000	0.000	1.167	−0.146	−0.151	2.365	−0.897	−0.468	2.846	0.507	−0.936	0.848	1.325	0.540
G_c	0.000	1.000	0.000	0.114	0.753	0.159	−0.515	1.426	0.089	−0.639	1.159	0.178	1.016	−0.265	−0.154
B_c	0.000	0.000	1.000	−0.001	0.059	1.128	0.005	−0.014	−1.009	1.521	−3.041	2.018	1.172	−1.247	1.688
	[2, P. 1-337]			[3, P. 413]			[2, P. 1-33]			[3, P. 413]					
R_N	0.842	0.156	0.091	1.000	0.000	0.000	1.910	−0.533	−0.288	2.432	0.332	−0.576	1.000	0.956	0.621
G_N	−0.129	1.320	−0.203	0.000	1.000	0.000	−0.985	2.000	−0.028	−1.519	2.083	−0.057	1.000	−0.272	−0.647
B_N	0.008	−0.069	0.897	0.000	0.000	1.000	0.058	−0.118	0.896	1.440	−2.823	1.803	1.000	−1.106	1.703
	[2, P. 1-34]						[2, P. 1-34]			[3, P. 413]					
X	0.490	0.310	0.200	0.607	0.174	0.201	1.000	0.000	0.000	1.500	0.000	0.000	0.967	0.318	0.594
Y	0.177	0.813	0.011	0.299	0.587	0.114	0.000	1.000	0.000	0.000	1.000	0.000	1.000	0.000	0.000
Z	0.000	0.010	0.990	0.000	0.066	1.117	0.000	0.000	1.000	1.500	−3.000	2.000	1.173	−1.238	1.870
	[2, P. 1-34]									[2, P. 486]			[3, P. 412]		
U	0.327	0.207	0.133	0.405	0.116	0.133	0.667	0.000	0.000	1.000	0.000	0.000	0.653	0.208	0.403
V	0.177	0.814	0.010	0.299	0.587	0.114	0.000	1.000	0.000	0.000	1.000	0.000	1.000	0.000	0.000
W	0.020	1.071	0.408	0.145	0.827	0.627	−0.500	1.500	0.500	0.000	0.000	1.000	1.599	−0.780	0.623
	[3, P. 412]						[2, P. 486]						[3, P. 412]		
Y	0.178	0.818	0.016	0.299	0.587	0.114	0.000	1.000	0.000	0.000	1.000	0.000	1.000	0.000	0.000
I	0.540	−0.263	−0.174	0.596	−0.274	−0.322	1.407	−0.842	−0.451	1.403	0.534	−0.907	−0.842	1.000	0.000
Q	0.246	−0.675	0.404	0.211	−0.523	0.312	0.932	1.189	0.233	1.757	−1.898	0.470	1.189	0.000	1.000
	[3, P. 412]						[2, P. 412]			[3, P. 412]					

and

$$\tilde{t}_1 \equiv \frac{\tilde{T}_1}{\tilde{T}_1 + \tilde{T}_2 + \tilde{T}_3} \tag{6}$$

$$\tilde{t}_2 \equiv \frac{\tilde{T}_2}{\tilde{T}_1 + \tilde{T}_2 + \tilde{T}_3} \tag{7}$$

represent the chromaticity coordinates in the original and new coordinate systems, respectively. Then from Eqs 1–3,

$$t_1 = \frac{\beta_1 T_1 + \beta_2 T_2 + \beta_3 T_3}{\beta_4 T_1 + \beta_5 T_2 + \beta_6 T_3} \tag{8}$$

$$t_2 = \frac{\beta_7 T_1 + \beta_8 T_2 + \beta_9 T_3}{\beta_4 T_1 + \beta_5 T_2 + \beta_6 T_3} \tag{9}$$

where

$$\beta_1 \equiv m_{11}$$
$$\beta_2 \equiv m_{12}$$
$$\beta_3 \equiv m_{13}$$
$$\beta_4 \equiv m_{11} + m_{21} + m_{31}$$
$$\beta_5 \equiv m_{12} + m_{22} + m_{32} \tag{10}$$
$$\beta_6 \equiv m_{13} + m_{23} + m_{33}$$
$$\beta_7 \equiv m_{21}$$
$$\beta_8 \equiv m_{22}$$
$$\beta_9 \equiv m_{23}$$

and the m_{ij} are conversion matrix elements from the $(T_1\text{-}T_2\text{-}T_3)$ to the $(\tilde{T}_1\text{-}\tilde{T}_2\text{-}\tilde{T}_3)$ coordinate systems. The luminance signal is related to the original tristimulus values by

$$Y = n_{21} T_1 + n_{22} T_2 + n_{23} T_3 \tag{11}$$

where the n_{ij} are conversion elements from the $(T_1\text{-}T_2\text{-}T_3)$ to the $(X\text{-}Y\text{-}Z)$ coordinate systems.

CASE 3. LUMINANCE/CHROMINANCE TO LUMINANCE/CHROMINANCE CONVERSION

Substitution of

$$T_1 = t_1(T_1 + T_2 + T_3) \tag{12}$$

$$T_2 = t_2(T_1 + T_2 + T_3) \tag{13}$$

$$T_3 = (1 - t_1 - t_2)(T_1 + T_2 + T_3) \tag{14}$$

into Eqs. 8 and 9 gives

$$\tilde{t}_1 = \frac{\alpha_1 t_1 + \alpha_2 t_2 + \alpha_3}{\alpha_4 t_1 + \alpha_5 t_2 + \alpha_6} \tag{15}$$

$$\tilde{t}_2 = \frac{\alpha_7 t_1 + \alpha_8 t_2 + \alpha_9}{\alpha_4 t_1 + \alpha_5 t_2 + \alpha_6} \tag{16}$$

where

$$\alpha_1 \equiv m_{11} - m_{13}$$

$$\alpha_2 \equiv m_{12} - m_{13}$$

$$\alpha_3 \equiv m_{13}$$

$$\alpha_4 \equiv m_{11} + m_{21} + m_{31} - m_{13} - m_{23} - m_{33}$$

$$\alpha_5 \equiv m_{12} + m_{22} + m_{32} - m_{13} - m_{23} - m_{33} \tag{17}$$

$$\alpha_6 \equiv m_{13} + m_{23} + m_{33}$$

$$\alpha_7 \equiv m_{21} - m_{23}$$

$$\alpha_8 \equiv m_{22} - m_{23}$$

$$\alpha_9 \equiv m_{23}$$

and the m_{ij} are conversion constants from the $(T_1\text{-}T_2\text{-}T_3)$ to the $(\tilde{T}_1\text{-}\tilde{T}_2\text{-}\tilde{T}_3)$ coordinate systems.

CASE 4. LUMINANCE/CHROMINANCE TO TRISTIMULUS CONVERSION

In the general situation in which the original chromaticity coordinates are not the C.I.E. x-y coordinates, the conversion is made in a two-stage process. From Eqs. 1–3

$$\tilde{T}_1 = n_{11}X + n_{12}Y + n_{13}Z \tag{18}$$

$$\tilde{T}_2 = n_{21}X + n_{22}Y + n_{23}Z \tag{19}$$

$$\tilde{T}_3 = n_{31}X + n_{32}Y + n_{33}Z \tag{20}$$

where the n_{ij} are the constants for a conversion from $(X\text{-}Y\text{-}Z)$ tristimulus values to $(T_1\text{-}T_2\text{-}T_3)$ tristimulus values.

Then from Eqs. 15 and 16

$$x = \frac{\alpha_1 t_1 + \alpha_2 t_2 + \alpha_3}{\alpha_4 t_1 + \alpha_5 t_2 + \alpha_6} \tag{21}$$

$$y = \frac{\alpha_7 t_1 + \alpha_8 t_2 + \alpha_9}{\alpha_4 t_1 + \alpha_5 t_3 + \alpha_6} \tag{22}$$

where the α_k are obtained from the m_{ij} of Eq. 17 for a conversion from a $(T_1\text{-}T_2\text{-}T_3)$ tristimulus system to an $(X\text{-}Y\text{-}Z)$ tristimulus system. Also, because

$$X = \frac{x}{y}Y \tag{23}$$

$$Z = \frac{1-x-y}{y}Y \tag{24}$$

the X and Z tristimulus values needed for substitution into Eqs. 18–20 become

$$X = \frac{\alpha_1 t_1 + \alpha_2 t_2 + \alpha_3}{\alpha_5 t_1 + \alpha_6 t_2 + \alpha_7} \tag{25}$$

$$Z = \frac{(\alpha_4 - \alpha_1 - \alpha_5)t_1 + (\alpha_5 - \alpha_2 - \alpha_6)t_2 + (\alpha_6 - \alpha_3 - \alpha_7)}{\alpha_5 t_1 + \alpha_6 t_2 + \alpha_7}Y \tag{26}$$

3 APPENDIX

STATISTICAL SOURCE CODING

This appendix describes two common methods of statistical source coding: Shannon–Fano and Huffman coding.

Figure 1 contains an example of Shannon–Fano coding. With this coding method a table of message symbols and their corresponding probabilities of occurrence is formed with the entries arranged in decreasing order of probability. Two groups of messages with probabilities as equal as possible are then formed. The first bit of each code word of one group is zero, and the first bit of the other group is one. The partitioning procedure is then continued for each subgroup for the additional bits of the code words. Average code word length and message source entropies are indicated in the figure.

Huffman coding of a message set is shown in the example of Figure 2. In this coding process the two messages with the lowest probability are combined in a tree structure, and their probabilities are summed at the junction. The next set of lowest probability messages or junctions is then combined as indicated until the tree converges to a single junction. The branches of the tree are denoted arbitrarily as ones and zeros. To form a code word for a message, the tree is traversed back to a message node recording the path designation, one or zero.

Message	Probability	Code Word
a_1	0.30	00
a_2	0.25	01
a_3	0.25	10
a_4	0.10	110
a_5	0.10	111

$$L_c = (2)[.3 + .25 + .25] + (3)[.1 + .1] = 2.2 \text{ BITS}$$

$$H = -(.3)\,\text{LOG}_2\,(.3) - (2)\,\text{LOG}_2\,(.25) - (2)(.1)\,\text{LOG}_2\,(.1)$$

$$H = 2.185 \text{ BITS}$$

$$E_F = \frac{L_c}{H} = 0.993$$

FIGURE 1. Shannon–Fano coding example.

Code Word	Message	Probability
10	a_1	.33
00	a_2	.22
01	a_3	.20
110	a_4	.15
1110	a_5	.05
1111	a_6	.05

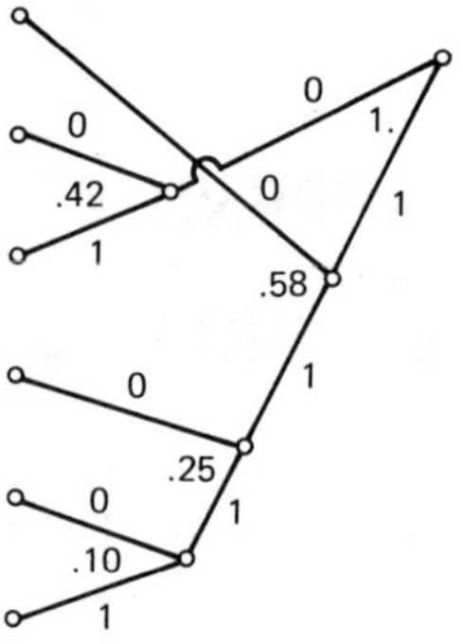

$$L_c = (2)[.33+.22+.20]+(3)(.15)+(4)(.05+.05)$$

$$L_c = 2.35 \text{ BITS}$$

$$H = -(.33)\,\text{LOG}_2\,(.33) - (.22)\,\text{LOG}_2\,(.22) - (.20)\,\text{LOG}_2\,(.20) - (.15)\,\text{LOG}_2\,(.15) - (2)(.05)\,\text{LOG}_2\,(.05)$$

$$H = 2.32 \text{ BITS}$$

$$E_F = \frac{L_c}{H} = 0.897$$

FIGURE 2. Example of Huffman coding.

There are algebraic methods for generating the Shannon–Fano and Huffman codes that do not require a recursive geometric tree construction. Often the Shannon–Fano and Huffman coding algorithms result in identical average length codes. For some set of message probabilities the average code words length is equal to the message source entropy. It can be shown that the Huffman code always provides a minimal average length set of code words.

INDEX

Aliasing error, definition, 104
  restoration, 426
Analytic continuation, 437
Area character coding, 705
Area measure, 529
Argyle edge detector, 485

Bartlett window, 294
Bessel function, 98
Bit assignment, algorithms, 149
  transform coding, 675
Bit plane coding, 635
Bit quads, 528
Blackman window, 294
Blind image restoration, 434
Block mode filtering, 290
Brightness, definition, 27
  metrics, 168
B-spline, 113

C.I.E., *see* Commission Internationale de
  l'Eclairage
Cepstrum, 327
Chain code, 703
Channel error effects, DPCM, 723
  PCM, color, 715
    monochrome, 712
  transform, 727
Channel error models, 710
Chirp Z-transform, 269
Chromatic adaption, 35, 47
Chromaticity coordinates, 68
Circular lens transfer function, 109
Coefficient rooting, 326
Color blindness, 35
Color coordinates, C.I.E. spectral, 72
  C.I.E. X-Y-Z, 24
  Karhunen-Loeve, 78
  L-a-b, 78
  N.T.S.C. receiver, 73
  N.T.S.C. transmission, 74
  retinal, 79

S-O-W*, 78
U*-V*-W*, 78
  uniform chromaticity, 75
Color differences, just noticeable, 76
Color film exposure estimation, 462
Color image display compensation, 466
Color image fidelity, 182
Colorimetry, 63
Color matching, 57
  additive, 58
  axioms, 62
  subtractive, 61
Color metrics, 170
Color solids, 84
Color space, definition, 67
  perceptual, 28
Color vision model, definition, 43
  verification, 64
Commission Internationale de l'Eclairage,
  51
Companding quantizer, 145, 617
Compass gradient edge detector, 481
Condition number, 393
Cones, description of, 29
  distribution of, 31
  sensitivity of, 30, 45
Connectivity, pixel, 514
Contour coding, 701
Contrast, clipping, 309
  enhancement, 307
  manipulation, 307
  scaling, 309
  stretching, 307
Contrast sensitivity, 32
Convex hull, 527
Convolution, continuous, definition, 10
  theorem, 14
  discrete, definitions, 216, 223, 227
    edge crispening masks, 323
    fast Fourier transform algorithm, 288
    noise cleaning masks, 320
    restoration model, 373

Convolution integral, 10
Correlation function, continuous, 20
  discrete, 129
  separable, 130
  system output, 23
Cosine transform, basis functions, 245
  even symmetrical, 243
  odd symmetrical, 244
Covariance, continuous, 20
  discrete, 130
  Markov matrix, 131
  matrix direct product form, 131
  stationary, 130
Cross-correlation function, 553
Curvature, definition, 530
  Fourier series of, 531
Curve fitting, 520
  iterative end point, 523
  polynomial, 521

Deltamodulation, 638
Delta-sigma modulation, 641
Differential operators, 11
Differential pulse code modulation, 641
  coding system, 642
  quantizer scales, 643
Dirac delta function, definition, 6
  sampling array, 94
  sifting property, 6
Directional graph, 580
Direct product, of covariance matrix, 131
  definition, 14
DPCM, *see* Differential pulse code
  modulation

Edge coding, 703
Edge crispening, 322
Edge detector, 478
  Argyle, 485
  compass gradient, 481
  differencing, 480
  Kirsch, 489
  Laplacian, 482
  linear edge enhancement, 479
  logarithmic, 489
  Macleod, 485
  nonlinear edge enhancement, 487
  product averaging mask, 491
  Roberts, 487
  Sobel, 487

  statistical mask, 485
Edge fitting, 492
  figure of merit for, 497
  Hueckel, 493
  performance of, 495
  statistical, 495
Entropy, definition, 185
  histogram feature, 473, 474
  image estimates, 188
  image source, 626
Euclidean color space, 170
Euler number, 527, 529
Eye, cones, 29
  cross-sectional view, 29
  elements of, 29
  fovea, 31
  rods, 29

False color, 333
Feature coding, 699
Film grain noise, definition, 368
  noise cheating method, 444
  restoration, 443
Fourier transform, continuous, properties,
    13
  two-dimensional, 12
  discrete, basis functions, 237
    computational method, 270
    display, 239
    filter design, 291
    matrix form, 241
    periodicity, 237
    redundancy, 239
    series form, 25
Fovea, 31
Frame rate reduction, 603
Frame replenishment coding, 636
Frames theory, 573

Gaussian probability density, 18, 134
Generalized linear systems, 16
Geodesic distance, 170
Geometric distortion correction, 429
Granularity error, 639
Grassman's laws, 62
Gray level dependency matrix, 507

Haar transform, basis functions, 255
  basis planes, 256
  definition, 254

Hadamard transform, basis functions, 252
  basis planes, 253
  computational algorithm, 266
  definition, 250
  sequency, 25
Hamming window, 294
Hanning window, 294
Heterarchical systems, 572
Hexagonal pixel grid, 517
Hierarchical systems, 570
Histogram, equalization, 312
  features, 471
  first order, definition, 136
  hyperbolization, 312
  image, 136
  modification, 311
  second order, definition, 138
Homomorphic filtering, definition, 17
  image restoration, 433
Hotelling transform, 259
Hough transform, 523
Hue, 27
Hueckel edge detector, 493
Hurter-Driffield curve, 356, 361
Hybrid transform/DPCM coding, 696

Ill-conditioned matrix, 393
Illuminance, 55
Illumination sources, C.I.E. standard, 52
  phosphor, 53
Image coding, analog processing, 591
  classification, 591
  digital point processing, 616
  digital spatial processing, 662
  performance, 710
Image feature extraction, 471
  amplitude features, 471
  color edge, 499
  histogram features, 471
  luminance edge, 478
  spot and line, 502
  texture, 503
  transform coefficient, 474
Image fidelity, 162
  cross-correlation measure, 176
  eye model measure, 178
  Laplacian correlation measure, 176
  least-square error, 177
  mean-square error, 177
  monochrome, 174

rectangular passband measure, 175
  Strehl definition, 175
Image function, 4
Image intelligibility, 162
  testing methods, 193
Image quality, 162
  goodness scale, 163
  impairment scale, 164
  K-factor rating, 166
  subjective rating, 163
  waveform rating, 166
Image reconstruction, exact, 93
  practical, 111
Image restoration models, digitization system, 363
  discrete restoration, 370
  display system, 364
  general, 345
  image noise, 365
  optical systems, 350
  photographic process, 353
Image sampling, deterministic fields, 93
  exact, 93
  practical, 101
  random fields, 99
Image understanding systems, 568
  blackboard, 573
  bottom-up, 570
  frames, 573
  heterarchical, 572
  hierarchical, 570
  top down, 571
Impulse response, Bessel function, 98
  definition, 9
  sinc function, 97
Interlace, dot, 607
  field patterns, 608
  line, 604
  picture, 603
Interpolation, cubic B-spline, 113
  error correction, 427
  one-dimensional, 114
  for spatial warping, 432
  two-dimensional, 115
Interpolative coding, 662
  destination, 665
  first order, 664
  source, 662
  zero order, 663
Isoplanatic, *see* Space invariant

Joint occurancy matrix, 507
Just noticeable color difference, 170

Kaiser window, 294
Karhunen-Loeve transform, basis functions, 263
  definition, 25
  for Markov process, 262
K-factor rating, 166
Kirsch edge detector, 489

L-a-b color coordinates, 78
Lambert's law, 55
Landolt C-charts, 193
Land's experiments, 36
Laplacian, continuous, 12
  edge detector, 482
  joint Laplacian density, 134
  probability density, 19
  thresholding, 537
Lateral inhibition, 42
Lightness scales, 169
Light sources, blackbody, 51
  phosphor, 53
  tungsten lamp, 51
  standard sources, 52
Linear operators, 201
  additive, 8
  computational requirements of, 204
  generalized, 201
  pseudoinverse, 206
  statistical representation of, 204
  structure of, 203
Linear systems, discrete, 208
  consistent, 209
  inconsistent, 211
  solutions to, 208
Lumen, 54
Luminance, calculation, 68
  definition, 4, 55
Luminance image restoration, display
    correction, 450
  sensor correction, 447
Luminosity coefficient, 69
Luminous efficiency functions, photopic,
    and scotopic, 53
Luminous flux, 52
Luminous intensity, 54

MacAdam's color ellipses, 172

Mach band, 33
Macleod edge detector, 485
Markov process, continuous, 21
  covariance matrix, 131
  discrete, 262
Matched filtering, derivative, 557
  deterministic continuous fields, 553
  discrete images, 560
  stochastic continuous fields, 558
Matrix, addition, 122
  correlation, 129
  covariance, 130
  definition, 122
  direct product, 124
  inverse, 123
  multiplication, 122
  rank, 125
  trace, 124
  transpose, 123
Max quantizer, 143
Maxwell triangle, 67
Mean, continuous, 20
  matrix, 129
  system output, 23
  vector, 129
Mean square error, continuous image, 177
  discrete image, 181
  image restoration, 411
  normalized, 181
  peak, 181
Medial axis transform, 519
Median filter, 330
  one-dimensional, 330
  two-dimensional, 332
Modulation transfer function, human
    visual system, 38, 46
  optical systems, 352
Moment approximation of image, 532
Multiplex coding, 612
Multispectral image, contrast enhancement, 310
  differencing, 338
  enhancement, 338
  histogram modification, 317
  principal components, 339
  ratioing, 339
Munsell color system, 28

Noise, cheating, 444
  cleaning, 319

film grain, 368
generation-recombination, 367
models, 365
photodetector, 365
shot, 367
thermal, 365
Norm, matrix, 124
vector, 124
NTSC, composite color video, 596
definition, 73
receiver color coordinates, 73
television system, 593
transmission color coordinates, 74
Nyquist rate criterion, 97

Object color, 89
Optical systems, 350
atmospheric model, 352
human vision, 37
lens, 109, 352
modulation transfer function, 352
optical transfer function, 352
Optical transfer function, 352
Orthogonality principle, 411
Overdetermined system, 207

PAL, 599
Parseval's theorem, 14
Pattern recognition, 568
PCM , *see* Pulse code modulation
Performance rating of image coders, 727
Perimeter measure, 529
Photographic process, 353
color, 358
color film exposure estimation,
462
color film model, 362
Hurter-Driffield curve, 356, 361
monochrome, 353
spectral dye densities, 360
spectral sensitivities, 359
transmittance versus exposure, 356
Photometry, 52
illuminance, 55
lumen, 54
luminous flux, 52
luminous intensity, 54
Photopic, 53
Planck's law, 50

Point spread function, *see* Impulse
response
Polyhedral analysis, 580-585
Power spectrum, continuous, 23
discrete, 132
Predictive coding, 637
adaptive, 646
color image, 648
design of, 650
differential frame, 649
rate-distortion, 656
spatial, 645
Principal components, 339
Probability density, conditional, 19
discrete image, 132
exponential, 19
Gaussian, scalar, 18
general image, 18
Laplacian, 19
log normal, 19
Rayleigh, 19
uniform, 19
vector Gaussian, 134
Pseudocolor, 336
Pseudoinverse, computational algorithms,
395
conditional inverse, 207
definition, 206
generalized inverse, 206
least-square inverse, 207
spatial image restoration, 387
SVD spatial image restoration, 402
transform domain, 295
Pulse code modulation, 616

Quadratic form, 125
Quantization, block, 149
coarse-fine, 623
color image, 155
companding, 145, 617
decision level, 141, 144
DPCM, 643, 655
improved gray scale, 622
Max, 143
monochrome image, 154
PCM error reduction, 624
pseudonoise, 618
reconstruction level, 141, 144
scalar, 141
split-band, 623

transform coding, 673
transform coding error reduction, 691
vector, 147

Rate distortion function, 189
  Gaussian source, 191
  Markov source, 192
Rayleigh probability density, 19
REARCS method, 601
Recursive filtering, 299
  computational requirements, 301
  stability condition, 300
Recursive image restoration, 441
Refraction of light, 27
Region growing, 541
Registration, image, 562
    correlation, 562
    statistical correlation, 563
Relational methods, 578
RETMA, 593
Riemannian color space, 170
Roberts edge detector, 487
Roberts modulation, 619
Rods, description of, 29
  distribution of, 31
  sensitivity of, 30
Run coding, 631
  bit plane, 635
  entropy of, 632
  run length, 632
Run length coding, 632

Saturation, 28
Scotopic, 53
SECAM, 598
Segmentation, image, 534
    amplitude, 534
    classification, 540
    contour following, 543
    edge, 542
    edge point linking, 544
    multidimensional, 539
    region growing, 541
    shape, 547
    texture, 546
Selection matrix, 229
Shape description, 525
  analytic attributes, 530
  metric attributes, 525
  topological attributed, 526

Shot noise, 367
Shrinking, 517
Sifting property, 6
Signal-to-noise ratio, image coding error,
    181
  Wiener filter, 383
Simultaneous contrast, 35
Sinc function, 97
Sine transform, basis functions, 248
  definition, 247
Singularity operators, 6
Singular value decomposition, coding, 706
  definition, 126
  spatial image restoration, 402
  transform, 264
Skeletonizing, 519
Slant transform, basis functions, 260
  definition, 257
Slope overload error, 639
SNR, *see* Signal-to-noise ratio
Sobel edge detector, 487
Space invariant, 9
Space variant restoration, 440
Spatial average, image, 5
Spatial frequency, 12
Spatial image restoration, algebraic
      spatial techniques, 378
    constrained least squares filter, 385
    constrained methods, 417
    continuous image techniques, 378
    geometrical mean filter, 385
    inverse filter, 378
    parametric estimation filter, 384
    power spectrum filter, 384
    pseudoinverse techniques, 387
    regression method, 409
    smoothing methods, 415
    Wiener estimation, 409
    Wiener filter, 381
Spectral factorization, 556
Spectral radiance estimation, 452
Spectral response correction, 456
Spectrum extrapolation, 693
Spectrum interpolation, 696
Stacking operator, 128
Statistical coding, 626
  previous pixel, 629
  single pixel, 627
Statistical differencing, 323
Statistical mask, 485, 565

Stochastic estimation, 420
  Bayes, 420
  maximum *a posteriori*, 420
  maximum likelihood, 420
Strehl measure, 175
Subjective color, 36
Superposition integral, 9
Superposition operator, 214
  circulant area, 226
  finite area, 215
  Fourier domain, 286
  Hadamard domain, 286
  relationship of, 229
  sampled infinite area, 217
  transform domain, 282
Superresolution, 438
SVD, *see* Singular value decomposition
Syntactic methods, 574
  definitions, 574
  examples, 576-579

Template matching, 551
Test colors, 458
Texture, artificial, 504
  autocorrelation measure, 506
  coarseness, 505
  definition, 503
  edge density measure, 506
  features, 503
  Fourier domain measure, 506
  joint histogram measure, 507
  natural, 505
  run length measure, 509
  synthesis, 510
Texture coding, 704
Thermal noise, 365
Thinness ratio, 526
Thinning, 517
Thresholding, dominant neighbor, 491
  iterative, 538
  luminance, 534
  Laplacian, 537
  multidimensional, 539
Time average, image, 5
Topological image attributes, 526
Transform domain processing, 279
Transform image coding, 667
  adaptive, 678
  color, 681
  interframe, 685

  monochrome, 667
  threshold coding, 678
  zonal coding, 673
  zonal sampling, 670
Transform processing, 326
Tristimulus value, calculation, 66
  definition, 60
  luminance limitation, 86
  positivity limitation, 84
  red, green, blue, 4
  transformation of, 68
Tristimulus value estimation, 457
Two dimensional unitary transforms, 232
  chirp-Z, 269
  computational algorithms, 266
  cosine, 242
  Fourier, 235
  Haar, 254
  Hadamard, 250
  Hotelling, 259
  Karhunen-Loeve, 259
  probability density models, 275
  series form, 233
  sine, 247
  slant, 257
  statistical analysis of, 270
  SVD, 264
  unitary transform operators, 232
  vector form, 233

U*-V*-W* color coordinates, 78
Underdetermined system, 207
Unsharp masking, 322

Variable spatial resolution, 602
Variable velocity scanning, 610
Variance function, 129
Vector, algebra, 121
  definition, 121
  differentiation, 125
  inner product, 15
  norm, 124
  outer product, 125
  quantization, 147
Vector space image representation, 127
Vision models, color, 43
  extended color, 46
  extended monochrome, 43
  logarithmic model, 40
  monochrome, 37

verification of, 64
Visual phenomena, chromatic aberration, 35
  color blindness, 35
  contrast sensitivity, 32
  Land's experiments, 36
  Mach band, 33
  simultaneous contrast, 35
  subjective color, 36

Weber fraction, 32
Wiener estimation, 410
Wiener filter, aliasing error correction, 427

film grain noise restoration, 443
  spatial restoration, 381
Wien's law, 51
Windowing operators, 292
  Bartlett, 294
  Blackman, 294
  Hamming, 294
  Hanning, 294
  Kaiser, 294
  rectangular, 294
Wrap around error, 289

Zonal coding, 673
Zonal sampling, 670